Study and Solutions Guide for

PRECALCULUS:
A GRAPHING APPROACH

Larson/Hostetler/Edwards

Bruce H. Edwards
University of Florida
Gainesville, Florida

Dianna L. Zook
Indiana University
Purdue University at Fort Wayne, Indiana

D. C. Heath and Company
Lexington, Massachusetts   Toronto

Published simultaneously in Canada.

Printed in the United States of America.

International Standard Book Number: 0-669-28501-3

10 9 8 7 6 5 4 3 2

TO THE STUDENT

The *Study and Solutions Guide for Precalculus: A Graphing Approach* is a supplement to the text by Roland E. Larson, Robert P. Hostetler, and Bruce H. Edwards.

As mathematics instructors, we often have students come to us with questions about the assigned homework. When we ask to see their work, the reply often is "I didn't know where to start." The purpose of the *Study Guide* is to provide brief summaries of the topics covered in the textbook and enough detailed solutions to problems so that you will be able to work the remaining exercises.

This *Study Guide* is the result of the efforts of Richard Bambauer, Lisa Bickel, Linda Bollinger, Laurie Brooks, Patti Jo Campbell, Darin Johnson, Linda Kifer, Deanna Larson, Timothy Larson, Amy Marshall, John Musser, Scott O'Neil, Louis Rieger, and Evelyn Wedzikowski. Thanks to Lisa Edwards for her help in preparing this project, and to Edward Schlindwein.

If you have any corrections or suggestions for improving this *Study Guide*, we would appreciate hearing from you.

Good luck with your study of precalculus.

Bruce H. Edwards
University of Florida
Gainesville, Florida 32611
(be@ math.ufl.edu)

Dianna L. Zook
Indiana University,
Purdue University
at Fort Wayne, Indiana 46805

CONTENTS

STUDY STRATEGIES

- Attend all classes and come prepared. Have your homework completed. Bring the text, paper, pen or pencil, and a graphing calculator to each class.

- Read the section in the text that is to be covered before class. As you read, use your graphing calculator to verify results and reproduce graphs in the text. Make notes about any questions that you have and, if they are not answered during the lecture, ask them at the appropriate time.

- Participate in class. As mentioned above, ask questions. Also, do not be afraid to answer questions.

- Take notes on all definitions, concepts, rules, formulas and examples. After class, read your notes and fill in any gaps, or make notations of any questions that you have. Make a habit of using your calculator often.

- DO THE HOMEWORK!!! You learn mathematics by doing it yourself. Mathematics is not a spectator sport! Allow **at least** two hours outside of each class for homework. Do not fall behind.

- Seek help when needed. Visit your instructor during office hours and come prepared with specific questions; check with your school's tutoring service; find a study partner in class; check additional books in the library for more examples—just do something before the problem becomes insurmountable.

- Do not cram for exams. Each chapter in the text contains a set of chapter review exercises. Work these problems a few days before the exam and review any areas of weakness.

CHAPTER P

Prerequisites: Review of Basic Algebra

Section P.1   The Real Number System

- ■ You should know the following sets.

  (a) The set of real numbers includes the rational numbers and the irrational numbers.

  (b) The set of rational numbers includes all real numbers that can be written as the ratio p/q of two integers, where $q \neq 0$.

  (c) The set of irrational numbers consists of all real numbers which are not rational.

  (d) The set of integers: $\{\ldots, -3, -2, -1, 0, 1, 2, 3, \ldots\}$

  (e) The set of whole numbers: $\{0, 1, 2, 3, 4, \ldots\}$

  (f) The set of natural numbers: $\{1, 2, 3, 4, \ldots\}$

- ■ The real number line is used to represent the real numbers.

- ■ Know the inequality symbols.

  (a) $a < b$ means a is less than b.

  (b) $a \leq b$ means a is less than or equal to b.

  (c) $a > b$ means a is greater than b.

  (d) $a \geq b$ means a is greater than or equal to b.

- ■ You should know the bounded and unbounded intervals on the real line.

- ■ You should know that

  $$|a| = \begin{cases} a, & \text{if } a \geq 0 \\ -a, & \text{if } a < 0. \end{cases}$$

- ■ Know the properties of absolute value.

  (a) $|a| \geq 0$ (b) $|-a| = |a|$ (c) $|ab| = |a|\,|b|$ (d) $\left|\dfrac{a}{b}\right| = \dfrac{|a|}{|b|}$

- ■ The distance between a and b on the real line is $|b - a| = |a - b|$.

1. (a) Natural numbers: $\{5, 1\}$

   (b) Integers: $\{-9, 5, 0, 1\}$

   (c) Rational numbers:
   $\left\{-9, -\frac{7}{2}, 5, \frac{2}{3}, 0, 1\right\}$

   (d) Irrational numbers: $\{\sqrt{2}\}$

3. Note that $\sqrt{4} = 2$.

   (a) Natural numbers: $\{12, 1, \sqrt{4}\}$

   (b) Integers: $\{12, -13, 1, \sqrt{4}\}$

   (c) Rational numbers:
   $\left\{12, -13, 1, \sqrt{4}, \frac{3}{2}\right\}$

   (d) Irrational numbers: $\{\sqrt{6}\}$

5. (a) Natural numbers: $\left\{\frac{6}{3}\right\}$

    (b) Integers: $\left\{\frac{6}{3}\right\}$

    (c) Rational numbers: $\left\{-\frac{1}{3}, \frac{6}{3}, -7.5\right\}$

    (d) Irrational numbers: $\left\{-\pi, \frac{1}{2}\sqrt{2}\right\}$

7. $\frac{3}{2} < 7$

9. $-4 > -8$

11. $\frac{5}{6} > \frac{2}{3}$

13. The interval $[-1, 3]$ denotes all real numbers greater than or equal to -1 and less than or equal to 3. That is, $-1 \le x \le 3$, which is bounded.

15. The interval $(10, \infty)$ denotes all real numbers greater than 10. That is, $x > 10$, which is unbounded.

17. The inequality $x \le 5$ denotes all real numbers less than or equal to 5. That is, $(-\infty, 5]$.

19. The inequality $x < 0$ denotes all real numbers that are less than zero. That is, $(-\infty, 0)$.

21. The inequality $x \ge 4$ denotes all real numbers greater than or equal to 4. That is, $[4, \infty)$.

23. The inequality $-2 < x < 2$ denotes all real numbers between -2 and 2, not including -2 or 2. That is, $(-2, 2)$.

25. The inequality $-1 \le x < 0$ denotes all real numbers between -1 and 0, including -1 but not including 0. That is, $[-1, 0)$.

27. $x < 0$, $(-\infty, 0)$

29. $y \le 25$, $(-\infty, 25]$

31. $A \ge 30$, $[30, \infty)$

33. $3.5\% \le r \le 6\%$, $[0.035, 0.06]$

35. $\dfrac{-5}{|-5|} = \dfrac{-5}{-(-5)} = \dfrac{-5}{5} = -1$

37. $-3|-3| = -3(3) = -9$

39. $-|16.25| + 20 = -16.25 + 20 = 3.75$

41. Since $|-3| = 3$ and $-|-3| = -3$,
we have $|-3| \boxed{>} -|-3|$.

43. Since $-|5| = -5$, we have $-5 \boxed{=} -|5|$.

45. Since $-|-2| = -2$ and $-|2| = -2$,
we have $-|-2| \boxed{=} -|2|$.

47. $d\left(-\frac{5}{2},\ 0\right) = \left|0 - \left(-\frac{5}{2}\right)\right| = \left|\frac{5}{2}\right| = \frac{5}{2}$

49. $d(126,\ 75) = |75 - 126| = 51$

51. $d(9.34,\ -5.65) = |9.34 - (-5.65)|$
$$= |9.34 + 5.65|$$
$$= |14.99| = 14.99$$

53. Since $d(x,\ 5) = |x - 5|$ and $d(x,\ 5) \le 3$,
we have $|x - 5| \le 3$.

55. Since $d\left(z,\ \frac{3}{2}\right) = \left|z - \frac{3}{2}\right|$ and $d\left(z,\ \frac{3}{2}\right) > 1$,
we have $\left|z - \frac{3}{2}\right| > 1$.

57. Since $d(y,\ 0) = |y - 0| = |y|$ and
$d(y,\ 0) \ge 6$, we have $|y| \ge 6$.

59. $\frac{7071}{5000} = 1.4142$

$\frac{584}{413} \approx 1.414043584$

$\sqrt{2} \approx 1.42\overline{42}$

$\frac{47}{33} = 1.42\overline{42}$

$\frac{127}{90} = 1.41\overline{1}$

$\frac{127}{90} < \frac{584}{413} < \frac{7071}{5000} < \sqrt{2} < \frac{47}{33}$

61. $\frac{5}{8} = 0.625$

63. $\frac{41}{333} = 0.123123\ldots$

65. False. The reciprocal of 2 is $\frac{1}{2}$ which is not
an integer.

67. True. If the real number can be written
as the quotient of two integers, p/q, it is
rational. Otherwise, the real number is
irrational.

Section P.2   Properties of Real Numbers and the Basic Rules of Algebra

■ You should be able to identify the terms in an algebraic expression.

■ You should know and be able to use the basic rules of algebra.

■ Commutative Property

(a) Addition: $a + b = b + a$ (b) Multiplication: $a \cdot b = b \cdot a$

■ Associative Property

(a) Addition: $(a + b) + c = a + (b + c)$ (b) Multiplication: $(ab)c = a(bc)$

■ Identity Property

(a) Addition: 0 is the identity; $a + 0 = 0 + a = a$.
(b) Multiplication: 1 is the identity; $a \cdot 1 = 1 \cdot a = a$.

■ Inverse Property

(a) Addition: $-a$ is the inverse of a; $a + (-a) = -a + a = 0$.
(b) Multiplication: $1/a$ is the inverse of a, $a \neq 0$; $a(1/a) = (1/a)a = 1$.

■ Distributive Property

(a) Left: $a(b + c) = ab + ac$ (b) Right: $(a + b)c = ac + bc$

■ Properties of Negatives

(a) $(-1)a = -a$ (b) $-(-a) = a$
(c) $(-a)b = a(-b) = -ab$ (d) $(-a)(-b) = ab$
(e) $-(a + b) = (-a) + (-b) = -a - b$

■ Properties of Zero

(a) $a \pm 0 = a$ (b) $a \cdot 0 = 0$
(c) $0 \div a = 0/a = 0$, $a \neq 0$ (d) If $ab = 0$, then $a = 0$ or $b = 0$.
(e) $a/0$ is undefined.

■ Properties of Fractions ($b \neq 0$, $d \neq 0$)

(a) Equivalent Fractions: $a/b = c/d$ if and only if $ad = bc$.
(b) Rule of Signs: $-a/b = a/-b = -(a/b)$ and $-a/-b = a/b$
(c) Equivalent Fractions: $a/b = ac/bc$, $c \neq 0$
(d) Addition and Subtraction
  1. Like Denominators: $(a/b) \pm (c/b) = (a \pm c)/b$
  2. Unlike Denominators: $(a/b) \pm (c/d) = (ad \pm bc)/bd$
(e) Multiplication: $(a/b) \cdot (c/d) = ac/bd$
(f) Division: $(a/b) \div (c/d) = (a/b) \cdot (d/c) = ad/bc$ if $c \neq 0$.

■ Properties of Equality

(a) Reflexive: $a = a$
(b) Symmetric: If $a = b$, then $b = a$.
(c) Transitive: If $a = b$ and $b = c$, then $a = c$.
(d) Substitution: If $a = b$, then a can be replaced by b in any statement involving a or b.
  1. If $a = b$, then $a + c = b + c$.
  2. If $a = b$, then $ac = bc$.

■ Cancellation Laws

(a) If $a + c = b + c$, then $a = b$.   (b) If $ac = bc$ and $c = 0$, then $a = b$.

■ You should know the properties of exponents.

(a) $a^1 = a$ (b) $a^0 = 1$, $a \neq 0$

(c) $a^m a^n = a^{m+n}$ (d) $a^m/a^n = a^{m-n}$, $a \neq 0$

(e) $a^{-n} = 1/a^n$, $a \neq 0$ (f) $(a^m)^n = a^{mn}$

(g) $(ab)^n = a^n b^n$ (h) $(a/b)^n = a^n/b^n$, $b \neq 0$

(i) $(a/b)^{-n} = (b/a)^n$, $a \neq 0$, $b \neq 0$ (j) $|a^2| = |a|^2 = a^2$

■ You should be able to write numbers in scientific notation, $c \times 10^n$, where $1 \leq c < 10$ and n is an integer.

■ You should be able to use your calculator to evaluate expressions involving exponents.

1. Terms: $7x$, 4

3. $x^2 - 4x + 8 = x^2 + (-4x) + 8$

Terms: x^2, $-4x$, 8

5. $4x^3 + x - 5 = 4x^3 + x + (-5)$

Terms: $4x^3$, x, -5

7. (a) $4(-1) - 6 = -4 - 6 = -10$

(b) $4(0) - 6 = 0 - 6 = -6$

9. (a) $(-2)^2 - 3(-2) + 4 = 4 + 6 + 4 = 14$

(b) $(2)^2 - 3(2) + 4 = 4 - 6 + 4 = 2$

11. (a) $\dfrac{1+1}{1-1} = \dfrac{2}{0}$ which is undefined.

You cannot divide by zero.

(b) $\dfrac{-1+1}{-1-1} = \dfrac{0}{-2} = 0$

13. $x + 9 = 9 + x$,

Commutative Property of Addition

15. $\dfrac{1}{(h+6)}(h+6) = 1$, $h \neq -6$

Inverse Property of Multiplication

17. $2(x+3) = 2 \cdot x + 2 \cdot 3 = 2x + 6$

Distributive Property

19. $1 \cdot (1 + x) = 1 + x$,

Identity Property of Multiplication

21. $x(3y) = (x \cdot 3)y$ by the Associative Property of Multiplication

$= (3x)y$ by the Commutative Property of Multiplication

23. $\dfrac{81 - (90 - 9)}{5} = \dfrac{81 - 81}{5} = \dfrac{0}{5} = 0$

25. $\dfrac{8-8}{-9+(6+3)} = \dfrac{8-8}{-9+9} = \dfrac{0}{0}$,

which is undefined since the denominator is zero.

27. $10 - 6 - 2 = 4 - 2 = 2$

29. $(4-7)(-2) = (-3)(-2)$

$= 6$

31. $\dfrac{3}{16} + \dfrac{5}{16} = \dfrac{3+5}{16}$

$= \dfrac{8}{16} = \dfrac{1}{2}$

33. $\dfrac{5}{8} - \dfrac{5}{12} + \dfrac{1}{6} = \dfrac{5 \cdot 3}{8 \cdot 3} - \dfrac{5 \cdot 2}{12 \cdot 2} + \dfrac{1 \cdot 4}{6 \cdot 4}$

$= \dfrac{15 - 10 + 4}{24} = \dfrac{9}{24} = \dfrac{3}{8}$

35. $\frac{4}{5} \cdot \frac{1}{2} \cdot \frac{3}{4} = \frac{1}{5} \cdot \frac{1}{2} \cdot \frac{3}{1} = \frac{3}{10}$

37. $\frac{2}{3} \div 8 = \frac{2}{3} \times \frac{1}{8} = \frac{1}{12}$

39. $12 \div \frac{1}{4} = 12 \times \frac{4}{1} = 12 \times 4 = 48$

41. $-3 + \dfrac{3}{7} = \dfrac{-18}{7} \approx -2.57$

43. $\dfrac{11.46 - 5.37}{3.91} = \dfrac{6.09}{3.91} \approx 1.56$

45. $5^{-1} + 2^{-3} = \dfrac{1}{5} + \dfrac{1}{2^3} = \dfrac{1}{5} + \dfrac{1}{8}$

$\qquad = \dfrac{8+5}{40} = \dfrac{13}{40} \approx 0.33$

47. $\dfrac{7^4 + 32}{7^4 - 200} = \dfrac{2401 + 32}{2401 - 200} = \dfrac{2433}{2201} \approx 1.11$

49. $\dfrac{5^5}{5^2} = 5^{5-2} = 5^3 = 125$

51. $(3^3)^2 = 3^6 = 729$

53. $(2^3 \cdot 3^2)^2 = (8 \cdot 9)^2 = 72^2 = 5184$

55. $\dfrac{4 \cdot 3^{-2}}{2^{-2} \cdot 3^{-1}} = \dfrac{4 \cdot 2^2 \cdot 3^1}{3^2} = \dfrac{4 \cdot 4}{3} = \dfrac{16}{3}$

57. $-3(2)^3 = -3(8) = -24$

59. $6(10)^0 - (6 \cdot 10)^0 = 6 \cdot 1 - (60)^0$

$\qquad\qquad = 6 - 1 = 5$

61. $(-5z)^3 = (-1)^3(5)^3(z^3) = -125z^3$

63. $6y^2(2y^4)^2 = 6y^2(2)^2(y^4)^2$

$\qquad\qquad = 6y^2(4)(y^8) = 24y^{10}$

65. $\dfrac{3x^5}{x^3} = 3x^{5-3} = 3x^2$

67. $\dfrac{7x^2}{x^3} = 7x^{2-3} = 7x^{-1} = \dfrac{7}{x}$

69. $\dfrac{12(x+y)^3}{9(x+y)} = \dfrac{3 \cdot 4(x+y)^{3-1}}{3 \cdot 3}$

$\qquad = \dfrac{4(x+y)^2}{3}$

71. $(x+5)^0 = 1, \ x \neq -5$

73. $(-2x^2)^3(4x^3)^{-1} = \dfrac{(-2x^2)^3}{4x^3}$

$\qquad = \dfrac{-8x^6}{4x^3} = -2x^3$

75. $\left(\dfrac{x}{10}\right)^{-1} = \dfrac{10}{x}$

77. $3^n \cdot 3^{2n} = 3^{n+2n} = 3^{3n}$ **79.** $57{,}500{,}000 = 5.75 \times 10^7$ **81.** $0.0000899 = 8.99 \times 10^{-5}$

83. $5.24 \times 10^8 = 524{,}000{,}000$

85. $4.8 \times 10^{-10} = 0.00000000048$

87. (a) $750\left(1 + \dfrac{0.11}{365}\right)^{800} \approx 954.448$

$\quad$ 750 $\boxed{\times}$ $\boxed{(}$ 1 $\boxed{+}$ 0.11 $\boxed{\div}$ 365 $\boxed{)}$ $\boxed{y^x}$ 800 $\boxed{=}$

$\quad$ (b) $\dfrac{67{,}000{,}000 + 93{,}000{,}000}{0.0052} \approx 3.077 \times 10^{10}$

$\quad$ $\boxed{(}$ 67000000 $\boxed{+}$ 93000000 $\boxed{)}$ $\boxed{\div}$ 0.0052 $\boxed{=}$

Section P.3   Radicals and Rational Exponents

- You should know the properties of radicals.

  (a) $\sqrt[n]{a^m} = (\sqrt[n]{a})^m$

  (b) $\sqrt[n]{a} \cdot \sqrt[n]{b} = \sqrt[n]{ab}$

  (c) $\dfrac{\sqrt[n]{a}}{\sqrt[n]{b}} = \sqrt[n]{\dfrac{a}{b}}$, $b \neq 0$

  (d) $\sqrt[m]{\sqrt[n]{a}} = \sqrt[mn]{a}$

  (e) $(\sqrt[n]{a})^n = a$

  (f) For n even, $\sqrt[n]{a^n} = |a|$

  For n odd, $\sqrt[n]{a^n} = a$

  (g) $a^{1/n} = \sqrt[n]{a}$

  (h) $a^{m/n} = (\sqrt[n]{a})^m = \sqrt[n]{a^m}$

- You should be able to simplify radicals.

  (a) All possible factors have been removed from the radical sign.

  (b) All fractions have radical-free denominators.

  (c) The index for the radical has been reduced as far as possible.

- You should be able to use your calculator to evaluate radicals.

1. Radical form: $\sqrt{9} = 3$
   Rational exponent form: $9^{1/2} = 3$

3. Radical form: $\sqrt{196} = 14$
   Rational exponent form: $196^{1/2} = 14$

5. Radical form: $\sqrt[3]{-216} = -6$
   Rational exponent form: $(-216)^{1/3} = -6$

7. Radical form: $\sqrt[3]{27^2} = 9$
   Rational exponent form:
   $(27^2)^{1/3} = 27^{2/3} = 9$

9. Radical form: $\sqrt[4]{81^3} = 27$
   Rational exponent form:
   $(81^3)^{1/4} = 81^{3/4} = 27$

11. $\sqrt{9} = 3$

13. $\sqrt[3]{8} = \sqrt[3]{2^3} = 2$

15. $\sqrt{36} = \sqrt{6^2} = 6$

17. $-\sqrt[3]{-27} = -\sqrt[3]{(-3)^3}$
    $= -(-3) = 3$

19. $\dfrac{4}{\sqrt{64}} = \dfrac{4}{8} = \dfrac{1}{2}$

21. $(\sqrt[3]{-125})^3 = -125$

23. $16^{1/2} = \sqrt{16} = 4$

25. $(32)^{-3/5} = (\sqrt[5]{32})^{-3}$

$\qquad = 2^{-3}$

$\qquad = \dfrac{1}{2^3}$

$\qquad = \dfrac{1}{8}$

27. $\left(\dfrac{16}{81}\right)^{-3/4} = \left(\dfrac{81}{16}\right)^{3/4}$

$\qquad = \left(\sqrt[4]{\dfrac{81}{16}}\right)^3$

$\qquad = \left(\dfrac{3}{2}\right)^3$

$\qquad = \dfrac{27}{8}$

29. $\left(-\dfrac{1}{64}\right)^{-1/3} = (-64)^{1/3}$

$\qquad = \sqrt[3]{-1}\sqrt[3]{64}$

$\qquad = -\sqrt[3]{4^3}$

$\qquad = -4$

31. $\sqrt{8} = \sqrt{4 \cdot 2}$

$\qquad = \sqrt{4}\sqrt{2}$

$\qquad = 2\sqrt{2}$

33. $\sqrt{9 \times 10^{-4}} = \sqrt{9}\sqrt{(10^{-2})^2}$

$\qquad = 3(10^{-2})$

$\qquad = 3 \times 10^{-2}$

$\qquad = \dfrac{3}{100}$

35. $\sqrt{72x^3} = \sqrt{36 \cdot 2 \cdot x^2 \cdot x}$

$\qquad = 6x\sqrt{2x}$

37. $\sqrt[3]{16x^5} = \sqrt[3]{8 \cdot 2 \cdot x^3 \cdot x^2}$

$\qquad = 2x\sqrt[3]{2x^2}$

39. $\sqrt{75x^2y^{-4}} = \sqrt{\dfrac{75x^2}{y^4}}$

$\qquad = \sqrt{\dfrac{25 \cdot 3x^2}{y^4}}$

$\qquad = \dfrac{5|x|\sqrt{3}}{y^2}$

41. $\dfrac{1}{\sqrt{3}} = \dfrac{1}{\sqrt{3}} \cdot \dfrac{\sqrt{3}}{\sqrt{3}}$

$\qquad = \dfrac{\sqrt{3}}{3}$

43. $\dfrac{8}{\sqrt[3]{2}} = \dfrac{8}{\sqrt[3]{2}} \cdot \dfrac{\sqrt[3]{2^2}}{\sqrt[3]{2^2}}$

$\qquad = \dfrac{8\sqrt[3]{2^2}}{\sqrt[3]{2^3}}$

$\qquad = \dfrac{8\sqrt[3]{4}}{2}$

$\qquad = 4\sqrt[3]{4}$

45. $\dfrac{2x}{5 - \sqrt{3}} = \dfrac{2x}{5 - \sqrt{3}} \cdot \dfrac{5 + \sqrt{3}}{5 + \sqrt{3}}$

$\qquad = \dfrac{2x(5 + \sqrt{3})}{25 - 3}$

$\qquad = \dfrac{2x(5 + \sqrt{3})}{22}$

$\qquad = \dfrac{x(5 + \sqrt{3})}{11}$

47. $\dfrac{3}{\sqrt{5}+\sqrt{6}} = \dfrac{3}{\sqrt{5}+\sqrt{6}} \cdot \dfrac{\sqrt{5}-\sqrt{6}}{\sqrt{5}-\sqrt{6}}$

$\qquad = \dfrac{3(\sqrt{5}-\sqrt{6})}{5-6}$

$\qquad = -3(\sqrt{5}-\sqrt{6})$

$\qquad = 3(\sqrt{6}-\sqrt{5})$

49. $\dfrac{\sqrt{8}}{2} = \dfrac{\sqrt{8}}{2} \cdot \dfrac{\sqrt{8}}{\sqrt{8}}$

$\qquad = \dfrac{8}{2\sqrt{8}} = \dfrac{4}{\sqrt{8}}$

$\qquad = \dfrac{4}{\sqrt{4\cdot 2}} = \dfrac{4}{2\sqrt{2}} = \dfrac{2}{\sqrt{2}}$

51. $\dfrac{\sqrt{5}+\sqrt{3}}{3} = \dfrac{\sqrt{5}+\sqrt{3}}{3} \cdot \dfrac{\sqrt{5}-\sqrt{3}}{\sqrt{5}-\sqrt{3}}$

$\qquad = \dfrac{5-3}{3(\sqrt{5}-\sqrt{3})}$

$\qquad = \dfrac{2}{3(\sqrt{5}-\sqrt{3})}$

53. $\dfrac{\sqrt{7}-3}{4} = \dfrac{\sqrt{7}-3}{4} \cdot \dfrac{\sqrt{7}+3}{\sqrt{7}+3}$

$\qquad = \dfrac{7-9}{4(\sqrt{7}+3)}$

$\qquad = \dfrac{-2}{4(\sqrt{7}+3)}$

$\qquad = \dfrac{-1}{2(\sqrt{7}+3)}$

55. $\sqrt[4]{3^2} = 3^{2/4}$

$\qquad = 3^{1/2}$

$\qquad = \sqrt{3}$

57. $\sqrt[6]{(x+1)^4} = (x+1)^{4/6}$

$\qquad = (x+1)^{2/3}$

$\qquad = \sqrt[3]{(x+1)^2}$

59. $\sqrt{\sqrt{32}} = (32^{1/2})^{1/2}$

$\qquad = 32^{1/4}$

$\qquad = \sqrt[4]{32}$

$\qquad = 2\sqrt[4]{2}$

61. $\sqrt{\sqrt[4]{2x}} = \left((2x)^{1/4}\right)^{1/2} = (2x)^{1/8} = \sqrt[8]{2x}$

63. $5\sqrt{x} - 3\sqrt{x} = (5-3)\sqrt{x} = 2\sqrt{x}$

65. $2\sqrt{50} + 12\sqrt{8} = 2\sqrt{25\cdot 2} + 12\sqrt{4\cdot 2}$

$\qquad = 2(5)\sqrt{2} + 12(2)\sqrt{2}$

$\qquad = 10\sqrt{2} + 24\sqrt{2} = 34\sqrt{2}$

67. $-2\sqrt{9y} + 10\sqrt{y} = -2\cdot 3\sqrt{y} + 10\sqrt{y}$

$\qquad = -6\sqrt{y} + 10\sqrt{y}$

$\qquad = 4\sqrt{y}$

69. $\dfrac{x^{-3}x^{1/2}}{x^{3/2}x^{-1}} = \dfrac{x^{1/2}x^1}{x^3 x^{3/2}} = \dfrac{x^{3/2}}{x^{9/2}}$

$\qquad = \dfrac{1}{x^{(9/2)-(3/2)}} = \dfrac{1}{x^{6/2}} = \dfrac{1}{x^3}$

71. $(3x^{-1/3}y^{3/4})^2 = \left(\dfrac{3y^{3/4}}{x^{1/3}}\right)^2 = \dfrac{9y^{3/2}}{x^{2/3}}$

73. $\dfrac{18y^{4/3}z^{-1/3}}{24y^{-2/3}z} = \dfrac{3y^{6/3}}{4z^{4/3}} = \dfrac{3y^2}{4z^{4/3}}$

75. $\left(\dfrac{x^{1/4}}{x^{1/6}}\right)^3 = (x^{1/12})^3 = x^{1/4}$

77. $(c^{3/2})^{1/3} = c^{1/2} = \sqrt{c}$

79. $\sqrt{57} \approx 7.550$

57 $\boxed{\sqrt{}}$ $\boxed{=}$

81. $\sqrt[6]{125} \approx 2.236$

125 $\boxed{y^x}$ $\boxed{(}$ 1 $\boxed{\div}$ 6 $\boxed{)}$ $\boxed{=}$

83. $\sqrt{75 + 3\sqrt{8}} \approx 9.137$

$\boxed{(}$ 75 $\boxed{+}$ $\boxed{(}$ 3 $\boxed{\times}$ 8 $\boxed{\sqrt{}}$ $\boxed{)}$ $\boxed{)}$ $\boxed{\sqrt{}}$

85. $\sqrt{5} + \sqrt{3} \approx 3.968$

$\sqrt{5+3} = \sqrt{8} \approx 2.828$

Therefore,

$\sqrt{5} + \sqrt{3} > \sqrt{5+3}.$

87. $\sqrt{3^2 + 2^2} = \sqrt{9+4}$

$= \sqrt{13}$

≈ 3.6056

Therefore,

$5 > \sqrt{3^2 + 2^2}.$

89. $\sqrt{3} \cdot \sqrt[4]{3} \approx 2.280$

$\sqrt[8]{3} \approx 1.147$

Therefore,

$\sqrt{3} \cdot \sqrt[4]{3} > \sqrt[8]{3}.$

91. Repeatedly taking the square root of a positive real number, the display appears to be approaching 1. For example,

$\sqrt{10} = 3.16227766$

$\sqrt{3.16227766} = 1.77827941$

$\sqrt{1.77827941} = 1.333521432$

$\sqrt{1.333521432} = 1.154781985$

and so on.

Section P.4   Polynomials and Special Products

- Given a polynomial in x, $a_n x^n + a_{n-1} x^{n-1} + \cdots + a_1 x + a_0$, where $a_n \neq 0$, you should be able to identify the following.
  - (a) Degree: n
  - (b) Terms: $a_n x^n$, $a_{n-1} x^{n-1}$, ..., $a_1 x$, a_0
  - (c) Coefficients: a_n, a_{n-1}, ..., a_1, a_0
  - (d) Leading coefficient: a_n
  - (e) Constant term: a_0

- You should be able to add and subtract polynomials.

- You should be able to multiply polynomials by either
  - (a) The Distributive Law or
  - (b) The Vertical Method.

- You should know the special binomial products.
  - (a) $(ax + b)(cx + d) = acx^2 + adx + bcx + bd$ FOIL
    $$= acx^2 + (ad + bc)x + bd$$
  - (b) $(u \pm v)^2 = u^2 \pm 2uv + v^2$
  - (c) $(u + v)(u - v) = u^2 - v^2$
  - (d) $(u \pm v)^3 = u^3 \pm 3u^2 v + 3uv^2 \pm v^3$

---

1. Standard form:
$2x^2 - x + 1$
Degree: 2
Leading coefficient: 2

3. Standard form: $x^5 - 1$
Degree: 5
Leading coefficient: 1

5. Standard form:
$4x^5 + 6x^4 - x - 1$
Degree: 5
Leading coefficient: 4

7. $2x - 3x^3 + 8$
This is a polynomial.
Standard form:
$-3x^3 + 2x + 8$

9. $\dfrac{3x + 4}{x} = \dfrac{3x}{x} + \dfrac{4}{x}$
$$= 3 + 4x^{-1}$$
This is not a polynomial because of the negative exponent.

11. $y^2 - y^4 + y^3$
This is a polynomial.
Standard form:
$-y^4 + y^3 + y^2$

13. $(6x + 5) - (8x + 15) = 6x + 5 - 8x - 15 = (6x - 8x) + (5 - 15) = -2x - 10$

15. $-(x^3 - 2) + (4x^3 - 2x) = -x^3 + 2 + 4x^3 - 2x = (4x^3 - x^3) - 2x + 2 = 3x^3 - 2x + 2$

17. $(15x^2 - 6) - (-8x^3 - 14x^2 - 17) = 15x^2 - 6 + 8x^3 + 14x^2 + 17$
$$= 8x^3 + (15x^2 + 14x^2) + (-6 + 17) = 8x^3 + 29x^2 + 11$$

19. $5z - [3z - (10z + 8)] = 5z - (3z - 10z - 8)$
$$= 5z - 3z + 10z + 8 = (5z - 3z + 10z) + 8 = 12z + 8$$

21. $3x(x^2 - 2x + 1) = 3x(x^2) + 3x(-2x) + 3x(1) = 3x^3 - 6x^2 + 3x$

23. $-5z(3z - 1) = -5z(3z) + (-5z)(-1)$
$$= -15z^2 + 5z$$

25. $(-2x)(-3x)(5x + 2) = 6x^2(5x + 2)$
$$= 6x^2(5x) + 6x^2(2)$$
$$= 30x^3 + 12x^2$$

27. $(x + 3)(x + 4) = x^2 + 4x + 3x + 12$
$$= x^2 + 7x + 12$$

29. $(3x - 5)(2x + 1) = 6x^2 + 3x - 10x - 5$
$$= 6x^2 - 7x - 5$$

31. $(x + 6)^2 = x^2 + 2(x)(6) + 6^2$
$$= x^2 + 12x + 36$$

33. $(2x - 5y)^2 = (2x)^2 - 2(2x)(5y) + (5y)^2$
$$= 4x^2 - 20xy + 25y^2$$

35. $[(x - 3) + y]^2 = (x - 3)^2 + 2(x - 3)y + y^2$
$$= x^2 - 6x + 9 + 2xy - 6y + y^2 = x^2 + 2xy + y^2 - 6x - 6y + 9$$

37. $(x + 10)(x - 10) = x^2 - 100$

39. $(x + 2y)(x - 2y) = x^2 - 4y^2$

41. $(m - 3 + n)(m - 3 - n) = [(m - 3) + n][(m - 3) - n]$
$$= (m - 3)^2 - n^2 = m^2 - 6m + 9 - n^2 = m^2 - n^2 - 6m + 9$$

43. $(2r^2 - 5)(2r^2 + 5) = 4r^4 - 25$

45. $(x + 1)^3 = x^3 + 3x^2(1) + 3x(1^2) + 1^3$
$$= x^3 + 3x^2 + 3x + 1$$

47. $(2x - y)^3 = (2x)^3 - 3(2x)^2y + 3(2x)y^2 - y^3 = 8x^3 - 12x^2y + 6xy^2 - y^3$

49. $(\sqrt{x} + \sqrt{y})(\sqrt{x} - \sqrt{y}) = (\sqrt{x})^2 - (\sqrt{y})^2$
$$= x - y$$

51. $(4x^3 - 3)^2 = (4x^3)^2 - 2(4x^3)(3) + (3)^2$
$$= 16x^6 - 24x^3 + 9$$

53. $(x^2 + 9)(x^2 - x - 4) = (x^2 + 9)x^2 - (x^2 + 9)(x) - (x^2 + 9)(4)$
$$= x^4 + 9x^2 - x^3 - 9x - 4x^2 - 36$$
$$= x^4 - x^3 + 5x^2 - 9x - 36$$

55. By the Vertical Method we have:

$$
\begin{array}{r}
x^2 - x \;+ 1 \\
x^2 + x \;+ 1 \\
\hline
x^4 - x^3 + x^2 \\
x^3 - x^2 + x \\
x^2 - x \;+ 1 \\
\hline
x^4 + 0x^3 + x^2 + 0x + 1
\end{array}
$$

which equals $x^4 + x^2 + 1$.

57. $5x(x+1) - 3x(x+1) = 5x^2 + 5x - 3x^2 - 3x = 2x^2 + 2x$

59. $(x + \sqrt{5})(x - \sqrt{5})(x + 4) = (x^2 - 5)(x + 4) = x^3 + 4x^2 - 5x - 20$

61. We form the product of two polynomials of degrees m and n, as follows.

$$
(a_m x^m + a_{m-1} x^{m-1} + \cdots + a_0)(b_n x^n + b_{n-1} x^{n-1} + \cdots + b_0)
$$

$$
= a_m x^m (b_n x^n + \cdots + b_0) + \cdots + a_0 (b_n x^n + \cdots + b_0)
$$

$$
= a_m b_n x^{m+n} + \cdots + a_0 b_0
$$

Thus, the degree of the product is $m + n$.

Section P.5   Factoring

- You should be able to factor out all common factors, the first step in factoring.
- You should be able to factor the following special polynomial forms.
  - (a) $u^2 - v^2 = (u + v)(u - v)$
  - (b) $u^2 \pm 2uv + v^2 = (u \pm v)^2$
  - (c) $mx^2 + nx + r = (ax + b)(cx + d)$, where $m = ac$, $r = bd$, $n = ad + bc$
    Note: Not all trinomials can be factored (using real coefficients).
  - (d) $u^3 \pm v^3 = (u \pm v)(u^2 \mp uv + v^2)$
- You should be able to factor by grouping.

1. $3x + 6 = 3(x + 2)$

3. $2x^3 - 6x = 2x(x^2 - 3)$

5. $(x - 1)^2 + 6(x - 1) = (x - 1)(x - 1 + 6)$
$$= (x - 1)(x + 5)$$

7. $x^2 - 36 = x^2 - 6^2 = (x + 6)(x - 6)$

9. $16y^2 - 9 = (4y)^2 - (3)^2 = (4y + 3)(4y - 3)$

11. $(x - 1)^2 - 4 = (x - 1)^2 - (2)^2$
$$= [(x - 1) + 2][(x - 1) - 2]$$
$$= (x + 1)(x - 3)$$

13. $x^2 - 4x + 4 = x^2 - 2(2)(x) + 2^2$
$$= (x - 2)^2$$

15. $4t^2 + 4t + 1 = (2t)^2 + 2(2t)(1) + (1)^2$
$$= (2t + 1)^2$$

17. $25y^2 - 10y + 1 = (5y)^2 - 2(5y)(1) + 1^2$
$$= (5y - 1)^2$$

19. $x^2 + x - 2 = (x + 2)(x - 1)$ since $(2)(-1) = -2$ and $(2) + (-1) = 1$.

21. $s^2 - 5s + 6 = (s - 2)(s - 3)$ since $(-2)(-3) = 6$ and $(-2) + (-3) = -5$.

23. $y^2 + y - 20 = (y + 5)(y - 4)$ since $(5)(-4) = -20$ and $(5) + (-4) = 1$.

25. $x^2 - 30x + 200 = (x - 10)(x - 20)$ since $(-10)(-20) = 200$ and $(-10) + (-20) = -30$.

27. $3x^2 - 5x + 2 = (3x - 2)(x - 1)$ since $(-2)(-1) = 2$ and $(-3) + (-2) = -5$.

29. $9z^2 - 3z - 2 = (3z + 1)(3z - 2)$ since $(1)(-2) = -2$ and $(-6) + (3) = -3$.

31. $5x^2 + 26x + 5 = (5x + 1)(x + 5)$ since $(1)(5) = 5$ and $(25) + (1) = 26$.

33. $x^3 - 8 = x^3 - 2^3 = (x - 2)(x^2 + 2x + 4)$ **35.** $y^3 + 64 = y^3 + 4^3 = (y + 4)(y^2 - 4y + 16)$

37. $8t^3 - 1 = (2t)^3 - 1^3 = (2t - 1)(4t^2 + 2t + 1)$ **39.** $x^3 - x^2 + 2x - 2 = (x^3 - x^2) + (2x - 2)$
$$= x^2(x - 1) + 2(x - 1)$$
$$= (x - 1)(x^2 + 2)$$

41. $2x^3 - x^2 - 6x + 3 = (2x^3 - x^2) + (-6x + 3)$ **43.** $6 + 2x - 3x^3 - x^4 = (6 + 2x) + (-3x^3 - x^4)$
$$= x^2(2x - 1) - 3(2x - 1) \qquad\qquad\qquad = 2(3 + x) - x^3(3 + x)$$
$$= (2x - 1)(x^2 - 3) \qquad\qquad\qquad\qquad = (3 + x)(2 - x^3)$$

45. $3x^2 + 10x + 8 = 3x^2 + 6x + 4x + 8$ **47.** $6x^2 + x - 2 = 6x^2 + 4x - 3x - 2$
$$= (3x^2 + 6x) + (4x + 8) \qquad\qquad = (6x^2 - 3x) + (4x - 2)$$
$$= 3x(x + 2) + 4(x + 2) \qquad\qquad = 3x(2x - 1) + 2(2x - 1)$$
$$= (x + 2)(3x + 4) \qquad\qquad\qquad = (2x - 1)(3x + 2)$$

49. $15x^2 - 11x + 2 = 15x^2 - 6x - 5x + 2$
$$= (15x^2 - 6x) - (5x - 2) = 3x(5x - 2) - (5x - 2) = (5x - 2)(3x - 1)$$

51. $3x^2 + 7x + 2 = (3x + 1)(x + 2)$ **53.** $2x^2 + 7x + 3 = (2x + 1)(x + 3)$

          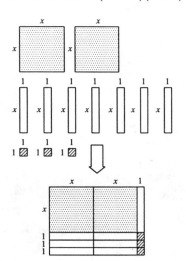

55. $x^3 - 9x = x(x^2 - 9)$
$$= x(x - 3)(x + 3)$$

57. $x^3 - 4x^2 = x^2(x - 4)$

59. $x^2 - 2x + 1 = (x - 1)^2$

61. $1 - 4x + 4x^2 = (1 - 2x)^2$

63. $-2x^2 - 4x + 2x^3 = 2x^3 - 2x^2 - 4x$
$$= 2x(x^2 - x - 2)$$
$$= 2x(x - 2)(x + 1)$$

65. $9x^2 + 10x + 1 = (9x + 1)(x + 1)$

67. $3x^3 + x^2 + 15x + 5 = x^2(3x + 1) + 5(3x + 1) = (3x + 1)(x^2 + 5)$

69. $x^4 - 4x^3 + x^2 - 4x = x(x^3 - 4x^2 + x - 4) = x[x^2(x - 4) + (x - 4)] = x(x - 4)(x^2 + 1)$

71. $25 - (x + 5)^2 = [5 - (x + 5)][5 + (x + 5)] = -x(x + 10)$

73. $(x^2 + 1)^2 - 4x^2 = [(x^2 + 1) + 2x][(x^2 + 1) - 2x]$
$$= (x^2 + 2x + 1)(x^2 - 2x + 1) = (x + 1)^2(x - 1)^2$$

75. $2t^3 - 16 = 2(t^3 - 8) = 2(t - 2)(t^2 + 2t + 4)$

77. $4x(2x - 1) + (2x - 1)^2 = (2x - 1)(4x + (2x - 1)) = (2x - 1)(6x - 1)$

79. $2(x + 1)(x - 3)^2 - 3(x + 1)^2(x - 3) = (x + 1)(x - 3)[2(x - 3) - 3(x + 1)]$
$$= (x + 1)(x - 3)[2x - 6 - 3x - 3]$$
$$= (x + 1)(x - 3)(-x - 9)$$
$$= -(x + 1)(x - 3)(x + 9)$$

Section P.6   Fractional Expressions

- You should know how to find the domain of an algebraic expression.
- You should know that a rational expression is the quotient of two polynomials.
- You should be able to simplify rational expressions by reducing them to lowest terms. This may involve factoring both the numerator and the denominator.
- You should be able to add, subtract, multiply, and divide rational expressions.
- You should be able to simplify compound fractions.

1. The domain of the polynomial $3x^2 - 4x + 7$ is the set of all real numbers.

3. The domain of the polynomial $4x^3 + 5x + 3$, $x \geq 0$ is the set of nonnegative real numbers, since the polynomial is restricted to that set.

5. The domain of $\dfrac{1}{x-2}$ is the set of all real numbers except $x = 2$, which would produce an undefined division by zero.

7. The domain of $\dfrac{x-1}{x(x-4)}$ is the set of all real numbers except $x = 0$ and $x = 4$, which would produce an undefined division by zero.

9. The domain of $\sqrt{x+1}$ is the set of real numbers greater than or equal to -1 since $x + 1 \geq 0$ when $x \geq -1$.

11. $\dfrac{5}{2x} = \dfrac{5(3x)}{(2x)(3x)} = \dfrac{15x}{6x^2}$

13. $\dfrac{x+1}{x} = \dfrac{x+1}{x} \cdot \dfrac{x-2}{x-2}$

$= \dfrac{(x+1)(x-2)}{x(x-2)}, \quad x \neq 2$

15. $\dfrac{3x}{x-3} = \dfrac{3x(x+2)}{(x-3)(x+2)}$

$= \dfrac{3x(x+2)}{x^2 - x - 6}, \quad x \neq -2$

17. $\dfrac{15x^2}{10x} = \dfrac{5x(3x)}{5x(2)} = \dfrac{3x}{2}, \quad x \neq 0$

19. $\dfrac{3xy}{xy+x} = \dfrac{3xy}{x(y+1)} = \dfrac{3y}{y+1}, \quad x \neq 0$

21. $\dfrac{x-5}{10-2x} = \dfrac{x-5}{-2(x-5)} = -\dfrac{1}{2}, \quad x \neq 5$

23. $\dfrac{x^3+5x^2+6x}{x^2-4} = \dfrac{x(x+2)(x+3)}{(x+2)(x-2)}$

$= \dfrac{x(x+3)}{x-2}, \quad x \neq -2$

25. $\dfrac{y^2-7y+12}{y^2+3y-18} = \dfrac{(y-3)(y-4)}{(y+6)(y-3)}$

$= \dfrac{y-4}{y+6}, \quad y \neq 3$

27. $\dfrac{2-x+2x^2-x^3}{x-2} = \dfrac{(2-x)+x^2(2-x)}{x-2}$

$= \dfrac{(2-x)(1+x^2)}{x-2} = \dfrac{-(x-2)(x^2+1)}{x-2} = -(x^2+1), \quad x \neq 2$

29. $\dfrac{z^3-8}{z^2+2z+4} = \dfrac{(z-2)(z^2+2z+4)}{z^2+2z+4} = z-2$

31. $\dfrac{5}{x-1} \cdot \dfrac{x-1}{25(x-2)} = \dfrac{1}{5(x-2)}, \quad x \neq 1$

33. $\dfrac{r}{r-1} \cdot \dfrac{r^2-1}{r^2} = \dfrac{r}{r-1} \cdot \dfrac{(r+1)(r-1)}{r^2} = \dfrac{r+1}{r}, \quad r \neq 1$

35. $\dfrac{y^3-8}{2y^3} \cdot \dfrac{4y}{y^2-5y+6} = \dfrac{(y-2)(y^2+2y+4)}{2y^3} \cdot \dfrac{4y}{(y-3)(y-2)} = \dfrac{2(y^2+2y+4)}{y^2(y-3)}, \quad y \neq 2$

37. $\dfrac{3(x+y)}{4} \div \dfrac{x+y}{2} = \dfrac{3(x+y)}{4} \cdot \dfrac{2}{x+y} = \dfrac{3}{2}, \quad x \neq -y$

39. $\dfrac{\left(-\dfrac{x^2}{(x+1)^2}\right)}{\left(\dfrac{x}{(x+1)^3}\right)} = \dfrac{x^2}{(x+1)^2} \div \dfrac{x}{(x+1)^3} = \dfrac{x^2}{(x+1)^2} \cdot \dfrac{(x+1)^3}{x} = x(x+1), \quad x \neq 0, -1$

41. $\dfrac{5}{x-1} + \dfrac{x}{x-1} = \dfrac{5+x}{x-1} = \dfrac{x+5}{x-1}$

43. $6 - \dfrac{5}{x+3} = \dfrac{6(x+3)}{(x+3)} - \dfrac{5}{x+3}$

$= \dfrac{6(x+3)-5}{x+3} = \dfrac{6x+13}{x+3}$

45. $\dfrac{3}{x-2} + \dfrac{5}{2-x} = \dfrac{3}{x-2} - \dfrac{5}{x-2} = \dfrac{3-5}{x-2} = -\dfrac{2}{x-2}$

47. $\dfrac{2}{x^2-4} - \dfrac{1}{x^2-3x+2} = \dfrac{2}{(x+2)(x-2)} - \dfrac{1}{(x-1)(x-2)}$

$$= \dfrac{2(x-1)}{(x+2)(x-2)(x-1)} - \dfrac{x+2}{(x+2)(x-2)(x-1)}$$

$$= \dfrac{2(x-1)-(x+2)}{(x+2)(x-2)(x-1)} = \dfrac{x-4}{(x+2)(x-2)(x-1)}$$

49. $-\dfrac{1}{x} + \dfrac{2}{x^2+1} + \dfrac{1}{x^3+x} = -\dfrac{1}{x} + \dfrac{2}{x^2+1} + \dfrac{1}{x(x^2+1)}$

$$= \dfrac{-(x^2+1)}{x(x^2+1)} + \dfrac{2x}{x(x^2+1)} + \dfrac{1}{x(x^2+1)} = \dfrac{-x^2-1+2x+1}{x(x^2+1)}$$

$$= \dfrac{-x^2+2x}{x(x^2+1)} = \dfrac{-x(x-2)}{x(x^2+1)} = -\dfrac{x-2}{x^2+1} = \dfrac{2-x}{x^2+1}, \quad x \neq 0$$

51. $x^2(x^2-1)^{-1/2} + (x^2-1)^{1/2} = (x^2-1)^{-1/2}(x^2+(x^2-1)) = \dfrac{2x^2-1}{(x^2-1)^{1/2}}$

53. $3(x-2)^{-1/3} - x(x-2)^{-4/3} = (x-2)^{-4/3}(3(x-2)-x) = \dfrac{2x-6}{(x-2)^{4/3}} = \dfrac{2(x-3)}{(x-2)^{4/3}}$

55. $\dfrac{\left(\dfrac{x}{2}-1\right)}{(x-2)} = \dfrac{\left(\dfrac{x}{2}-1\right)}{(x-2)} \cdot \dfrac{2}{2}$

$$= \dfrac{(x-2)}{2(x-2)} = \dfrac{1}{2}, \quad x \neq 2$$

57. $\dfrac{\left(\dfrac{1}{x}-\dfrac{1}{x+1}\right)}{\left(\dfrac{1}{x+1}\right)} = \dfrac{\dfrac{(x+1)-x}{x(x+1)}}{\dfrac{1}{x+1}}$

$$= \dfrac{1}{x(x+1)} \cdot \dfrac{x+1}{1}$$

$$= \dfrac{1}{x}, \quad x \neq -1$$

59. $\dfrac{\left(\dfrac{1}{(x+h)^2}-\dfrac{1}{x^2}\right)}{h} = \dfrac{\left(\dfrac{1}{(x+h)^2}-\dfrac{1}{x^2}\right)}{h} \cdot \dfrac{x^2(x+h)^2}{x^2(x+h)^2} = \dfrac{x^2-(x+h)^2}{hx^2(x+h)^2}$

$$= \dfrac{[x+(x+h)][x-(x+h)]}{hx^2(x+h)^2} = \dfrac{(2x+h)(-h)}{hx^2(x+h)^2} = -\dfrac{2x+h}{x^2(x+h)^2}, \quad h \neq 0$$

61. $\dfrac{2a^{-1}+b^{-1}}{ab} = \dfrac{2a^{-1}}{ab} + \dfrac{b^{-1}}{ab}$

$$= \dfrac{2}{a^2b} + \dfrac{1}{ab^2}$$

$$= \dfrac{2b+a}{a^2b^2}$$

63. $\dfrac{\left(\sqrt{x}-\dfrac{1}{2\sqrt{x}}\right)}{\sqrt{x}} = \dfrac{\left(\sqrt{x}-\dfrac{1}{2\sqrt{x}}\right)}{\sqrt{x}} \cdot \dfrac{2\sqrt{x}}{2\sqrt{x}}$

$$= \dfrac{2x-1}{2x}, \quad x > 0$$

65. $\dfrac{\dfrac{t^2}{\sqrt{t^2+1}}-\sqrt{t^2+1}}{t^2} = \dfrac{\dfrac{t^2}{\sqrt{t^2+1}}-\sqrt{t^2+1}}{t^2} \cdot \dfrac{\sqrt{t^2+1}}{\sqrt{t^2+1}} = \dfrac{t^2-(t^2+1)}{t^2\sqrt{t^2+1}} = -\dfrac{1}{t^2\sqrt{t^2+1}}$

67. $\dfrac{\sqrt{x+2}-\sqrt{x}}{2} = \dfrac{\sqrt{x+2}-\sqrt{x}}{2} \cdot \dfrac{\sqrt{x+2}+\sqrt{x}}{\sqrt{x+2}+\sqrt{x}}$

$\qquad = \dfrac{(x+2)-x}{2(\sqrt{x+2}+\sqrt{x})} = \dfrac{2}{2(\sqrt{x+2}+\sqrt{x})} = \dfrac{1}{\sqrt{x+2}+\sqrt{x}}$

Section P.7   The Cartesian Plane

- You should be able to plot points.
- You should know that the distance between (x_1, y_1) and (x_2, y_2) in the plane is
  $$d = \sqrt{(x_2 - x_1)^2 + (y_2 - y_1)^2}.$$
- You should know that the midpoint of the line segment joining (x_1, y_1) and (x_2, y_2) is
  $$\left(\frac{x_1 + x_2}{2}, \frac{y_1 + y_2}{2}\right).$$
- You should know the equation of a circle:
  $$(x - h)^2 + (y - k)^2 = r^2.$$

1.

3.

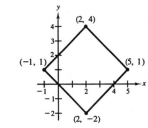

5. Since the points $(6, -3)$ and $(6, 5)$ lie on the same horizontal line, the distance between the points is given by the absolute value of the difference of their y-coordinates.
$$d = |5 - (-3)| = |5 + 3| = |8| = 8$$

7. Since the points $(-3, -1)$ and $(2, -1)$ lie on the same vertical line, the distance between the points is given by the absolute value of the difference of their x-coordinates.
$$d = |-3 - 2| = 5$$

9. (a) $a = |4 - 0| = 4$
  $$b = |3 - 0| = 3$$
  $$c = \sqrt{4^2 + 3^2} = \sqrt{25} = 5$$
  (b) $d = \sqrt{(4 - 0)^2 + (3 - 0)^2}$
  $$= \sqrt{16 + 9} = \sqrt{25} = 5$$

11. (a) $a = |-3 - 7| = 10$
  $$b = |4 - 1| = 3$$
  $$c = \sqrt{10^2 + 3^2} = \sqrt{109}$$
  (b) $c = \sqrt{(7 - (-3))^2 + (4 - 1)^2}$
  $$= \sqrt{10^2 + 3^2} = \sqrt{109}$$

13. (a)

(b) $d = \sqrt{(9-1)^2 + (7-1)^2}$

$\quad = \sqrt{8^2 + 6^2}$

$\quad = \sqrt{100} = 10$

(c) $m = \left(\dfrac{1+9}{2}, \dfrac{1+7}{2}\right) = (5,\ 4)$

15. (a)

(b) $d = \sqrt{(-4-4)^2 + (10-(-5))^2}$

$\quad = \sqrt{(-8)^2 + (15)^2}$

$\quad = \sqrt{289} = 17$

(c) $m = \left(\dfrac{-4+4}{2}, \dfrac{10+(-5)}{2}\right) = \left(0,\ \dfrac{5}{2}\right)$

17. (a)

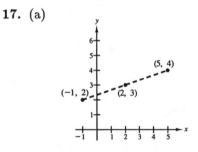

(b) $d = \sqrt{(5+1)^2 + (4-2)^2}$

$\quad = \sqrt{36+4} = 2\sqrt{10}$

(c) $m = \left(\dfrac{-1+5}{2}, \dfrac{2+4}{2}\right) = (2,\ 3)$

19. (a)

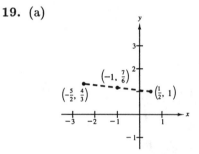

(b) $d = \sqrt{\left(\frac{1}{2}+\frac{5}{2}\right)^2 + \left(1-\frac{4}{3}\right)^2}$

$\quad = \sqrt{9+\frac{1}{9}} = \dfrac{\sqrt{82}}{3}$

(c) $m = \left(\dfrac{-\frac{5}{2}+\frac{1}{2}}{2}, \dfrac{\frac{4}{3}+1}{2}\right) = \left(-1,\ \dfrac{7}{6}\right)$

21. (a)

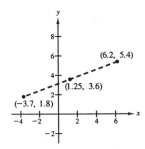

(b) $d = \sqrt{(6.2 - (-3.7))^2 + (5.4 - 1.8)^2}$

$\quad = \sqrt{(9.9)^2 + (3.6)^2}$

$\quad = \sqrt{110.97}$

(c) $m = \left(\dfrac{6.2 + (-3.7)}{2}, \dfrac{5.4 + 1.8}{2} \right)$

$\quad = (1.25,\ 3.6)$

23. (a)

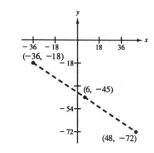

(b) $d = \sqrt{(48 + 36)^2 + (-72 + 18)^2}$

$\quad = \sqrt{7056 + 2916}$

$\quad = \sqrt{9972} = 6\sqrt{277}$

(c) $m = \left(\dfrac{-36 + 48}{2}, \dfrac{-18 - 72}{2} \right)$

$\quad = (6,\ -45)$

25. $\dfrac{520{,}000 + 740{,}000}{2} = 630{,}000$

The estimated sales for 1991 is \$630,000.

27. $d_1 = \sqrt{(-1 - 2)^2 + (-5 - 1)^2} = \sqrt{45}$

$\quad d_2 = \sqrt{(2 - 4)^2 + (1 - 0)^2} = \sqrt{5}$

$\quad d_3 = \sqrt{(4 - (-1))^2 + (0 - (-5))^2} = \sqrt{50}$

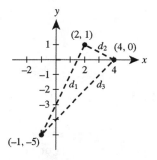

Since $d_1{}^2 + d_2{}^2 = d_3{}^2$, we can conclude by the Pythagorean Theorem that the triangle is a right triangle.

29. $d_1 = \sqrt{(0 - 1)^2 + (0 - 2)^2} = \sqrt{5}$

$\quad d_2 = \sqrt{(0 - 2)^2 + (0 - 1)^2} = \sqrt{5}$

$\quad d_3 = \sqrt{(3 - 1)^2 + (3 - 2)^2} = \sqrt{5}$

$\quad d_4 = \sqrt{(3 - 2)^2 + (3 - 1)^2} = \sqrt{5}$

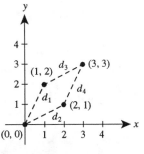

Since $d_1 = d_2 = d_3 = d_4$, we can conclude that the points form the vertices of a rhombus.

31. $\sqrt{(x-1)^2 + (-10-2)^2} = 13$

$\sqrt{x^2 - 2x + 1 + 144} = 13$

$x^2 - 2x + 145 = 169$

$x^2 - 2x - 24 = 0$

$(x+4)(x-6) = 0$

$x = -4 \quad \text{or} \quad x = 6$

33. $\sqrt{(8-0)^2 + (y-0)^2} = 17$

$\sqrt{64 + y^2} = 17$

$64 + y^2 = 289$

$y^2 = 225$

$y = \pm 15$

35. The distance between $(4, -1)$ and (x, y) is equal to the distance between $(-2, 3)$ and (x, y).

$$\sqrt{(x-4)^2 + (y+1)^2} = \sqrt{(x+2)^2 + (y-3)^2}$$

$$(x-4)^2 + (y+1)^2 = (x+2)^2 + (y-3)^2$$

$$x^2 - 8x + 16 + y^2 + 2y + 1 = x^2 + 4x + 4 + y^2 - 6y + 9$$

$$-12x + 8y + 4 = 0$$

$$3x - 2y - 1 = 0$$

37. $x > 0 \Rightarrow x$ lies in Quadrant I or in Quadrant IV.

$y < 0 \Rightarrow y$ lies in Quadrant III or in Quadrant IV.

$x > 0$ and $y < 0 \Rightarrow (x, y)$ lies in Quadrant IV.

39. $x > 0 \Rightarrow x$ lies in Quadrant I or in Quadrant IV.

$y > 0 \Rightarrow y$ lies in Quadrant I or in Quadrant II.

$x > 0$ and $y > 0 \Rightarrow (x, y)$ lies in Quadrant I.

41. $x = -4 \Rightarrow x$ is negative $\Rightarrow x$ lies in Quadrant II or Quadrant III.

$y > 0 \Rightarrow y$ lies in Quadrant I or Quadrant II.

$x = -4$ and $y > 0 \Rightarrow (x, y)$ lies in Quadrant II.

43. $y < -5 \Rightarrow y$ is negative $\Rightarrow y$ lies in either Quadrant III or Quadrant IV.

45. If $xy > 0$, then either x and y are both positive, or both negative. Hence, (x, y) lies in either Quadrant I or Quadrant III.

47. Since $(x, -y)$ is in Quadrant II, we know that

$x < 0$ and $-y > 0$. If $-y > 0$, then $y < 0$.

$x < 0 \Rightarrow x$ lies in Quadrant II or in Quadrant III.

$y < 0 \Rightarrow y$ lies in Quadrant III or in Quadrant IV.

$x < 0$ and $y < 0 \Rightarrow (x, y)$ lies in Quadrant III.

49.

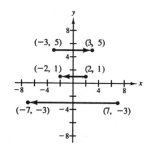

The points are reflected through the y-axis.

51. $(x - 0)^2 + (y - 0)^2 = 3^2$

$\qquad x^2 + y^2 = 9$

53. $(x - 2)^2 + (y + 1)^2 = 4^2$

$\qquad (x - 2)^2 + (y + 1)^2 = 16$

55. $(x + 1)^2 + (y - 2)^2 = r^2$

$\qquad (0 + 1)^2 + (0 - 2)^2 = r^2 \ \Rightarrow \ r^2 = 5$

$\qquad (x + 1)^2 + (y - 2)^2 = 5$

57. $r = \dfrac{1}{2}\sqrt{(6 - 0)^2 + (8 - 0)^2} = \dfrac{1}{2}\sqrt{100} = 5$

$\qquad$ Center $= \left(\dfrac{0 + 6}{2}, \ \dfrac{0 + 8}{2} \right) = (3, \ 4)$

$\qquad (x - 3)^2 + (y - 4)^2 = 25$

CHAPTER 1
Functions and Graphs

Section 1.1   Graphs and Graphing Utilities

- You should be able to graph an equation by the point-plotting method.
- You should be able to find the intercepts of a graph of an equation.
- You should be able to graph an equation using a graphing utility.
- You should be able to determine an appropriate viewing rectangle to show all the important features of a graph.
- You should be able to use the zoom and trace features of a graphing utility.

1. (a) $\sqrt{0+4} = 2$, yes

(b) $\sqrt{5+4} = 3$, yes

3. (a) $2(1) - 2 - 3 = -3 \neq 0$, no

(b) $2(1) - (-1) - 3 = 0$, yes

5. (a) $1^2\left(\frac{1}{5}\right) - 1^2 + 4\left(\frac{1}{5}\right) = 0$
yes

(b) $2^2\left(\frac{1}{2}\right) - 2^2 + 4\left(\frac{1}{2}\right) = 0$
yes

7. $y = x^2 + C$

$6 = (2)^2 + C$

$6 = 4 + C$

$C = 2$

9. $y = C\sqrt{x+1}$

$8 = C\sqrt{3+1}$

$2C = 8$

$C = 4$

11. $2x + y = 3$

$y = -2x + 3$

x	-4	-2	0	2	4
y	11	7	3	-1	-5
$(x,\ y)$	$(-4,\ 11)$	$(-2,\ 7)$	$(0,\ 3)$	$(2,\ -1)$	$(4,\ -5)$

13. $y = 4 - x$

x-intercept: $(4, 0)$

y-intercept: $(0, 4)$

Matches graph (c)

```
RANGE
Xmin=-2
Xmax=6
Xscl=1
Ymin=-1
Ymax=5
Yscl=1
```

15. $y = \sqrt{4 - x^2}$

x-intercepts:

$(2, 0), (-2, 0)$

y-intercept: $(0, 2)$

Matches graph (d)

```
RANGE
Xmin=-3
Xmax=3
Xscl=1
Ymin=-1
Ymax=3
Yscl=1
```

17. $y = x^3 - x$

x-intercepts:

$(-1, 0), (0, 0), (1, 0)$

y-intercept: $(0, 0)$

Matches graph (e)

```
RANGE
Xmin=-2
Xmax=2
Xscl=1
Ymin=-2
Ymax=2
Yscl=1
```

19. $y = -3x + 2$

Intercepts: $(0, 2), \left(\frac{2}{3}, 0\right)$

21. $y = 1 - x^2$

Intercepts:

$(-1, 0), (0, 1), (1, 0)$

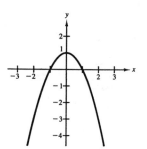

23. $y = x^3 + 2$

Intercepts:

$(-\sqrt[3]{2}, 0), (0, 2)$

25. $y = (x - 3)(x + 2)$

Intercepts:

$(3, 0), (-2, 0), (0, -6)$

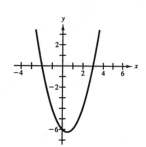

27. $y = \sqrt{x - 3}$

Intercept: $(3, 0)$

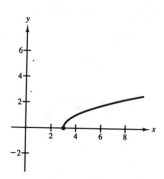

29. $y = |x - 2|$

Intercepts: $(0, 2), (2, 0)$

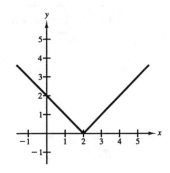

31. $y = x^2 - 4x + 3$

The graph intersects the x-axis twice and the y-axis once.

33. $y = 3x^4 - 6x^2$

The graph intersects the x-axis three times and the y-axis once.

35. $y = x\sqrt{4 - x}$

The graph intersects the x-axis twice and the y-axis once.

37. $y = \dfrac{10x}{x^2 + 1}$

The graph intersects the x-axis once and the y-axis once.

39. $y = x^4 - 4x^3 + 16x$

The graph intersects the x-axis twice and the y-axis once.

41. $y = 100x\sqrt{25 - x}$

The graph intersects the x-axis twice and the y-axis once.

43. $x^2 - 100y - 1000 = 0 \Rightarrow 100y = x^2 - 1000$

$$\Rightarrow y = \tfrac{1}{100}x^2 - 10$$

The graph intersects the x-axis twice and the y-axis once.

45. $x^2 + y^2 = 64 \Rightarrow y^2 = 64 - x^2$

$$\Rightarrow y = \pm\sqrt{64 - x^2}$$

$$y_1 = \sqrt{64 - x^2}, \quad y_2 = -\sqrt{64 - x^2}$$

47. $6x^2 + y^2 = 72 \Rightarrow y^2 = 72 - 6x^2$

$$\Rightarrow y = \pm\sqrt{72 - 6x^2}$$

$$y_1 = \sqrt{72 - 6x^2}, \quad y_2 = -\sqrt{72 - 6x^2}$$

49. $9x + 27y - 1000 = 0 \Rightarrow 27y = -9x + 1000$

$$\Rightarrow y = -\tfrac{1}{3}x + \tfrac{1000}{27}$$

Since the y-intercept is $\tfrac{1000}{27} \approx 37.04$, we can use:

Xmin=−1   Ymin=−1
Xmax=100   Ymax=40
Xscl=5   Yscl=2

(Answer is not unique.)

51. $y = -(x-5)^2(x-15)$

Since the x-intercepts are 5 and 15, we can use:

Xmin=−1   Ymin=−25
Xmax=20   Ymax=150
Xscl=1   Yscl=10

(Answer is not unique.)

53. $y = 0.25x - 50$

The first viewing rectangle is preferred because it shows a greater rate of increase.

55. $y = \sqrt[3]{x}$

(a)

x	-1	0	1
y	-1	0	1

(b)

x	-1	$-\frac{3}{4}$	$-\frac{1}{2}$	$-\frac{1}{4}$	0	$\frac{1}{4}$	$\frac{1}{2}$	$\frac{3}{4}$	1
y	-1	-0.91	-0.79	-0.63	0	0.63	0.79	0.91	-1

(c)

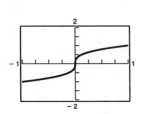

57. $y = \sqrt{5 - x}$
    (a) $(2, y)$, $y = 1.73$
    (b) $(x, 3)$, $x = -4.00$

59. $y = x^5 - 5x$
    (a) $(-0.5, y)$, $y = 2.47$
    (b) $(x, -4)$, $x = 1, -1.65$

61. $y = 225,000 - 20,000x$, $0 \le x \le 8$
    (a)

```
RANGE
Xmin=0
Xmax=8
Xscl=1
Ymin=0
Ymax=250000
Yscl=50000
```

    (b)

63. $y = 0.40x^3 - 9.42x^2 + 1053.24$
    (a)

65. $y = 1.097x + 0.15$, $0 \le x \le 6$

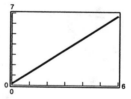

    (b) Using the zoom and trace features,
        we have $y = 16889.72$ when $x = 44$
        (year 1994).

67. If the x-intercept of the graph of $y = \sqrt{ax + b}$ is $(5, 0)$, then $0 = \sqrt{5a + b}$ or $5a + b = 0$. Hence, there are many correct answers. For instance, $a = 1$, $b = -5$.

Section 1.2   Lines in the Plane

> You should know the following important facts about lines.
>
> ■ The slope of the line through $(x_1, \ y_1)$ and $(x_2, \ y_2)$ is
>
> $$m = \frac{y_2 - y_1}{x_2 - x_1}.$$
>
> ■ (a) If $m > 0$, the line rises from left to right.
> (b) If $m = 0$, the line is horizontal.
> (c) If $m < 0$, the line falls from left to right.
> (d) If m is undefined, the line is vertical.
>
> ■ Equations of Lines
> (a) Point-Slope: $y - y_1 = m(x - x_1)$
> (b) Two-Point: $y - y_1 = \dfrac{y_2 - y_1}{x_2 - x_1}(x - x_1)$
> (c) Slope-Intercept: $y = mx + b$
> (d) General: $Ax + By + C = 0$
> (e) Vertical: $x = a$
> (f) Horizontal: $y = b$
>
> ■ You should be able to graph a line using a graphing utility. This graph may not appear to have the slope indicated by its equation unless you are using the "square" viewing rectangle.
>
> ■ Given two distinct nonvertical lines
>
> $$L_1 : y = m_1 x + b_1 \quad \text{and} \quad L_2 : y = m_2 x + b_2$$
>
> (a) L_1 is parallel to L_2 if and only if $m_1 = m_2$ and $b_1 \neq b_2$.
> (b) L_1 is perpendicular to L_2 if and only if $m_1 = -1/m_2$.

1. Slope $= \dfrac{\text{rise}}{\text{run}} = \dfrac{6}{5}$

3. Since the line is horizontal, it has a slope of zero.

5. Slope $= \dfrac{\text{rise}}{\text{run}} = \dfrac{-3}{1} = -3$

7.

9. $m = \dfrac{6 - (-2)}{1 - (-3)} = \dfrac{8}{4} = 2$

11. $m = \dfrac{4 - (-1)}{-6 - (-6)} = \dfrac{5}{0}$

The slope is undefined.

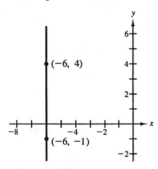

13. $\text{Slope} = \dfrac{2 + 2}{1 + 2} = \dfrac{4}{3}$

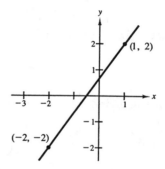

15. Since $m = 0$, the line is horizontal, and since the line passes through $(2, 1)$, all other points on the line will be of the form $(x, 1)$. Three additional points are $(0, 1)$, $(3, 1)$, and $(-1, 1)$.

17. Since $m = 1$, y increases by 1 for every one unit increase in x. Three points are $(6, -5)$, $(7, -4)$, and $(8, -3)$.

19. The slope of L_1 is
$$m_1 = \frac{9 - (-1)}{5 - 0} = \frac{10}{5} = 2.$$
The slope of L_2 is
$$m_2 = \frac{1 - 3}{4 - 0} = -\frac{2}{4} = -\frac{1}{2}.$$
Since m_1 and m_2 are negative reciprocals of each other, the lines are perpendicular.

21. The slope of L_1 is
$$m_1 = \frac{6 - 0}{3 - (-6)} = \frac{6}{9} = \frac{2}{3}.$$
The slope of L_2 is
$$m_2 = \frac{\frac{7}{3} - (-1)}{5 - 0} = \frac{\frac{10}{3}}{5} = \frac{2}{3}.$$
Since $m_1 = m_2$, the lines are parallel.

23. The slope between the first two points is
$$\frac{0-(-4)}{2-0}=2$$ and the slope between the
second and third points is $\dfrac{2-0}{3-2}=2.$
Hence, the three points are collinear.

25. Since the slope is $-12/100$ and you have
descended 2000 feet, $-12/100 = -2000/x$,
which gives $x = 16{,}666.67$ feet
horizontally.

27. $5x - y + 3 = 0$

$$-y = -5x - 3$$
$$y = 5x + 3$$

Slope: $m = 5$

y-intercept: $(0, 3)$

29. $5x - 2 = 0$

$$5x = 2$$
$$x = \tfrac{2}{5} \quad \text{Vertical line}$$

Slope: Undefined

y-intercept: None

31. $m = \dfrac{5-(-1)}{-5-5} = \dfrac{6}{-10} = -\dfrac{3}{5}$

$$y + 1 = -\frac{3}{5}(x - 5)$$
$$5y + 5 = -3(x - 5)$$
$$5y + 5 = -3x + 15$$
$$3x + 5y - 10 = 0$$

33. $m = \dfrac{\frac{5}{4}-\frac{1}{2}}{\frac{1}{2}-2} = \dfrac{\frac{3}{4}}{-\frac{3}{2}} = -\dfrac{1}{2}$

$$y - \frac{1}{2} = -\frac{1}{2}(x - 2)$$
$$2y - 1 = -(x - 2)$$
$$2y - 1 = -x + 2$$
$$x + 2y - 3 = 0$$

35. $m = \dfrac{7-1}{-8-(-8)} = \dfrac{6}{0}$

Undefined

$$x = -8$$
$$x + 8 = 0$$

37.
$$y + 2 = 3(x - 0)$$
$$y + 2 = 3x$$
$$3x - y - 2 = 0$$

39.
$$y - \tfrac{5}{2} = -\tfrac{4}{3}(x - 4)$$
$$y - \tfrac{5}{2} = -\tfrac{4}{3}x + \tfrac{16}{3}$$
$$y = -\tfrac{4}{3}x + \tfrac{47}{6}$$

$$6y + 8x - 47 = 0$$

41. Since the slope is undefined, the line is vertical, and since the line passes through $(6, -1)$, its equation is $x = 6$ or $x - 6 = 0$.

43. $y = 0.5x - 3$

45.

$$y = 2x$$
$$y = -2x$$
$$y = \tfrac{1}{2}x$$

47.

$$y = -\tfrac{1}{2}x$$
$$y = -\tfrac{1}{2}x + 3$$
$$y = 2x - 4$$

49. $\dfrac{x}{5} + \dfrac{y}{-3} = 1 \Rightarrow \dfrac{y}{-3} = \dfrac{-x}{5} + 1 \Rightarrow y = \dfrac{3}{5}x - 3$

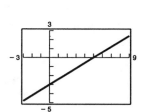

$a = 5$ is the x-intercept and $b = -3$ is the y-intercept.

51. $\dfrac{x}{2} + \dfrac{y}{3} = 1$

$3x + 2y = 6$

$3x + 2y - 6 = 0$

53. $4x - 2y = 3$

$\qquad -2y = -4x + 3$

$\qquad y = 2x - \dfrac{3}{2}$

The slope of the given line is $m_1 = 2$.

(a) The slope of the parallel line
is $m_2 = m_1 = 2$.

$\qquad y - 1 = 2(x - 2)$

$\qquad y - 1 = 2x - 4$

$\qquad 2x - y - 3 = 0$

(b) The slope of the perpendicular line
is $m_2 = -1/m_1 = -1/2$.

$\qquad y - 1 = -\tfrac{1}{2}(x - 2)$

$\qquad 2y - 2 = -(x - 2)$

$\qquad 2y - 2 = -x + 2$

$\qquad x + 2y - 4 = 0$

55. $y = -3$

The slope of the given line is $m_1 = 0$.

(a) The slope of the parallel line is
$m_2 = m_1 = 0$.

$\qquad y - 0 = 0(x + 1)$

$\qquad y = 0$

(b) The slope of the perpendicular line
is $m_2 = -1/m$, undefined.

$\qquad x = -1$

$\qquad x + 1 = 0$

57. Value = \$2540 + (\$125)(the number of years t after 1990)

$\qquad V = 125t + 2540, \quad 0 \le t \le 5$

59. Value = \$20,400 + (\$2000)(the number of years t after 1990)

$\qquad V = 2000t + 20,400, \quad 0 \le t \le 5$

61. A person is paying $10 per week to a friend to repay a $100 loan, $y = 100 - 10x$. Matches graph (b). The slope is $m = -10$. This represents the decrease in the amount of the loan each week.

63. A sales representative receives $20 per day for food plus $0.25 for each mile traveled, $y = 20 + 0.25x$. Matches graph (a). The slope is 0.25 and the y-intercept is 20.

65. Using the points $(0, 32)$ and $(100, 212)$, we have

$$m = \frac{212 - 32}{100 - 0} = \frac{180}{100} = \frac{9}{5}$$

$$F - 32 = \frac{9}{5}(C - 0)$$

$$F = \frac{9}{5}C + 32.$$

67. Let $t = 0$ represent 1990.

$$(0, \ 28{,}500), \ (2, \ 32{,}900)$$

$$m = \frac{32{,}900 - 28{,}500}{2 - 0} = \frac{4400}{2} = 2200$$

$$S - 28{,}500 = 2200(t - 0)$$

$$S = 2200t + 28{,}500$$

When $t = 5$,

$$S = 2200(5) + 28{,}500 = \$39{,}500.$$

69. (a) Using the points $(0, \ 875)$ and $(5, \ 0)$ where the first coordinate represents the year x and the second coordinate represents the value y, we have:

$$m = \frac{0 - 875}{5 - 0} = -175$$

$$y - 875 = -175(x - 0)$$

$$y = -175x + 875, \ \ 0 \leq x \leq 5$$

(c) When $x = 2$, $y = 525.00$ dollars.

(d) When $y = 200$, $x = 3.86$ years.

(b)

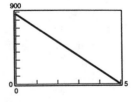

71. Monthly wage = Monthly salary + 7% of sales

$$W = 2500 + 0.07S$$

73. (a) $C = 5.25t + 11.50t + 36{,}500$

   $C = 16.75t + 36{,}500$

   (b) $R = 37t$

   (c) The break-even point is $t = 1802$ hours, the t-value of the point where the two lines intersect.

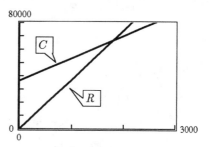

75. (Many answers possible) The cost of producing each toy is $25, and the fixed costs are $450. Find the cost function for producing x toys.

77. Since the triangles are similar, the result immediately follows.

$$\frac{y_2{}^* - y_1{}^*}{x_2{}^* - x_1{}^*} = \frac{y_2 - y_1}{x_2 - x_1}$$

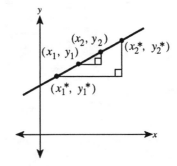

Section 1.3   Functions

■ You should know the definition of a function, domain, and range.

■ Given a set or an equation, you should be able to determine if it represents a function.

■ You should understand function notation.

■ Given a function, you should be able to do the following.
(a) Find the domain.
(b) Evaluate the function at specific values.

■ You should be able to use the function keys on your calculator.

---

1. (a) Each element of A is matched with exactly one element of B, so it does represent a function.

(b) The element 1 in A is matched with two elements, -2 and 1 of B, so it does not represent a function.

(c) Each element of A is matched with exactly one element of B, so it does represent a function.

(d) The element 2 in A is not matched with an element of B, so it does not represent a function.

3. y is not a function of x since some values of x give two values for y. For example, if $x = 0$, then $y = \pm 2$.

5. $x^2 + y = 4$

$$y = -x^2 + 4$$

y is a function of x. No value of x yields more than one value of y.

7. $x^2 y - x^2 + 4y = 0$

$$(x^2 - 4)y = x^2$$

$$y = \frac{x^2}{x^2 - 4}$$

y is a function of x. No value of x yields more than one value of y.

9. y is not a function of x since some values of x give two values for y. For example, if $x = 3$, then $y = \pm\sqrt{8}$.

11. (a) $f(3) = 6 - 4(3) = -6$
(b) $f(-7) = 6 - 4(-7) = 34$
(c) $f(t) = 6 - 4(t) = 6 - 4t$
(d) $f(c + 1) = 6 - 4(c + 1)$

$$= 2 - 4c$$

$$= 2(1 - 2c)$$

13. (a) $f(4) = \dfrac{1}{(4) + 1} = \dfrac{1}{5}$
(b) $f(0) = \dfrac{1}{(0) + 1} = 1$
(c) $f(4x) = \dfrac{1}{(4x) + 1} = \dfrac{1}{4x + 1}$
(d) $f(x + h) = \dfrac{1}{(x + h) + 1} = \dfrac{1}{x + h + 1}$

15. (a) $f(1) = 2(1) - 3 = -1$
(b) $f(-3) = 2(-3) - 3 = -9$
(c) $f(x - 1) = 2(x - 1) - 3 = 2x - 5$
(d) $f\left(\frac{1}{4}\right) = 2\left(\frac{1}{4}\right) - 3 = -\frac{5}{2}$

17. (a) $h(2) = 2^2 - 2(2) = 0$
(b) $h(-1) = (-1)^2 - 2(-1) = 3$
(c) $h(x + 2) = (x + 2)^2 - 2(x + 2) = x^2 + 2x$
(d) $h(1.5) = (1.5)^2 - 2(1.5) = -0.75$

19. (a) $f(2) = \dfrac{|2|}{2} = 1$
(b) $f(-2) = \dfrac{|-2|}{-2} = -1$
(c) $f(x^2) = \dfrac{|x^2|}{x^2} = 1$
(d) $f(x - 1) = \dfrac{|x - 1|}{x - 1}$

21. (a) $f(-1) = 2(-1) + 1$
$$= -1$$
(b) $f(0) = 2(0) + 2 = 2$
(c) $f(1) = 2(1) + 2 = 4$
(d) $f(2) = 2(2) + 2 = 6$

23. All real numbers x

25. $y - 10 \geq 0$

$$y \geq 10$$

Therefore, the domain is $y \geq 10$.

27. All real numbers except $t = 0$

29. $x \neq 0, x+2 \neq 0 \Rightarrow x \neq -2$
Therefore, the domain is all real numbers except $x = 0, -2$.

31. $\{(-2, f(-2)), (-1, f(-1)), (0, f(0)), (1, f(1)), 2, f(2))\}$
$\{(-2, 4), (-1, 1), (0, 0), (1, 1), (2, 4)\}$

33. $\{(-2, f(-2)), (-1, f(-1)), (0, f(0)), (1, f(1)), (2, f(2))\}$
$\{(-2, 0), (-1, 1), (0, \sqrt{2}), (1, \sqrt{3}), (2, 2)\}$

35. (a) $(32.5)^2 = 1056.250$
(b) $(4.3)^5 = 1470.084$

37. (a) $\dfrac{1}{8.5} = 0.118$
(b) $\dfrac{1}{0.047} = 21.277$

39. The data fits the quadratic model $y = cx^2$ with $c = -2$.

41. Since y is undefined for $x = 0$, the data fits the model $y = c/x$ with $c = 32$.

43.
$$f(x) = 2x$$
$$f(x + h) = 2(x + h) = 2x + 2h$$
$$f(x + h) - f(x) = 2h$$
$$\frac{f(x + h) - f(x)}{h} = 2, \quad h \neq 0$$

45.
$$f(x) = x^3$$
$$f(x + h) = (x + h)^3 = x^3 + 3x(h)^2 + 3x^2 h + (h)^3$$
$$f(x + h) - f(x) = 3x(h)^2 + 3x^2 h + (h)^3$$
$$\frac{f(x + h) - f(x)}{h} = 3xh + 3x^2 + (h)^2, \quad h \neq 0$$

47. $A = \pi r^2, \quad C = 2\pi r$
$$r = \frac{C}{2\pi}$$
$$A = \pi \left(\frac{C}{2\pi}\right)^2 = \frac{C^2}{4\pi}$$

49. $A = \dfrac{1}{2}bh = \dfrac{1}{2}xy$

Since $(0, y)$, $(1, 2)$ and $(x, 0)$ all lie on the same line, the slopes between any pair are equal.
$$\frac{2 - y}{1 - 0} = \frac{0 - 2}{x - 1}$$
$$2 - y = -\frac{2}{x - 1}$$
$$y = \frac{2}{x - 1} + 2 = \frac{2x}{x - 1}$$
Therefore, $A = \dfrac{1}{2}x \left(\dfrac{2x}{x - 1}\right) = \dfrac{x^2}{x - 1}$.

Since $\dfrac{x^2}{x - 1} > 0$, $x > 1$.

Therefore, the domain is $x > 1$.

51. $y + 4x = 108$

$$y = 108 - 4x$$

$$V = x(x)y = x^2(108 - 4x)$$

$$= 108x^2 - 4x^3$$

$$= 4x^2(27 - x)$$

$$x > 0 \quad \text{and} \quad 108 - 4x > 0$$

$$-4x > -108$$

$$x < 27$$

Therefore, the domain is $0 < x < 27$.

55. (a) Cost = Variable costs + Fixed costs

$$C = 12.30x + 98,000$$

(b) Revenue = Price per unit × Number of units

$$R = 17.98x$$

(c) Profit = Revenue − Cost

$$P = 17.98x - (12.30x + 98,000)$$

$$P = 5.68x - 98,000$$

53. By the Pythagorean Theorem we have:

$$h^2 + 2000^2 = d^2$$

$$h^2 = d^2 - 2000^2$$

$$h = \sqrt{d^2 - 2000^2}$$

Since $d^2 - 2000^2 \geq 0$ and $d \geq 0$, we have a domain of $d \geq 2000$ feet.

Section 1.4   Graphs of Functions

■ You should be able to determine the domain and range of a function from its graph.

■ You should be able to use the vertical line test for functions.

■ You should be able to graph functions using your graphing utility.

■ You should know that the graph of $f(x) = c$ is a horizontal line through $(0, c)$.

■ You should be able to determine when a function is constant, increasing, or decreasing.

■ You should be able to approximate relative minimum and maximum values of a function using your graphing utility.

■ You should know the definition and graph of the greatest integer function.

■ You should know that f is
   (a) Odd if $f(-x) = -f(x)$.
   (b) Even if $f(-x) = f(x)$.

1. From the graph we see that the x-values are greater than or equal to 1. Therefore, the domain is $[1, \infty)$. Similarly, the y-values are greater than or equal to 0. Therefore, the range is $[0, \infty)$.

3. From the graph we see that the x-values are less than or equal to -2 and greater than or equal to 2. Therefore, the domain is $(-\infty, -2]$, $[2, \infty)$. Similarly, the y-values are greater than or equal to 0. Therefore, the range is $[0, \infty)$.

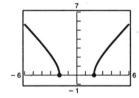

5. From the graph we see that the x-values are between -5 and 5 including -5 and 5. Therefore, the domain is $[-5, 5]$. Similarly, the y-values are between 0 and 5 including 0 and 5. Therefore, the range is $[0, 5]$.

7. Since no vertical line would ever cross the graph more than one time, y *is* a function of x. You could use the following viewing window to produce the given graph.

```
RANGE
Xmin=-3
Xmax=3
Xscl=1
Ymin=-1
Ymax=4
Yscl=1
```

9. Some vertical lines cross the graph more than once. For example, the vertical line $x = 4$ crosses the graph at $(4,\ 2)$ and $(4, -2)$. Therefore, y is not a function of x. You could use the following viewing window and the equations $y_1 = \sqrt{x}$ and $y_2 = -\sqrt{x}$ to produce the given graph.

```
RANGE
Xmin=-1
Xmax=5
Xscl=1
Ymin=-3
Ymax=3
Yscl=1
```

11. Since no vertical line would ever cross the graph more than one time, y *is* a function of x. You could use the following viewing window and the equation

$$y = \frac{x^2 + 1}{x}$$

to produce the given graph.

```
RANGE
Xmin=-5
Xmax=5
Xscl=1
Ymin=-4
Ymax=4
Yscl=1
```

13. $f(x) = -0.2x^2 + 3x + 32$
    (b) shows the most complete graph.

15. $f(x) = 4x^3 - x^4$
    (a) shows the most complete graph.

17. By its graph we see that f is increasing on $(-\infty, \infty)$.

19. By its graph we see that f is increasing on $(-\infty, 0)$ and $(2, \infty)$ and is decreasing on $(0, 2)$.

21. By its graph we see that f is increasing on $(-1, 0)$ and $(1, \infty)$ and is decreasing on $(-\infty, -1)$ and $(0, 1)$.

23. By its graph we see that f is increasing on $(-2, \infty)$ and decreasing on $(-3, -2)$.

25. Using the zoom and trace features, we find that $(3.00, -9.00)$ is a relative minimum of $f(x) = x^2 - 6x$.

27. Using the zoom and trace features, we find that $(-2.00, 20.00)$ is a relative maximum, and $(1.00, -7.00)$ is a relative minimum.

29. Using the zoom and trace features, we find that $(0.33, -0.38)$ is a relative minimum.

31. (a) Since the perimeter is 100 feet and x is the length of one side of the rectangle, the width is $50 - x$. The area is the length times the width, $A = x(50 - x)$.

(b)

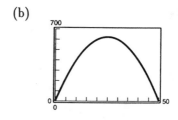

(c) Using the zoom and trace features, the maximum of the area function is 625.00. This occurs when $x = 25.00$, and hence, the dimensions of the rectangle which yields the maximum area are 25×25 (a square!).

33. $P = R - C = xp - C$

$$= x(100 - 0.0001x) - (350,000 + 30x)$$

$$= -0.0001x^2 + 70x - 350,000$$

$x = 350,000$ units would produce a maximum profit.

35. $f(x) = \begin{cases} 2x + 3, & x < 0 \\ 3 - x, & x \geq 0 \end{cases}$

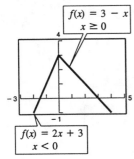

37. $f(x) = \begin{cases} x^2 + 5, & x \leq 1 \\ -x^2 + 4x + 3, & x > 1 \end{cases}$

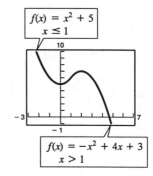

39. $s(x) = 2[\![x - 1]\!]$

(*Hint:* use dot mode, not connected.)

Domain: all x

Range: $\{\ldots,\; -4,\; -2,\; 0,\; 2,\; 4,\; \ldots\}$

41. (a) $C = 0.65 + 0.42[\![t]\!]$

(b)

(c) Less than 13 minutes

43. (a) $(-5,\; 6)$

(b) $(-5,\; -6)$

45. (a) $\left(\frac{3}{2},\; -2\right)$

(b) $\left(\frac{3}{2},\; 2\right)$

47. $f(x) = 3$

$f(-x) = 3 = f(x)$

f is even. The graph is symmetric with respect to the y-axis.

49. $f(x) = 5 - 3x$

$f(-x) = 5 - 3(-x)$

$\qquad = 5 + 3x$

$\qquad \neq f(x) \neq -f(x)$

f is neither odd nor even. The graph is not symmetric with respect to the origin nor the y-axis.

51. $g(s) = \dfrac{s^3}{4}$

$$g(-s) = \dfrac{(-s)^3}{4}$$

$$= -\dfrac{s^3}{4} = -g(s)$$

g is odd. The graph is symmetric with respect to the origin.

53. $f(x) = \sqrt{1-x}$

$$f(-x) = \sqrt{1-(-x)}$$

$$= \sqrt{1+x}$$

$$\neq f(x) \neq -f(x)$$

f is neither odd nor even. The graph is not symmetric with respect to the origin nor the y-axis.

55. $g(x) = \dfrac{5x}{x^2+1}$

$$g(-x) = \dfrac{5(-x)}{(-x)^2+1}$$

$$= \dfrac{-5x}{x^2+1}$$

$$= -g(x)$$

g is odd. The graph is symmetric with respect to the origin.

57. $f(x) = \dfrac{x^6}{3} - 2x^2$

$$f(-x) = \dfrac{(-x)^6}{3} - 2(-x)^2$$

$$= \dfrac{x^6}{3} - 2x^2$$

$$= f(x)$$

f is even.

59. $g(x) = x^3 - 5x$

$$g(-x) = (-x)^3 - 5(-x)$$

$$= -x^3 + 5x$$

$$= -(x^3 - 5x)$$

$$= -g(x)$$

g is odd.

61.

$$f(t) = t^2 + 2t - 3$$

$$f(-t) = (-t)^2 + 2(-t) - 3$$

$$= t^2 - 2t - 3$$

$$\neq f(t) \neq -f(t)$$

f is neither even nor odd.

63. $f(x) \geq 0$

   $4 - x \geq 0$

   $x \leq 4$

   $f(x) \geq 0$ on the interval $(-\infty, 4]$.

65. $f(x) \geq 0$

   $1 - x^4 \geq 0$

   $x^4 \leq 1$

   $|x| \leq 1$

   $-1 \leq x \leq 1$

   $f(x) \geq 0$ on the interval $[-1, 1]$.

67. $f(x) \geq 0$

   $5 \geq 0$

   $f(x) > 0$ for all x.

69. $h = $ top $-$ bottom

   $h = (4x - x^2) - 3$

71. $h = $ top $-$ bottom

   $h = (4x - x^2) - x^2$

   $h = 4x - 2x^2$

73. $L = $ right $-$ left

   $L = (4 - y^2) - (y + 2)$

   $L = -y^2 - y + 2$

75.

Interval	Intake Pipe	Drain Pipe 1	Drain Pipe 2
[0, 5]	Open	Closed	Closed
[5, 10]	Open	Open	Closed
[10, 20]	Closed	Closed	Closed
[20, 30]	Closed	Closed	Open
[30, 40]	Open	Open	Open
[40, 45]	Open	Closed	Open
[45, 50]	Open	Open	Open
[50, 60]	Open	Open	Closed

77. $f(x) = a_{2n}x^{2n} + a_{2n-2}x^{2n-2} + \cdots + a_2x^2 + a_0$

   $f(-x) = a_{2n}(-x)^{2n} + a_{2n-2}(-x)^{2n-2} + \cdots + a_2(-x)^2 + a_0$

   $\quad\quad = a_{2n}x^{2n} + a_{2n-2}x^{2n-2} + \cdots + a_2x^2 + a_0 = f(x)$

Section 1.5   Shifting, Reflecting, and Stretching Graphs

■ You should know the graphs of the most commonly used functions in algebra, and be able to reproduce them on your graphing utility.

(a) Constant function: $f(x) = c$ (b) Identity function: $f(x) = x$

(c) Absolute value function: $f(x) = |x|$ (d) Square root function: $f(x) = \sqrt{x}$

(e) Squaring function: $f(x) = x^2$ (f) Cubing function: $f(x) = x^3$

■ You should know how the graph of a function is changed by vertical and horizontal shifts.

■ You should know how the graph of a function is changed by a reflection.

■ You should know how the graph of a function is changed by nonrigid transformations, like stretches and shrinks.

■ You should know how the graph of a function is changed by a sequence of transformations.

1.

3.

5.

7.

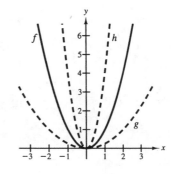

9. Since the vertex of g is at $(1,\ 1)$, $g(x) = (x-1)^2 + 1$. Since the vertex of h is at $(2,\ 4)$ and h opens downward, $h(x) = -(x-2)^2 + 4$.

11. Since the vertex of g is at $(3,\ -2)$, $g(x) = (x-3)^2 - 2$. Since the vertex of h is at $(0,\ 3)$ and h opens downward, $h(x) = -x^2 + 3$.

13. $f(x) = x^3 - 3x^2$

$g(x) = f(x+2) = (x+2)^3 - 3(x+2)^2$ horizontal shift 2 units to the left

$h(x) = f\left(\tfrac{1}{2}x\right) = \left(\tfrac{1}{2}x\right)^3 - 3\left(\tfrac{1}{2}x\right)^2$ stretched horizontally by factor of 2

15. $f(x) = x^3 - 3x^2$

$g(x) = -\tfrac{1}{3}f(x) = -\tfrac{1}{3}(x^3 - 3x^2)$ reflection in the x-axis and vertical shrink

$h(x) = f(-x) = (-x)^3 - 3(-x)^2$ reflection in the y-axis

17. The graph of g is obtained from that of f by first negating f, and then shifting vertically one unit upward: $g(x) = -x^3 + 3x^2 + 1$.

19. $y = \sqrt{x} + 2$ is $f(x)$ shifted up two units.

21. $y = \sqrt{x-2}$ is $f(x)$ shifted right two units.

23. $y = \sqrt{2x}$ is a vertical stretch of $f(x)$ by $\sqrt{2}$.

25. $y = \sqrt[3]{x} - 1$ is $f(x)$ shifted down one unit.

27. $y = \sqrt[3]{x-1}$ is $f(x)$ shifted right one unit.

29. $y = \sqrt[3]{-x} = -\sqrt[3]{x}$ is $f(x)$ reflected in the y-axis.

31. $f(x - 4)$

33. $f(x) + 4$

35. $2f(x)$

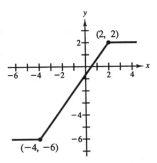

37. $g(x) = 4 - x^3$ is obtained from $f(x)$ by a reflection in the x-axis followed by a vertical shift upward of four units.

39. $h(x) = \frac{1}{4}(x + 2)^3$ is obtained from $f(x)$ by a left shift of two units and a vertical shrink by a factor of $\frac{1}{4}$.

41. $p(x) = \left(\frac{1}{3}x\right)^3 + 2$ is obtained from $f(x)$ by a horizontal stretch, followed by a vertical shift of two units upward.

43. (a) $P(x) = 80 + 20x - 0.5x^2$, $\quad 0 \le x \le 20$

(b) $P(x)$ is shifted downward by a vertical shift of -2500.

$$P(x) = -2420 + 20x - 0.5x^2$$
$$0 \le x \le 20$$

(c) $P(x)$ is changed by a *horizontal stretch.*

$$P(x) = 80 + 20\left(\frac{x}{100}\right) - 0.5\left(\frac{x}{100}\right)^2$$
$$= 80 + 0.2x - 0.00005x^2$$

45. These three even functions are nonnegative. As the exponent increases, the graphs become flatter in the interval $(-1, 1)$ while they grow more rapidly as x tends to infinity.

47.

49. $f(x) = x^2(x-6)^2$

51. $f(x) = x^2(x-6)^3$

Section 1.6   Combinations of Functions

- Given two functions, f and g, you should be able to form the following functions, (if defined).
  1. Sum: $(f+g)(x) = f(x) + g(x)$
  2. Difference: $(f-g)(x) = f(x) - g(x)$
  3. Product: $(fg)(x) = f(x)g(x)$
  4. Quotient: $(f/g)(x) = f(x)/g(x)$, $g(x) \neq 0$
  5. Composition of f with g: $(f \circ g)(x) = f(g(x))$
  6. Composition of g with f: $(g \circ f)(x) = g(f(x))$

1. (a) $(f+g)(x) = f(x) + g(x)$
$$= (x+1) + (x-1) = 2x$$
   (b) $(f-g)(x) = f(x) - g(x)$
$$= (x+1) - (x-1) = 2$$
   (c) $(fg)(x) = f(x) \cdot g(x)$
$$= (x+1)(x-1) = x^2 - 1$$
   (d) $\left(\dfrac{f}{g}\right)(x) = \dfrac{f(x)}{g(x)} = \dfrac{x+1}{x-1}, \quad x \neq 1$
   The domain of f/g is $(-\infty, 1)$, $(1, \infty)$.

3. (a) $(f+g)(x) = f(x) + g(x)$
$$= (x^2 + 5) + \sqrt{1-x}$$
   (b) $(f-g)(x) = f(x) - g(x)$
$$= (x^2 + 5) - \sqrt{1-x}$$
   (c) $(fg)(x) = f(x) \cdot g(x)$
$$= (x^2 + 5)\sqrt{1-x}$$
   (d) $\left(\dfrac{f}{g}\right)(x) = \dfrac{f(x)}{g(x)} = \dfrac{x^2 + 5}{\sqrt{1-x}}, \quad x < 1$
   The domain of f/g is $(-\infty, 1)$.

5. (a) $(f+g)(x) = f(x) + g(x) = \dfrac{1}{x} + \dfrac{1}{x^2} = \dfrac{x+1}{x^2}$
   (b) $(f-g)(x) = f(x) - g(x) = \dfrac{1}{x} - \dfrac{1}{x^2} = \dfrac{x-1}{x^2}$
   (c) $(fg)(x) = f(x) \cdot g(x) = \dfrac{1}{x}\left(\dfrac{1}{x^2}\right) = \dfrac{1}{x^3}$
   (d) $\left(\dfrac{f}{g}\right)(x) = \dfrac{f(x)}{g(x)} = \dfrac{1/x}{1/x^2} = \dfrac{x^2}{x} = x, \quad x \neq 0$
   The domain of f/g is $(-\infty, 0)$, $(0, \infty)$.

7. $(f+g)(3)$

$\quad = f(3) + g(3)$

$\quad = [(3)^2 + 1] + (3 - 4)$

$\quad = 10 - 1$

$\quad = 9$

9. $(f-g)(2t)$

$\quad = f(2t) - g(2t)$

$\quad = [(2t)^2 + 1] - [(2t) - 4]$

$\quad = 4t^2 + 1 - 2t + 4$

$\quad = 4t^2 - 2t + 5$

11. $(fg)(4) = f(4)g(4)$

$\quad = [4^2 + 1][4 - 4]$

$\quad = 0$

13. $\left(\dfrac{f}{g}\right)(5) = \dfrac{f(5)}{g(5)}$

$\qquad = \dfrac{5^2 + 1}{5 - 4}$

$\qquad = 26$

15. $\left(\dfrac{f}{g}\right)(-1) - g(3) = \dfrac{f(-1)}{g(-1)} - g(3)$

$\qquad = \dfrac{(-1)^2 + 1}{-1 - 4} - (3 - 4)$

$\qquad = -\dfrac{2}{5} + 1 = \dfrac{3}{5}$

17.

19.

21. When $0 \le x \le 2$, f contributes the most. When $x > 5$, g contributes the most.

23. $R(x) = \frac{3}{4}x$, $B(x) = \frac{1}{15}x^2$,

$\quad T = R(x) + B(x) = \frac{3}{4}x + \frac{1}{15}x^2$

25. (a) $(f \circ g)(x) = f(g(x)) = f(x - 1) = (x - 1)^2 = x^2 - 2x + 1$

$\quad$ (b) $(g \circ f)(x) = g(f(x)) = g(x^2) = x^2 - 1$

$\quad$ (c) $(f \circ f)(x) = f(f(x)) = f(x^2) = (x^2)^2 = x^4$

Section 1.7   Inverse Functions

- You should know the definition of the inverse of a function.
- Two functions f and g are inverses of each other if $f(g(x)) = x$ for every x in the domain of g and $g(f(x)) = x$ for every x in the domain of f.
- A function f has an inverse if and only if f is one-to-one.
- You should be able to find the inverse of a function, if it exists.
- You should be able to use your graphing utility to graphically verify if two functions are inverses of each other.

1. To "undo" 8 times x, let f^{-1} divide x by 8.
$$f^{-1}(x) = \frac{x}{8}$$
Now, we have
$$f(f^{-1}(x)) = f\left(\frac{x}{8}\right) = 8\left(\frac{x}{8}\right) = x$$
and
$$f^{-1}(f(x)) = f^{-1}(8x) = \frac{8x}{8} = x.$$

3. To "undo" x plus 10, let f^{-1} equal x minus 10.
$$f^{-1}(x) = x - 10$$
Now, we have
$$f(f^{-1}(x)) = f(x - 10)$$
$$= x - 10 + 10 = x$$
and
$$f^{-1}(f(x)) = f^{-1}(x + 10)$$
$$= x + 10 - 10 = x.$$

5. To "undo" the cubed root of x, let f^{-1} equal x cubed.
$$f^{-1}(x) = x^3$$
Now, we have
$$f(f^{-1}(x)) = f(x^3) = \sqrt[3]{x^3} = x$$
and
$$f^{-1}(f(x)) = f^{-1}\left(\sqrt[3]{x}\right) = \left(\sqrt[3]{x}\right)^3 = x.$$

7. (a) $f(g(x)) = f\left(\frac{x}{2}\right) = 2\left(\frac{x}{2}\right) = x$
$$g(f(x)) = g(2x) = \frac{(2x)}{2} = x$$

(b)

The graphs of f and g are reflections in the line $y = x$.

9. (a) $f(g(x)) = f\left(\dfrac{x-1}{5}\right)$

$$= 5\left(\dfrac{x-1}{5}\right) + 1 = x$$

$g(f(x)) = g(5x+1)$

$$= \dfrac{(5x+1)-1}{5} = x$$

(b)

The graphs of f and g are reflections in the line $y = x$.

11. (a) $f(g(x)) = f(\sqrt[3]{x}) = (\sqrt[3]{x})^3 = x$

$g(f(x)) = g(x^3) = \sqrt[3]{x^3} = x$

(b)

The graphs of f and g are reflections in the line $y = x$.

13. (a) $f(g(x)) = f(x^2 + 4), \quad x \geq 0$

$$= \sqrt{(x^2+4)-4} = x$$

$g(f(x)) = g(\sqrt{x-4})$

$$= (\sqrt{x-4})^2 + 4 = x$$

(b)

The graphs of f and g are reflections in the line $y = x$.

15. (a) $f(g(x)) = f(\sqrt{9-x}), \quad x \leq 9$

$$= 9 - (\sqrt{9-x})^2 = x$$

$g(f(x)) = g(9 - x^2), \quad x \geq 0$

$$= \sqrt{9-(9-x^2)} = x$$

(b)

The graphs of f and g are reflections in the line $y = x$.

17. $g(x) = \dfrac{4 - x}{6}$

By the horizontal line test, g is one-to-one.

19. $h(x) = |x + 4| - |x - 4|$

By the horizontal line test, h is not one-to-one.

21. $f(x) = -2x\sqrt{16 - x^2}$

By the horizontal line test, f is not one-to-one.

23. $f(x) = 2x - 3$

$y = 2x - 3$

$x = 2y - 3$

$2y = x + 3$

$y = \dfrac{x + 3}{2}$

$f^{-1}(x) = \dfrac{x + 3}{2}$

25. $f(x) = x^5$

$y = x^5$

$x = y^5$

$y = \sqrt[5]{x}$

$f^{-1}(x) = \sqrt[5]{x}$

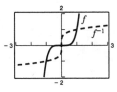

27. $f(x) = \sqrt{x}$

$y = \sqrt{x}$

$x = \sqrt{y}$

$y = x^2$

$f^{-1}(x) = x^2, \quad x \geq 0$

29. $f(x) = \sqrt{4 - x^2}, \ 0 \le x \le 2$

$y = \sqrt{4 - x^2}$

$x = \sqrt{4 - y^2}$

$4 - y^2 = x^2$

$y^2 = 4 - x^2$

$y = \sqrt{4 - x^2}$

$f^{-1}(x) = \sqrt{4 - x^2}, \ 0 \le x \le 2$

31. $f(x) = \sqrt[3]{x - 1}$

$y = \sqrt[3]{x - 1}$

$x = \sqrt[3]{y - 1}$

$y - 1 = x^3$

$y = x^3 + 1$

$f^{-1}(x) = x^3 + 1$

33. Since $f(1) = 1$ and $f(-1) = 1$, f is not one-to-one and does not have an inverse. Or, notice that the graph of f fails the horizontal line test.

35. $g(a) = g(b)$

$\dfrac{a}{8} = \dfrac{b}{8}$

$a = b$

Therefore, g is one-to-one.

$g(x) = \dfrac{x}{8}$

$y = \dfrac{x}{8}$

$x = \dfrac{y}{8}$

$8x = y$

$g^{-1}(x) = 8x$

37. $f(a) = f(b)$

$(a + 3)^2 = (b + 3)^2$

$a + 3 = b + 3, \ \text{since } a, \ b \ge -3$

$a = b$

Therefore, f is one-to-one.

$f(x) = (x + 3)^2, \ x \ge -3$

$y = (x + 3)^2$

$x = (y + 3)^2$

$y + 3 = \sqrt{x}$

$y = \sqrt{x} - 3$

$f^{-1}(x) = \sqrt{x} - 3, \ x \ge 0$

39. $h(a) = h(b)$

$$\frac{1}{a} = \frac{1}{b}$$

$$a = b$$

Therefore, h is one-to-one.

$$h(x) = \frac{1}{x}$$

$$y = \frac{1}{x}$$

$$x = \frac{1}{y}$$

$$xy = 1$$

$$y = \frac{1}{x}$$

$$f^{-1}(x) = \frac{1}{x}$$

41. $f(a) = f(b)$

$$\sqrt{2a+3} = \sqrt{2b+3}$$

$$2a + 3 = 2b + 3$$

$$2a = 2b$$

$$a = b$$

Therefore, f is one-to-one.

$$f(x) = \sqrt{2x+3}$$

$$y = \sqrt{2x+3}$$

$$x = \sqrt{2y+3}$$

$$2y + 3 = x^2$$

$$2y = x^2 - 3$$

$$y = \frac{x^2 - 3}{2}$$

$$f^{-1}(x) = \frac{x^2 - 3}{2}, \quad x \geq 0$$

43. Since $g(0) = 0$ and $g(1) = 0$, g is not one-to-one and does not have an inverse. Or, notice that the graph of g fails the horizontal line test.

45. $f(a) = f(b)$

$$25 - a^2 = 25 - b^2$$

$$a^2 = b^2$$

$$a = b, \quad \text{since } a, \ b \leq 0$$

Therefore, f is one-to-one.

$$f(x) = 25 - x^2, \quad x \leq 0$$

$$y = 25 - x^2$$

$$x = 25 - y^2$$

$$y^2 = 25 - x$$

$$y = -\sqrt{25 - x}$$

$$f^{-1}(x) = -\sqrt{25 - x}$$

47. Delete the part corresponding to $x < 3$.

$$f(x) = (x-3)^2, \quad x \geq 3$$

$$y = (x-3)^2$$

$$x = (y-3)^2$$

$$y - 3 = \sqrt{x}$$

$$y = \sqrt{x} + 3$$

$$f^{-1}(x) = \sqrt{x} + 3, \quad x \geq 0$$

49. Delete the part corresponding to $x < -3$.

51.

x	0	1	2	3	4
$f^{-1}(x)$	-2	0	1	2	4

$$f(x) = |x + 3|, \quad x \geq -3$$
$$f(x) = x + 3$$
$$y = x + 3$$
$$x = y + 3$$
$$y = x - 3$$
$$f^{-1}(x) = x - 3, \quad x \geq 0$$

In Exercises 53 and 55, $f(x) = \frac{1}{8}x - 3$, $f^{-1}(x) = 8(x + 3)$, $g(x) = x^3$, $g^{-1}(x) = \sqrt[3]{x}$.

53. $(f^{-1} \circ g^{-1})(1) = f^{-1}(g^{-1}(1))$
$$= f^{-1}(\sqrt[3]{1})$$
$$= 8(1 + 3)$$
$$= 32$$

55. $(f^{-1} \circ f^{-1})(6) = f^{-1}(f^{-1}(6))$
$$= f^{-1}(8[6 + 3])$$
$$= 8[8(6 + 3) + 3]$$
$$= 600$$

In Exercises 57 and 59, $f(x) = x + 4$, $f^{-1}(x) = x - 4$, $g(x) = 2x - 5$, $g^{-1}(x) = \frac{1}{2}(x + 5)$.

57. $(g^{-1} \circ f^{-1})(x) = g^{-1}(x - 4) = \frac{1}{2}(x - 4 + 5) = \frac{1}{2}(x + 1)$

59. $(f \circ g)(x) = f(2x - 5) = (2x - 5) + 4 = 2x - 1$
Hence, $(f \circ g)^{-1}(x) = \frac{1}{2}(x + 1)$. Alternatively, observe that $(f \circ g)^{-1}(x) = (g^{-1} \circ f^{-1})(x)$, as in Exercise 57.

61. (a)
$$y = 0.03x^2 + 254.50, \quad 0 < x < 100$$

$$x = 0.03y^2 + 254.50$$

$$0.03y^2 = x - 254.50$$

$$y^2 = \frac{100}{3}x - \frac{25{,}450}{3}$$

$$y = \sqrt{\frac{50}{3}(2x - 509)}$$

$$y = \frac{5\sqrt{2}}{\sqrt{3}}\sqrt{2x - 509}$$

$$y = \frac{5\sqrt{6}}{3}\sqrt{2x - 509}$$

(b)

y represents the percentage load and x
represents the exhaust temperature.

63. If f is an even function, then $f(-x) = f(x)$. This implies that f is not one-to-one. Thus f^{-1} does not exist. The statement is false. For example, $f(x) = x^2$ is even and is not one-to-one.

65. $f(x) = x^n$, where n is odd

$$f(a) = f(b)$$

$$a^n = b^n$$

$$a = b$$

Therefore, f is one-to-one and its inverse exists. The statement is true.

Chapter 1   Review Exercises

1. $y - 2x - 3 = 0$

3. $x - 5 = 0$

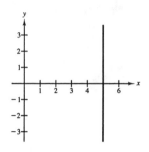

5. $y = \sqrt{5 - x}$

7. $y + 2x^2 = 0$

9. $y = \sqrt{25 - x^2}$

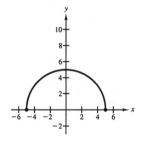

11. $y = \frac{1}{4}(x + 1)^3$ intersects the x-axis once and the y-axis once.

13. $y = \frac{1}{4}x^4 - 2x^2$ intersects the x-axis three times and the y-axis once.

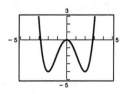

15. $y = x\sqrt{9 - x^2}$ intersects the x-axis three times and the y-axis once.

17. $y = |x - 4| - 4$ intersects the x-axis twice and the y-axis once.

19. $2y^2 = x^3$

$$y = \pm\sqrt{x^3/2}$$

$$y_1 = \sqrt{x^3/2}$$

$$y_2 = -\sqrt{x^3/2}$$

21. The line through $(-2, 5)$ and $(1, 1)$ is:

$$y - 5 = \frac{1-5}{1+2}(x+2)$$

$$y - 5 = -\frac{4}{3}(x+2)$$

$$3y - 15 = -4x - 8$$

$$4x + 3y = 7$$

For $(0, t)$ to be on this line also, it must satisfy the equation $4x + 3y = 7$.

$$4(0) + 3(t) = 7$$

Thus, $t = \frac{7}{3}$.

23. The line through $(1, -4)$ and $(5, 10)$ is:

$$y + 4 = \frac{10+4}{5-1}(x-1)$$

$$y + 4 = \frac{7}{2}(x-1)$$

$$2y + 8 = 7(x-1)$$

$$2y + 8 = 7x - 7$$

$$7x - 2y = 15$$

For $(t, 3)$ to be on this line also, it must satisfy the equation $7x - 2y = 15$.

$$7(t) - 2(3) = 15$$

$$7t = 21$$

Thus, $t = 3$.

25. Since the points lie on a vertical line, $x = 0$.

27. $y - 1 = \dfrac{6-1}{14-2}(x-2) = \dfrac{5}{12}(x-2) \Rightarrow y = \dfrac{5}{12}x + \dfrac{1}{6}$ or $5x - 12y + 2 = 0$

29. $y - 0 = \dfrac{2-0}{6+1}(x+1) = \dfrac{2}{7}(x+1) \Rightarrow y = \dfrac{2}{7}x + \dfrac{2}{7}$ or $2x - 7y + 2 = 0$

31.
$$y + 5 = \tfrac{3}{2}(x - 0)$$
$$2y + 10 = 3x$$
$$3x - 2y - 10 = 0$$

33.
$$y - 0 = -\tfrac{2}{3}(x - 3)$$
$$3y = -2(x - 3)$$
$$3y = -2x + 6$$
$$2x + 3y - 6 = 0$$

35. $5x - 4y = 8$
$$-4y = -5x + 8$$
$$y = \tfrac{5}{4}x - 2 \quad \Rightarrow \quad m_1 = \tfrac{5}{4}$$
(a) Parallel slope $m_2 = \tfrac{5}{4}$
$$y - (-2) = \tfrac{5}{4}(x - 3)$$
$$y + 2 = \tfrac{5}{4}x - \tfrac{15}{4}$$
$$4y + 8 = 5x - 15$$
$$5x - 4y - 23 = 0$$
(b) Perpendicular slope $m_2 = -\tfrac{4}{5}$
$$y - (-2) = -\tfrac{4}{5}(x - 3)$$
$$y + 2 = -\tfrac{4}{5}x + \tfrac{12}{5}$$
$$5y + 10 = -4x + 12$$
$$4x + 5y - 2 = 0$$

37. $(2, \ 160{,}000), \quad (3, \ 185{,}000)$
$$m = \frac{185{,}000 - 160{,}000}{3 - 2} = 25{,}000$$
$$S - 160{,}000 = 25{,}000(t - 2)$$
$$S = 25{,}000t + 110{,}000$$
For the fourth quarter let $t = 4$. Then we have
$$S = 25{,}000(4) + 110{,}000 = \$210{,}000.$$

39. $f(x) = x^2 + 1$
(a) $f(2) = 2^2 + 1 = 5$
(c) $f(t^2) = (t^2)^2 + 1 = t^4 + 1$

(b) $f(-4) = (-4)^2 + 1 = 17$
(d) $-f(x) = -(x^2 + 1) = -x^2 - 1$

41. $h(x) = 6 - 5x^2$

(a) $h(2) = 6 - 5(2)^2 = -14$

(b) $h(x + 3) = 6 - 5(x + 3)^2 = -5x^2 - 30x - 39$

(c) $\dfrac{h(4) - h(2)}{4 - 2} = \dfrac{-74 + 14}{4 - 2} = -30$

(d) $\dfrac{h(x + t) - h(x)}{t} = \dfrac{6 - 5(x + t)^2 - 6 + 5x^2}{t}$

$$= \dfrac{-5(x^2 + 2xt + (t)^2 - x^2)}{t}$$

$$= \dfrac{-5t(2x + t)}{t} = -5(2x + t) = -10x - 5t, \quad t \neq 0$$

43. (a) $f(x) = \frac{1}{2}x + c$

$c = -2$: $\quad f(x) = \frac{1}{2}x - 2$

$c = 0$: $\quad f(x) = \frac{1}{2}x$

$c = 2$: $\quad f(x) = \frac{1}{2}x + 2$

(b) $f(x) = \frac{1}{2}(x - c)$

$c = -2$: $\quad f(x) = \frac{1}{2}(x + 2)$

$\qquad\qquad = \frac{1}{2}x + 1$

$c = 0$: $\quad f(x) = \frac{1}{2}x$

$c = 2$: $\quad f(x) = \frac{1}{2}(x - 2)$

$\qquad\qquad = \frac{1}{2}x - 1$

(c) $f(x) = \frac{1}{2}(cx)$

$c = -2$: $\quad f(x) = \frac{1}{2}(-2x)$

$\qquad\qquad = -x$

$c = 0$: $\quad f(x) = \frac{1}{2}(0x)$

$\qquad\qquad = 0$

$c = 2$: $\quad f(x) = \frac{1}{2}(2x)$

$\qquad\qquad = x$

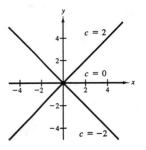

45. $25 - x^2 \geq 0$

$x^2 \leq 25$

$-5 \leq x \leq 5$

The domain is $[-5, 5]$.

47. $3s - 9 \neq 0$

$3s \neq 9$

$s \neq 3$

The domain is all real numbers except $s = 3$.

49. $x^2 - x - 6 \neq 0$

$(x - 3)(x + 2) \neq 0$

$x \neq -2, 3$

The domain is all real numbers except $x = -2, 3$.

51. $v(t) = -32t + 48$

 (a) $v(1) = -32(1) + 48 = 16$ ft/sec

 (c) $v(2) = -32(2) + 48 = -16$ ft/sec

        (b) $v(t) = 0$

$$-32t + 48 = 0$$

$$-32t = -48$$

$$t = 1.5 \text{ seconds}$$

53. If x and y are the two sides, then the perimeter P is given by $P = 2x + 2y = 24$. Hence,

$$x + y = 12$$

$$y = 12 - x.$$

$$A = xy = x(12 - x)$$

$$A = 12x - x^2$$

Since $A > 0$ and x is the shortest side, the domain is $(0,\ 6)$.

55. (a) Constant on $(-\infty,\ -2)$ and $(2,\ \infty)$

   Increasing on $(-2,\ 2)$

 (b) Minimum is -4 on $(-\infty,\ -2)$.

   Maximum is 4 on $(2,\ \infty)$.

 (c) Since

$$g(-x) = |-x + 2| - |-x - 2|$$

$$= |x - 2| - |x + 2|$$

$$= -g(x),$$

  the function is odd.

57. (a) Increasing on $(-\infty,\ 0)$ and $(0,\ 3)$

   Decreasing on $(3,\ \infty)$

 (b) Relative maximum at $(3,\ 27)$

 (c) Since

$$h(-x) = 4(-x)^3 - (-x)^4$$

$$= -4x^3 + x^4,$$

  h is neither even nor odd.

59. (a) At time t, ship A is $100 - 12t$ miles east of $(0, 0)$, whereas, ship B is $-10t$ south of $(0, 0)$. Hence, by the Pythagorean Theorem, the distance between the ships is
$$d = \sqrt{(100 - 12t)^2 + (-10t)^2}.$$

(b) Using the zoom and trace features, we see that the minimum distance of $d = 64.02$ miles occurs at $t = 4.92$ hours.

61. $f(x) = \frac{1}{2}x - 3$

(a) $f^{-1}(x) = 2x + 6$

(b)

63. $f(x) = \sqrt{x + 1}$

(a) $f^{-1}(x) = x^2 - 1, \quad x \geq 0$

(b)

(c) $f^{-1}(f(x)) = f^{-1}\left(\frac{1}{2}x - 3\right)$
$$= 2\left(\frac{1}{2}x - 3\right) + 6 = x$$
$f(f^{-1}(x)) = f(2x + 6)$
$$= \frac{1}{2}(2x + 6) - 3 = x$$

(c) $f^{-1}(f(x)) = f^{-1}(\sqrt{x + 1})$
$$= (x + 1) - 1 = x$$
$f(f^{-1}(x)) = f(x^2 - 1), \quad x \geq 0$
$$= \sqrt{x^2 - 1 + 1} = x$$

65. $f(x) = x^2 - 5, \quad x \geq 0$

(a) $f^{-1}(x) = \sqrt{x + 5}, \quad x \geq -5$

(b)

(c) $f^{-1}(f(x)) = f^{-1}(x^2 - 5), \quad x \geq 0$
$$= \sqrt{x^2 - 5 + 5}$$
$$= x$$

$f(f^{-1}(x)) = f(\sqrt{x + 5})$
$$= (x + 5) - 5$$
$$= x$$

67. $f(x) = 2(x-4)^2$ is increasing on the interval $[4, \infty)$.

$$f(x) = 2(x-4)^2, \quad x \geq 4$$

$$y = 2(x-4)^2, \quad x \geq 4$$

$$x = 2(y-4)^2$$

$$\sqrt{x} = \sqrt{2}(y-4)$$

$$\frac{\sqrt{x}}{\sqrt{2}} + 4 = y$$

$$f^{-1}(x) = \sqrt{\frac{x}{2}} + 4, \quad x \geq 0$$

69. $f(x) = \sqrt{x^2 - 4}$ is increasing on the interval $[2, \infty)$.

$$f(x) = \sqrt{x^2 - 4}, \quad x \geq 2$$

$$y = \sqrt{x^2 - 4}, \quad x \geq 2$$

$$x = \sqrt{y^2 - 4}$$

$$y^2 - 4 = x^2$$

$$y^2 = x^2 + 4$$

$$y = \sqrt{x^2 + 4}$$

$$f^{-1}(x) = \sqrt{x^2 + 4}, \quad x \geq 0$$

71. $(f - g)(4) = f(4) - g(4)$

$$= (3 - 2 \cdot 4) - \sqrt{4}$$

$$= -7$$

73. $(fh)(1) = f(1) \cdot h(1)$

$$= (3 - 2 \cdot 1)(3 \cdot 1^2 + 2)$$

$$= 5$$

75. $(h \circ g)(7) = h(g(7))$

$$= h(\sqrt{7})$$

$$= 3(\sqrt{7})^2 + 2$$

$$= 23$$

77. $g^{-1}(x) = x^2, \quad x \geq 0$

$$g^{-1}(3) = 3^2 = 9$$

CHAPTER 2

Solving Equations and Inequalities

Section 2.1   Linear Equations

■ You should know how to solve linear equations: $ax + b = 0$

■ An identity is an equation whose solution consists of every real number in its domain.

■ To solve an equation you can:

(a) Add or subtract the same quantity from both sides.
(b) Multiply or divide both sides by the same nonzero quantity.

■ To solve an equation that can be simplified to a linear equation:

(a) Remove all symbols of grouping and all fractions.
(b) Combine like terms.
(c) Solve by algebra.
(d) Check the answer algebraically and graphically.

■ A "solution" that does not satisfy the original equation is called an extraneous solution.

1. $2(x - 1) = 2x - 2$

$2x - 2 = 2x - 2$

Identity

3. $-2(x - 3) + 5 = -2x + 10$

$-2x + 6 + 5 = -2x + 10$

$-2x + 11 = -2x + 10$

$11 \neq 10$

No solution; conditional

5. $4(x + 1) - 2x = 2(x + 2)$

$4x + 4 - 2x = 2x + 4$

$2x + 4 = 2x + 4$

Identity

7. $x^2 - 8x + 5 = (x - 4)^2 - 11$

$\qquad = x^2 - 8x + 16 - 11$

$\qquad = x^2 - 8x + 5$

Identity

9. $3 + \dfrac{1}{x + 1} = \dfrac{4x}{x + 1}$

$\dfrac{3x + 4}{x + 1} = \dfrac{4x}{x + 1}$

$3x + 4 = 4x$

$x = 4$

Conditional

11. $5x - 3 = 3x + 5$

(a) $5(0) - 3 \overset{?}{=} 3(0) + 5$

$$-3 \neq 5$$

$x = 0$ *is not* a solution.

(c) $5(4) - 3 \overset{?}{=} 3(4) + 5$

$$17 = 17$$

$x = 4$ *is* a solution.

(b) $5(-5) - 3 \overset{?}{=} 3(-5) + 5$

$$-28 \neq -10$$

$x = -5$ *is not* a solution.

(d) $5(10) - 3 \overset{?}{=} 3(10) + 5$

$$47 \neq 35$$

$x = 10$ *is not* a solution.

13. $3x^2 + 2x - 5 = 2x^2 - 2$

(a) $3(-3)^2 + 2(-3) - 5 \overset{?}{=} 2(-3)^2 - 2$

$$16 = 16$$

$x = -3$ *is* a solution.

(c) $3(4)^2 + 2(4) - 5 \overset{?}{=} 2(4)^2 - 2$

$$51 \neq 30$$

$x = 4$ is *not* a solution.

(b) $3(1)^2 + 2(1) - 5 \overset{?}{=} 2(1)^2 - 2$

$$0 = 0$$

$x = 1$ *is* a solution.

(d) $3(-5)^2 + 2(-5) - 5 \overset{?}{=} 2(-5)^2 - 2$

$$60 \neq 48$$

$x = -5$ is *not* a solution.

15. $\dfrac{5}{2x} - \dfrac{4}{x} = 3$

(a) $\dfrac{5}{2(-1/2)} - \dfrac{4}{(-1/2)} \overset{?}{=} 3$

$$3 = 3$$

$x = -\frac{1}{2}$ *is* a solution.

(c) $\dfrac{5}{2(0)} - \dfrac{4}{0}$ is undefined.

$x = 0$ *is not* a solution.

(b) $\dfrac{5}{2(4)} - \dfrac{4}{4} \overset{?}{=} 3$

$$-\dfrac{3}{8} \neq 3$$

$x = 4$ *is not* a solution.

(d) $\dfrac{5}{2(1/4)} - \dfrac{4}{1/4} \overset{?}{=} 3$

$$-6 \neq 3$$

$x = \frac{1}{4}$ *is not* a solution.

17. $(x + 5)(x - 3) = 20$

(a) $(3 + 5)(3 - 3) \overset{?}{=} 20$

$$0 \neq 20$$

$x = 3$ *is not* a solution.

(c) $(5 + 5)(5 - 3) \overset{?}{=} 20$

$$20 = 20$$

$x = 5$ *is* a solution.

(b) $(-5 + 5)(-5 - 3) \overset{?}{=} 20$

$$0 \neq 20$$

$x = -5$ *is not* a solution.

(d) $(-7 + 5)(-7 - 3) \overset{?}{=} 20$

$$20 = 20$$

$x = -7$ *is* a solution.

19. $x + 10 = 15$

$\quad x = 5$

21. $7 - 2x = 15$

$\quad -2x = 8$

$\quad x = -4$

23. $8x - 5 = 3x + 10$

$\quad 5x = 15$

$\quad x = 3$

25. $2(x + 5) - 7 = 3(x - 2)$

$\quad 2x + 10 - 7 = 3x - 6$

$\quad 2x + 3 = 3x - 6$

$\quad -x = -9$

$\quad x = 9$

27. $6[x - (2x + 3)] = 8 - 5x$

$\quad 6[-x - 3] = 8 - 5x$

$\quad -6x - 18 = 8 - 5x$

$\quad -x = 26$

$\quad x = -26$

29. $\dfrac{5x}{4} + \dfrac{1}{2} = x - \dfrac{1}{2}$

$\quad 4\left(\dfrac{5x}{4}\right) + 4\left(\dfrac{1}{2}\right) = 4(x) + 4\left(-\dfrac{1}{2}\right)$

$\quad 5x + 2 = 4x - 2$

$\quad x = -4$

31. $\dfrac{3}{2}(z + 5) - \dfrac{1}{4}(z + 24) = 0$

$\quad 4\left(\dfrac{3}{2}\right)(z + 5) - 4\left(\dfrac{1}{4}\right)(z + 24) = 4(0)$

$\quad 6(z + 5) - (z + 24) = 0$

$\quad 6z + 30 - z - 24 = 0$

$\quad 5z = -6$

$\quad z = -\dfrac{6}{5}$

33. $x + 8 = 2(x - 2) - x$

$\quad x + 8 = 2x - 4 - x$

$\quad x + 8 = x - 4$

$\quad 8 = -4$

Not possible; no solution

35. $\dfrac{100 - 4u}{3} = \dfrac{5u + 6}{4} + 6$

$\quad 12\left(\dfrac{100 - 4u}{3}\right) = 12\left(\dfrac{5u + 6}{4}\right) + 12(6)$

$\quad 4(100 - 4u) = 3(5u + 6) + 72$

$\quad 400 - 16u = 15u + 18 + 72$

$\quad -31u = -310$

$\quad u = 10$

37. $\dfrac{5x - 4}{5x + 4} = \dfrac{2}{3}$

$\quad 3(5x - 4) = 2(5x + 4)$

$\quad 15x - 12 = 10x + 8$

$\quad 5x = 20$

$\quad x = 4$

39. $10 - \dfrac{13}{x} = 4 + \dfrac{5}{x}$

$\quad (x)10 - (x)\dfrac{13}{x} = (x)4 + (x)\dfrac{5}{x}$

$\quad 10x - 13 = 4x + 5$

$\quad 6x = 18$

$\quad x = 3$

41.
$$\frac{1}{x-3} + \frac{1}{x+3} = \frac{10}{x^2-9}$$

$$\frac{1}{x-3}(x+3)(x-3) + \frac{1}{x+3}(x+3)(x-3) = \frac{10}{x^2-9}(x+3)(x-3)$$

$$x + 3 + x - 3 = 10$$

$$2x = 10$$

$$x = 5$$

43.
$$\frac{x}{x+4} + \frac{4}{x+4} + 2 = 0$$

$$\frac{x}{x+4}(x+4) + \frac{4}{x+4}(x+4) + 2(x+4) = 0$$

$$x + 4 + 2x + 8 = 0$$

$$3x = -12$$

$$x = -4$$

A check reveals that $x = -4$ is an extraneous solution, so there is no solution. Or, notice that the graph of

$$y = \frac{x}{x+4} + \frac{4}{x+4} + 2$$

lies entirely above the x-axis.

45.
$$\frac{7}{2x+1} - \frac{8x}{2x-1} = -4$$

$$\frac{7}{2x+1}(2x+1)(2x-1) - \frac{8x}{2x-1}(2x+1)(2x-1) = -4(2x+1)(2x-1)$$

$$7(2x-1) - 8x(2x+1) = -4(4x^2-1)$$

$$14x - 7 - 16x^2 - 8x = -16x^2 + 4$$

$$6x = 11$$

$$x = \frac{11}{6}$$

47.
$$\frac{1}{x} + \frac{2}{x-5} = 0$$

$$\frac{1}{x}(x)(x-5) + \frac{2}{x-5}(x)(x-5) = 0(x)(x-5)$$

$$x - 5 + 2x = 0$$

$$3x = 5$$

$$x = \frac{5}{3}$$

49.

$$\frac{3}{x(x-3)} + \frac{4}{x} = \frac{1}{x-3}$$

$$\frac{3}{x(x-3)}(x)(x-3) + \frac{4}{x}(x)(x-3) = \frac{1}{x-3}(x)(x-3)$$

$$3 + 4(x-3) = x$$

$$3 + 4x - 12 = x$$

$$3x = 9$$

$$x = 3$$

A check reveals that $x = 3$ is an extraneous solution, so there is no solution.

51.

$$(x+2)^2 - x^2 = 4(x+1)$$

$$x^2 + 4x + 4 - x^2 = 4x + 4$$

$$4 = 4$$

The equation is an identity; every real number is a solution.

53.

$$4(x+1) - ax = x + 5$$

$$4x + 4 - ax = x + 5$$

$$3x - ax = 1$$

$$x(3-a) = 1$$

$$x = \frac{1}{3-a}, \ a \neq 3$$

If $a = 3$, there is no solution.

55.

$$4 - 2(x - 2b) = ax + 3$$

$$4 - 2x + 4b = ax + 3$$

$$4b + 1 = ax + 2x$$

$$4b + 1 = x(a + 2)$$

$$x = \frac{4b+1}{a+2}, \ a \neq -2$$

If $a = -2$, there are two possibilities. If $b = -\frac{1}{4}$, every x is a solution, and if $b \neq -\frac{1}{4}$, there is no solution.

57.

$$0.275x + 0.725(500 - x) = 300$$

$$0.275x + 362.5 - 0.725x = 300$$

$$-0.45x = -62.5$$

$$x \approx 138.889$$

Or, using a graphing utility, you can show that the x-intercept of the function $y = 0.275x + 0.725(500 - x) - 300$ is $x = 138.89$.

59.
$$\frac{x}{0.6321} + \frac{x}{0.0692} = 1000$$

$$\frac{x}{0.6321}(0.6321)(0.0692) + \frac{x}{0.0692}(0.6321)(0.0692) = 1000(0.6321)(0.0692)$$

$$0.0692x + 0.6321x = 1000(0.6321)(0.0692)$$

$$(0.0692 + 0.6321)x = 1000(0.6321)(0.0692)$$

$$x = \frac{1000(0.6321)(0.0692)}{(0.0692 + 0.6321)}$$

$$x \approx 62.372$$

Or, using a graphing utility, you can show that the x-intercept of the function

$$y = \frac{x}{0.6321} + \frac{x}{0.0692} - 1000$$

is $x = 62.37$.

61.
$$(x + 5.62)^2 + 10.83 = (x + 7)^2$$

$$x^2 + 11.24x + 31.5844 + 10.83 = x^2 + 14x + 49$$

$$-6.5856 = 2.76x$$

$$-2.386 = x$$

Or, using a graphing utility, you can show that the x-intercept of the function $y = (x + 5.62)^2 + 10.83 - (x + 7)^2$ is $x = -2.39$.

63. $ax + b = cx$

$ax - cx = -b$

$x(a - c) = -b$

$$x = \frac{-b}{a - c}$$

Since $x = 2$, we have $2 = -b/(a - c)$. Choose any combination of a, b and c that satisfies this equation. One possibility is $a = 1$, $b = 4$, and $c = 3$. The equation is $x + 4 = 3x$.

65. $248 = 2(24) + 2(4x) + 2(6x)$

$248 = 48 + 8x + 12x$

$200 = 20x$

$x = 10$ inches

67. $16 = 0.432x - 10.44$

$26.44 = 0.432x$

$x \approx 61.2$ inches

Section 2.2   Linear Equations and Modeling

- ■ You should be able to set up mathematical models to solve problems.

- ■ You should be able to translate key words and phrases.
  - (a) **Consecutive**: Next, subsequent
  - (b) **Addition**: Sum, plus, greater, increased by, more than, exceeds, total of
  - (c) **Subtraction**: Difference, minus, less than, decreased by, subtracted from, reduced by, the remainder
  - (d) **Multiplication**: Product, multiplied by, twice, times, percent of
  - (e) **Division**: Quotient, divided by, ratio, per
  - (f) **Equality**: Equals, equal to, is, are, was, will be, represents

- ■ You should know the following formulas:
  - (a) Perimeter
    1. Square: $P = 4s$
    2. Rectangle: $P = 2L + 2W$
    3. Circle: $C = 2\pi r$

  - (b) Area
    1. Square: $A = s^2$
    2. Rectangle: $A = LW$
    3. Circle: $A = \pi r^2$
    4. Triangle: $A = \left(\frac{1}{2}\right) bh$

  - (c) Volume
    1. Cube: $V = s^3$
    2. Rectangular solid: $V = LWH$
    3. Cylinder: $V = \pi r^2 h$
    4. Sphere: $V = \left(\frac{4}{3}\right) \pi r^3$

  - (d) Simple interest: $I = Prt$

  - (e) Compound Interest: $A = P\left(1 + \dfrac{r}{n}\right)^{nt}$

  - (f) Distance: $D = r \cdot t$

  - (g) Temperature: $F = \frac{9}{5}C + 32$

- ■ You should be able to solve word problems. Study the examples in the text carefully. Use your graphing utility when appropriate.

---

1. *Verbal Model*   Sum = First number + Second number

   Labels   Sum = S

First number = n

Second number = $n + 1$

   Algebraic Equation $S = n + (n + 1) = 2n + 1$

3. *Verbal Model*   Distance = Rate × Time

     Labels   Distance = d
                      Rate (in miles per hour) = 50
                      Time (in hours) = t

     Algebraic Equation $d = 50t$

5. *Verbal Model*   Amount of acid = 20% • Amount of solution

     Labels   Amount of acid (in gallons) = A
                      Amount of solution (in gallons) = x

     Algebraic Equation $A = 0.20x$

7. *Verbal Model*   Perimeter = 2 • Width + 2 • Length

     Labels   Perimeter = P
                      Width = x
                      Length = 2 • Width = $2x$

     Algebraic Equation $P = 2x + 2(2x) = 6x$

9. *Verbal Model*   (Total cost) = (Fixed cost) + (Unit cost)(Number of units)

     Labels   Total cost = C
                      Fixed cost = \$1200
                      Unit cost = \$25
                      Number of units = x

     Algebraic Equation $C = 1200 + 25x$

11. *Verbal Model*   Sum = First number + Second number

     Labels   Sum = 525
                      First number = n
                      Second number = $n + 1$

     Algebraic Equation $525 = n + (n + 1)$

$$525 = 2n + 1$$

$$524 = 2n$$

$$n = 262$$

First number = $n = 262$,   second number = $n + 1 = 263$

13. *Verbal Model*   Difference = One number − Another number

  Labels   Difference = 148
           One number = $5x$
           Another number = x

  Algebraic Equation $148 = 5x - x$
           $148 = 4x$
           $x = 37$

One number = $5x = 185$, another number = $x = 37$

15. *Verbal Model*   Product = (First number) × (Second number)

  Labels   Product = (First number)^2 − 5 = $n^2 - 5$
           First number = n
           Second number = $n + 1$

  Algebraic Equation $n^2 - 5 = n(n + 1)$

           $n = -5$

First number = $n = -5$, second number = $n + 1 = -4$

17. x = Percent • Number

  $x = 30\% \times 45$

  $x = (0.30)(45)$

  $x = 13.5$

19. x = Percent • Number

  $x = 0.045\% \times 2,650,000$

  $x = (0.00045)(2,650,000)$

  $x = 1192.5$

21. 459 = Percent • 340

  Percent = $\frac{459}{340} = 1.35 = 135\%$

23. $70 = 40\%$ • Number

  Number $= \dfrac{70}{40\%} = \dfrac{70}{0.40} = 175$

25. Income taxes = 45%(990,800,000,000)

       = 0.45(990,800,000,000)

       = 445,860,000,000

       ≈ \$446 billion

  Corporation taxes = 10.4%(990,800,000,000)

       = 0.104(990,800,000,000)

       = 103,043,200,000

       ≈ \$103 billion

  Social Security taxes = 36.3%(990,800,000,000)

       = 0.363(990,800,000,000)

       = 359,660,400,000

       ≈ \$360 billion

  Other taxes = 8.3%(990,800,000,000)

       = 0.083(990,800,000,000)

       = 82,236,400,000

       ≈ \$82 billion

27. *Verbal Model*   Loan payments = 58.6% • Annual income

   Labels   Loan payments = 13,077.75
         Annual income = I

   Algebraic Equation $13,077.75 = 0.586I$
              $I \approx 22,316.98$

The family's annual income is $22,316.98.

29. *Verbal Model*   Total profit = January profit + February profit

   Labels   Total profit = $157,498
         January profit = p
         February profit = $p + 0.2p = 1.2p$

   Algebraic Equation $157,498 = p + 1.2p$

              $157,498 = 2.2p$

                $p = 71,590$

January's profit was $71,590. February's profit was 1.2(71,590) or $85,908.

31. *Verbal Model*   1990 annual earnings
         = Percentage increase • 1940 annual earnings + 1940 annual earnings

   Labels   1990 annual earnings = $27,000
         Percentage increase = p
         1940 annual earnings = 1500

   Algebraic Equation $27,000 = 1500p + 1500$

              $\dfrac{25,500}{1500} = p$

                $p = 17 = 1700\%$

Percentage increase = $p = 1700\%$

33. *Verbal Model*   1990 lb of ground beef price
         = Percentage increase • 1940 lb of ground beef price
                    + 1940 lb of ground beef price

   Labels   1990 lb of ground beef price = $1.44
         Percentage increase = p
         1940 lb of ground beef price = $0.15

   Algebraic Equation $1.44 = p(0.15) + 0.15$

              $1.29 = 0.15p$

                $p = 8.6 = 860\%$

Percentage increase = $p = 860\%$

35. *Verbal Model*   Perimeter $= 2 \cdot$ Width $+ 2 \cdot$ Length

   Labels   Perimeter $= 75$ feet
   Width (in feet) $= x$
   Length (in feet) $= 1.5 \cdot$ Width $= 1.5x$

Algebraic Equation $75 = 2x + 2(1.5x)$

   $75 = 5x$

   $x = 15$

Width $= x = 15$ feet, length $= 1.5x = 22.5$ feet

37. *Verbal Model* $\dfrac{\text{Sum of scores}}{\text{Sum of possible points}} = \text{Average}$

   Labels   Sum of scores $= 87 + 92 + 84 + x$
   Sum of possible points $= 400$
   Average $= 0.9$

Algebraic Equation $\dfrac{87 + 92 + 84 + x}{400} = 0.9$

   $\dfrac{263 + x}{400} = 0.9$

   $263 + x = 360$

   $x = 97$ (or greater)

39. $(\text{Time}) = \dfrac{(\text{Distance})}{(\text{Rate})}$

   $(\text{Rate}) = \dfrac{25 \text{ miles}}{30 \text{ minutes}}$

   $= \dfrac{25 \text{ miles}}{\frac{1}{2} \text{ hour}}$

   $= 50\dfrac{\text{miles}}{\text{hour}}$

   $t = \dfrac{150}{50} = 3$ hours

41. Distance $=$ Rate $\cdot$ Time

   $d_1 = 40$ miles per hour $\cdot\, t$

   $d_2 = 55$ miles per hour $\cdot\, t$

Distance between cars $=$ Second distance $-$ First distance

   $5 = d_2 - d_1$

   $5 = 55t - 40t = 15t$

   $t = \frac{1}{3}$ hour

43. (a) Time for the first family: $t_1 = \dfrac{d}{r_1} = \dfrac{160}{42} \approx 3.8$ hours

Time for the other family: $t_2 = \dfrac{d}{r_2} = \dfrac{160}{50} = 3.2$ hours

(b) $t = \dfrac{d}{r} = \dfrac{100}{42 + 50} = \dfrac{100}{92} \approx 1.1$ hours

(c) $d = rt = 42\left(\dfrac{160}{42} - \dfrac{160}{50}\right) = 25.6$ miles

45. Total speed $=$ (Air speed) $+$ (Wind speed)

$$s_1 = 600 \text{ mph} + x \qquad \text{(trip out)}$$

$$s_2 = 600 \text{ mph} + (-x) \quad \text{(return trip)}$$

(Time out) $=$ (Return time)

$$\frac{1500 \text{ miles}}{s_1} = \frac{1500 \text{ miles} - 300 \text{ miles to go}}{s_2}$$

$$\frac{1500}{600 + x} = \frac{1200}{600 - x}$$

$$1500(600 - x) = 1200(600 + x)$$

$$2700x = 180{,}000$$

$$x = \frac{200}{3} \approx 66.7 \text{ mph}$$

47. $d = rt$

$$3.86 \times 10^8 = (3.0 \times 10^8)\,t$$

$$t = \frac{3.86 \times 10^8}{3.0 \times 10^8} \approx 1.29 \text{ seconds}$$

49. By similar triangles,

$$\frac{\text{Height of building}}{\text{Building's shadow}} = \frac{\text{Height of stake}}{\text{Stake's shadow}}$$

$$\frac{x}{50} = \frac{4}{3.5}$$

$$x = 50\left(\frac{4}{3.5}\right)$$

$$\approx 57.1 \text{ feet}$$

51. By similar triangles,

$$\frac{\text{Height of silo}}{\text{Silo's shadow}} = \frac{\text{Height of person}}{\text{Person's shadow}}$$

$$\frac{50}{32 + x} = \frac{6}{x}$$

$$50x = 6(32 + x)$$

$$50x = 192 + 6x$$

$$44x = 192$$

$$x \approx 4.36 \text{ feet}$$

53. Interest = Interest rate × Principal

$$i_1 = 11\% \times \$x$$

$$i_2 = 12.5\% \times \$(25{,}000 - x)$$

Total interest = (Interest in first account) + (Interest in second account)

$$2975 = i_1 + i_2$$

$$2975 = 0.11x + 0.125(25{,}000 - x)$$

$$2975 = -0.015x + 3125$$

$$x = \frac{150}{0.015} = 10{,}000$$

You have \$10,000 in the 11% fund and \$15,000 in the $12\frac{1}{2}$% fund.

55. Interest = Interest rate × Principal × Portion of year

$$i_1 = x \times \$10{,}000 \times \tfrac{3}{4} \text{ year}$$

$$i_2 = (x - 1.5\%) \times \$10{,}000 \times \tfrac{1}{4} \text{ year}$$

Total interest = (First three quarter's interest) + (Last quarter's interest)

$$\$1112.50 = i_1 + i_2$$

$$1112.50 = 7500x + 2500(x - 0.015)$$

$$x = \tfrac{1150}{10{,}000} = 0.115 = 11.5\%$$

The first three quarter's rate was 11.5% and the last quarter's rate was 10%.

57. (Final concentration)(Amount) = (Solution 1 concentration)(Amount)

$$+ \text{(Solution 2 concentration)(Amount)}$$

$$(75\%)(55 \text{ gal}) = (40\%)(55 - x) + (100\%)x$$

$$41.25 = 0.60x + 22$$

$$x \approx 32.1 \text{ gallons}$$

59. (Final mix cost)(Amount) = (Nut 1 cost)(Amount) + (Nut 2 cost)(Amount)

$$(\$3.19)(100 \text{ lbs}) = (\$2.49)x + (\$3.89)(100 - x)$$

$$319 = 389 - 1.40x$$

$$1.40x = 70$$

$$x = 50 \text{ lbs of Nut 1}$$

$$100 - x = 50 \text{ lbs of Nut 2}$$

61.   Cost = (Fixed costs) + (Variable cost)(Number of units)

$$\$85,000 = \$10,000 + \$9.30x$$

$$x = \frac{75,000}{9.3} \approx 8064.52 \text{ units}$$

At most, the company can manufacture 8064 units.

63. $W_1 x = W_2(L - x)$

$$50x = 75(10 - x)$$

$$50x = 750 - 75x$$

$$125x = 750$$

$$x = 6 \text{ ft from}$$

$$\text{the 50-lb child}$$

65. $A = \dfrac{1}{2}bh$

$$2A = bh$$

$$\frac{2A}{b} = h$$

67. $I = Prt$

$$r = \frac{I}{Pt}$$

69. $A = \dfrac{1}{2}(a + b)h$

$$\frac{2A}{h} = a + b$$

$$\frac{2A - ah}{h} = b$$

71. $V = \dfrac{1}{3}\pi h^2(3r - h)$

$$\frac{3V}{\pi h^2} = 3r - h$$

$$\frac{3V + \pi h^3}{\pi h^2} = 3r$$

$$\frac{3V + \pi h^3}{3\pi h^2} = r$$

73. $F = \alpha\dfrac{m_1 m_2}{r^2}$

$$Fr^2 = \alpha m_1 m_2$$

$$\frac{Fr^2}{\alpha m_1} = m_2$$

75. $S = \dfrac{rL - a}{r - 1}$

$$S(r - 1) = rL - a$$

$$Sr - S = rL - a$$

$$Sr - rL = S - a$$

$$r(S - L) = S - a$$

$$r = \frac{S - a}{S - L}$$

Section 2.3   Solving Equations Graphically

- You should be able to find the intercepts of the graph of an equation.

- You should be able to find the zeros of a function $y = f(x)$ by solving the equation $f(x) = 0$.

- You should be able to find the solutions of an equation graphically using a graphing utility.

- You should be able to use the zoom and trace features to find solutions to any desired accuracy.

- You should be able to find the points of intersection of two graphs.

1. $y = x - 5$

   Let $y = 0$: $0 = x - 5 \Rightarrow x = 5 \Rightarrow (5,\ 0)$ x-intercept
   Let $x = 0$: $y = 0 - 5 \Rightarrow y = -5 \Rightarrow (0,\ -5)$ y-intercept

3. $y = x^2 + x - 2$

   Let $y = 0$: $(x^2 + x - 2) = (x + 2)(x - 1) = 0 \Rightarrow x = -2,\ 1 \Rightarrow (-2,\ 0),\ (1,\ 0)$ x-intercepts
   Let $x = 0$: $y = 0^2 + 0 - 2 = -2 \Rightarrow (0,\ -2)$ y-intercept

5. $y = x\sqrt{x + 2}$

   Let $y = 0$: $0 = x\sqrt{x + 2} \Rightarrow x = 0,\ -2 \Rightarrow (0,\ 0),\ (-2,\ 0)$ x-intercepts
   Let $x = 0$: $y = 0\sqrt{0 + 2} = 0 \Rightarrow (0,\ 0)$ y-intercept

7. $xy - 2y - x + 1 = 0$

   Let $y = 0$: $-x + 1 = 0 \Rightarrow x = 1 \Rightarrow (1,\ 0)$ x-intercept
   Let $x = 0$: $-2y + 1 = 0 \Rightarrow y = \frac{1}{2} \Rightarrow \left(0,\ \frac{1}{2}\right)$ y-intercept

9. $f(x) = 12 - 4x$

11. $f(x) = x^2 - 2.5x - 6$

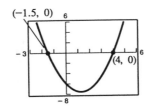

13. $f(x) = \dfrac{x+2}{3} - \dfrac{x-1}{5} - 1$

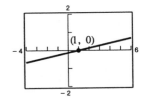

15. $25(x - 3) = 12(x + 2) - 10$

$25x - 75 = 12x + 24 - 10$

$13x - 89 = 0$

17. $\dfrac{2x}{3} = 10 - \dfrac{1}{x}$

$\dfrac{2x}{3} + \dfrac{1}{x} - 10 = 0$

19. $\dfrac{3}{x+2} - \dfrac{4}{x-2} = 5$

$\dfrac{3}{x+2} - \dfrac{4}{x-2} - 5 = 0$

21. $27 - 4x = 12$

$-4x = -15$

$x = \dfrac{15}{4}$

$27 - 4x - 12 = 0$

$f(x) = 15 - 4x = 0$

$x = 3.75$

23. $\dfrac{3x}{2} + \dfrac{1}{4}(x - 2) = 10$

$\dfrac{6x}{4} + \dfrac{x}{4} = 10 + \dfrac{1}{2}$

$\dfrac{7x}{4} = \dfrac{21}{2}$

$x = 6$

$f(x) = \dfrac{3x}{2} + \dfrac{1}{4}(x - 2) - 10 = 0$

$x = 6.0$

25. $3(x+3) = 5(1-x) - 1$

$\qquad 3x + 9 = 5 - 5x - 1$

$\qquad\quad 8x = -5$

$\qquad\quad\ \ x = -\frac{5}{8}$

$\quad f(x) = 3(x+3) - 5(1-x) + 1 = 0$

$\qquad\quad\ \ x = -0.625$

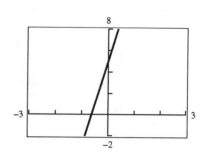

27. $\frac{1}{4}(x^2 - 10x + 17) = 0$

$\quad x = 2.172,\ 7.828$

29. $x^3 + x + 4 = 0$

$\quad x = -1.379$

31. $2x^3 - x^2 - 18x + 9 = 0$

$\quad x = -3.0,\ 0.5,\ 3.0$

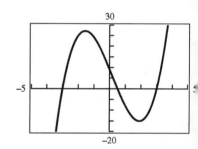

33. $\qquad\qquad x^4 = 2x^3 + 1$

$\quad\ \ x^4 - 2x^3 - 1 = 0$

$\quad\ \ x = -0.717,\ 2.107$

35. $\qquad \dfrac{2}{z+2} = 3$

$\qquad \dfrac{2}{z+2} - 3 = 0$

$\quad z = -1.333$

37. $y = 2 - x$

$\quad y = 2x - 1$

$\quad (x,\ y) = (1,\ 1)$

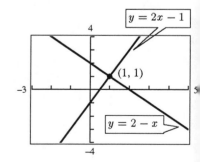

39. $y = 4 - x^2$

$y = 2x - 1$

$(x,\ y) = (1.449,\ 1.898),\ (-3.449,\ -7.898)$

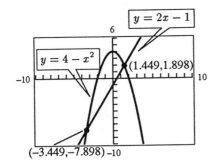

41. $y = 8$

$y = 3x^2 + 2x$

$(x,\ y) = (-2,\ 8),\ (1.333,\ 8)$

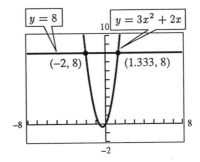

43. $y = 3(x + 1)$

$y = x^2 + 2x + 1$

$(x,\ y) = (-1,\ 0),\ (2,\ 9)$

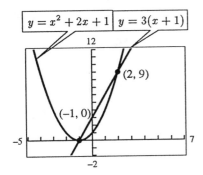

45. $y = 2x^2$

$y = x^4 - 2x^2$

$(x,\ y) = (0,\ 0),\ (2,\ 8),\ (-2,\ 8)$

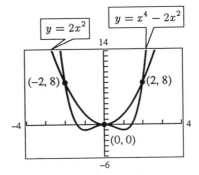

47. (a) $\dfrac{1 + 0.73205}{1 - 0.73205} = \dfrac{1.73205}{0.26795}$

$\qquad = 6.464079 = 6.46$

(b) $\dfrac{1 + 0.73205}{1 - 0.73205} = \dfrac{1.73205}{0.26795}$

$\qquad = \dfrac{1.73}{0.27}$

$\qquad = 6.407407 = 6.41$

The second method decreases accuracy.

49. (a) $\dfrac{3.33 + (1.98/0.74)}{4 + (6.25/3.15)} = \dfrac{6.005675676}{5.984126984}$

$\qquad = 1.00360098$

$\qquad = 1.00$

(b) $\dfrac{3.33 + (1.98/0.74)}{4 + (6.25/3.15)} = \dfrac{6.01}{5.98}$

$\qquad = 1.005016722$

$\qquad = 1.01$

The second method decreases accuracy.

51. (a) $T = \dfrac{x}{63} + \dfrac{(280 - x)}{54}$

(b) Domain: $0 \le x \le 280$

(c) If the time was 4 hours and 45 minutes, then $T = 4\frac{3}{4}$ and $x \approx 164.5$ miles.

53. (a) $C = x + 0.33(55 - x)$

(b) Domain: $0 \le x \le 55$

(c) If the final mixture is 60% concentrate, then $C = 0.6(55) = 33$ and $x = 22.2$.

55. $S = I + G$

$\quad S = x + 8000 - \frac{1}{2}x$

$\quad = \frac{1}{2}x + 8000, \quad 0 \le x \le 16,000$

(a) The government payment decreases.

(b) The spendable income increases.

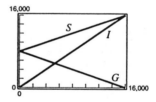

57. If $S = 11,800$, then:

$\quad 11,800 = \frac{1}{2}x + 8000$

$\quad\quad x = 7600$

Section 2.4   Quadratic Equations

- A quadratic equation is of the form $ax^2 + bx + c = 0$, $a \neq 0$.
- You should be able to factor a quadratic.
- You should be able to solve a quadratic by extracting square roots.
- You should be able to complete the square on any quadratic.

1.
$$2x^2 = 3 - 5x$$
$$2x^2 + 5x - 3 = 0$$

3.
$$(x - 3)^2 = 2$$
$$x^2 - 6x + 9 = 2$$
$$x^2 - 6x + 7 = 0$$

5.
$$\frac{3x^2 - 10}{5} = 12x$$
$$3x^2 - 10 = 60x$$
$$3x^2 - 60x - 10 = 0$$

7.
$$6x^2 + 3x = 0$$
$$3x(2x + 1) = 0$$
$$3x = 0 \ \Rightarrow \ x = 0$$
$$2x + 1 = 0 \ \Rightarrow \ x = -\tfrac{1}{2}$$

9.
$$x^2 - 2x - 8 = 0$$
$$(x + 2)(x - 4) = 0$$
$$x + 2 = 0 \ \Rightarrow \ x = -2$$
$$x - 4 = 0 \ \Rightarrow \ x = \ \ 4$$

11.
$$x^2 + 10x + 25 = 0$$
$$(x + 5)^2 = 0$$
$$x + 5 = 0 \ \Rightarrow \ x = -5$$

13.
$$3 + 5x - 2x^2 = 0$$
$$(3 - x)(1 + 2x) = 0$$
$$3 - x = 0 \ \Rightarrow \ x = 3$$
$$1 + 2x = 0 \ \Rightarrow \ x = -\tfrac{1}{2}$$

15.
$$2x^2 + 8x - 6 = x^2 + 4x + 6$$
$$x^2 + 4x = 12$$
$$x^2 + 4x - 12 = 0$$
$$(x + 6)(x - 2) = 0$$
$$x + 6 = 0 \ \Rightarrow \ x = -6$$
$$x - 2 = 0 \ \Rightarrow \ x = 2$$

17.
$$x^2 + 2ax + a^2 = 0$$
$$(x + a)^2 = 0$$
$$x + a = 0$$
$$x = -a$$

19. $x^2 = 16$

$\quad x = \pm\sqrt{16}$

$\quad x = \pm 4 = \pm 4.00$

21. $x^2 = 7$

$\quad x = \pm\sqrt{7} \approx \pm 2.65$

23. $3x^2 = 36$

$\quad x^2 = 12$

$\quad x = \pm\sqrt{12}$

$\quad x = \pm 2\sqrt{3} \approx \pm 3.46$

25. $(x-12)^2 = 18$

$\quad x - 12 = \pm 3\sqrt{2}$

$\quad x = 12 \pm 3\sqrt{2}$

$\quad x \approx 16.24 \text{ or } x \approx 7.76$

27. $(x+2)^2 = 12$

$\quad x + 2 = \pm\sqrt{12}$

$\quad x = -2 \pm 2\sqrt{3}$

$\quad x \approx 1.46 \text{ or } x \approx -5.46$

29. $(x-7)^2 = (x+3)^2$

$\quad x - 7 = \pm(x+3)$

$\quad \text{For } x - 7 = +(x+3)$

$\quad\quad -7 = +3, \text{ No solution}$

$\quad \text{For } x - 7 = -(x+3)$

$\quad\quad x - 7 = -x - 3$

$\quad\quad 2x = 4$

$\quad\quad x = 2$

31. $\quad x^2 - 2x = 0$

$\quad x^2 - 2x + 1^2 = 1^2$

$\quad (x-1)^2 = 1$

$\quad x - 1 = \pm 1$

$\quad x = 1 \pm 1$

$\quad x = 2, \ 0$

$\quad x = 2 \text{ or } x = 0$

33. $x^2 + 4x - 32 = 0$

$\quad x^2 + 4x = 32$

$\quad x^2 + 4x + 2^2 = 32 + 2^2$

$\quad (x+2)^2 = 36$

$\quad x + 2 = \pm 6$

$\quad x = -2 \pm 6$

$\quad x = 4 \text{ or } x = -8$

35. $\quad x^2 + 6x + 2 = 0$

$\quad x^2 + 6x = -2$

$\quad x^2 + 6x + 3^2 = -2 + 3^2$

$\quad (x+3)^2 = 7$

$\quad x + 3 = \pm\sqrt{7}$

$\quad x = -3 \pm \sqrt{7}$

37. $9x^2 - 18x + 3 = 0$

$x^2 - 2x + \frac{1}{3} = 0$

$x^2 - 2x = -\frac{1}{3}$

$x^2 - 2x + 1^2 = -\frac{1}{3} + 1^2$

$(x - 1)^2 = \frac{2}{3}$

$x - 1 = \pm\sqrt{\frac{2}{3}}$

$x = 1 \pm \sqrt{\frac{2}{3}}$

$x = 1 \pm \frac{\sqrt{6}}{3}$

39. $8 + 4x - x^2 = 0$

$x^2 - 4x - 8 = 0$

$x^2 - 4x = 8$

$x^2 - 4x + 2^2 = 8 + 2^2$

$(x - 2)^2 = 12$

$x - 2 = \pm\sqrt{12}$

$x = 2 \pm 2\sqrt{3}$

41. $0.23x^2 - 0.78x - 1.15 = 0$

Begin with the standard viewing rectangle. By zooming in and using the trace feature, we find $x = -1.111$ and 4.502.

43. $\frac{1}{50}x(41 - x) + 55 = 0$

Begin with the standard viewing rectangle. By zooming *out* twice, we see that there are two solutions. By zooming in and using the trace feature, we find $x = 76.805$ and -35.805.

45. $x^2 - 2x - 1 = 0$

$x^2 - 2x = 1$

$x^2 - 2x + 1^2 = 1 + 1^2$

$(x - 1)^2 = 2$

$x - 1 = \pm\sqrt{2}$

$x = 1 \pm \sqrt{2}$

47. $16x^2 - 9 = 0$

$16x^2 = 9$

$x^2 = \frac{9}{16}$

$x = \pm\frac{3}{4}$

49. $4x^2 - 12x + 9 = 0$

$(2x - 3)^2 = 0$

$2x - 3 = 0$

$x = \frac{3}{2}$

51. $(x + 3)^2 = 81$

$x + 3 = \pm 9$

$x = -3 \pm 9$

$x = 6$ or $x = -12$

53. $50 + 5x = 3x^2$

$$0 = 3x^2 - 5x - 50$$

$$0 = (3x + 10)(x - 5)$$

$$0 = 3x + 10 \;\Rightarrow\; -\tfrac{10}{3} = x$$

$$0 = x - 5 \quad\;\Rightarrow\quad\; 5 = x$$

55. $12x = x^2 + 27$

$$0 = x^2 - 12x + 27$$

$$0 = (x - 9)(x - 3)$$

$$x - 9 = 0 \;\Rightarrow\; x = 9$$

$$x - 3 = 0 \;\Rightarrow\; x = 3$$

57. $x^2 - x - \tfrac{11}{4} = 0$

$$x^2 - x = \tfrac{11}{4}$$

$$x^2 - x + \left(\tfrac{1}{2}\right)^2 = \tfrac{11}{4} + \left(\tfrac{1}{2}\right)^2$$

$$\left(x - \tfrac{1}{2}\right)^2 = \tfrac{12}{4}$$

$$x - \tfrac{1}{2} = \pm\sqrt{\tfrac{12}{4}}$$

$$x = \tfrac{1}{2} \pm \sqrt{3}$$

Or, by using the zoom and trace features of a graphing utility, we find that $y = x^2 - x - \tfrac{11}{4}$ has two x-intercepts: $x = -1.23$ and $x = 2.23$.

59. $50x^2 - 60x - 7 = 0$

$$x^2 - \frac{6}{5}x - \frac{7}{50} = 0$$

$$x^2 - \frac{6}{5}x = \frac{7}{50}$$

$$x^2 - \frac{6}{5}x + \left(\frac{3}{5}\right)^2 = \frac{7}{50} + \left(\frac{3}{5}\right)^2$$

$$\left(x - \frac{3}{5}\right)^2 = \frac{1}{2}$$

$$x - \frac{3}{5} = \pm\frac{\sqrt{2}}{2}$$

$$x = \frac{3}{5} \pm \frac{\sqrt{2}}{2}$$

Or, by using the zoom and trace features of a graphing utility, we find that $y = 50x^2 - 60x - 7$ has two x-intercepts: $x = 1.31$ and $x = -0.11$.

61. $(x + 3)^2 - 4 = 0$

$$(x + 3)^2 = 4$$

$$x + 3 = \pm 2$$

$$x = -3 \pm 2$$

$$x = -5 \text{ or } x = -1$$

63. $(x + 1)^2 = x^2$

$$x^2 = (x + 1)^2$$

$$x = \pm(x + 1)$$

For $x = +(x + 1)$

$$0 = 1, \quad \text{No solution}$$

For $x = -(x + 1)$

$$2x = -1$$

$$x = -\tfrac{1}{2}$$

65. $\dfrac{1}{x^2 + 2x + 5} = \dfrac{1}{x^2 + 2x + 1 + 4}$

$$= \dfrac{1}{(x + 1)^2 + 4}$$

67. $\dfrac{1}{x^2 - 4x - 12} = \dfrac{1}{x^2 - 4x + 2^2 - 2^2 - 12}$

$$= \dfrac{1}{(x - 2)^2 - 16}$$

69. $\dfrac{1}{\sqrt{6x - x^2}} = \dfrac{1}{\sqrt{-(x^2 - 6x)}} = \dfrac{1}{\sqrt{-(x^2 - 6x + 3^2 - 3^2)}} = \dfrac{1}{\sqrt{-[(x-3)^2 - 9]}} = \dfrac{1}{\sqrt{9 - (x-3)^2}}$

71. $\quad w(w + 14) = 1632$

$w^2 + 14w - 1632 = 0$

$(w + 48)(w - 34) = 0$

Since $w > 0$, we have $w = 34$ feet and the length is $w + 14 = 48$ feet.

73. $\quad 0 = -16t^2 + 1821$

$16t^2 = 1821$

$t^2 = \frac{1821}{16}$

$t = \pm\sqrt{\frac{1821}{16}}$

$t \approx \pm 10.67$

Since $t > 0$, it will take ≈ 10.67 seconds for the object to hit the ground.

75. $x^2 + x^2 = 5^2$ $\quad$ Pythagorean Theorem

$2x^2 = 25$

$x^2 = \dfrac{25}{2}$

$x = \sqrt{\dfrac{25}{2}}$

$= \dfrac{5}{\sqrt{2}}$

$= \dfrac{5\sqrt{2}}{2}$

≈ 3.54 centimeters

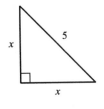

77. Since the angle is $45°$, the triangle is isosceles.

$x^2 + x^2 = 3000^2$

$2x^2 = 9{,}000{,}000$

$x^2 = 4{,}500{,}000$

$x = 1500\sqrt{2} \approx 2121.32$ feet

79. $p = 20 - 0.0002x$

$$R = xp = x(20 - 0.0002x)$$

(a)

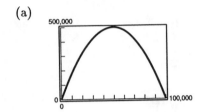

(b) R will be a maximum when $x = 50,000$. In this case, $p = 10$.

(c) If $R = 400,000$, then $x = 27,639$ ($p = 14.47$) or $x = 72,361$ ($p = 5.53$). It would be better to select the higher price because that would require selling less units.

81. $ax^2 + bx = 0$

$x(ax + b) = 0$

$x = 0$

$ax + b = 0 \Rightarrow x = -\dfrac{b}{a}$

83. $x = -4$ or $x = 6$

$(x + 4)(x - 6) = 0$

$x^2 - 2x - 24 = 0$ or

any multiple of this equation

Section 2.5   The Quadratic Formula

- You should know the Quadratic Formula: For $ax^2 + bx + c = 0$, $a \neq 0$,

$$x = \frac{-b \pm \sqrt{b^2 - 4ac}}{2a}$$

- You should be able to determine the types of solutions of a quadratic equation by checking the discriminant $b^2 - 4ac$.
  - (a) If $b^2 - 4ac > 0$, there are two distinct real solutions.
  - (b) If $b^2 - 4ac = 0$, there is one repeated real solution.
  - (c) If $b^2 - 4ac < 0$, there are no real solutions.

- You should be able to use your calculator to solve quadratic equations.

- You should be able to solve word problems involving quadratic equations. Study the examples in the text carefully. Use your graphing calculator to verify your answers.

---

1. $4x^2 - 4x + 1 = 0$; $a = 4$, $b = -4$, $c = 1$

$b^2 - 4ac = (-4)^2 - 4(4)(1) = 0$

One real solution

3. $2x^2 - 5x + 5 = 0$; $a = 2$, $b = -5$, $c = 5$

$b^2 - 4ac = (-5)^2 - 4(2)(5) = -15 < 0$

No real solutions

5. $\frac{1}{5}x^2 + \frac{6}{5}x - 8 = 0$

$x^2 + 6x - 40 = 0$; $a = 1$, $b = 6$, $c = -40$

$b^2 - 4ac = (6)^2 - 4(1)(-40) = 36 + 160 = 196 > 0$

Two real solutions

7. $2x^2 + x - 1 = 0$

$a = 2$, $b = 1$, $c = -1$

$x = \dfrac{-1 \pm \sqrt{1^2 - 4(2)(-1)}}{2(2)}$

$= \dfrac{-1 \pm \sqrt{9}}{4} = \dfrac{-1 \pm 3}{4}$

$x = \dfrac{-1 + 3}{4} = \dfrac{1}{2}$ or

$x = \dfrac{-1 - 3}{4} = -1$

9. $16x^2 + 8x - 3 = 0$

$a = 16$, $b = 8$, $c = -3$

$x = \dfrac{-8 \pm \sqrt{8^2 - 4(16)(-3)}}{2(16)}$

$= \dfrac{-8 \pm \sqrt{256}}{32} = \dfrac{-8 \pm 16}{32}$

$x = \dfrac{-8 + 16}{32} = \dfrac{1}{4}$ or

$x = \dfrac{-8 - 16}{32} = -\dfrac{3}{4}$

11. $2 + 2x - x^2 = 0$

$x^2 - 2x - 2 = 0$

$a = 1, \; b = -2, \; c = -2$

$x = \dfrac{-(-2) \pm \sqrt{(-2)^2 - 4(1)(-2)}}{2(1)}$

$= \dfrac{2 \pm \sqrt{12}}{2} = \dfrac{2 \pm 2\sqrt{3}}{2}$

$x = 1 \pm \sqrt{3}$

13. $x^2 + 14x + 44 = 0$

$a = 1, \; b = 14, \; c = 44$

$x = \dfrac{-14 \pm \sqrt{14^2 - 4(1)(44)}}{2(1)}$

$= \dfrac{-14 \pm \sqrt{20}}{2} = \dfrac{-14 \pm 2\sqrt{5}}{2}$

$x = -7 \pm \sqrt{5}$

15. $x^2 + 8x - 4 = 0; \; a = 1, \; b = 8, \; c = -4$

$x = \dfrac{-8 \pm \sqrt{8^2 - 4(1)(-4)}}{2(1)}$

$= \dfrac{-8 \pm \sqrt{80}}{2} = \dfrac{-8 \pm 4\sqrt{5}}{2}$

$x = -4 \pm 2\sqrt{5}$

17. $12x - 9x^2 = -3$

$9x^2 - 12x - 3 = 0$

$3x^2 - 4x - 1 = 0$

$a = 3, \; b = -4, \; c = -1$

$x = \dfrac{-(-4) \pm \sqrt{(-4)^2 - 4(3)(-1)}}{2(3)}$

$= \dfrac{4 \pm \sqrt{28}}{6} = \dfrac{4 \pm 2\sqrt{7}}{6}$

$x = \dfrac{2}{3} \pm \dfrac{\sqrt{7}}{3}$

19. $36x^2 + 24x - 7 = 0$

$a = 36, \; b = 24, \; c = -7$

$x = \dfrac{-24 \pm \sqrt{24^2 - 4(36)(-7)}}{2(36)}$

$= \dfrac{-24 \pm \sqrt{1584}}{72} = \dfrac{-24 \pm 12\sqrt{11}}{72}$

$x = \dfrac{-2 \pm \sqrt{11}}{6} = -\dfrac{1}{3} \pm \dfrac{\sqrt{11}}{6}$

21. $4x^2 + 4x = 7$

$4x^2 + 4x - 7 = 0; \; a = 4, \; b = 4, \; c = -7$

$x = \dfrac{-4 \pm \sqrt{4^2 - 4(4)(-7)}}{2(4)}$

$= \dfrac{-4 \pm \sqrt{128}}{8} = \dfrac{-4 \pm 8\sqrt{2}}{8}$

$x = -\dfrac{1}{2} \pm \sqrt{2}$

23. $28x - 49x^2 = 4$

$49x^2 - 28x + 4 = 0$

$a = 49, \ b = -28, \ c = 4$

$x = \dfrac{-(-28) \pm \sqrt{(-28)^2 - 4(49)(4)}}{2(49)}$

$= \dfrac{28 \pm \sqrt{0}}{98} = \dfrac{2}{7}$

27. $(y - 5)^2 = 2y$

$y^2 - 10y + 25 = 2y$

$y^2 - 12y + 25 = 0$

$a = 1, \ b = -12, \ c = 25$

$x = \dfrac{-(-12) \pm \sqrt{(-12)^2 - 4(1)(25)}}{2(1)}$

$= \dfrac{12 \pm \sqrt{44}}{2} = \dfrac{12 \pm 2\sqrt{11}}{2}$

$x = 6 \pm \sqrt{11}$

31. $422x^2 - 506x - 347 = 0$

$a = 422, \ b = -506, \ c = -347$

$x = \dfrac{-(-506) \pm \sqrt{(-506)^2 - 4(422)(-347)}}{2(422)}$

$x = \dfrac{506 \pm \sqrt{841{,}772}}{844} \approx \dfrac{506 \pm 917.481335}{844}$

$x \approx 1.687 \quad \text{or} \quad x \approx -0.488$

25. $25h^2 + 80h + 61 = 0$

$a = 25, \ b = 80, \ c = 61$

$h = \dfrac{-80 \pm \sqrt{(80)^2 - 4(25)(61)}}{2(25)}$

$= \dfrac{-80 \pm \sqrt{300}}{50} = \dfrac{-80 \pm 10\sqrt{3}}{50}$

$h = \dfrac{-8 \pm \sqrt{3}}{5} = -\dfrac{8}{5} \pm \dfrac{\sqrt{3}}{5}$

29. $5.1x^2 - 1.7x - 3.2 = 0$

$a = 5.1, \ b = -1.7, \ c = -3.2$

$x = \dfrac{-(-1.7) \pm \sqrt{(-1.7)^2 - 4(5.1)(-3.2)}}{2(5.1)}$

$x = \dfrac{1.7 \pm \sqrt{68.17}}{10.2} \approx \dfrac{1.7 \pm 8.2565}{10.2}$

$x \approx 0.976 \quad \text{or} \quad x \approx -0.643$

Alternate Solution:
$5.1x^2 - 1.7x - 3.2 = 0$
Beginning with the standard viewing rectangle, we see that there are two solutions. Using the zoom feature, we obtain $x = 0.976$ and -0.643.

Alternate Solution:
$422x^2 - 506x - 347 = 0$
Beginning with the standard viewing rectangle, we see that there are two solutions. Using the zoom feature, we obtain $x = 1.687$ and -0.488.

33. $3x + 4 = 2x - 7$

$\quad x + 4 = -7$

$\quad\quad x = -11$

35. $4x^2 - 15 = 25$

$\quad\quad 4x^2 = 40$

$\quad\quad x^2 = 10$

$\quad\quad x = \pm\sqrt{10}$

37. $x^2 + 3x + 1 = 0$

$$x = \frac{-3 \pm \sqrt{3^2 - 4(1)(1)}}{2(1)}$$

$$= \frac{-3 \pm \sqrt{5}}{2}$$

39. $(x - 1)^2 = 9$

$\quad x - 1 = \pm\sqrt{9}$

$\quad\quad x = 1 \pm 3$

$\quad\quad x = 4 \text{ or } x = -2$

41. $100x^2 - 400 = 0$

$\quad\quad 100x^2 = 400$

$\quad\quad x^2 = 4$

$\quad\quad x = \pm 2$

43. *Verbal Model:*   The sum of Bill and Harry's ages is 100. The product of their ages is 2500. How old is Bill? How old is Harry?

Let $x =$ one number and $100 - x =$ other number.

$\quad x(100 - x) = 2500$

$\quad 100x - x^2 = 2500$

$\quad\quad\quad 0 = x^2 - 100x + 2500$

$\quad\quad\quad 0 = (x - 50)^2$

$\quad\quad\quad x = 50, \quad 100 - x = 50$

45. *Verbal Model:*   One leg of a right triangle is one foot longer than the other leg. The hypotenuse is $\sqrt{113}$ feet. Find the length of each leg, given that they are both integers.

Let $n =$ first integer and $n + 1 =$ next integer.

$\quad\quad n^2 + (n + 1)^2 = 113$

$\quad n^2 + n^2 + 2n + 1 = 113$

$\quad\quad 2n^2 + 2n - 112 = 0$

$\quad\quad\quad n^2 + n - 56 = 0$

$\quad\quad (n + 8)(n - 7) = 0$

$\quad\quad n = -8 \quad \text{or} \quad n = 7$

Since we want a positive integer, $n = 7$ and $n + 1 = 8$.

47. $14,000 = 0.125x^2 + 20x + 500$

$\qquad 0 = 0.125x^2 + 20x - 13,500$

Thus, $a = 0.125,\ b = 20,\ c = -13,500.$

$$x = \frac{-20 \pm \sqrt{20^2 - 4(0.125)(-13,500)}}{2(0.125)} \approx \frac{-20 \pm 84.5577}{0.25}$$

$$x \approx \frac{-20 + 84.5577}{0.25} \quad \text{or} \quad x \approx \frac{-20 - 84.5577}{0.25}$$

$$x \approx 258.2 \qquad\qquad\qquad x \approx -418.2, \quad \text{not a valid solution}$$

The manufacturer can produce 258 units for the given cost $C = \$14,000.$

Alternate Solution: Using a graphing utility, we find that the positive solution to $y = 0.125x^2 + 20x - 13,500$ is $x = 258.2,$ or 258 units.

49. $1680 = 800 + 0.04x + 0.002x^2$

$\qquad 0 = 0.002x^2 + 0.04x - 880$

Thus, $a = 0.002,\ b = 0.04,\ c = -880.$

$$x = \frac{-0.04 \pm \sqrt{(0.04)^2 - 4(0.002)(-880)}}{2(0.002)} \approx \frac{-0.04 \pm 2.6536}{0.004}$$

$$x \approx \frac{-0.04 + 2.6536}{0.004} \quad \text{or} \quad x \approx \frac{-0.04 - 2.6536}{0.004}$$

$$x \approx 653.4 \qquad\qquad\qquad x \approx -673.4, \quad \text{not a valid solution}$$

The manufacturer can produce 653 units for the given cost $C = \$1680.$

Alternate Solution: Using a graphing utility, we find that the positive solution to $y = 0.002x^2 + 0.04x - 880$ is $x = 653.4,$ or 653 units.

51. Number of rows $= x$; Number of seats/row $= \dfrac{72}{x}$

$$\left(\frac{72}{x} + 3\right)(x - 2) = 72$$

$$(72 + 3x)(x - 2) = 72x$$

$$3x^2 - 6x - 144 = 0$$

Thus, $a = 3,\ b = -6,\ c = -144.$

$$x = \frac{-(-6) \pm \sqrt{(-6)^2 - 4(3)(-144)}}{2(3)} = \frac{6 \pm 42}{6}$$

$$x = 8 \quad \text{or} \quad x = -6, \quad \text{not a valid solution}$$

$$\frac{72}{x} = \frac{72}{8} = 9 \text{ seats/row}$$

53. $(200 - 2x)(100 - 2x) = \dfrac{1}{4}(100)(200)$

$\qquad 20{,}000 - 600x + 4x^2 = 5000$

$\qquad 4x^2 - 600x + 15{,}000 = 0$

$\qquad x^2 - 150x + 3750 = 0$

Thus, $a = 1,\ b = -150,\ c = 3750.$

$$x = \frac{-(-150) \pm \sqrt{(-150)^2 - 4(1)(3750)}}{2(1)} \approx \frac{150 \pm 86.6025}{2}$$

$$x \approx \frac{150 + 86.6025}{2} \approx 118.301 \text{ ft}, \quad \text{not possible since the lot is only 100 feet wide.}$$

$$x \approx \frac{150 - 86.6025}{2} \approx 31.699 \text{ ft}$$

The person must go around the lot $\dfrac{31.699 \text{ ft}}{24 \text{ in.}} = \dfrac{31.699 \text{ ft}}{2 \text{ ft}} = 15.8$ times or 16 times.

Alternate Solution:

$$\text{Small area} = \frac{1}{4}(\text{Large area})$$

$$(200 - 2x)(100 - 2x) = \frac{1}{4}(200)(100)$$

$$4x^2 = 600x + 20{,}000 = 5000$$

$$4x^2 - 600x + 15{,}000 = 0$$

$$x^2 - 150x + 3750 = 0$$

Using the zoom feature, we obtain $x = 31.699$. (The other solution, $x = 118.301$, is extraneous.)

55. $S = x^2 + 4xh$

$\qquad 108 = x^2 + 4x(3)$

$\qquad 0 = x^2 + 12x - 108$

$\qquad 0 = (x - 6)(x + 18)$

$\qquad x = 6 \quad \text{or} \quad x = -18$

Choosing the positive value, we have
$x = 6$. The dimensions of the base are
6 in. × 6 in.

Open Box

57. (a) $S = 116{,}289 + 9506.7t + 841.45t^2$

(b) Tracing to the right, $S = 300{,}000$
when $t = 10.170$ years.

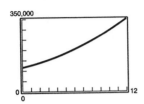

59. Let $S = $ rate of the southbound plane and $E = S + 50 = $ rate of the eastbound plane.

$$d_S = tr_S = 3S$$

$$d_E = tr_E = 3(S + 50)$$

By the Pythagorean Theorem:

$$d_S{}^2 + d_E{}^2 = (2440)^2$$

$$[3S]^2 + [3(S + 50)]^2 = (2440)^2$$

$$9S^2 + 9(S^2 + 100S + 2500) = 5{,}953{,}600$$

$$18S^2 + 900S - 5{,}931{,}100 = 0$$

$$S = \frac{-900 \pm \sqrt{(900)^2 - 4(18)(-5931100)}}{2(18)}$$

$$S \approx \frac{-900 \pm 20684.51595}{36}$$

Considering the positive solution, $S \approx 550$ mph, and $E = S + 50 \approx 600$ mph. Or, graphing the function $y = 18S^2 + 900S - 5{,}931{,}100$, we see that the positive x-intercept is $S = 549.57$ and $E = S + 50 = 599.57$.

61. $x^2 + 15^2 = 75^2$ Pythagorean Theorem

$x^2 = 75^2 - 15^2$

$x^2 = 5400$

$x = \sqrt{5400} \approx 73.48$ feet

63. (a) $D = -0.024s^2 + 1.455s + 431.5$

$\quad 0 < s \le 75$

(b) The greatest distance is $D = 453.552$ corresponding to $s = 30.313$. The trip will take $D/s = 453.552/30.313 = 14.962$ hours.

(c) The distance traveled in 8 hours is $8s$. The point of intersection of D with $y_2 = 8s$ is $s = 54.883$ mph, corresponding to a distance of 439.063 miles.

Section 2.6   Other Types of Equations

- You should be able to solve certain types of nonlinear or nonquadratic equations. The zoom and trace features on your graphing utility are especially effective for such equations.

- For equations involving radicals or fractional powers, raise both sides to the same power.

- For equations that are of the quadratic type, $au^2 + bu + c = 0$, $a \neq 0$, use either factoring or the quadratic formula.

- You should be able to solve equations involving fractions or absolute values.

- Always check for extraneous solutions. This can be done either algebraically or using your graphing calculator.

---

1. $x^3 - 2x^2 - 3x = 0$

$\quad x(x^2 - 2x - 3) = 0$

$\quad x(x - 3)(x + 1) = 0$

$\quad\quad x = 0$

$\quad x - 3 = 0 \Rightarrow x = 3$

$\quad x + 1 = 0 \Rightarrow x = -1$

5. $x^3 - 3x^2 - x + 3 = 0$

$\quad x^2(x - 3) - (x - 3) = 0$

$\quad\quad (x - 3)(x^2 - 1) = 0$

$\quad (x - 3)(x + 1)(x - 1) = 0$

$\quad x - 3 = 0 \Rightarrow x = 3$

$\quad x + 1 = 0 \Rightarrow x = -1$

$\quad x - 1 = 0 \Rightarrow x = 1$

3. $5x^3 + 30x^2 + 45x = 0$

$\quad 5x(x^2 + 6x + 9) = 0$

$\quad\quad 5x(x + 3)^2 = 0$

$\quad 5x = 0 \Rightarrow x = 0$

$\quad x + 3 = 0 \Rightarrow x = -3$

7. $x^4 - 10x^2 + 9 = 0$

$\quad (x^2 - 1)(x^2 - 9) = 0$

$\quad (x + 1)(x - 1)(x + 3)(x - 3) = 0$

$\quad x + 1 = 0 \Rightarrow x = -1$

$\quad x - 1 = 0 \Rightarrow x = 1$

$\quad x + 3 = 0 \Rightarrow x = -3$

$\quad x - 3 = 0 \Rightarrow x = 3$

9. $\dfrac{1}{t^2} + \dfrac{8}{t} + 15 = 0$

$1 + 8t + 15t^2 = 0$

$(1 + 3t)(1 + 5t) = 0$

$1 + 3t = 0 \Rightarrow t = -\dfrac{1}{3}$

$1 + 5t = 0 \Rightarrow t = -\dfrac{1}{5}$

11. $5 - 3x^{1/3} - 2x^{2/3} = 0$

$(5 + 2x^{1/3})(1 - x^{1/3}) = 0$

$x^{1/3} = -\dfrac{5}{2} \Rightarrow x = -\dfrac{125}{8}$

$x^{1/3} = 1 \Rightarrow x = 1$

13. $\sqrt{2x} - 10 = 0$

$\sqrt{2x} = 10$

$2x = 100$

$x = 50$

15. $\sqrt[3]{2x + 5} + 3 = 0$

$\sqrt[3]{2x + 5} = -3$

$2x + 5 = -27$

$2x = -32$

$x = -16$

17. $\sqrt{x + 1} - 3x = 1$

$\sqrt{x + 1} = 3x + 1$

$(\sqrt{x + 1})^2 = (3x + 1)^2$

$x + 1 = 9x^2 + 6x + 1$

$0 = 9x^2 + 5x = x(9x + 5)$

$x = 0$

$9x + 5 = 0 \Rightarrow x = -\dfrac{5}{9},$ extraneous

19. $\sqrt{x} + \sqrt{x - 20} = 10$

$\sqrt{x} = 10 - \sqrt{x - 20}$

$(\sqrt{x})^2 = (10 - \sqrt{x - 20})^2$

$x = 100 - 20\sqrt{x - 20} + x - 20$

$-80 = -20\sqrt{x - 20}$

$4 = \sqrt{x - 20}$

$16 = x - 20$

$36 = x$

21. $\sqrt{x + 5} + \sqrt{x - 5} = 10$

$\sqrt{x + 5} = 10 - \sqrt{x - 5}$

$(\sqrt{x + 5})^2 = (10 - \sqrt{x - 5})^2$

$x + 5 = 100 - 20\sqrt{x - 5} + x - 5$

$20\sqrt{x - 5} = 90$

$\sqrt{x - 5} = \dfrac{9}{2}$

$x - 5 = \dfrac{81}{4}$

$x = \dfrac{101}{4}$

23. $(x - 5)^{2/3} = 16$

$x - 5 = \pm 16^{3/2}$

$x - 5 = \pm 64$

$x = 69$ or

$x = -59$

25. $3x(x-1)^{1/2} + 2(x-1)^{3/2} = 0$

$\qquad (x-1)^{1/2}[3x + 2(x-1)] = 0$

$\qquad\quad (x-1)^{1/2}(5x-2) = 0$

$\qquad x - 1 = 0 \Rightarrow x = 1$

$\qquad\qquad\quad x = \frac{2}{5}, \text{ not valid}$

27. $\qquad\qquad \dfrac{20-x}{x} = x$

$\qquad\qquad\quad 20 - x = x^2$

$\qquad\qquad\quad x^2 + x - 20 = 0$

$\qquad\qquad\quad (x+5)(x-4) = 0$

$\qquad\qquad\quad x + 5 = 0 \Rightarrow x = -5$

$\qquad\qquad\quad x - 4 = 0 \Rightarrow x = 4$

29. $\qquad\qquad\qquad \dfrac{1}{x} - \dfrac{1}{x+1} = 3$

$x(x+1)\dfrac{1}{x} - x(x+1)\dfrac{1}{x+1} = x(x+1)(3)$

$\qquad\qquad x + 1 - x = 3x(x+1)$

$\qquad\qquad\qquad 1 = 3x^2 + 3x$

$\qquad\qquad\qquad 0 = 3x^2 + 3x - 1$

$a = 3, \; b = 3, \; c = -1$

$x = \dfrac{-3 \pm \sqrt{(3)^2 - 4(3)(-1)}}{2(3)} = \dfrac{-3 \pm \sqrt{21}}{6} = -\dfrac{1}{2} \pm \dfrac{\sqrt{21}}{6}$

Or, using a graphing utility to graph

$\qquad y = \dfrac{1}{x} - \dfrac{1}{x+1} - 3,$

we see that there are two x-intercepts: $x = -1.264$ and $x = 0.264$.

31. $\qquad\qquad\qquad \dfrac{4}{x+1} - \dfrac{3}{x+2} = 1$

$(x+1)(x+2)\dfrac{4}{x+1} - (x+1)(x+2)\dfrac{3}{x+2} = (x+1)(x+2)(1)$

$\qquad\qquad 4(x+2) - 3(x+1) = (x+1)(x+2)$

$\qquad\qquad 4x + 8 - 3x - 3 = x^2 + 3x + 2$

$\qquad\qquad\qquad\qquad 0 = x^2 + 2x - 3$

$\qquad\qquad\qquad\qquad 0 = (x+3)(x-1)$

$\qquad\qquad x + 3 = 0 \Rightarrow x = -3$

$\qquad\qquad x - 1 = 0 \Rightarrow x = 1$

33. $|2x - 1| = 5$

$\qquad 2x - 1 = 5 \Rightarrow x = 3$

$\qquad -(2x-1) = 5 \Rightarrow x = -2$

35. $|x| = x^2 + x - 3$

$$x = x^2 + x - 3 \qquad\qquad -x = x^2 + x - 3$$
$$x^2 - 3 = 0 \qquad\qquad x^2 + 2x - 3 = 0$$
$$x = \pm\sqrt{3} \qquad\qquad (x - 1)(x + 3) = 0$$
$$x - 1 = 0 \;\Rightarrow\; x = 1$$
$$x + 3 = 0 \;\Rightarrow\; x = -3$$

Only $x = \sqrt{3}$ and $x = -3$ are solutions. Or, using a graphing utility we see that $y = |x| - x^2 - x + 3$ has two x-intercepts: $x = -3$ and $x = 1.732$.

37. $x^4 - x^3 + x - 1 = 0$

Using the zoom and trace features, we find that $x = 1, \ -1$.

39. $x^4 + 5x^2 - 36 = 0$

Using the zoom and trace features, we find that $x = 2, \ -2$.

41. $2x + 9\sqrt{x} - 5 = 0$

Using the zoom and trace features, we find that $x = 0.25$.

43. $-\sqrt{26 - 11x} + 4 = x$

Using the zoom and trace features, we find that $x = 2, \ -5$.

45. $\sqrt{7x + 36} - \sqrt{5x + 16} = 2$

Using the zoom and trace features, we find that $x = 0, \ 4$.

47. $x = \dfrac{3}{x} + \dfrac{1}{2}$

Using the zoom and trace features, we find that $x = 2, \ -1.5$.

49. $\dfrac{1}{x} = \dfrac{4}{x - 1} + 1$

Using the zoom and trace features, we find that $x = -1$.

51. $|x - 10| = x^2 - 10x$

Using the zoom and trace features, we find that $x = -1, \ 10$.

53. $3.2x^4 - 1.5x^2 - 2.1 = 0$

Using the zoom and trace features, we find that $x = \pm 1.04$.

55. $1.8x - 6\sqrt{x} - 5.6 = 0$

Using the zoom and trace features, we find that $x = 16.76$.

57. Number of students $= x$; Cost per student $= f$

$$fx = 1700 \Rightarrow f = \frac{1700}{x}$$

$$(f - 7.50)(x + 6) = 1700$$

$$\left(\frac{1700}{x} - 7.50\right)(x + 6) = 1700$$

$$(2x)\left(\frac{1700}{x} - 7.50\right)(x + 6) = (2x)(1700)$$

$$(3400 - 15x)(x + 6) = 3400x$$

$$-15x^2 - 90x + 20{,}400 = 0$$

$$x = \frac{90 \pm \sqrt{(-90)^2 - 4(-15)(20{,}400)}}{2(-15)} = \frac{90 \pm 1110}{-30}$$

The original number was $x = 34$. Or, using a graphing utility to graph

$$y = \left(\frac{1700}{x} - 7.50\right)(x + 6) - 1700,$$

we see that there is one x-intercept: $x = 34$.

59. Let $x =$ average speed of the plane, then we have a travel time of $t = 720/x$. If the average speed is increased by 40 mph,

$$t - \frac{12}{60} = \frac{720}{x + 40}$$

$$t = \frac{720}{x + 40} + \frac{1}{5}.$$

Equate these two equations and solve for x.

$$\frac{720}{x} = \frac{720}{x + 40} + \frac{1}{5}$$

$$720(5)(x + 40) = 720(5)x + x(x + 40)$$

$$3600x + 144{,}000 = 3600x + x^2 + 40x$$

$$0 = x^2 + 40x - 144{,}000$$

$$0 = (x + 400)(x - 360)$$

Using the positive value for x we have $x = 360$ mph and $x + 40 = 400$ mph. The airspeed required to obtain the decrease in travel time is 400 miles per hour.

61. Compound Interest Formula:

$$A = P\left(1 + \frac{r}{n}\right)^{nt}$$

$$3544.06 = 2500\left(1 + \frac{r}{12}\right)^{12 \cdot 5}$$

$$\frac{3544.06}{2500} = \left(1 + \frac{r}{12}\right)^{60}$$

$$\left(\frac{3544.06}{2500}\right)^{1/60} = 1 + \frac{r}{12}$$

$$\left(\frac{3544.06}{2500}\right)^{1/60} - 1 = \frac{r}{12}$$

$$12\left[\left(\frac{3544.06}{2500}\right)^{1/60} - 1\right] = r$$

$$r \approx 0.07$$

The annual percentage rate is 7%. Or, using a graphing utility to graph

$$y = 2500\left(1 + \frac{x}{12}\right)^{60} - 3544.06,$$

the *x*-intercept is $x = 0.07$, corresponding to a 7% annual percentage rate.

63. (a) $T = 75.82 - 2.11x + 43.51\sqrt{x}$
$\qquad 5 \le x \le 40$
(b) When $x = 14.696$, the model predicts
$\qquad T = 211.609$, which is very accurate.
(c) If $T = 240$, then $x = 24.725$.

65.
$$37.55 = 40 - \sqrt{0.01x + 1}$$
$$\sqrt{0.01x + 1} = 2.45$$
$$0.01x + 1 = 6.0025$$
$$0.01x = 5.0025$$
$$x = 500.25$$

Rounding *x* to the nearest whole unit yields $x \approx 500$ units.

67. (a) Let $6 - x$ be the distance over land. Then the cost is the sum of the cost across water, $24(5280)\sqrt{x^2 + (1/4)}$, and the cost along land, $18(5280)(6 - x)$.

$$C = 24(5280)\sqrt{x^2 + (1/4)} + 18(5280)(6 - x)$$

(b) Domain: $0 \le x \le 6$

(c)

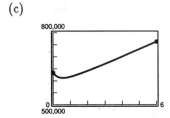

(d) If $C = 625{,}000$, then $x = 1.38$ or 0.11 miles.

69.
$$S = \pi r\sqrt{r^2 + h^2}$$
$$S^2 = \pi^2 r^2(r^2 + h^2)$$
$$S^2 = \pi^2 r^4 + \pi^2 r^2 h^2$$
$$\frac{S^2 - \pi^2 r^4}{\pi^2 r^2} = h^2$$
$$h = \frac{\sqrt{S^2 - \pi^2 r^4}}{\pi r}$$

Section 2.7 Linear Inequalities and Graphing Utilities

- You should know the properties of inequalities.
  - (a) Transitive: $a < b$ and $b < c$ implies $a < c$.
  - (b) Addition: $a < b$ and $c < d$ implies $a + c < b + d$.
  - (c) Adding or Subtracting a Constant: $a \pm c < b \pm c$ if $a < b$.
  - (d) Multiplying or Dividing by a Constant: For $a < b$,
    1. If $c > 0$, then $ac < bc$ and $\dfrac{a}{c} < \dfrac{b}{c}$.

    2. If $c < 0$, then $ac > bc$ and $\dfrac{a}{c} > \dfrac{b}{c}$.

- You should be able to solve inequalities algebraically and graphically.

- You should know that
$$|x| = \begin{cases} x & \text{if } x \geq 0 \\ -x & \text{if } x < 0. \end{cases}$$

- You should be able to solve inequalities involving absolute value.
  - (a) $|x| < a$ if and only if $-a < x < a$.
  - (b) $|x| > a$ if and only if $x < -a$ or $x > a$.

1. $5x - 12 > 0$

   (a) $x = 3$

   $5(3) - 12 \overset{?}{>} 0$

   $3 > 0$

   $x = 3$ *is* a solution.

   (b) $x = -3$

   $5(-3) - 12 \overset{?}{>} 0$

   $-27 \not> 0$

   $x = -3$ *is not* a solution.

   (c) $x = \frac{5}{2}$

   $5\left(\frac{5}{2}\right) - 12 \overset{?}{>} 0$

   $\frac{1}{2} > 0$

   $x = \frac{5}{2}$ *is* a solution.

   (d) $x = \frac{3}{2}$

   $5\left(\frac{3}{2}\right) - 12 \overset{?}{>} 0$

   $-\frac{9}{2} \not> 0$

   $x = \frac{3}{2}$ *is not* a solution.

3. $0 < \dfrac{x-2}{4} < 2$

(a) $x = 4$

$0 \overset{?}{<} \dfrac{4-2}{4} \overset{?}{<} 2$

$0 < \dfrac{1}{2} < 2$

$x = 4$ *is* a solution.

(b) $x = 10$

$0 \overset{?}{<} \dfrac{10-2}{4} \overset{?}{<} 2$

$0 < \quad 2 \quad \not< 2$

$x = 10$ *is not* a solution.

(c) $x = 0$

$0 \overset{?}{<} \dfrac{0-2}{4} \overset{?}{<} 2$

$0 \not< -\dfrac{1}{2} < 2$

$x = 0$ *is not* a solution.

(d) $x = \dfrac{7}{2}$

$0 \overset{?}{<} \dfrac{(7/2)-2}{4} \overset{?}{<} 2$

$0 < \quad \dfrac{3}{8} \quad < 2$

$x = \dfrac{7}{2}$ *is* a solution.

5. $x < 4$ indicates all points to the left of $x = 4$; graph (c).

7. $-2 < x \le 5$ indicates all points from $x = -2$ up to and including $x = 5$; graph (f).

9. $|x| < 4$ indicates all points less than 4 units from $x = 0$; graph (g).

11. $|x - 5| > 2$

$x - 5 < -2$ or $x - 5 > 2$

$x < 3 \qquad\qquad x > 7$

Graph (b)

13. $4x < 12$

$x < 3$

15. $-10x < 40$

$x > -4$

17. $x - 5 \ge 7$

$x \ge 12$

19. $4(x + 1) < 2x + 3$

$4x + 4 < 2x + 3$

$2x < -1$

$x < -\dfrac{1}{2}$

21. $1 < 2x + 3 < 9$
$$-2 < \quad 2x \quad < 6$$
$$-1 < \quad x \quad < 3$$

23. $-4 < \dfrac{2x - 3}{3} < 4$
$$-12 < 2x - 3 < 12$$
$$-9 < \quad 2x \quad < 15$$
$$-\frac{9}{2} < \quad x \quad < \frac{15}{2}$$

25. $\frac{3}{4} > x + 1 > \frac{1}{4}$
$$-\frac{1}{4} > \quad x \quad > -\frac{3}{4}$$

27. $|x| < 5$
$$-5 < x < 5$$

29. $\left|\dfrac{x}{2}\right| > 3$
$$\frac{x}{2} < -3 \quad \text{or} \quad \frac{x}{2} > 3$$
$$x < -6 \qquad\qquad x > 6$$

31. $|x - 20| \le 4$
$$-4 \le x - 20 \le 4$$
$$16 \le \quad x \quad \le 24$$

33. $|x - 20| \ge 4$
$$x - 20 \le -4 \quad \text{or} \quad x - 20 \ge 4$$
$$x \le 16 \qquad\qquad x \ge 24$$

35. $|9 - 2x| - 2 < -1$
$$|9 - 2x| < 1$$
$$-1 < 9 - 2x < 1$$
$$-10 < \quad -2x \quad < -8$$
$$5 > \quad x \quad > 4$$

37. $|x - 5| < 0$
No solution

39. Graphing $y_1 = 4 - 2x - 3 = 1 - 2x$ on $[-2, 2] \times [-2, 2]$ shows that the solution to $4 - 2x < 3$ is $x > 0.5$.

41. Graphing

$$y_1 = \frac{-4x + 25}{5} - \frac{3x - 10}{10}$$

on the standard viewing rectangle shows that the solution is $x \leq 5.45$.

43. Graphing both $y_1 = -\frac{5}{2} - 0.75x - 2 = -0.75x - 4.5$ and $y_2 = 0.75x + 2 - 4 = 0.75x - 2$ on the same viewing rectangle shows that the solution to $-\frac{5}{2} < 0.75x + 2 < 4$ is $-3 < x < 2.67$.

45. Graphing

$$y_1 = \left| \frac{x - 3}{2} \right| - 5$$

on $[-10, 20] \times [-10, 10]$ shows that the solution is $x \leq -7$ or $x \geq 13$.

47. Graphing $y_1 = 2|x + 10| - 9$ on $[-20, 10] \times [-10, 10]$ shows that the solution is $x \leq -14.5$ or $x \geq -5.5$.

49. The radicand of $\sqrt{3 - x}$ is $3 - x$.

$$3 - x \geq 0$$
$$-x \geq -3$$
$$x \leq 3$$

Therefore, the interval is $(-\infty, 3]$.

51. The radicand of $\sqrt[4]{7 - 2x}$ is $7 - 2x$.

$$7 - 2x \geq 0$$
$$-2x \geq -7$$
$$x \leq \frac{7}{2}$$

Therefore, the interval is $\left(-\infty, \frac{7}{2}\right]$.

53. $|x| \leq 2$

55. $|x - 9| \geq 3$

57. $|x - 12| \leq 10$

59. $|x - (-3)| > 5$

$$|x + 3| > 5$$

61. $150 + 0.25x > 250$

$$0.25x > 100$$
$$x > 400$$

If you drive more than 400 miles in a week, the rental fee for Company B is greater than the rental fee for Company A.

63. $1250 < 1000[1 + r(2)]$

$$1.25 < 1 + 2r$$
$$0.25 < 2r$$
$$0.125 < r \quad \text{or} \quad r > 12.5\%$$

65. $R > C$

$115.95x > 95x + 750$

$20.95x > 750$

$x > 35.7995$

$x \geq 36$ units

Using the zoom and trace features, we find
that $x = 35.80$.

67. (a) $C = 1.45x + 150$

(b) $R = 2.95x$

(c) $P = R - C = 2.95x - (1.45x + 150)$

$= 1.50x - 150$

(d) If $50 \leq P \leq 200$, then

$133.333 \leq x \leq 233.333$

$134 \ \leq x \leq \ 23.3$

(e) Let x be the number of dozen *sold*.
$C = 1.45(x + 10) + 150$, since there
are 10 dozen unsold.

$R = 2.95x$

$P = R - C = 1.50x - 164.5$

If $50 \leq P \leq 200$, then $143 \leq x \leq 243$.

69. Subscribers $= 3.657t + 14.784$

$3.657t + 14.784 > 55$

Using the zoom and trace features, we find
that $t = 1991$. Or, solving the inequality
algebraically,

$3.657t > 40.216$

$t > 10.997$

$(t = 1991)$

71. $\left(10.4 - \dfrac{1}{16}\right)^2 \leq \text{area} \leq \left(10.4 + \dfrac{1}{16}\right)^2$

$(10.3375)^2 \leq \text{area} \leq (10.4625)^2$

$106.86390625 \leq \text{area} \leq \ 109.46390625$

73. $\left| \dfrac{h - 68.5}{2.7} \right| \leq 1$

$-1 \leq \dfrac{h - 68.5}{2.7} \leq 1$

$-2.7 \leq h - 68.5 \leq 2.7$

$65.8 \text{ inches } \leq h \leq 71.2 \text{ inches}$

75. $a > b > 0$

$b < a$ a, b are both positive

$1 < \dfrac{a}{b}$

$1 \cdot \dfrac{1}{a} < \dfrac{a}{b} \cdot \dfrac{1}{a}$

$\dfrac{1}{a} < \dfrac{1}{b}$

Section 2.8   Other Types of Inequalities and Graphing Utilities

- You should be able to solve inequalities.
  - (a) Find the critical numbers.
    - 1. Values that make the expression zero
    - 2. Values that make the expression undefined
  - (b) Test one value in each interval on the real number line resulting from the critical numbers.
  - (c) Determine the solution intervals.
- You should be able to solve inequalities graphically.

1.
$$x^2 \leq 9$$
$$x^2 - 9 \leq 0$$
$$(x + 3)(x - 3) \leq 0$$
Critical numbers: $x = \pm 3$
Test intervals:
$$(-\infty, \ -3) \Rightarrow (x + 3)(x - 3) > 0$$
$$(-3, \ 3) \Rightarrow (x + 3)(x - 3) < 0$$
$$(3, \ \infty) \Rightarrow (x + 3)(x - 3) > 0$$
Solution interval: $[-3, \ 3]$

3.
$$x^2 + 4x + 4 \geq 9$$
$$x^2 + 4x - 5 \geq 0$$
$$(x + 5)(x - 1) \geq 0$$
Critical numbers: $x = -5, \ x = 1$
Test intervals:
$$(-\infty, \ -5) \Rightarrow (x + 5)(x - 1) > 0$$
$$(-5, \ 1) \Rightarrow (x + 5)(x - 1) < 0$$
$$(1, \ \infty) \Rightarrow (x + 5)(x - 1) > 0$$
Solution intervals: $(-\infty, \ -5] \cup [1, \ \infty)$

5.
$$x^2 + x < 6$$
$$x^2 + x - 6 < 0$$
$$(x + 3)(x - 2) < 0$$
Critical numbers: $x = -3, \ x = 2$
Test intervals:
$$(-\infty, \ -3) \Rightarrow (x + 3)(x - 2) > 0$$
$$(-3, \ 2) \Rightarrow (x + 3)(x - 2) < 0$$
$$(2, \ \infty) \Rightarrow (x + 3)(x - 2) > 0$$
Solution interval: $(-3, \ 2)$

7. $3(x - 1)(x + 1) > 0$
Critical numbers: $x = -1, \ x = 1$
Test intervals:
$$(-\infty, \ -1) \Rightarrow 3(x - 1)(x + 1) > 0$$
$$(-1, \ 1) \Rightarrow 3(x - 1)(x + 1) < 0$$
$$(1, \ \infty) \Rightarrow 3(x - 1)(x + 1) > 0$$
Solution intervals: $(-\infty, \ -1) \cup (1, \ \infty)$

9. $x^2 + 2x - 3 < 0$

$(x + 3)(x - 1) < 0$

Critical numbers: $x = -3$, $x = 1$

Test intervals:

$(-\infty, -3) \Rightarrow (x + 3)(x - 1) > 0$

$(-3, 1) \Rightarrow (x + 3)(x - 1) < 0$

$(1, \infty) \Rightarrow (x + 3)(x - 1) > 0$

Solution interval: $(-3, 1)$

11. $4x^3 - 6x^2 < 0$

$2x^2(2x - 3) < 0$

Critical numbers: $x = 0$, $x = \frac{3}{2}$

Test intervals:

$(-\infty, 0) \Rightarrow 2x^2(2x - 3) < 0$

$\left(0, \frac{3}{2}\right) \Rightarrow 2x^2(2x - 3) < 0$

$\left(\frac{3}{2}, \infty\right) \Rightarrow 2x^2(2x - 3) > 0$

Solution intervals: $(-\infty, 0) \cup \left(0, \frac{3}{2}\right)$

Note: $x = 0$ is not a solution.

13. $x^3 - 4x \geq 0$

$x(x + 2)(x - 2) \geq 0$

Critical numbers: $x = -2$, $x = 0$, $x = 2$

Test intervals:

$(-\infty, -2) \Rightarrow x(x + 2)(x - 2) < 0$

$(-2, 0) \Rightarrow x(x + 2)(x - 2) > 0$

$(0, 2) \Rightarrow x(x + 2)(x - 2) < 0$

$(2, \infty) \Rightarrow x(x + 2)(x - 2) > 0$

Solution intervals: $[-2, 0] \cup [2, \infty)$

15. Graphing $y_1 = (1/x) - x$ on the standard viewing rectangle, we see that $(1/x) - x > 0$ on $(-\infty, -1) \cup (0, 1)$.

Algebraically:

$$\frac{1}{x} > x$$

$$\frac{1}{x} - x > 0$$

$$\frac{1 - x^2}{x} > 0$$

$$\frac{(1 + x)(1 - x)}{x} > 0$$

Critical numbers: $x = -1$, $x = 0$, $x = 1$

Analyzing the four test intervals, we obtain the same solution as before.

Solution intervals: $(-\infty, -1) \cup (0, 1)$

17. Graphing $y_1 = [(x + 6)/(x + 1)] - 2$ on the standard viewing rectangle, we see that $[(x + 6)/(x + 1)] - 2 < 0$ on $(-\infty, -1) \cup (4, \infty)$. Algebraically:

$$\frac{x + 6}{x + 1} < 2$$

$$\frac{x + 6}{x + 1} - 2 < 0$$

$$\frac{x + 6 - 2(x + 1)}{x + 1} < 0$$

$$\frac{4 - x}{x + 1} < 0$$

Critical numbers: $x = -1$, $x = 4$
Test intervals:

$$(-\infty, -1) \Rightarrow \frac{4 - x}{x + 1} < 0$$

$$(-1, 4) \Rightarrow \frac{4 - x}{x + 1} > 0$$

$$(4, \infty) \Rightarrow \frac{4 - x}{x + 1} < 0$$

Solution intervals: $(-\infty, -1) \cup (4, \infty)$

21.

$$\frac{4}{x + 5} > \frac{1}{2x + 3}$$

$$\frac{4(2x + 3) - 1(x + 5)}{(x + 5)(2x + 3)} > 0$$

$$\frac{7x + 7}{(x + 5)(2x + 3)} > 0$$

Critical numbers:

$$x = -5, \ x = -\tfrac{3}{2}, \ x = -1$$

Test intervals:

$$(-\infty, -5) \Rightarrow \frac{7x + 7}{(x + 5)(2x + 3)} < 0$$

$$\left(-5, -\frac{3}{2}\right) \Rightarrow \frac{7x + 7}{(x + 5)(2x + 3)} > 0$$

$$\left(-\frac{3}{2}, -1\right) \Rightarrow \frac{7x + 7}{(x + 5)(2x + 3)} < 0$$

$$(-1, \infty) \Rightarrow \frac{7x + 7}{(x + 5)(2x + 3)} > 0$$

Solution intervals: $\left(-5, -\tfrac{3}{2}\right) \cup (-1, \infty)$

19. Graphing $y_1 = [(3x - 5)/(x - 5)] - 4$ on the viewing rectangle $[-10, 20] \times [-5, 5]$, we see that $[(3x - 5)/(x - 5)] > 4$ on $(5, 15)$. Algebraically:

$$\frac{3x - 5}{x - 5} > 4$$

$$\frac{3x - 5 - 4(x - 5)}{x - 5} > 0$$

$$\frac{15 - x}{x - 5} > 0$$

Critical numbers: $x = 5$, $x = 15$
Test intervals:

$$(-\infty, 5) \Rightarrow \frac{15 - x}{x - 5} < 0$$

$$(5, 15) \Rightarrow \frac{15 - x}{x - 5} > 0$$

$$(15, \infty) \Rightarrow \frac{15 - x}{x - 5} < 0$$

Solution interval: $(5, 15)$

23. $|x^2 - 4x + 5| < 2x^{-1} = \dfrac{2}{x}$

Graphing $y_1 = |x^2 - 4x + 5|$ and $y_2 = 2/x$ on the same viewing rectangle, we see that the solution satisfies $0 < x < 1$ or $1 < x < 2$.

25. $(x-1)^2(x+2)^3 \geq 0$

Using the zoom and trace features, we find that $x \geq -2$.

27. $-0.5x^2 + 12.5x + 1.6 > 0$

Using the zoom and trace features, we find that $-0.13 < x < 25.13$.

29. $\dfrac{5}{x-6} > \dfrac{3}{x+2}$

Using the zoom and trace features, we find that $x > 6$ or $-14 < x < -2$.

31. $\dfrac{3}{x-1} - \dfrac{2}{x+1} < 1$

Using the zoom and trace features, we find that $x < -2$ or $-1 < x < 1$ or $x > 3$.

33. $4 - x^2 \geq 0$

$(2-x)(2+x) \geq 0$

Critical numbers: $x = 2$, $x = -2$

Test intervals:

$(-\infty, -2) \Rightarrow (2-x)(2+x) < 0$

$(-2, 2) \Rightarrow (2-x)(2+x) > 0$

$(2, \infty) \Rightarrow (2-x)(2+x) < 0$

Domain: $[-2, 2]$

35. $x^2 - 7x + 12 \geq 0$

$(x-3)(x-4) \geq 0$

Critical numbers: $x = 3$, $x = 4$

Test intervals:

$(-\infty, 3) \Rightarrow (x-3)(x-4) > 0$

$(3, 4) \Rightarrow (x-3)(x-4) < 0$

$(4, \infty) \Rightarrow (x-3)(x-4) > 0$

Domain: $(-\infty, 3] \cup [4, \infty)$

37. $12 - x - x^2 \geq 0$

$(4+x)(3-x) \geq 0$

Critical numbers: $x = -4$, $x = 3$

Test intervals:

$(-\infty, -4) \Rightarrow (4+x)(3-x) < 0$

$(-4, 3) \Rightarrow (4+x)(3-x) > 0$

$(3, \infty) \Rightarrow (4+x)(3-x) < 0$

Domain: $[-4, 3]$

39. $\dfrac{x}{x^2-9} \geq 0$

$\dfrac{x}{(x+3)(x-3)} \geq 0$

Critical numbers: $x = -3$, $x = 0$, $x = 3$

Test intervals:

$(-\infty, -3) \Rightarrow \dfrac{x}{(x+3)(x-3)} < 0$

$(3, 0) \Rightarrow \dfrac{x}{(x+3)(x-3)} > 0$

$(0, 3) \Rightarrow \dfrac{x}{(x+3)(x-3)} < 0$

$(3, \infty) \Rightarrow \dfrac{x}{(x+3)(x-3)} > 0$

Domain: $(-3, 0] \cup (3, \infty)$

41. $s = -16t^2 + v_0t + s_0 = -16t^2 + 160t = -16t(t - 10)$

(a) $t - 10 = 0$

$t = 10$ seconds later

(b) $-16t^2 + 160t > 384$

$t^2 - 10t + 24 < 0$

$(t - 4)(t - 6) < 0$

Critical numbers: $t = 4$, $t = 6$

Test intervals: $(0, 4) \Rightarrow (t - 4)(t - 6) > 0$

$(4, 6) \Rightarrow (t - 4)(t - 6) < 0$

$(6, 10) \Rightarrow (t - 4)(t - 6) > 0$

Solution interval: $(4, 6)$ or $4 \text{ sec} < t < 6 \text{ sec}$

Or, graphing $y_1 = -16t^2 + 160t$ and $y_2 = 384$ on the viewing rectangle $[0, 10] \times [0, 450]$, we can determine that $y_1 > y_2$ on the interval $(4, 6)$.

43. $2L + 2W = 100$

$$W = \frac{100 - 2L}{2} = 50 - L$$

$LW \geq 500$

$L(50 - L) \geq 500$

$50L - L^2 \geq 500$

$0 \geq L^2 - 50L + 500$

Using a graphing utility to graph $y_1 = x^2 - 50x + 500$ on the viewing rectangle $[0, 50] \times [-150, 150]$, we see that $y_1 \leq 0$ on $[13.82, 36.18]$. Algebraically, we obtain:
Critical numbers:

$$L = \frac{50 \pm \sqrt{(50)^2 - 4(500)}}{2} = \frac{50 \pm \sqrt{500}}{2} = \frac{50 \pm 10\sqrt{5}}{2} = 25 \pm 5\sqrt{5}$$

Test intervals:

$(0, 25 - 5\sqrt{5}) \Rightarrow L^2 - 50L + 500 > 0$

$(25 - 5\sqrt{5}, 25 + 5\sqrt{5}) \Rightarrow L^2 - 50L + 500 < 0$

$(25 + 5\sqrt{5}, 50) \Rightarrow L^2 - 50L + 500 > 0$

Solution interval: $[25 - 5\sqrt{5}, 25 + 5\sqrt{5}]$ or 13.8197 meters $\leq L \leq 36.1803$ meters

45. (a) $\dfrac{1}{R} = \dfrac{1}{R_1} + \dfrac{1}{R_2} = \dfrac{R_2 + R_1}{R_1 R_2}$

$\Rightarrow R = \dfrac{R_1 R_2}{R_1 + R_2}$

(b) If $R_2 = 2,\quad R = \dfrac{R_1(2)}{R_1 + 2}$.

(c) If $R \geq 1$, then

$\dfrac{2R_1}{R_1 + 2} \geq 1 \Rightarrow 2R_1 \geq R_1 + 2 \Rightarrow R_1 \geq 2.$

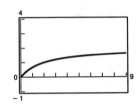

47. $5.136 + 0.0069t^2 \geq 25 \Rightarrow t \geq 53.655$
or the year 1994

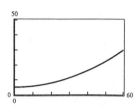

Chapter 2   Review Exercises

1. $6 - (x-2)^2 = 2 + 4x - x^2$

$6 - (x^2 - 4x + 4) = 2 + 4x - x^2$

$2 + 4x - x^2 = 2 + 4x - x^2$

$0 = 0$ Identity

3. (a) $3(0)^2 + 7(0) + 5 \stackrel{?}{=} (0)^2 + 9$

$5 \neq 9$

$x = 0$ *is not* a solution.

(b) $3(-4)^2 + 7(-4) + 5 \stackrel{?}{=} (-4)^2 + 9$

$25 = 25$

$x = -4$ *is* a solution.

(c) $3\left(\dfrac{1}{2}\right)^2 + 7\left(\dfrac{1}{2}\right) + 5 \stackrel{?}{=} \left(\dfrac{1}{2}\right)^2 + 9$

$\dfrac{37}{4} = \dfrac{37}{4}$

$x = \frac{1}{2}$ *is* a solution.

(d) $3(-1)^2 + 7(-1) + 5 \stackrel{?}{=} (-1)^2 + 9$

$1 \neq 10$

$x = -1$ *is not* a solution.

5. $3x - 2(x+5) = 10$

$3x - 2x - 10 = 10$

$x = 20$

7. $3\left(1 - \dfrac{1}{5t}\right) = 0$

$1 - \dfrac{1}{5t} = 0$

$1 = \dfrac{1}{5t}$

$5t = 1$

$t = \dfrac{1}{5}$

9. $6x^2 = 5x + 4$

$6x^2 - 5x - 4 = 0$

$(3x - 4)(2x + 1) = 0$

$3x - 4 = 0 \;\Rightarrow\; x = \;\frac{4}{3}$

$2x + 1 = 0 \;\Rightarrow\; x = -\frac{1}{2}$

11. $(x+4)^2 = 18$

$x + 4 = \pm\sqrt{18}$

$x = -4 \pm 3\sqrt{2}$

13. $x^2 - 12x + 30 = 0$

$x = \dfrac{-(-12) \pm \sqrt{(-12)^2 - 4(1)(30)}}{2(1)}$

$x = 6 \pm \sqrt{6}$

15. $4t^3 - 12t^2 + 8t = 0$

$4t(t^2 - 3t + 2) = 0$

$4t(t-1)(t-2) = 0$

$4t = 0 \Rightarrow t = 0$

$t - 1 = 0 \Rightarrow t = 1$

$t - 2 = 0 \Rightarrow t = 2$

17. $\dfrac{4}{(x-4)^2} = 1$

$4 = (x-4)^2$

$\pm 2 = x - 4$

$4 \pm 2 = x$

$x = 6 \quad \text{or} \quad x = 2$

19. $\sqrt{x+4} = 3$

$(\sqrt{x+4})^2 = (3)^2$

$x + 4 = 9$

$x = 5$

21. $2\sqrt{x} - 5 = 0$

$(2\sqrt{x})^2 = 5^2$

$4x = 25$

$x = \frac{25}{4}$

23. $(x-1)^{2/3} - 25 = 0$

$(x-1)^{2/3} = 25$

$x - 1 = \pm 25^{3/2}$

$x = 1 \pm 125$

$x = 126 \text{ or } x = -124$

25. $(x+4)^{1/2} + 5x(x+4)^{3/2} = 0$

$(x+4)^{1/2}[1 + 5x(x+4)] = 0$

$(x+4)^{1/2}(5x^2 + 20x + 1) = 0$

$x + 4 = 0 \Rightarrow x = -4$

$5x^2 + 20x + 1 = 0 \Rightarrow x = \dfrac{-20 \pm \sqrt{380}}{10}$

$= -2 \pm \dfrac{\sqrt{95}}{5}$

27. $|x - 5| = 10$

$x - 5 = -10 \quad \text{or} \quad x - 5 = 10$

$x = -5 \qquad\qquad x = 15$

29. $x^2 + 6x - 3 = 0$

Using the zoom and trace features, we find that $x = 0.464, -6.464$.

31. $5\sqrt{x} - \sqrt{x-1} = 6$

Using the zoom and trace features, we find that $x = 1.944$.

33. $\dfrac{1}{x} + \dfrac{1}{x+1} = 2$

Using the zoom and trace features, we find that $x = \pm 0.707$.

35. $|x^2 - 3| = 2x$

Using the zoom and trace features, we find that $x = 1, 3$.

37. $V = \dfrac{1}{3}\pi r^2 h$

$3V = \pi r^2 h$

$\dfrac{3V}{\pi h} = r^2$

$r = \sqrt{\dfrac{3V}{\pi h}}, \qquad \text{(assuming } r > 0)$

39.
$$L = \frac{k}{3\pi r^2 p}$$

$$3\pi r^2 p L = k$$

$$p = \frac{k}{3\pi r^2 L}$$

41. $\frac{1}{2}(3 - x) > \frac{1}{3}(2 - 3x)$

$$3(3 - x) > 2(2 - 3x)$$

$$9 - 3x > 4 - 6x$$

$$3x > -5$$

$$x > -\frac{5}{3} \text{ or } (-\frac{5}{3}, \infty)$$

43. $\dfrac{x - 5}{3 - x} < 0$

Test intervals:

$$(-\infty, 3) \Rightarrow \frac{x - 5}{3 - x} < 0$$

$$(3, 5) \Rightarrow \frac{x - 5}{3 - x} > 0$$

$$(5, \infty) \Rightarrow \frac{x - 5}{3 - x} < 0$$

Solution intervals: $(-\infty, 3) \cup (5, \infty)$

45.
$$|x - 2| < 1$$

$$-1 < x - 2 < 1$$

$$1 < x < 3 \text{ or } (1, 3)$$

47. $\left|x - \frac{3}{2}\right| \geq \frac{3}{2}$

$$x - \frac{3}{2} \leq -\frac{3}{2} \quad \text{or} \quad x - \frac{3}{2} \geq \frac{3}{2}$$

$$x \leq 0 \qquad\qquad x \geq 3 \text{ or } (-\infty, 0] \cup [3, \infty)$$

49. $\dfrac{x}{5} - 6 \leq -\dfrac{x}{2} + 6$

Using the zoom and trace features, we find that $x \leq 17.143$.

51. $(x - 4)|x| > 0$

Using the zoom and trace features, we find that $x = (4, \infty)$.

53. $2x - 10 \geq 0$

$$2x \geq 10$$

$$x \geq 5 \text{ or } [5, \infty)$$

55. September's profit $= x$

October's profit $= 1.12x$

$$x + 1.12x = 689,000$$

$$2.12x = 689,000$$

$$x = 325,000$$

September's profit $= x = \$325,000$

October's profit $= 1.12x = \$364,000$

57. Let x = the number of quarts of pure antifreeze.

$$30\% \text{ of } (10 - x) + 100\% \text{ of } x = 50\% \text{ of } 10$$
$$0.30(10 - x) + 1.00x = 0.50(10)$$
$$3 - 0.30x + 1.00x = 5$$
$$0.70x = 2$$
$$x = \frac{2}{0.70}$$
$$\approx 2.857 \text{ quarts}$$

59. Since the angle is 45°, the triangle is isosceles.

$$x^2 + x^2 = 2000^2$$
$$2x^2 = 4{,}000{,}000$$
$$x^2 = 2{,}000{,}000$$
$$x = 1000\sqrt{2} \approx 1414.21 \text{ feet}$$

61. Let x = number of farmers in the group.

Cost per farmer: $48{,}000/x$

If two more farmers join the group, the cost per farmer will be $48{,}000/(x + 2)$. Since this new cost is $4000 less than the original cost:

$$\frac{48{,}000}{x} - 4000 = \frac{48{,}000}{x + 2}$$
$$48{,}000(x + 2) - 4000x(x + 2) = 48{,}000x$$
$$12(x + 2) - x(x + 2) = 12x$$
$$12x + 24 - x^2 - 2x = 12x$$
$$0 = x^2 + 2x - 24$$
$$0 = (x + 6)(x - 4)$$
$$x = -6, \text{ extraneous or } x = 4$$

Thus, $x = 4$ farmers. Or, using a graphing utility to graph

$$y_1 = \frac{48{,}000}{x} - 4000 - \frac{48{,}000}{x + 2}$$

we see that the positive x-intercept is 4.00.

63.
$$29.95 = 42 - \sqrt{0.001x + 2}$$
$$\left(\sqrt{0.001x + 2}\right)^2 = (12.05)^2$$
$$0.001x + 2 = 145.2025$$
$$0.001x = 143.2025$$
$$x \approx 143{,}203$$

The demand would be for 143,203 units per day.

65.
$$R > C$$
$$125.95x > 92x + 1200$$
$$33.95x > 1200$$
$$x > 35.346$$

When $x \geq 36$ units, this product will return a profit.

CHAPTER 3

Polynomial Functions: Graphs and Zeros

Section 3.1 Quadratic Functions

> You should know the following facts about parabolas.
>
> ■ $f(x) = ax^2 + bx + c$, $a \neq 0$, is a quadratic function and its graph is a parabola.
>
> ■ If $a > 0$, the parabola opens upward and the vertex is the minimum point. If $a < 0$, the parabola opens downward and the vertex is the maximum point.
>
> ■ The vertex is $(-b/2a, \ f(-b/2a))$.
>
> ■ To find the x-intercepts (if any), solve $ax^2 + bx + c = 0$.
>
> ■ The standard form of the equation of a parabola is $f(x) = a(x - h)^2 + k$, where $a \neq 0$.
>   (a) The vertex is $(h, \ k)$.
>   (b) The axis is the vertical line $x = h$.

1. $f(x) = (x - 3)^2$ opens upward and has vertex $(3, 0)$; graph (f)

```
RANGE
Xmin=-1
Xmax=6
Xscl=1
Ymin=-1
Ymax=5
Yscl=1
```

3. $f(x) = x^2 - 4$ opens upward and has vertex $(0, -4)$; graph (c)

```
RANGE
Xmin=-4
Xmax=4
Xscl=1
Ymin=-5
Ymax=2
Yscl=1
```

5. $f(x) = 4 - (x - 1)^2$ opens downward and has vertex $(1, 4)$; graph (b)

```
RANGE
Xmin=-3
Xmax=5
Xscl=1
Ymin=-2
Ymax=5
Yscl=1
```

7. (a) f is a parabola that opens upward and is broader than $y = x^2$.

   (b) g is a parabola that opens downward and is narrower than $y = x^2$.

9. (a) f is shifted 3 units to the left, 3 units upward, and opens downward.

   (b) g is shifted 4 units to the right and 3 units downward. It opens upward and is narrower than $y = x^2$.

11. Vertex: $(2, 0)$

$y = a(x - 2)^2 + 0$

$(0, 4)$ is on graph

$4 = a(0 - 2)^2$

$a = 1$

$y = (x - 2)^2$

13. Vertex: $(-2, 4)$

$y = a(x + 2)^2 + 4$

$(0, 0)$ is on graph

$0 = a(0 + 2)^2 + 4$

$a = -1$

$y = -(x + 2)^2 + 4$

15. Vertex: $(-3, 3)$

$y = a(x + 3)^2 + 3$

$(-2, 1)$ is on graph

$1 = a(-2 + 3)^2 + 3$

$a = -2$

$y = -2(x + 3)^2 + 3$

17. $f(x) = x^2 - 5$
Vertex: $(0, -5)$
Intercepts: $(-\sqrt{5}, 0)$, $(0, -5)$, $(\sqrt{5}, 0)$

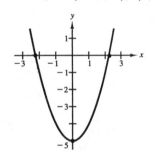

19. $f(x) = (x + 5)^2 - 6$
Vertex: $(-5, -6)$
Intercepts: $(-5 - \sqrt{6}, 0)$,
$(-5 + \sqrt{6}, 0)$, $(0, 19)$

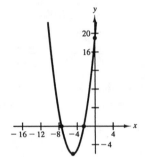

21. $h(x) = x^2 - 8x + 16 = (x - 4)^2$
Vertex: $(4, 0)$
Intercepts: $(0, 16)$, $(4, 0)$

23. $f(x) = -x^2 + 2x + 5$

$= -(x^2 - 2x + 1) + 5 + 1$

$= -(x - 1)^2 + 6$

Vertex: $(1, 6)$
Intercepts: $(1 - \sqrt{6}, 0)$, $(0, 5)$, $(1 + \sqrt{6}, 0)$

25. $h(x) = 4x^2 - 4x + 21$

$\qquad = 4\left(x^2 - x + \frac{1}{4}\right) + 21 - 1$

$\qquad = 4\left(x - \frac{1}{2}\right)^2 + 20$

Vertex: $\left(\frac{1}{2},\ 20\right)$

Intercept: $(0, 21)$

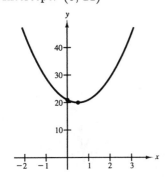

27. $f(x) = -(x^2 + 2x - 3)$

$\qquad = -(x^2 + 2x + 1) + 3 + 1$

$\qquad = -(x + 1)^2 + 4$

Vertex: $(-1,\ 4)$

Intercepts: $(1,\ 0),\ (-3,\ 0),\ (0,\ 3)$

29. $f(x) = 2x^2 - 16x + 31$

$\qquad = 2(x^2 - 8x + 16) + 31 - 32$

$\qquad = 2(x - 4)^2 - 1$

Vertex: $(4,\ -1)$

Intercepts: $(3.29,\ 0),\ (4.71,\ 0),\ (0,\ 31)$

31. $y = a(x - 3)^2 + 4$

$\qquad 2 = a(1 - 3)^2 + 4$

$\qquad 4a = -2$

$\qquad a = -\frac{1}{2}$

$\qquad y = -\frac{1}{2}(x - 3)^2 + 4$

33. $y = a(x - 5)^2 + 12$

$\qquad 15 = a(7 - 5)^2 + 12$

$\qquad 4a = 3$

$\qquad a = \frac{3}{4}$

$\qquad y = \frac{3}{4}(x - 5)^2 + 12$

35. $y = (x + 1)(x - 3) = x^2 - 2x - 3$

$\qquad y = -(x + 1)(x - 3) = -x^2 + 2x + 3$

37. $y = x(x - 10) = x^2 - 10x$

$y = -x(x - 10) = -x^2 + 10x$

39. $y = (x + 3)(2x + 1) = 2x^2 + 7x + 3$

$y = -(x + 3)(2x + 1) = -2x^2 - 7x - 3$

41. $f(x) = x(110 - x) = -x^2 + 110x = -(x^2 - 110x + 3025) + 3025 = -(x - 55)^2 + 3025$

Vertex: $(55, 3025)$

The two numbers are $x = 55$ and $110 - x = 55$. Or, by graphing $f(x) = -x^2 + 110x$, we see that the maximum value of f occurs at $(55, 3025)$.

43. (a) $2x + 2w = 100$

$w = 50 - x$

$A(x) = xw = x(50 - x)$

Domain: $0 < x < 50$

(c) $x = w = 25$ for maximum area (square)

(b)

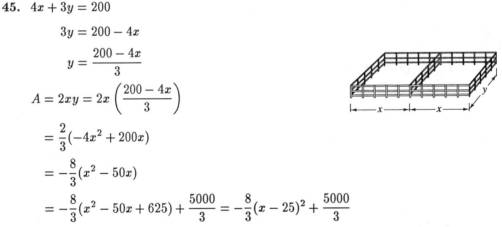

45. $4x + 3y = 200$

$3y = 200 - 4x$

$y = \dfrac{200 - 4x}{3}$

$A = 2xy = 2x \left(\dfrac{200 - 4x}{3} \right)$

$= \dfrac{2}{3}(-4x^2 + 200x)$

$= -\dfrac{8}{3}(x^2 - 50x)$

$= -\dfrac{8}{3}(x^2 - 50x + 625) + \dfrac{5000}{3} = -\dfrac{8}{3}(x - 25)^2 + \dfrac{5000}{3}$

The maximum area occurs at the vertex and is $5000/3$ square feet. This happens when $x = 25$ feet and $y = [200 - 4(25)]/3 = 100/3$ feet. The dimensions are $2x = 50$ feet by $33\frac{1}{3}$ feet.

47. $R = 900x - 0.1x^2 = -0.1(x^2 - 9000 + (4500)^2) + 2,025,000 = -0.1(x - 4500)^2 + 2,025,000$

Vertex: $(4500, 2,025,000)$

Maximum when $x = 4500$ units. Or, by graphing $R = 900x - 0.1x^2$, we see that the maximum value of R occurs at $(4500.00, 2,025,000.00)$.

49. $C = 4024.5 + 51.4t - 3.1t^2$, $(t = 0$ is 1960.)

    (a) Yes, the average annual consumption dropped after 1968.

    (b) $\dfrac{(4024.5)(116{,}530{,}000)}{48{,}500{,}000} = 9669.6$ cigarettes/smoker

$$\dfrac{9669.6}{365} = 26.5 \text{ cigarettes/day}$$

51. $y = -\frac{1}{12}x^2 + 2x + 4$

    (a)

53. $V = 0.77x^2 - 1.32x - 9.31$, $0 \le x \le 40$

    (a)

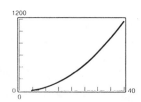

    (b) $y = 4$ feet when $x = 0$.

    (c) $y = 16$ feet is the maximum height (when $x = 12$).

    (d) $x = 25.86$ feet when the ball strikes the ground ($y = 0$).

    (b) If $x = 16$, $V = 166.69$ board-feet.

    (c) If $V = 500$, $x = 26.59$ inches.

55. $f(x) = ax^2 + bx + c = a\left(x^2 + \dfrac{b}{a}x + \left(\dfrac{b}{2a}\right)^2\right) + c - \dfrac{b^2}{4a} = a\left(x + \dfrac{b}{2a}\right)^2 + \dfrac{4ac - b^2}{4a}$

Vertex: $\left(-\dfrac{b}{2a},\ -\dfrac{b^2 - 4ac}{4a}\right)$

59. If $f(x) = ax^2 + bx + c$ has two real zeros, then by the Quadratic Formula they are

$x = \dfrac{-b \pm \sqrt{b^2 - 4ac}}{2a}$. The average of the zeros of f is

$$\dfrac{\dfrac{-b - \sqrt{b^2 - 4ac}}{2a} + \dfrac{-b + \sqrt{b^2 - 4ac}}{2a}}{2} = \dfrac{\dfrac{-2b}{2a}}{2} = -\dfrac{b}{2a}.$$

This is the x-coordinate of the vertex of the graph. (See Exercise 55.)

Section 3.2   Polynomial Functions of Higher Degree

You should know the following basic principles about polynomials.

- $f(x) = a_n x^n + a_{n-1} x^{n-1} + \cdots + a_2 x^2 + a_1 x + a_0,\ a_n \neq 0$ is a polynomial function of degree n.

- The graph of a polynomial function is continuous, as you can verify with a graphing utility.

- If f is of odd degree and

  (a) $a_n > 0$, then:
  1. $f(x) \to \infty$ as $x \to \infty$
  2. $f(x) \to -\infty$ as $x \to -\infty$

  (b) $a_n < 0$, then:
  1. $f(x) \to -\infty$ as $x \to \infty$
  2. $f(x) \to \infty$ as $x \to -\infty$

- If f is of even degree and

  (a) $a_n > 0$, then:
  1. $f(x) \to \infty$ as $x \to \infty$
  2. $f(x) \to \infty$ as $x \to -\infty$

  (b) $a_n < 0$, then:
  1. $f(x) \to -\infty$ as $x \to \infty$
  2. $f(x) \to -\infty$ as $x \to -\infty$

- The following are equivalent for a polynomial function.

  (a) $x = a$ is a zero of a function.
  (b) $x = a$ is a solution of the polynomial equation $f(x) = 0$.
  (c) $(x - a)$ is a factor of the polynomial.
  (d) $(a,\ 0)$ is an x-intercept of the graph of f.

- A polynomial of degree n has at most n distinct zeros. These can be found using a graphing utility.

- If f is a polynomial function such that $a < b$ and $f(a) \neq f(b)$, then the Intermediate Value Theorem says that f takes on every value between $f(a)$ and $f(b)$ in the interval $[a,\ b]$.

- If you can find a value where a polynomial is positive and another value where it is negative, then there is at least one real zero between the values. You can find this zero using a graphing utility.

1. (a) $f(x) = (x-2)^3$ is a right shift by 2 units of $y = x^3$.

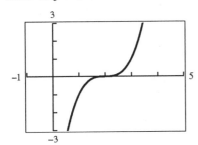

(b) $f(x) = x^3 - 2$ is a downward shift of 2 units of $y = x^3$.

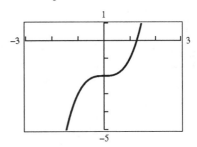

(c) $f(x) = (x-2)^3 - 2$ is a right shift of 2 units, and a downward shift of 2 units of $y = x^3$.

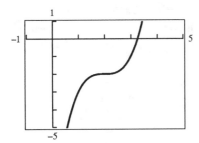

(d) $f(x) = -\frac{1}{2}x^3$ is a reflection in the x-axis, and wider, compared to $y = x^3$.

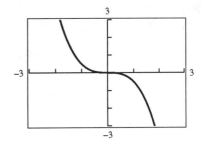

3. $f(x) = -3x + 5$ is a line with y-intercept $(0, 5)$; graph (e)

```
RANGE
Xmin=-3
Xmax=5
Xscl=1
Ymin=-1
Ymax=6
Yscl=1
```

5. $f(x) = -2x^2 - 8x - 9$ is a parabola opening downward; graph (b)

```
RANGE
Xmin=-5
Xmax=1
Xscl=1
Ymin=-12
Ymax=3
Yscl=3
```

7. $f(x) = -\frac{1}{3}x^3 + x - \frac{2}{3}$ is a cubic with y-intercept $\left(0, -\frac{2}{3}\right)$; graph (a)

```
RANGE
Xmin=-3
Xmax=3
Xscl=1
Ymin=-3
Ymax=2
Yscl=1
```

9. $f(x) = 3x^4 + 4x^3$ has intercepts $(0, 0)$ and $\left(-\frac{4}{3}, 0\right)$; graph (d)

```
RANGE
Xmin=-3
Xmax=2
Xscl=1
Ymin=-2
Ymax=4
Yscl=1
```

11.

13.

15. $f(x) = 2x^2 - 3x + 1$

The degree is even and the leading coefficient is positive. The graph rises to the left and right.

17. $h(t) = -\frac{2}{3}(t^2 - 5t + 3)$

The degree is even and the leading coefficient is negative. The graph falls to the left and right.

19. $f(x) = 6 - 2x + 4x^2 - 5x^3$

The degree is odd and the leading coefficient is negative. The graph rises to the left and falls to the right.

21. $f(x) = x^2 - 25$

$$= (x + 5)(x - 5)$$

Thus, the real zeros are -5 and 5.

23. $h(t) = t^2 - 6t + 9$

$$= (t - 3)^2$$

Thus, the real zero is 3.

25. $f(x) = x^2 + x - 2$

$$= (x + 2)(x - 1)$$

Thus, the real zeros are -2 and 1.

27. $f(x) = 3x^2 - 12x + 3$

$$= 3(x^2 - 4x + 1)$$

$$= \frac{4 \pm \sqrt{16 - 4}}{2} = 2 \pm \sqrt{3}$$

Thus, the real zeros are $2 \pm \sqrt{3}$.

29. $f(t) = t^3 - 4t^2 + 4t$

$$= t(t - 2)^2$$

Thus, the real zeros are 0 and 2.

31. $g(t) = \frac{1}{2}t^4 - \frac{1}{2}$

$$= \frac{1}{2}(t + 1)(t - 1)(t^2 + 1)$$

Thus, the real zeros are -1 and 1.

33. $f(x) = 2x^4 - 2x^2 - 40$

$= 2(x^2 + 4)(x^2 - 5)$

$= 2(x^2 + 4)(x + \sqrt{5})(x - \sqrt{5})$

Thus, the real zeros are $-\sqrt{5}$ and $\sqrt{5}$.

35. $f(x) = 5x^4 + 15x^2 + 10$

$= 5(x^4 + 3x^2 + 2)$

$= 5(x^2 + 2)(x^2 + 1)$

No real zeros; or, by graphing f, we see the graph lies entirely above the x-axis.

37. $f(x) = (x - 0)(x - 10)$

$= x^2 - 10x$

39. $f(x) = (x - 2)(x + 6)$

$= x^2 + 4x - 12$

41. $f(x) = (x - 0)(x + 2)(x + 3)$

$= x(x^2 + 5x + 6)$

$= x^3 + 5x^2 + 6x$

43. $f(x) = (x - 4)(x + 3)(x - 3)(x - 0)$

$= (x^2 - 4x)(x^2 - 9)$

$= x^4 - 4x^3 - 9x^2 + 36x$

45. $f(x) = [x - (1 + \sqrt{3})][x - (1 - \sqrt{3})]$

$= [(x - 1) - \sqrt{3}][(x - 1) + \sqrt{3}]$

$= (x - 1)^2 - 3$

$= x^2 - 2x + 1 - 3$

$= x^2 - 2x - 2$

47.

49.

51.

53.

55.

57.

59.

61.

63. $f(x) = x^3 - 3x^2 + 3$
$[-1, 0], [1, 2], [2, 3]$

65. $g(x) = 3x^4 + 4x^3 - 3$
$[-2, -1], [0, 1]$

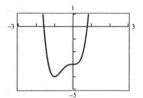

67. (a) Volume $= (12 - 2x)(12 - 2x)x$
$= 4x(6 - x)^2$

(b) Domain: $0 < x < 6$

(c) $V(x)$ is maximum for $x = 2.00$.

69. $R = \frac{1}{50,000}(-x^3 + 600x^2), \ 0 \le x \le 400$

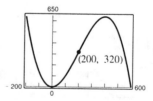

$x = 200$ is approximately the point where R is increasing most rapidly.

Section 3.3   Polynomial Division and Synthetic Division

You should know the following basic techniques and principles of polynomial division.

■ The Division Algorithm (Long Division of Polynomials)

■ Synthetic Division

■ $f(k)$ is equal to the remainder of $f(x)$ divided by $(x - k)$.

■ $f(k) = 0$ if and only if $(x - k)$ is a factor of $f(x)$.

1.
$$
\begin{array}{r}
2x + 4 \\
x+3\ \overline{)\ 2x^2 + 10x + 12} \\
\underline{2x^2 + 6x} \\
4x + 12 \\
\underline{4x + 12} \\
0
\end{array}
$$

3.
$$
\begin{array}{r}
x^2 - 3x + 1 \\
4x+5\ \overline{)\ 4x^3 - 7x^2 - 11x + 5} \\
\underline{4x^3 + 5x^2} \\
-12x^2 - 11x \\
\underline{-12x^2 - 15x} \\
4x + 5 \\
\underline{4x + 5} \\
0
\end{array}
$$

5.
$$
\begin{array}{r}
x^3 + 3x^2 - 1 \\
x+2\ \overline{)\ x^4 + 5x^3 + 6x^2 - x - 2} \\
\underline{x^4 + 2x^3} \\
3x^3 + 6x^2 \\
\underline{3x^3 + 6x^2} \\
-x - 2 \\
\underline{-x - 2} \\
0
\end{array}
$$

7.
$$
\begin{array}{r}
7 \\
x+2\ \overline{)\ 7x + 3} \\
\underline{7x + 14} \\
-11
\end{array}
$$

$$\frac{7x + 3}{x + 2} = 7 - \frac{11}{x + 2}$$

9.
$$
\begin{array}{r}
3x + 5 \\
2x^2 + 1\ \overline{)\ 6x^3 + 10x^2 + x + 8} \\
\underline{6x^3 \qquad\quad + 3x} \\
10x^2 - 2x + 8 \\
\underline{10x^2 \qquad + 5} \\
-2x + 3
\end{array}
$$

$$\frac{6x^3 + 10x^2 + x + 8}{2x^2 + 1} = 3x + 5 - \frac{2x - 3}{2x^2 + 1}$$

11.
$$
\begin{array}{r}
x^2 + 2x \ + 4 \\
x^2 - 2x + 3 \overline{\smash{)}\; x^4 \qquad\quad + 3x^2 \qquad + 1} \\
\underline{x^4 - 2x^3 + 3x^2} \\
2x^3 \\
\underline{2x^3 - 4x^2 + 6x} \\
4x^2 - 6x + \ 1 \\
\underline{4x^2 - 8x + 12} \\
2x - 11
\end{array}
$$
$\Rightarrow \quad \dfrac{x^4 + 3x^2 + 1}{x^2 - 2x + 3} = x^2 + 2x + 4 + \dfrac{2x - 11}{x^2 - 2x + 3}$

13. Observe that $(x - 1)^2 = x^2 - 2x + 1$.

$$
\begin{array}{r}
2x \\
x^2 - 2x + 1 \overline{\smash{)}\; 2x^3 - 4x^2 - 15x + 5} \\
\underline{2x^3 - 4x^2 + \ 2x} \\
- 17x + 5
\end{array}
$$
$\Rightarrow \quad \dfrac{2x^3 - 4x^2 - 15x + 5}{(x - 1)^2} = 2x - \dfrac{17x - 5}{(x - 1)^2}$

15.
$$
\begin{array}{r|rrrr}
5 & 3 & -17 & 15 & -25 \\
  &   & 15 & -10 & 25 \\
\hline
  & 3 & -2 & 5 & 0
\end{array}
$$
$(3x^3 - 17x^2 + 15x - 25) \div (x - 5)$
$= 3x^2 - 2x + 5$

17.
$$
\begin{array}{r|rrrr}
-2 & 4 & 8 & -9 & -18 \\
   &   & -8 & 0 & 18 \\
\hline
   & 4 & 0 & -9 & 0
\end{array}
$$
$(4x^3 - 9x + 8x^2 - 18) \div (x + 2) = 4x^2 - 9$

19.
$$
\begin{array}{r|rrrr}
-10 & -1 & 0 & 75 & -250 \\
    &   & 10 & -100 & 250 \\
\hline
    & -1 & 10 & -25 & 0
\end{array}
$$
$(-x^3 + 75x - 250) \div (x + 10)$
$= -x^2 + 10x - 25$

21.
$$
\begin{array}{r|rrrr}
4 & 5 & -6 & 0 & 8 \\
  &   & 20 & 56 & 224 \\
\hline
  & 5 & 14 & 56 & 232
\end{array}
$$
$(5x^3 - 6x^2 + 8) \div (x - 4)$
$= 5x^2 + 14x + 56 + \dfrac{232}{x - 4}$

23.
$$
\begin{array}{r|rrrrr}
6 & 10 & -50 & 0 & 0 & -800 \\
  &   & 60 & 60 & 360 & 2160 \\
\hline
  & 10 & 10 & 60 & 360 & 1360
\end{array}
$$
$(10x^4 - 50x^3 - 800) \div (x - 6)$
$= 10x^3 + 10x^2 + 60x + 360 + \dfrac{1360}{x - 6}$

25.
$$
\begin{array}{r|rrrr}
-8 & 1 & 0 & 0 & 512 \\
   &   & -8 & 64 & -512 \\
\hline
   & 1 & -8 & 64 & 0
\end{array}
$$
$(x^3 + 512) \div (x + 8) = x^2 - 8x + 64$

27. 2 | $\begin{array}{ccccc} -3 & 0 & 0 & 0 & 0 \end{array}$

 | $\begin{array}{cccc} -6 & -12 & -24 & -48 \end{array}$

 | $\begin{array}{ccccc} -3 & -6 & -12 & -24 & -48 \end{array}$

$-3x^4 \div (x - 2)$

$$= -3x^3 - 6x^2 - 12x - 24 - \frac{48}{x - 2}$$

29. −1 | $\begin{array}{cccc} -1 & 2 & -3 & 5 \end{array}$

 | $\begin{array}{ccc} 1 & -3 & 6 \end{array}$

 | $\begin{array}{cccc} -1 & 3 & -6 & 11 \end{array}$

$(5 - 3x + 2x^2 - x^3) \div (x + 1)$

$$= -x^2 + 3x - 6 + \frac{11}{x + 1}$$

31. $-\frac{1}{2}$ | $\begin{array}{cccc} 4 & 16 & -23 & -15 \end{array}$

$\phantom{-\frac{1}{2}}$ | $\begin{array}{ccc} -2 & -7 & 15 \end{array}$

$\phantom{-\frac{1}{2}}$ | $\begin{array}{cccc} 4 & 14 & -30 & 0 \end{array}$

$(4x^3 + 16x^2 - 23x - 15) \div \left(x + \frac{1}{2}\right)$

$$= 4x^2 + 14x - 30$$

33. 2 | $\begin{array}{cccc} 1 & 0 & -7 & 6 \end{array}$

 | $\begin{array}{ccc} 2 & 4 & -6 \end{array}$

 | $\begin{array}{cccc} 1 & 2 & -3 & 0 \end{array}$

$x^3 - 7x + 6 = (x - 2)(x^2 + 2x - 3)$

$$= (x - 2)(x + 3)(x - 1)$$

Real zeros: 2, −3, 1

35. $\frac{1}{2}$ | $\begin{array}{cccc} 2 & -15 & 27 & -10 \end{array}$

$\phantom{\frac{1}{2}}$ | $\begin{array}{ccc} 1 & -7 & 10 \end{array}$

$\phantom{\frac{1}{2}}$ | $\begin{array}{cccc} 2 & -14 & 20 & 0 \end{array}$

$2x^3 - 15x^2 + 27x - 10 = \left(x - \frac{1}{2}\right)(2x^2 - 14x + 20) = (2x - 1)(x - 2)(x - 5)$

Real zeros: $\frac{1}{2}$, 2, 5

37. $\sqrt{3}$ | $\begin{array}{cccc} 1 & 2 & -3 & -6 \end{array}$

$\phantom{\sqrt{3}}$ | $\begin{array}{ccc} \sqrt{3} & 2\sqrt{3} + 3 & 6 \end{array}$

$\phantom{\sqrt{3}}$ | $\begin{array}{cccc} 1 & 2 + \sqrt{3} & 2\sqrt{3} & 0 \end{array}$

$x^3 + 2x^2 - 3x - 6 = (x - \sqrt{3})(x^2 + (2 + \sqrt{3})x + 2\sqrt{3}) = (x - \sqrt{3})(x + 2)(x + \sqrt{3})$

Real zeros: $\sqrt{3}$, −2, $-\sqrt{3}$

39.

$$1+\sqrt{3} \, \bigg| \begin{array}{cccc} 1 & -3 & 0 & 2 \\ & 1+\sqrt{3} & 1-\sqrt{3} & -2 \end{array}$$

$$\begin{array}{cccc} 1 & -2+\sqrt{3} & 1-\sqrt{3} & 0 \end{array}$$

Real zeros: $1+\sqrt{3}$, 1, $1-\sqrt{3}$

$x^3 - 3x^2 + 2 = [x - (1+\sqrt{3})][x^2 + (-2+\sqrt{3})x + (1-\sqrt{\ }$

$= (x - 1 - \sqrt{3})(x - 1)(x - 1 + \sqrt{3})$

41. $f(x) = x^3 - x^2 - 14x + 11, \quad k = 4$

$$4 \, \bigg| \begin{array}{cccc} 1 & -1 & -14 & 11 \\ & 4 & 12 & -8 \end{array}$$

$$\begin{array}{cccc} 1 & 3 & -2 & 3 \end{array}$$

$f(x) = (x - 4)(x^2 + 3x - 2) + 3$

$f(4) = (0)(26) + 3 = 3$

43. $f(x) = x^3 + 3x^2 - 2x - 14, \quad k = \sqrt{2}$

$$\sqrt{2} \, \bigg| \begin{array}{cccc} 1 & 3 & -2 & -14 \\ & \sqrt{2} & 2+3\sqrt{2} & 6 \end{array}$$

$$\begin{array}{cccc} 1 & 3+\sqrt{2} & 3\sqrt{2} & -8 \end{array}$$

$f(x) = (x - \sqrt{2})[x^2 + (3 + \sqrt{2})x + 3\sqrt{2}] - 8$

$f(\sqrt{2}) = (0)(4 + 6\sqrt{2}) - 8 = -8$

45. $f(x) = 4x^3 - 13x + 10$

(a) $1 \, \bigg| \begin{array}{cccc} 4 & 0 & -13 & 10 \\ & 4 & 4 & -9 \end{array}$

$\begin{array}{ccccc} 4 & 4 & -9 & 1 & = f(1) \end{array}$

(b) $-2 \, \bigg| \begin{array}{cccc} 4 & 0 & -13 & 10 \\ & -8 & 16 & -6 \end{array}$

$\begin{array}{ccccc} 4 & -8 & 3 & 4 & = f(-2) \end{array}$

(c) $\frac{1}{2} \, \bigg| \begin{array}{cccc} 4 & 0 & -13 & 10 \\ & 2 & 1 & -6 \end{array}$

$\begin{array}{ccccc} 4 & 2 & -12 & 4 & = f(\frac{1}{2}) \end{array}$

(d) $8 \, \bigg| \begin{array}{cccc} 4 & 0 & -13 & 10 \\ & 32 & 256 & 1944 \end{array}$

$\begin{array}{ccccc} 4 & 32 & 243 & 1954 & = f(8) \end{array}$

47. $h(x) = 3x^3 + 5x^2 - 10x + 1$

(a) $3 \, \bigg| \begin{array}{cccc} 3 & 5 & -10 & 1 \\ & 9 & 42 & 96 \end{array}$

$\begin{array}{ccccc} 3 & 14 & 32 & 97 & = h(3) \end{array}$

(b) $\frac{1}{3} \, \bigg| \begin{array}{cccc} 3 & 5 & -10 & 1 \\ & 1 & 2 & -\frac{8}{3} \end{array}$

$\begin{array}{ccccc} 3 & 6 & -8 & -\frac{5}{3} & = h(\frac{1}{3}) \end{array}$

(c) $-2 \, \bigg| \begin{array}{cccc} 3 & 5 & -10 & 1 \\ & -6 & 2 & 16 \end{array}$

$\begin{array}{ccccc} 3 & -1 & -8 & 17 & = h(-2) \end{array}$

(d) $-5 \, \bigg| \begin{array}{cccc} 3 & 5 & -10 & 1 \\ & -15 & 50 & -200 \end{array}$

$\begin{array}{ccccc} 3 & -10 & 40 & -199 & = h(-5) \end{array}$

49. $f(x) = x^3 - 2x^2 - 11x + 52$

(a)

5	1	-2	-11	52
		5	15	20
	1	3	4	72 = $f(5)$

(b)

-4	1	-2	-11	52
		-4	24	-52
	1	-6	13	0 = $f(-4)$

(c)

1.2	1	-2	-11	52
		1.2	-0.96	-14.352
	1	-0.8	-11.96	37.648 = $f(1.2)$

(d)

2	1	-2	-11	52
		2	0	-22
	1	0	-11	30 = $f(2)$

51. $\dfrac{4x^3 - 8x^2 + x + 3}{2x - 3} = \dfrac{2x^3 - 4x^2 + \frac{1}{2}x + \frac{3}{2}}{x - \frac{3}{2}}$

$\frac{3}{2}$	2	-4	$\frac{1}{2}$	$\frac{3}{2}$
		3	$-\frac{3}{2}$	$-\frac{3}{2}$
	2	-1	-1	0

$2x^2 - x - 1$

53. $\dfrac{x^3 + 3x^2 - x - 3}{x + 1}$

-1	1	3	-1	-3
		-1	-2	3
	1	2	-3	0

$\dfrac{x^3 + 3x^2 - x - 3}{x + 1} = x^2 + 2x - 3$

55. $\dfrac{x^4 + 6x^3 + 11x^2 + 6x}{x^2 + 3x + 2} = \dfrac{x^4 + 6x^3 + 11x^2 + 6x}{(x + 1)(x + 2)}$

-1	1	6	11	6	0
		-1	-5	-6	0
	1	5	6	0	0

-2	1	5	6	0
		-2	-6	0
	1	3	0	0

$\dfrac{x^4 + 6x^3 + 11x^2 + 6x}{(x + 1)(x + 2)} = x^2 + 3x$

57. $y = -1.42x^3 + 5.04x^2 + 32.45x - 0.75,\ 1 \leq x \leq 5$

(a)

(b) If $y = 110$, then $x = 3.29$ (or $x = 5$).

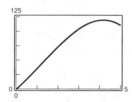

(c) Since $y = 110$ when $x = 5$ we have $x = 5$ as a zero to the equation $y - 110$.

$$f(x) = y - 110, \quad 1 \leq x \leq 5$$

$$= -1.42x^3 + 5.04x^2 + 32.45x - 110.75$$

$$
\begin{array}{r|rrrr}
5 & -1.42 & 5.04 & 32.45 & -110.75 \\
  &   & -7.10 & -10.30 & 110.75 \\
\hline
  & -1.42 & -2.06 & 22.15 & 0
\end{array}
$$

$$x = \frac{-(-2.06) \pm \sqrt{(-2.06)^2 - 4(-1.42)(22.15)}}{2(-1.42)} = \frac{2.06 \pm \sqrt{130.0556}}{-2.84}$$

$x \approx -4.74$ or $x \approx 3.3$.

Since $1 \leq x \leq 5$, we choose $x = 3.3$ which corresponds to 3300 rpm.

59. $f(x) = (x - k)q(x) + r$

(a) Since the point passes through $(2, 5)$, we know $f(x) = (x - 2)q(x) + 5$. Suppose the graph falls to the left and rises to the right, we know then that the function is odd and positive.

$$f(x) = (x - 2)x^2 + 5 = x^3 - 2x^2 + 5$$

(b) Since the point passes through $(-3, 1)$, we know $f(x) = (x + 3)q(x) + 1$. Suppose the graph rises to the left and falls to the right, we know then that the function is odd and negative.

$$f(x) = (x + 3)(-x^2) + 1 = -x^3 - 3x^2 + 1$$

Section 3.4   Real Zeros of Polynomial Functions

- You should know Descartes's Rule of Signs.
  - (a) The number of positive real zeros of f is either equal to the number of variations of sign of f or is less than that number by an even integer.
  - (b) The number of negative real zeros of f is either equal to the number of variations in sign of $f(-x)$ or is less than that number by an even integer.
  - (c) When there is only one variation in sign, there is exactly one positive (or negative) real zero.

- You should know the Rational Zero Test.

- You should know shortcuts for the Rational Zero Test.
  - (a) Use a graphing calculator to give a good estimate of the location of the zero.
  - (b) After finding a root, use synthetic division to reduce the degree of the polynomial.

- You should be able to observe the last row obtained from synthetic division in order to determine upper or lower bounds.
  - (a) If the test value is positive and all of the entries in the last row are positive or zero, then the test value is an upper bound.
  - (b) If the test value is negative and the entries in the last row alternate from positive to negative, then the test value is a lower bound. (Zero entries count as positive or negative.)

- You should know the Bisection Method for approximating zeros.

---

1. $f(x) = x^3 + 3$

Sign variations: 0, positive zeros: 0

$f(-x) = -x^3 + 3$

Sign variations: 1, negative zeros: 1

3. $h(x) = 3x^4 + 2x^2 + 1$

Sign variations: 0, positive zeros: 0

$h(-x) = 3x^4 + 2x^2 + 1$

Sign variations: 0, negative zeros: 0

5. $g(x) = 2x^3 - 3x^2 - 3$

Sign variations: 1, positive zeros: 1

$g(-x) = -2x^3 - 3x^2 - 3$

Sign variations: 0, negative zeros: 0

7. $f(x) = -5x^3 + x^2 - x + 5$

Sign variations: 3, positive zeros: 3 or 1

$f(-x) = 5x^3 + x^2 + x + 5$

Sign variations: 0, negative zeros: 0

9. $h(x) = 4x^2 - 8x + 3$

   Sign variations: 2, positive zeros: 2 or 0

   $h(-x) = 4x^2 + 8x + 3$

   Sign variations: 0, negative zeros: 0

11. $f(x) = x^3 + x^2 - 4x - 4$

    Possible rational zeros: $\pm 1, \ \pm 2, \ \pm 4$

    $-2, \ -1, \ 2$ on graph

13. $f(x) = -4x^3 + 15x^2 - 8x - 3$

    Possible rational zeros: $\dfrac{\pm 1, \ \pm 3}{\pm 1, \ \pm 2, \ \pm 4} = \pm\dfrac{1}{4}, \ \pm\dfrac{1}{2}, \ \pm\dfrac{3}{4}, \ \pm 1, \ \pm\dfrac{3}{2}, \ \pm 3$

    $-\dfrac{1}{4}, \ 1, \ 3$ on graph

15. $f(x) = -2x^4 + 13x^3 - 21x^2 + 2x + 8$

    (a) Possible rational zeros:

    $$\dfrac{\pm 1, \ \pm 2, \ \pm 4, \ \pm 8}{\pm 1, \ \pm 2}$$

    $$= \pm\dfrac{1}{2}, \ \pm 1, \ \pm 2, \ \pm 4, \ \pm 8$$

    (c) $-\frac{1}{2}, \ 1, \ 2, \ 4$ on graph

    (b)

17. $f(x) = 32x^3 - 52x^2 + 17x + 3$

    (a) Possible rational zeros:

    $\pm\frac{1}{32}, \ \pm\frac{1}{16}, \ \pm\frac{3}{32}, \ \pm\frac{1}{8}, \ \pm\frac{3}{16}, \ \pm\frac{1}{4},$

    $\pm\frac{3}{8}, \ \pm\frac{1}{2}, \ \pm\frac{3}{4}, \ \pm 1, \ \pm\frac{3}{2}, \ \pm 3$

    (b)

    (c) $-\frac{1}{8}, \ \frac{3}{4}, \ 1$ on graph

19. $f(x) = 4x^3 + 7x^2 - 11x - 18$

    (a) Possible rational zeros:

    $\pm\frac{1}{4}, \ \pm\frac{1}{2}, \ \pm\frac{3}{4}, \ \pm 1, \ \pm\frac{3}{2}, \ \pm\frac{9}{4},$

    $\pm\frac{9}{2}, \ \pm 2 \pm 3, \ \pm 6, \ \pm 9, \ \pm 18$

    (b)

    (c) $-2, \ \dfrac{1 \pm \sqrt{145}}{8}$ on graph

21. $f(x) = x^4 - 4x^3 + 15$

(a)
$$
\begin{array}{r|rrrrr}
4 & 1 & -4 & 0 & 0 & 15 \\
  &   & 4 & 0 & 0 & 0 \\
\hline
  & 1 & 0 & 0 & 0 & 15
\end{array}
$$

4 is an upper bound.

(b)
$$
\begin{array}{r|rrrrr}
-1 & 1 & -4 & 0 & 0 & 15 \\
   &   & -1 & 5 & -5 & 5 \\
\hline
   & 1 & -5 & 5 & -5 & 20
\end{array}
$$

−1 is a lower bound.

(c)
$$
\begin{array}{r|rrrrr}
3 & 1 & -4 & 0 & 0 & 15 \\
  &   & 3 & -3 & -9 & -27 \\
\hline
  & 1 & -1 & -3 & -9 & -12
\end{array}
$$

3 is neither an upper nor lower bound.

23. $f(x) = x^4 - 4x^3 + 16x - 16$

(a)
$$
\begin{array}{r|rrrrr}
-1 & 1 & -4 & 0 & 16 & -16 \\
   &   & -1 & 5 & -5 & -11 \\
\hline
   & 1 & -5 & 5 & 11 & -27
\end{array}
$$

−1 is neither an upper nor lower bound.

(b)
$$
\begin{array}{r|rrrrr}
-3 & 1 & -4 & 0 & 16 & -16 \\
   &   & -3 & 21 & -63 & 141 \\
\hline
   & 1 & -7 & 21 & -47 & 125
\end{array}
$$

−3 is a lower bound.

(c)
$$
\begin{array}{r|rrrrr}
5 & 1 & -4 & 0 & 16 & -16 \\
  &   & 5 & 5 & 25 & 205 \\
\hline
  & 1 & 1 & 5 & 41 & 189
\end{array}
$$

5 is an upper bound.

25. Possible rational zeros: $\pm 1, \pm 2, \pm 3, \pm 6$

$$
\begin{array}{r|rrrr}
1 & 1 & -6 & 11 & -6 \\
  &   & 1 & -5 & 6 \\
\hline
  & 1 & -5 & 6 & 0
\end{array}
$$

$$x^3 - 6x^2 + 11x - 6 = (x-1)(x^2 - 5x + 6)$$
$$= (x-1)(x-2)(x-3)$$

The zeros are 1, 2, and 3.

27. Possible rational zeros: $\pm 1, \pm 2, \pm 2$

$$
\begin{array}{r|rrrr}
1 & 1 & -4 & -1 & 4 \\
  &   & 1 & -3 & -4 \\
\hline
  & 1 & -3 & -4 & 0
\end{array}
$$

$$x^3 - 4x^2 - x + 4 = (x-1)(x^2 - 3x - 4)$$
$$= (x-1)(x-4)(x+1)$$

The zeros are −1, 1, and 4.

29. Possible rational zeros: $\pm 1, \pm 2, \pm 5, \pm 10$

$$
\begin{array}{r|rrrr}
-1 & 1 & 12 & 21 & 10 \\
   &   & -1 & -11 & -10 \\
\hline
   & 1 & 11 & 10 & 0
\end{array}
$$

$$t^3 + 12t^2 + 21t + 10 = (t+1)(t^2 + 11t + 10) = (t+1)(t+1)(t+10)$$

The zeros are −1 and −10.

31. Possible rational zeros: $\pm 1, \pm 2$

$$
\begin{array}{r|rrrr}
1 & 1 & -4 & 5 & -2 \\
  &   & 1 & -3 & 2 \\
\hline
  & 1 & -3 & 2 & 0
\end{array}
$$

$$
\begin{aligned}
x^3 - 4x^2 + 5x - 2 &= (x-1)(x^2 - 3x + 2) \\
&= (x-1)(x-1)(x-2)
\end{aligned}
$$

The zeros are 1 and 2.

33. Possible rational zeros: $\pm 1, \pm \frac{1}{2}$

$$
\begin{array}{r|rrrr}
-1 & 2 & 3 & 0 & -1 \\
   &   & -2 & -1 & 1 \\
\hline
   & 2 & 1 & -1 & 0
\end{array}
$$

$$
\begin{aligned}
2x^3 + 3x^2 - 1 &= (x+1)(2x^2 + x - 1) \\
&= (x+1)(2x-1)(x+1)
\end{aligned}
$$

The zeros are -1 and $\frac{1}{2}$.

35. Possible rational zeros: $\pm 1, \pm \frac{1}{2}, \pm \frac{1}{4}$

$$
\begin{array}{r|rrrr}
1 & 4 & 0 & -3 & -1 \\
  &   & 4 & 4 & 1 \\
\hline
  & 4 & 4 & 1 & 0
\end{array}
$$

$$
\begin{aligned}
4x^3 - 3x - 1 &= (x-1)(4x^2 + 4x + 1) \\
&= (x-1)(2x+1)^2
\end{aligned}
$$

The zeros are $-\frac{1}{2}$ and 1.

37. Possible rational zeros:

$$\pm 1, \pm 2, \pm 3, \pm 6,$$
$$\pm \frac{1}{2}, \pm \frac{3}{2}, \pm \frac{1}{4}, \pm \frac{3}{4}$$

$$
\begin{array}{r|rrrr}
-\frac{3}{4} & 4 & 3 & 8 & 6 \\
   &   & -3 & 0 & -6 \\
\hline
   & 4 & 0 & 8 & 0
\end{array}
$$

$$4y^3 + 3y^2 + 8y + 6 = \left(y + \frac{3}{4}\right)\left(4y^2 + 8\right)$$

The zero is $-\frac{3}{4}$.

39.
$$
\begin{aligned}
f(x) &= x^4 - 3x^2 + 2 \\
&= (x^2 - 1)(x^2 - 2) \\
&= (x+1)(x-1)(x+\sqrt{2})(x-\sqrt{2})
\end{aligned}
$$

The zeros are ± 1 and $\pm \sqrt{2}$.

41.
$$
\begin{aligned}
x^4 - 13x^2 - 12x &= 0 \\
x(x^3 - 13x - 12) &= 0
\end{aligned}
$$

$$
\begin{array}{r|rrrr}
-1 & 1 & 0 & -13 & -12 \\
   &   & -1 & 1 & 12 \\
\hline
   & 1 & -1 & -12 & 0
\end{array}
$$

$$
\begin{aligned}
x(x^3 - 13x - 12) &= x(x+1)(x^2 - x - 12) \\
&= x(x+1)(x-4)(x+3) \\
&= 0
\end{aligned}
$$

The real solutions are -3, -1, 0, and 4.

43. $2x^4 - 11x^3 - 6x^2 + 64x + 32 = 0$

$$
\begin{array}{r|rrrrr}
-2 & 2 & -11 & -6 & 64 & 32 \\
 & & -4 & 30 & -48 & -32 \\
\hline
4 & 2 & -15 & 24 & 16 & 0 \\
 & & 8 & -28 & -16 & \\
\hline
 & 2 & -7 & -4 & 0 &
\end{array}
$$

$2x^4 - 11x^3 - 6x^2 + 64x + 32 = (x+2)(x-4)(2x^2 - 7x - 4)$

$\qquad\qquad\qquad\qquad = (x+2)(x-4)(2x+1)(x-4) = 0$

The real solutions are -2, $-\frac{1}{2}$, and 4.

45. $P(x) = x^4 - \frac{25}{4}x^2 + 9$

$\qquad = \frac{1}{4}(4x^4 - 25x^2 + 36)$

Possible rational zeros:

$\qquad \pm\frac{1}{4}, \pm\frac{1}{2}, \pm\frac{3}{4}, \pm 1, \pm\frac{3}{2}, \pm 2, \pm\frac{9}{4}$

$\qquad \pm 3, \pm 4, \pm\frac{9}{2}, \pm 6, \pm 9, \pm 12, \pm 18, \pm 36$

$x = \pm 2, \pm\frac{3}{2}$

47. $f(x) = x^3 - \frac{1}{4}x^2 - x + \frac{1}{4}$

$\qquad = \frac{1}{4}(4x^3 - x^2 - 4x + 1)$

Possible rational zeros: $\pm\frac{1}{4}, \pm\frac{1}{2}, \pm 1$

$x = -1, \frac{1}{4}, 1$

49. $f(x) = x^3 - 1 = (x-1)(x^2 + x + 1)$

Zeros: 1

One rational zero; zero irrational zeros

Matches (d)

51. $f(x) = x^3 - x = x(x^2 - 1) = x(x+1)(x-1)$

Zeros: 0, ± 1

Three rational zeros; no irrational zeros

Matches (b)

53. $f(x) = 3x^3 - 2x^2 - 15x + 10$

$\qquad = \left(x - \frac{2}{3}\right)(3x^2 - 15) = 0 \Rightarrow x = \frac{2}{3}$ (rational), $\pm\sqrt{5}$ (irrational)

55. $g(x) = x^3 + 3x^2 - 34x - 42$

$\qquad = (x+7)(x^2 - 4x - 6) \Rightarrow x = -7$ (rational), $2 \pm \sqrt{10}$ (irrational)

57. $f(x) = x^3 + x - 1$

    (a) ±1

    (b)

    (c) 0.68

59. $f(x) = x^4 - x - 3$

    (a) ±1, ±3

    (b)

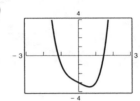

    (c) −1.16, 1.45

61. $V = 18 = (9 - 2x)(5 - 2x)(x), \quad 0 < x < \dfrac{5}{2}$

$$x(45 - 28x + 4x^2) = 18$$

$$4x^3 - 28x^2 + 45x - 18 = 0$$

Using a graphing utility, we see that there are two solutions in the interval $\left(0, \frac{5}{2}\right)$: $x = 1.5$ and $x = 0.614$ or

$$(2x - 3)(2x^2 - 11x + 6) = 0$$

$$x = \frac{3}{2}, \frac{11 - \sqrt{73}}{4}$$

$x = \dfrac{3}{2}, \ 9 - 2x = 6, \ 5 - 2x = 2$

$x = \dfrac{11 - \sqrt{73}}{4} \approx 0.614, \ 9 - 2x = 7.77, \ 5 - 2x = 3.77$

Dimensions: $\frac{3}{2}$ inches × 2 inches × 6 inches or 0.614 in × 3.77 inches × 7.77 inches

63. $2{,}500{,}000 = -76x^3 + 4{,}830x^2 - 320{,}000$

$76x^3 - 4{,}830x^2 + 2{,}820{,}000 = 0$

Using a graphing utility with the viewing rectangle $[0, 50] \times [-10, 10]$, we see that there are two solutions, $x \approx 38.4$ or $x \approx 46.1$ which corresponds to \$384,000 or \$461,000 being spent on advertising. The smaller is 384,000.

65. $C = 100 \left(\dfrac{200}{x^2} + \dfrac{x}{x+30} \right), \quad 1 \le x$

$3x^3 - 40x^2 - 2400x - 36{,}000 = 0$

Graphing this function, we see that $x = 4000$. You can also graph C directly and zoom in on the minimum value.

67.

Iteration	a	c	b	$f(a)$	$f(c)$	$f(b)$	Error
1	0.0000	0.5000	1.0000	−8.0000	−0.5000	10.0000	0.5000
2	0.5000	0.7500	1.0000	−0.5000	4.1875	10.0000	0.2500
3	0.5000	0.6250	0.7500	−0.5000	1.7266	4.1875	0.1250
4	0.5000	0.5625	0.6250	−0.5000	0.5869	1.7266	0.0625
5	0.5000	0.5313	0.5625	−0.5000	0.0372	0.5869	0.0313
6	0.5000	0.5156	0.5313	−0.5000	−0.2329	0.0372	0.0156
7	0.5156	0.5234	0.5313	−0.2329	−0.0982	0.0372	0.0078
8	0.5234	0.5273	0.5313	−0.0982	−0.0306	0.0372	0.0039
9	0.5273	0.5293	0.5313	−0.0306	0.0033	0.0372	0.0020

The zero of f is approximately 0.53.

69.

Iteration	a	c	b	$f(a)$	$f(c)$	$f(b)$	Error
1	1.0000	1.5000	2.0000	−100.0000	−9.5625	56.0000	0.5000
2	1.5000	1.7500	2.0000	−9.5625	26.2461	56.0000	0.2500
3	1.5000	1.6250	1.7500	−9.5625	9.1345	26.2461	0.1250
4	1.5000	1.5625	1.6250	−9.5625	−0.0135	9.1345	0.0625
5	1.5625	1.5938	1.6250	−0.0135	4.6104	9.1345	0.0313
6	1.5625	1.5781	1.5938	−0.0135	2.3109	4.6104	0.0156
7	1.5625	1.5703	1.5781	−0.0135	1.1518	2.3109	0.0078
8	1.5625	1.5664	1.5703	−0.0135	0.5699	1.1518	0.0039
9	1.5625	1.5645	1.5664	−0.0135	0.2784	0.5699	0.0020
10	1.5625	1.5635	1.5645	−0.0135	0.1324	0.2784	0.0010

The zero of f is approximately 1.56.

Section 3.5   Complex Numbers

- You should know how to work with complex numbers, $a + bi$, where $i = \sqrt{-1}$.
- Operations on Complex Numbers
  - (a) Addition: $(a + bi) + (c + di) = (a + c) + (b + d)i$
  - (b) Subtraction: $(a + bi) - (c + di) = (a - c) + (b - d)i$
  - (c) Multiplication: $(a + bi)(c + di) = (ac - bd) + (ad + bc)i$
  - (d) Division: $\dfrac{a + bi}{c + di} = \dfrac{a + bi}{c + di} \cdot \dfrac{c - di}{c - di} = \dfrac{ac + bd}{c^2 + d^2} + \dfrac{bc - ad}{c^2 + d^2} i$

- The complex conjugate of $a + bi$ is $a - bi$: $(a + bi)(a - bi) = a^2 + b^2$
- The additive inverse of $a + bi$ is $-a - bi$.
- The multiplicative inverse of $a + bi$ is $\dfrac{a - bi}{a^2 + b^2}$.
- $\sqrt{-a} = \sqrt{a}\, i$ for $a > 0$.
- You should be able to find the complex solutions to a quadratic equation.
- You should be able to plot complex numbers in the complex plane.

1.
$i = i \quad i^5 = i \quad i^9 = i \quad i^{13} = i$
$i^2 = -1 \quad i^6 = -1 \quad i^{10} = -1 \quad i^{14} = -1$
$i^3 = -i \quad i^7 = -i \quad i^{11} = -i \quad i^{15} = -i$
$i^4 = 1 \quad i^8 = 1 \quad i^{12} = 1 \quad i^{16} = 1$

3. $a + bi = -10 + 6i$
$\qquad a = -10$
$\qquad b = 6$

5. $(a - 1) + (b + 3)i = 5 + 8i$
$\qquad a - 1 = 5 \ \Rightarrow \ a = 6$
$\qquad b + 3 = 8 \ \Rightarrow \ b = 5$

7. $4 + \sqrt{-9} = 4 + \sqrt{9}\, i$
$\qquad\quad = 4 + 3i$

9. $2 - \sqrt{-27} = 2 - \sqrt{27}\, i$
$\qquad\qquad = 2 - 3\sqrt{3}\, i$

11. $\sqrt{-75} = \sqrt{75}\, i$
$\qquad\quad = 5\sqrt{3}\, i$

13. $-6i + i^2 = -6i + (-1)$
$\qquad\qquad = -1 - 6i$

15. $-5i^5 = -5(i^4)i = -5i$

17. 8 is in standard form.
The imaginary part is 0.

19. $(5+i) + (6-2i) = 5 + i + 6 - 2i$
$$= (5+6) + (1-2)i$$
$$= 11 - i$$

21. $(8-i) - (4-i) = 8 - i - 4 + 1$
$$= (8-4) + (-1+1)i$$
$$= 4 + 0i$$
$$= 4$$

23. $(-2 + \sqrt{-8}) + (5 - \sqrt{-50}) = -2 + 2\sqrt{2}\,i + 5 - 5\sqrt{2}\,i = (-2+5) + \sqrt{2}(2-5)i = 3 - 3\sqrt{2}\,i$

25. $-\left(\frac{3}{2} + \frac{5}{2}i\right) + \left(\frac{5}{3} + \frac{11}{3}i\right) = -\frac{3}{2} - \frac{5}{2}i + \frac{5}{3} + \frac{11}{3}i = \left(-\frac{3}{2} + \frac{5}{3}\right) + \left(-\frac{5}{2} + \frac{11}{3}\right)i = \frac{1}{6} + \frac{7}{6}i$

27. The complex conjugate of $5 + 3i$ is $5 - 3i$.
$$(5+3i)(5-3i) = 5^2 - (3i)^2 = 25 - 9i^2 = 25 + 9 = 34$$

29. The complex conjugate of $-2 - \sqrt{5}\,i$ is $-2 + \sqrt{5}\,i$.
$$(-2 - \sqrt{5}\,i)(-2 + \sqrt{5}\,i) = (-2)^2 - (\sqrt{5}\,i)^2$$
$$= 4 - 5i^2$$
$$= 4 + 5$$
$$= 9$$

31. $\sqrt{-6} \cdot \sqrt{-2} = (\sqrt{6}\,i)(\sqrt{2}\,i)$
$$= \sqrt{12}\,i^2$$
$$= -2\sqrt{3}$$

(Note that it is incorrect to write
$\sqrt{-6} \cdot \sqrt{-2} = \sqrt{(-6)(-2)} = \sqrt{12} = 2\sqrt{3}$.)

33. $(\sqrt{-10})^2 = (\sqrt{10}\,i)^2$
$$= (\sqrt{10})^2(i^2)$$
$$= -10$$

35. $(1+i)(3-2i) = 3 - 2i + 3i - 2i^2$
$$= 3 + i + 2$$
$$= 5 + i$$

37. $6i(5-2i) = 30i - 12i^2 = 12 + 30i$

39. $(\sqrt{14} + \sqrt{10}\,i)(\sqrt{14} - \sqrt{10}\,i) = 14 - 10i^2$
$$= 14 + 10$$
$$= 24$$

41. $(4+5i)^2 = 16 + 40i + 25i^2$
$$= 16 + 40i - 25$$
$$= -9 + 40i$$

43. $(2+3i)^2 + (2-3i)^2 = (4+12i+9i^2) + (4-12i+9i^2)$

$$= 8 + 18i^2$$

$$= 8 - 18$$

$$= -10$$

45. $\dfrac{4}{4-5i} = \dfrac{4}{4-5i} \cdot \dfrac{4+5i}{4+5i}$

$$= \dfrac{16+20i}{16+25}$$

$$= \dfrac{16}{41} + \dfrac{20}{41}i$$

47. $\dfrac{2+i}{2-i} = \dfrac{2+i}{2-i} \cdot \dfrac{2+i}{2+i}$

$$= \dfrac{4+4i+i^2}{4+1}$$

$$= \dfrac{3+4i}{5}$$

$$= \dfrac{3}{5} + \dfrac{4}{5}i$$

49. $\dfrac{6-7i}{i} = \dfrac{6-7i}{i} \cdot \dfrac{-i}{-i}$

$$= \dfrac{-6i+7i^2}{1}$$

$$= -7 - 6i$$

51. First, note that

$$(1+i)^3 = (1+i)(1+i)^2$$

$$= (1+i)(2i) = -2 + 2i.$$

Then

$$\dfrac{5}{(1+i)^3} = \dfrac{5}{-2+2i} \cdot \dfrac{-2-2i}{-2-2i}$$

$$= \dfrac{-10-10i}{8} = \dfrac{-5}{4} - \dfrac{5}{4}i.$$

53. $\dfrac{(21-7i)(4+3i)}{(2-5i)} = \dfrac{105+35i}{2-5i} \cdot \dfrac{2+5i}{2+5i}$

$$= \dfrac{(210-175)+(70+525)i}{4+25} = \dfrac{35+595i}{29} = \dfrac{35}{29} + \dfrac{595}{29}i$$

55. $x^2 - 2x + 2 = 0$

$a = 1,\ b = -2,\ c = 2$

$$x = \dfrac{-(-2) \pm \sqrt{(-2)^2 - 4(1)(2)}}{2(1)}$$

$$= \dfrac{2 \pm \sqrt{-4}}{2} = \dfrac{2 \pm 2i}{2}$$

$$= 1 \pm i$$

57. $4x^2 + 16x + 17 = 0$

$a = 4,\ b = 16,\ c = 17$

$$x = \dfrac{-16 \pm \sqrt{(16)^2 - 4(4)(17)}}{2(4)}$$

$$= \dfrac{-16 \pm \sqrt{-16}}{8} = \dfrac{-16 \pm 4i}{8}$$

$$= -2 \pm \dfrac{1}{2}i$$

59. $4x^2 + 16x + 15 = 0$

$a = 4, \ b = 16, \ c = 15$

$x = \dfrac{-16 \pm \sqrt{16^2 - 4(4)(15)}}{2(4)} = \dfrac{-16 \pm 4}{8}$

$x = \dfrac{-16 + 4}{8} = -\dfrac{3}{2}$

$x = \dfrac{-16 - 4}{8} = -\dfrac{5}{2}$

61. $16t^2 - 4t + 3 = 0; \ a = 16, \ b = -4, \ c = 3$

$t = \dfrac{-(-4) \pm \sqrt{(-4)^2 - 4(16)(3)}}{2(16)}$

$= \dfrac{4 \pm \sqrt{-176}}{32} = \dfrac{4 \pm 4\sqrt{11}\,i}{32}$

$= \dfrac{1}{8} \pm \dfrac{\sqrt{11}}{8}i$

63.

65.

67.

69. The complex number 0 is in the Mandelbrot Set since for $c = 0$, the corresponding Mandelbrot sequence is 0, 0, 0, 0, 0, 0, ... which is bounded.

71. The complex number $\frac{1}{2}i$ is in the Mandelbrot Set since for $c = \frac{1}{2}i$, the corresponding Mandelbrot sequence is

$\frac{1}{2}i, \ -\frac{1}{4} + \frac{1}{2}i, \ -\frac{3}{16} + \frac{1}{4}i, \ -\frac{7}{256} + \frac{13}{32}i, \ \frac{-10{,}767}{65{,}536} + \frac{1957}{4096}i, \ -\frac{864{,}513{,}055}{4{,}294{,}967{,}296} + \frac{46{,}037{,}845}{134{,}217{,}728}i$

which is bounded. Or in decimal form

$0.5i, \ -0.25 + 0.5i, \ -0.1875 + 0.25i, \ -0.02734 + 0.40625i,$
$-0.164291 + 0.477783i, \ -0.201285 + 0.343009i.$

73. The complex number 1 is not in the Mandelbrot Set since for $c = 1$, the corresponding Mandelbrot sequence is 1, 2, 5, 26, 677, 458,330 which is unbounded.

75. $2^3 = 8$

$$(-1 + \sqrt{3}\,i)^3 = (-1)^3 + 3(-1)^2(\sqrt{3}\,i) + 3(-1)(\sqrt{3}\,i)^2 + (\sqrt{3}\,i)^3$$

$$= -1 + 3\sqrt{3}\,i + 9 - 3\sqrt{3}\,i = 8$$

$$(-1 - \sqrt{3}\,i)^3 = (-1)^3 - 3(-1)^2(\sqrt{3}\,i) + 3(-1)(\sqrt{3}\,i)^2 - (\sqrt{3}\,i)^3$$

$$= -1 - 3\sqrt{3}\,i + 9 + 3\sqrt{3}\,i = 8$$

All three numbers are cube roots of 8.

77. $(a + bi) + (a - bi) = (a + a) + (b - b)i$

$$= 2a + 0i$$

$$= 2a$$

which is a real number.

79. $(a + bi)(a - bi) = a^2 - abi + abi - (bi)^2$

$$= a^2 - b^2 i^2$$

$$= a^2 + b^2$$

which is a real number.

Section 3.6   Complex Zeros and The Fundamental Theorem of Algebra

---

- You should know that if f is a polynomial of degree $n > 0$, then f has exactly n zeros (roots) in the complex number system.

- You should know that if $a + bi$ is a complex zero of a polynomial f, with real coefficients, then $a - bi$ is also a complex zero of f.

- You should know the difference between a factor that is irreducible over the rationals (such as $x^2 - 7$) and a factor that is irreducible over the reals (such as $x^2 + 9$).

---

1. $f(x) = x^2 + 25$
Zeros: $x = \pm 5i$
$f(x) = (x + 5i)(x - 5i)$

3. $h(x) = x^2 - 4x + 1$
Zeros: $x = \dfrac{4 \pm \sqrt{12}}{2} = 2 \pm \sqrt{3}$
$h(x) = (x - 2 + \sqrt{3})(x - 2 - \sqrt{3})$

5. $f(x) = x^4 - 81$
Zeros: $x = \pm 3, \ \pm 3i$
$f(x) = (x + 3)(x - 3)(x + 3i)(x - 3i)$

7. $f(z) = z^2 - 2z + 2$
Zeros: $z = \dfrac{2 \pm \sqrt{4}\,i}{2} = 1 \pm i$
$f(z) = (z - 1 + i)(z - 1 - i)$

9. $f(t) = t^3 - 3t^2 - 15t + 125$

$$
\begin{array}{r|rrrr}
-5 & 1 & -3 & -15 & 125 \\
   &   & -5 & 40 & -125 \\
\hline
   & 1 & -8 & 25 & 0
\end{array}
$$

Zeros: $t = -5, \ \dfrac{8 \pm \sqrt{36}\,i}{2} = 4 \pm 3i$
$f(t) = (t + 5)(t - 4 - 3i)(t - 4 + 3i)$

11. $f(x) = 16x^3 - 20x^2 - 4x + 15$

$$
\begin{array}{r|rrrr}
-\frac{3}{4} & 16 & -20 & -4 & 15 \\
   &   & -12 & 24 & -15 \\
\hline
   & 16 & -32 & 20 & 0
\end{array}
$$

Zeros: $x = -\dfrac{3}{4}, \ \dfrac{32 \pm \sqrt{256}\,i}{32} = 1 \pm \dfrac{1}{2}i$
$f(x) = (4x + 3)(2x - 2 + i)(2x - 2 - i)$

13. $f(x) = 5x^3 - 9x^2 + 28x + 6$

$$
\begin{array}{r|rrrr}
-\frac{1}{5} & 5 & -9 & 28 & 6 \\
 & & -1 & 2 & -6 \\
\hline
 & 5 & -10 & 30 & 0
\end{array}
$$

$x = -\dfrac{1}{5}, \quad \dfrac{10 \pm \sqrt{500}\,i}{10} = 1 \pm \sqrt{5}\,i$

$f(x) = (5x + 1)(x - 1 + \sqrt{5}\,i)(x - 1 - \sqrt{5}\,i)$

15. $f(x) = x^4 + 10x^2 + 9$

$\qquad = (x^2 + 9)(x^2 + 1)$

Zeros: $x = \pm i,\ \pm 3i$

$\qquad f(x) = (x + i)(x - i)(x + 3i)(x - 3i)$

17. $g(x) = x^4 - 4x^3 + 8x^2 - 16x + 16$

$$
\begin{array}{r|rrrrr}
2 & 1 & -4 & 8 & -16 & 16 \\
 & & 2 & -4 & 8 & -16 \\
\hline
2 & 1 & -2 & 4 & -8 & 0 \\
 & & 2 & 0 & 8 & \\
\hline
 & 1 & 0 & 4 & 0 &
\end{array}
$$

Zeros: $x = 2,\ \pm 2i$

$g(x) = (x - 2)^2(x + 2i)(x - 2i)$

19. $f(x) = 2x^4 + 5x^3 + 4x^2 + 5x + 2$

$\qquad = 2x^4 + 5x^3 + 2x^2 + 2x^2 + 5x + 2$

$\qquad = x^2(2x^2 + 5x + 2) + (2x^2 + 5x + 2)$

$\qquad = (x^2 + 1)(2x^2 + 5x + 2)$

Zeros: $x = \pm i$

$\qquad x = \dfrac{-5 \pm \sqrt{9}}{4} = -2,\ -\dfrac{1}{2}$

$\qquad f(x) = (2x + 1)(x + 2)(x + i)(x - i)$

21. $f(x) = (x - 1)(x - 5i)(x + 5i)$

$\qquad = (x - 1)(x^2 + 25)$

$\qquad = x^3 - x^2 + 25x - 25$

23. $f(x) = (x - 2)(x - 4 - i)(x - 4 + i)$

$\qquad = (x - 2)(x^2 - 8x + 17)$

$\qquad = x^3 - 10x^2 + 33x - 34$

25. $f(x) = (x - i)(x + i)(x - 6i)(x + 6i) = (x^2 + 1)(x^2 + 36) = x^4 + 37x^2 + 36$

27. $f(x) = (x + 5)^2(x - 1 - \sqrt{3}\,i)(x - 1 + \sqrt{3}\,i)$

$\qquad = (x^2 + 10x + 25)(x^2 - 2x + 4) = x^4 + 8x^3 + 9x^2 - 10x + 100$

29. $f(x) = (4x - 3)(x + 2)(2x + 1 - 2i)(2x + 1 + 2i)$

$\qquad = (4x^2 + 5x - 6)(4x^2 + 4x + 5) = 16x^4 + 36x^3 + 16x^2 + x - 30$

31. $f(x) = x^4 + 6x^2 - 27$

(a) $f(x) = (x^2 + 9)(x^2 - 3)$

(b) $f(x) = (x^2 + 9)(x + \sqrt{3})(x - \sqrt{3})$

(c) $f(x) = (x + 3i)(x - 3i)(x + \sqrt{3})(x - \sqrt{3})$

33. $f(x) = x^4 - 4x^3 + 5x^2 - 2x - 6$

(a) $f(x) = (x^2 - 2x - 2)(x^2 - 2x + 3)$

(b) $f(x) = (x - 1 - \sqrt{3})(x - 1 + \sqrt{3})(x^2 - 2x + 3)$

(c) $f(x) = (x - 1 - \sqrt{3})(x - 1 + \sqrt{3})(x - 1 - \sqrt{2}\,i)(x - 1 + \sqrt{2}\,i)$

35.

$5i$	2	3	50	75
		$10i$	$-50 + 15i$	-75
$-5i$	2	$3 + 10i$	$15i$	0
		$-10i$	$-15i$	
	2	3	0	

Zeros: $-\frac{3}{2}$, $\pm 5i$

Since $5i$ is a zero, so is $-5i$. Using a graphing utility, we can determine that the real zero is -1.50.

37.

$2i$	2	-1	7	-4	-4
		$4i$	$-8 - 2i$	$4 - 2i$	4
$-2i$	2	$-1 + 4i$	$-1 - 2i$	$-2i$	0
		$-4i$	$2i$	$2i$	
1	2	-1	-1	0	
		2	1		
	2	1	0		

Zeros: $-\frac{1}{2}$, 1, $\pm 2i$

Since $2i$ is a zero, so is $-2i$. Using a graphing utility, we can determine that the real zeros are -0.50 and 1.00.

39.

$-3 + i$	4	23	34	-10
		$-12 + 4i$	$-37 - i$	10
$-3 - i$	4	$11 + 4i$	$-3 - i$	0
		$-12 - 4i$	$3 + i$	
	4	-1	0	

Zeros: $\frac{1}{4}$, $-3 \pm i$

41.

$-3 + \sqrt{2}\,i$	1	2	-9	-20	44
		$-3 + \sqrt{2}\,i$	$1 - 4\sqrt{2}\,i$	$32 + 4\sqrt{2}\,i$	-44
$-3 - \sqrt{2}\,i$	1	$-1 + \sqrt{2}\,i$	$-8 - 4\sqrt{2}\,i$	$12 + 4\sqrt{2}\,i$	0
		$-3 - \sqrt{2}\,i$	$12 + 4\sqrt{2}\,i$	$-12 - 4\sqrt{2}\,i$	
	1	-4	4	0	

Zeros: 2, $-3 \pm \sqrt{2}\,i$

43.

$$\dfrac{1-\sqrt{5}i}{2}\ \Big|\ \begin{array}{cccc} 8 & -14 & 18 & -9 \\[4pt] & 4-4\sqrt{5}i & -15+3\sqrt{5}i & 9 \end{array}$$

$$\dfrac{1+\sqrt{5}i}{2}\ \Big|\ \begin{array}{cccc} 8 & -10-4\sqrt{5}i & 3+3\sqrt{5}i & 0 \\[4pt] & 4+4\sqrt{5}i & -3-3\sqrt{5}i & \end{array}$$

$$\begin{array}{ccc} 8 & -6 & 0 \end{array}$$

Zeros: $\dfrac{3}{4},\ \dfrac{1}{2}\pm\dfrac{\sqrt{5}}{2}i$

Since $\dfrac{1-\sqrt{5}i}{2}$ is a zero, so is $\dfrac{1+\sqrt{5}i}{2}$. Using a graphing utility, we can determine that the real zero is 0.75.

45.

$$-16t^2+48t = 64, \quad 0 \le t \le 3$$

$$-16t^2+48t-64 \doteq 0$$

$$t = \dfrac{-48\pm\sqrt{1792}i}{-32}$$

Since this results in imaginary roots, the ball will never reach a height of 64 feet. Verifying this with a graphing utility, we can graph $y_1 = h = -16t^2 + 48t$ and $y_2 = 64$ which do not intersect.

47. $f(x) = (x - \sqrt{b}i)(x + \sqrt{b}i)$

$$= x^2 + b$$

Chapter 3   Review Exercises

1. $y = \left(x + \dfrac{3}{2}\right)^2 + 1$

When $x = 0$, $y = \left(0 + \dfrac{3}{2}\right)^2 + 1 = \dfrac{13}{4}$.

Vertex: $\left(-\dfrac{3}{2},\ 1\right)$

Intercept: $\left(0,\ \dfrac{13}{4}\right)$

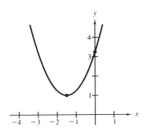

3. $y = \dfrac{1}{3}(x^2 + 5x - 4)$

$ = \dfrac{1}{3}\left(x^2 + 5x + \dfrac{25}{4}\right) - \dfrac{4}{3} - \dfrac{25}{12}$

$ = \dfrac{1}{3}\left(x + \dfrac{5}{2}\right)^2 - \dfrac{41}{12}$

When $x = 0$, $y = \dfrac{1}{3}\left(0 + \dfrac{5}{2}\right)^2 - \dfrac{41}{12} = -\dfrac{4}{3}$.

When $y = 0$,

$0 = \dfrac{1}{3}\left(x + \dfrac{5}{2}\right)^2 - \dfrac{41}{12} \Rightarrow x = \dfrac{-5 \pm \sqrt{41}}{2}$.

Vertex: $\left(-\dfrac{5}{2},\ -\dfrac{41}{12}\right)$

Intercepts: $\left(0,\ -\dfrac{4}{3}\right),\ \left(\dfrac{-5 \pm \sqrt{41}}{2},\ 0\right)$

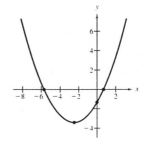

5. $f(x) = a(x - 1)^2 - 4$

$ -3 = a(2 - 1)^2 - 4$

$ 1 = a$

$ f(x) = (x - 1)^2 - 4$

7. $g(x) = x^2 - 2x$

$ = (x^2 - 2x + 1) - 1$

$ = (x - 1)^2 - 1$

Minimum: $(1,\ -1)$

9. $f(x) = 6x - x^2$

$ = -(x^2 - 6x + 9) + 9$

$ = -(x - 3)^2 + 9$

Maximum: $(3,\ 9)$

11. $f(t) = -2t^2 + 4t + 1$

$ = -2(t^2 - 2t + 1) + 1 + 2$

$ = -2(t - 1)^2 + 3$

Maximum: $(1,\ 3)$

13. $h(x) = x^2 + 5x - 4$

$$= \left(x^2 + 5x + \frac{25}{4}\right) - 4 - \frac{25}{4}$$

$$= \left(x + \frac{5}{2}\right)^2 - \frac{41}{4}$$

Minimum: $\left(-\frac{5}{2}, -\frac{41}{4}\right)$

15. $x + 2y - 6 = 0 \quad \Rightarrow \quad x = 6 - 2y$

$$A = xy = (6 - 2y)y = 6y - 2y^2$$

$$= -2\left(y^2 - 3y + \frac{9}{4}\right) + \frac{9}{2}$$

$$= -2\left(y - \frac{3}{2}\right)^2 + \frac{9}{2}$$

A is a maximum when

$x = 6 - 2\left(\frac{3}{2}\right) = 3$ and $y = \frac{3}{2}$.

17. $R = 900x - 0.1x^2$

Using the zoom and trace features, the number of units that produces a maximum revenue is $x = 4500$.

19. (50, 540), (49, 570)

$$p - 540 = \frac{570 - 540}{49 - 50}(x - 50)$$

$$p = -30(x - 50) + 540 = -30x + 1500 + 540 = -30x + 2040$$

$$P = xp - C$$

$$P = x(-30x + 2040) - 18x = -30x^2 + 2022x$$

Graphing P on the viewing rectangle $[0, 60] \times [0, 40{,}000]$, and using the zoom and trace features, we see that $x = 33.70$ produces a maximum profit. Or, completing the square

$$P = -30\left[x^2 - \frac{337}{5}x + \left(\frac{337}{10}\right)^2\right] + \frac{(337)^2}{100} \cdot 30 = -30\left(x - \frac{337}{10}\right)^2 + \frac{340{,}707}{10}.$$

P is maximum when $x = 33.7$. Therefore, to obtain a maximum profit, $p = -30(33.7) + 2040 = \$1029$ should be charged for rent.

21. $f(x) = -x^2 + 6x + 9$

Since the degree is even and the leading coefficient is negative, the graph falls to the left and falls to the right.

23. $g(x) = \frac{3}{4}(x^4 + 3x^2 + 2)$

Since the degree is even and the leading coefficient is positive, the graph rises to the left and rises to the right.

25. $f(x) = -(x-2)^3$

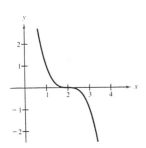

27. $g(x) = x^4 - x^3 - 2x^2$
$$= x^2(x^2 - x - 2)$$
$$= x^2(x-2)(x+1)$$

29. $f(t) = t^3 - 3t$
$$= t(t^2 - 3)$$
$$= t(t + \sqrt{3})(t - \sqrt{3})$$

31. $f(x) = x(x+3)^2$

33.
$$
\begin{array}{r}
8x \;+\; 5 \\
3x - 2 \overline{\smash{)}\; 24x^2 - x - 8} \\
\underline{24x^2 - 16x} \\
15x - 8 \\
\underline{15x - 10} \\
2
\end{array}
$$

$$\frac{24x^2 - x - 8}{3x - 2} = 8x + 5 + \frac{2}{3x - 2}$$

35.
$$
\begin{array}{r}
x^2 - 2 \\
x^2 - 1 \overline{\smash{)}\; x^4 - 3x^2 + 2} \\
\underline{x^4 - x^2} \\
-2x^2 + 2 \\
\underline{-2x^2 + 2} \\
0
\end{array}
$$

$$\frac{x^4 - 3x^2 + 2}{x^2 - 1} = x^2 - 2$$

37.
$$
\begin{array}{r}
x^2 - 3x \;+\; 2 \\
x^2 + 2 \overline{\smash{)}\; x^4 - 3x^3 + 4x^2 - 6x + 3} \\
\underline{x^4 + 2x^2} \\
-3x^3 + 2x^2 - 6x \\
\underline{-3x^3 - 6x} \\
2x^2 + 3 \\
\underline{2x^2 + 4} \\
-1
\end{array}
$$

$$\frac{x^4 - 3x^3 + 4x^2 - 6x + 3}{x^2 + 2}$$

$$= x^2 - 3x + 2 - \frac{1}{x^2 + 2}$$

39.

$$
\begin{array}{r|rrrrr}
2 & 0.25 & -4 & 0 & 0 & 0 \\
  &   & 0.5 & -7 & -14 & -28 \\
\hline
  & 0.25 & -3.5 & -7 & -14 & -28 \\
\end{array}
$$

$$\frac{0.25x^4 - 4x^3}{x - 2}$$

$$= 0.25x^3 - 3.5x^2 - 7x - 14 - \frac{28}{x-2}$$

41.

$$
\begin{array}{r|rrrr}
1+2i & 2 & -5 & 12 & -5 \\
     &   & 2+4i & -11-2i & 5 \\
\hline
     & 2 & -3+4i & 1-2i & 0 \\
\end{array}
$$

$$\frac{2x^3 - 5x^2 + 12x - 5}{x - (1+2i)}$$

$$= 2x^2 + (-3+4i)x + (1-2i)$$

43. $f(x) = 2x^3 + 3x^2 - 20x - 21$

(a) $x = 4$ is not a zero.

$$
\begin{array}{r|rrrr}
4 & 2 & 3 & -20 & -21 \\
  &   & 8 & 44 & 96 \\
\hline
  & 2 & 11 & 24 & 75 \\
\end{array}
$$

(b) $x = -1$ is a zero.

$$
\begin{array}{r|rrrr}
-1 & 2 & 3 & -20 & -21 \\
   &   & -2 & -1 & 21 \\
\hline
   & 2 & 1 & -21 & 0 \\
\end{array}
$$

(c) $x = -\frac{7}{2}$ is a zero.

$$
\begin{array}{r|rrrr}
-\frac{7}{2} & 2 & 3 & -20 & -21 \\
             &   & -7 & 14 & 21 \\
\hline
             & 2 & -4 & -6 & 0 \\
\end{array}
$$

(d) $x = 0$ is not a zero.

$$
\begin{array}{r|rrrr}
0 & 2 & 3 & -20 & -21 \\
  &   & 0 & 0 & 0 \\
\hline
  & 2 & 3 & -20 & -21 \\
\end{array}
$$

45. $f(x) = 2x^3 + 7x^2 - 18x - 30$

(a) $x = 1$ is not a zero.

$$
\begin{array}{r|rrrr}
1 & 2 & 7 & -18 & -30 \\
  &   & 2 & 9 & -9 \\
\hline
  & 2 & 9 & -9 & -39 \\
\end{array}
$$

(b) $x = \frac{5}{2}$ is a zero.

$$
\begin{array}{r|rrrr}
\frac{5}{2} & 2 & 7 & -18 & -30 \\
            &   & 5 & 30 & 30 \\
\hline
            & 2 & 12 & 12 & 0 \\
\end{array}
$$

(c) $x = -3 + \sqrt{3}$ is a zero.

$$
\begin{array}{r|rrrr}
-3+\sqrt{3} & 2 & 7 & -18 & -30 \\
            &   & -6+2\sqrt{3} & 3-5\sqrt{3} & 30 \\
\hline
            & 2 & 1+2\sqrt{3} & -15-5\sqrt{3} & 0 \\
\end{array}
$$

(d) $x = 0$ is not a zero.

$$
\begin{array}{r|rrrr}
0 & 2 & 7 & -18 & -30 \\
  &   & 0 & 0 & 0 \\
\hline
  & 2 & 7 & -18 & -30 \\
\end{array}
$$

47. $g(x) = 2x^4 - 17x^3 + 58x^2 - 77x + 26$

(a) -2

	2	-17	58	-77	26
		-4	42	-200	554
	2	-21	100	-277	580

$= g(-2)$

(b) $\frac{1}{2}$

	2	-17	58	-77	26
		1	-8	25	-26
	2	-16	50	-52	0

$= g\left(\frac{1}{2}\right)$

49. $f(x) = x^4 + 10x^3 - 24x^2 + 20x + 44$

(a) -3

	1	10	-24	20	44
		-3	-21	135	-465
	1	7	-45	155	-421

$= f(-3)$

(b) $\sqrt{2}\,i$

	1	10	-24	20	44
		$\sqrt{2}\,i$	$-2 + 10\sqrt{2}\,i$	$-20 - 26\sqrt{2}\,i$	52
	1	$10 + \sqrt{2}\,i$	$-26 + 10\sqrt{2}\,i$	$-26\sqrt{2}\,i$	96

$= f(\sqrt{2}\,i)$

51. $-(6 - 2i) + (-8 + 3i) = -6 - 8 + (2 + 3)i = -14 + 5i$

53. $5i(13 - 8i) = 65i - 40i^2$

$\qquad = 40 + 65i$

55. $\dfrac{6 + i}{i} = \dfrac{6 + i}{i} \cdot \dfrac{-i}{-i}$

$\qquad = \dfrac{-6i + 1}{1}$

$\qquad = 1 - 6i$

57. $f(x) = (x + 1)(x + 1)(3x - 1)(2x + 1)$

$\qquad = (x^2 + 2x + 1)(6x^2 + x - 1)$

$\qquad = 6x^4 + 13x^3 + 7x^2 - x - 1$

59. $f(x) = (3x - 2)(x - 4)(x - \sqrt{3}i)(x + \sqrt{3}i)$

$\qquad = (3x^2 - 14x + 8)(x^2 + 3)$

$\qquad = 3x^4 - 14x^3 + 17x^2 - 42x + 24$

61. $g(x) = 5x^3 + 3x^2 - 6x + 9$

Sign variations; 2, positive zeros: 2 or 0

$g(-x) = -5x^3 + 3x^2 + 6x + 9$

Sign variations; 1, negative zeros: 1

63. $f(x) = -4x^3 + 8x^2 - 3x + 15$

Possible rational zeros:

$\dfrac{\pm 1, \ \pm 3, \ \pm 5, \ \pm 15}{\pm 1, \ \pm 2, \ \pm 4} = \pm 1, \ \pm 3, \ \pm 5, \ \pm 15,$

$\qquad \pm \dfrac{1}{2}, \ \pm \dfrac{3}{2}, \ \pm \dfrac{5}{2}, \ \pm \dfrac{15}{2},$

$\qquad \pm \dfrac{1}{4}, \ \pm \dfrac{3}{4}, \ \pm \dfrac{5}{4}, \ \pm \dfrac{15}{4}$

65. $f(x) = 4x^3 - 11x^2 + 10x - 3$

1	4	−11	10	−3
		4	−7	3
	4	−7	3	0

Zeros: $\frac{3}{4}$, 1

67. $f(x) = 6x^3 - 5x^2 + 24x - 20$

$\frac{5}{6}$	6	−5	24	−20
		5	0	20
	6	0	24	0

Zeros: $\frac{5}{6}$, $\pm 2i$

69. $f(x) = 6x^4 - 25x^3 + 14x^2 + 27x - 18$

−1	6	−25	14	27	−18
		−6	31	−45	18
3	6	−31	45	−18	0
		18	−39	18	
	6	−13	6	0	

Zeros: -1, $\frac{2}{3}$, $\frac{3}{2}$, 3

71. $f(x) = x^4 + 2x - 1$

(a) ± 1

(b)

(c) -1.40, 0.47

73. $h(x) = x^3 - 6x^2 + 12x - 10$

(a) ± 1, ± 2, ± 5, ± 10

(b)

(c) 3.26

75. $3x^3 - 22{,}500x + 250{,}000 = 0$

Using a graphing utility, we find $x = 11.30$.

CHAPTER 4

Rational Functions and Conic Sections

Section 4.1   Rational Functions and Asymptotes

■ You should know the following basic facts about rational functions.

(a) A function of the form $f(x) = P(x)/Q(x)$, $Q(x) \neq 0$, where $P(x)$ and $Q(x)$ are polynomials, is called a rational function.

(b) The domain of a rational function is the set of all real numbers except those which make the denominator zero.

(c) If $f(x) = P(x)/Q(x)$ is in reduced form, and a is a value such that $Q(a) = 0$, then the line $x = a$ is a vertical asymptote of the graph of f.

(d) The line $y = b$ is a horizontal asymptote of the graph of f if $f(x) \to b$ as $x \to \infty$ or $x \to -\infty$.

■ Be able to graph rational functions with your graphing utility.

1. $f(x) = \dfrac{1}{x - 2}$

(a)

x	1	1.5	1.9	1.99	1.999
$f(x)$	-1	-2	-10	-100	-1000

x	3	2.5	2.1	2.01	2.001
$f(x)$	1	2	10	100	1000

x	3	5	10	100	1000
$f(x)$	1	0.3333	0.125	0.0102	0.0010

(b) Vertical asymptote: $x = 2$
Horizontal asymptote: $y = 0$

(c) Domain: $x \neq 2$

3. $f(x) = \dfrac{3x}{|x - 2|}$

(a)

x	1	1.5	1.9	1.99	1.999
$f(x)$	3	9	57	597	5997

x	3	2.5	2.1	2.01	2.001
$f(x)$	9	15	63	603	6003

x	3	5	10	100	1000
$f(x)$	9	5	3.75	3.0612	3.0060

(b) Vertical asymptote: $x = 2$
   Horizontal asymptote: $y = \pm 3$

(c) Domain: $x \neq 2$

5. $f(x) = \dfrac{3x^2}{x^2 - 4}$

(a)

x	1	1.5	1.9	1.99	1.999
$f(x)$	-1	-3.8571	-27.7692	-297.752	-2997.75

x	3	2.5	2.1	2.01	2.001
$f(x)$	5.4	8.3333	32.2683	302.2519	3002.25

x	3	5	10	100	1000
$f(x)$	5.4	3.5714	3.125	3.0012	3.0000

(b) Vertical asymptote:
   $x = \pm 2$
   Horizontal asymptote:
   $y = 3$

(c) Domain: $x \neq \pm 2$

7. $f(x) = \dfrac{1}{x^2}$

Domain: all real numbers except 0
Vertical asymptote: $x = 0$
Horizontal asymptote: $y = 0$

9. $f(x) = \dfrac{2 + x}{2 - x} = \dfrac{x + 2}{-x + 2}$

Domain: all real numbers except 2
Vertical asymptote: $x = 2$
Horizontal asymptote: $y = -1$

11. $f(x) = \dfrac{x^3}{x^2 - 1} = x + \dfrac{x}{x^2 - 1}$

Domain: all real numbers except 1 and -1
Vertical asymptotes: $x = \pm 1$
No horizontal asymptote
(Slant asymptote: $y = x$)

13. $f(x) = \dfrac{3x^2 + 1}{x^2 + 9}$

Domain: all real numbers
Horizontal asymptote: $y = 3$

15. $f(x) = \dfrac{2}{x+1}$

Vertical asymptote:
$x = -1$
Horizontal asymptote:
$y = 0$
y-intercept: $(0, 2)$
Graph (f)

```
RANGE
Xmin=-5
Xmax=3
Xscl=1
Ymin=-3
Ymax=3
Yscl=1
```

17. $f(x) = \dfrac{x+1}{x}$

Vertical asymptote:
$x = 0$
Horizontal asymptote:
$y = 1$
x-intercept: $(-1, 0)$
Graph (a)

```
RANGE
Xmin=-3
Xmax=3
Xscl=1
Ymin=-1
Ymax=3
Yscl=1
```

19. $f(x) = \dfrac{x-2}{x-1}$

Vertical asymptote:
$x = 1$
Horizontal asymptote:
$y = 1$
x-intercept: $(2, 0)$
y-intercept: $(0, 2)$
Graph (c)

```
RANGE
Xmin=-2
Xmax=4
Xscl=1
Ymin=-1
Ymax=3
Yscl=1
```

21. $f(x) = \dfrac{x^2 - 4}{x + 2}$, $g(x) = x - 2$

(a) Domain of f: $x \neq -2$
    Domain of g: all x
(b) No vertical asymptote of f
(d) Some viewing rectangles will show the difference in domains. For instance, on the TI–81, use the standard viewing rectangle.

(c)

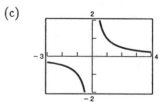

23. $f(x) = \dfrac{x-3}{x^2 - 3x}$, $g(x) = \dfrac{1}{x}$

(a) Domain of f: $x \neq 0, 3$
    Domain of g: $x \neq 0$
(b) f has a vertical asymptote at $x = 0$.
(d) Some viewing rectangles will show the difference in domains. For instance, on the TI–81, use the following range.

```
RANGE
Xmin=-4.5
Xmax=5
Xscl=1
Ymin=-2
Ymax=2
Yscl=1
```

(c)

25. (a) $C = \dfrac{255(10)}{100 - 10} = 28\frac{1}{3}$

     The cost would be $28\frac{1}{3}$ million.

(b) $C = \dfrac{255(40)}{100 - 40} = 170$

     The cost would be \$170 million.

(c) $C = \dfrac{255(75)}{100 - 75} = 765$

     The cost would be \$765 million.

(d) No. The model is undefined for $p = 100$.

27. $N = \dfrac{10(5 + 3t)}{1 + 0.04t} = \dfrac{30t + 50}{0.04t + 1}$

(a) $N(5) \approx 167$ deer

     $N(10) = 250$ deer

     $N(25) = 400$ deer

(b) The herd is limited by a horizontal asymptote:

     $N = \dfrac{30}{0.04} = 750$ deer

     Verify this result by graphing N and $y = 750$ on the same viewing rectangle.

29. $P = \dfrac{0.5 + 0.9(n - 1)}{1 + 0.9(n - 1)}, \quad 0 < n$

(a)

n	1	2	3	4	5	6	7	8	9	10
P	0.50	0.74	0.82	0.86	0.89	0.91	0.92	0.93	0.94	0.95

(b) The percentage of correct responses is limited by a horizontal asymptote:

     $P = 0.9/0.9 = 1.0 = 100\%$. Verify this result by graphing P and $y = 1.0$ on the same viewing rectangle.

Section 4.2   Graphs of Rational Functions

■ You should know how to graph rational functions with a graphing utility.

■ Let $f(x) = p(x)/q(x)$ be a rational function, where $p(x)$ and $q(x)$ are polynomials with no common factors.

(a) The y-intercept (if any) is the value $f(0)$.

(b) The x-intercepts (if any) are the zeros of the numerator.

(c) The vertical asymptotes (if any) are the zeros of the denominator.

(d) The horizontal asymptote (if there is one) is the value that $f(x)$ approaches as x increases or decreases without bound.

■ You should be able to determine the behavior of the graph of a rational function between and beyond each x-intercept and vertical asymptote.

■ You should know how to determine whether or not a rational function has a slant asymptote.

1. $g(x) = f(x) + 1 = \dfrac{1}{x} + 1$

Vertical shift one unit upward

3. $g(x) = -f(x) = -\dfrac{1}{x}$

Reflection in the x-axis

5. $g(x) = f(x) - 2 = \dfrac{4}{x^2} - 2$

Vertical shift two units downward

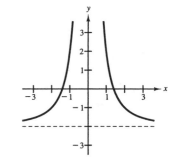

7. $g(x) = f(x - 2)$

$$= \frac{4}{(x - 2)^2}$$

Horizontal shift two units right

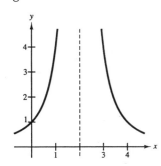

9. $g(x) = f(x + 2)$

$$= \frac{8}{(x + 2)^3}$$

Horizontal shift two units to the left

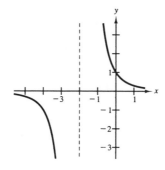

11. $g(x) = -f(x) = -\dfrac{8}{x^3}$

Reflection in the x-axis

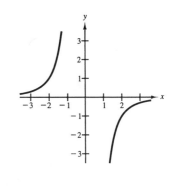

13. $f(x) = \dfrac{1}{x + 2}$

y-intercept: $\left(0, \frac{1}{2}\right)$
Vertical asymptote:
   $x = -2$
Horizontal asymptote:
   $y = 0$

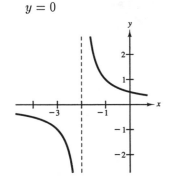

15. $h(x) = \dfrac{-1}{x + 2}$

y-intercept: $\left(0, -\frac{1}{2}\right)$
Vertical asymptote:
   $x = -2$
Horizontal asymptote:
   $y = 0$

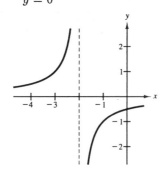

17. $C(x) = \dfrac{5 + 2x}{1 + x} = \dfrac{2x + 5}{x + 1}$

x-intercept: $\left(-\frac{5}{2}, 0\right)$
y-intercept: $(0, 5)$
Vertical asymptote:
   $x = -1$
Horizontal asymptote:
   $y = 2$

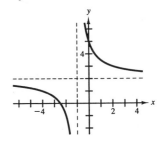

19. $g(x) = \dfrac{1}{x+2} + 2$

$= \dfrac{1 + 2(x+2)}{x+2}$

$= \dfrac{2x+5}{x+2}$

x-intercept: $\left(-\frac{5}{2}, 0\right)$
y-intercept: $\left(0, \frac{5}{2}\right)$
Vertical asymptote: $x = -2$
Horizontal asymptote: $y = 2$

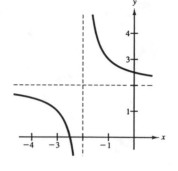

21. $f(x) = \dfrac{x^2}{x^2+9}$

Intercept: $(0, 0)$
Horizontal asymptote: $y = 1$
No vertical asymptotes
y-axis symmetry

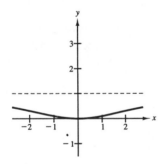

23. $h(x) = \dfrac{x^2}{x^2-9}$

Intercept: $(0, 0)$
Vertical asymptotes: $x = \pm 3$
Horizontal asymptote: $y = 1$
y-axis symmetry

25. $g(x) = -\dfrac{1}{(x-2)^2} + 3$

$= \dfrac{-1 + 3(x-2)^2}{(x-2)^2}$

$= \dfrac{3x^2 - 12x + 11}{(x-2)^2}$

Using the quadratic formula, we see
that the solutions to $3x^2 - 12x + 11$ are
$2 \pm \left(\sqrt{3}/3\right) \approx 2.577, 1.423$.

Intercepts: $\left(2 \pm \left(\sqrt{3}/3\right), 0\right)$, $(0, 2.75)$
Vertical asymptote: $x = 2$
Horizontal asymptote: $y = 3$

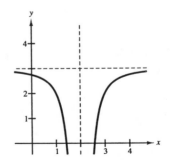

27. $f(x) = \dfrac{3x}{x^2 - x - 2}$

$\qquad = \dfrac{3x}{(x+1)(x-2)}$

Intercept: $(0, 0)$
Vertical asymptotes:
$\quad x = -1,\ 2$
Horizontal asymptote:
$\quad y = 0$

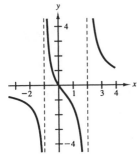

29. $f(x) = \dfrac{2 + x}{1 - x}$

Domain:
$\quad$ all real numbers $x \neq 1$
Range:
$\quad$ all real numbers $y \neq -1$

31. $f(t) = \dfrac{3t + 1}{t}$

Domain:
$\quad$ all real numbers $t \neq 0$
Range:
$\quad$ all real numbers $y \neq 3$

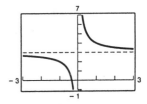

33. $h(t) = \dfrac{4}{t^2 + 1}$

Domain: all real numbers
Range: $0 < y \leq 4$

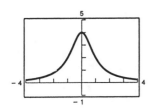

35. $f(x) = \dfrac{20x}{x^2 + 1} - \dfrac{1}{x}$

Domain:
$\quad$ all real numbers $x \neq 0$
Range: $-\infty < y < \infty$

37. $f(x) = \dfrac{2x^2 + 1}{x} = 2x + \dfrac{1}{x}$

Vertical asymptote:
$x = 0$
Slant asymptote: $y = 2x$
Origin symmetry

39. $g(x) = \dfrac{x^2 + 1}{x} = x + \dfrac{1}{x}$

Vertical asymptote:
   $x = 0$
Slant asymptote: $y = x$
Origin symmetry

41. $f(x) = \dfrac{x^3}{x^2 - 1}$

$= x + \dfrac{x}{x^2 - 1}$

Intercept: $(0, 0)$
Vertical asymptotes:
   $x = \pm 1$
Slant asymptote: $y = x$
Origin symmetry

43. $f(x) = \dfrac{x^2 - x + 1}{x - 1}$

$= x + \dfrac{1}{x - 1}$

y-intercept: $(0, -1)$
Vertical asymptote:
   $x = 1$
Slant asymptote: $y = x$

45. $f(x) = \dfrac{x^2 + 5x + 8}{x + 3}$

$= x + 2 + \dfrac{2}{x + 3}$

y-intercept: $\left(0, \dfrac{8}{3}\right)$
Vertical asymptote:
   $x = -3$
Slant asymptote:
   $y = x + 2$

47. $h(x) = \dfrac{6x}{\sqrt{x^2 + 1}}$

Notice that the graph
has two horizontal
asymptotes:
   $y = \pm 6$

49. $f(x) = \dfrac{4(x - 1)^2}{x^2 - 4x + 5}$

Notice that the graph
crosses the horizontal
asymptote $y = 4$.

51.

There is no vertical asymptote since

$$\frac{6 - 2x}{3 - x} = 2, \quad (x \neq 3).$$

53. $f(x) = \dfrac{3(x + 1)}{x^2 + x + 1}$

Relative maximum: $(0, \ 3)$
Relative minimum: $(-2, \ -1)$

55. (a) $C = \dfrac{\text{Amount of brine}}{\text{Number of gallons}}$

$= \dfrac{\text{Original brine} + \text{added brine}}{\text{Original gallons} + \text{added gallons}}$

$= \dfrac{(5/2) + (3/4)x}{10 + x}$

$= \dfrac{3x + 10}{4(x + 10)}$

(b) Since the tank holds 250 gallons,
$0 \leq x \leq 240.$

(c)

The rate of increase of brine gets
slower and approaches 0.75, or 75%.

57. (a) $(x - 2)(y - 4) = 30$ square inches of print $\Rightarrow$

$$y = \frac{30}{x - 2} + 4$$

$$= \frac{22 + 4x}{x - 2}$$

$$A = xy = x \left(\frac{22 + 4x}{x - 2} \right)$$

$$= \frac{2x(2x + 11)}{x - 2}$$

(b) Domain: $x > 2$

(c)

Minimum at $x = 5.87$ inches
and $y = 11.75$ inches

59. $C = 100 \left(\dfrac{200}{x^2} + \dfrac{x}{x + 30} \right)$, $1 \le x$

C is a minimum when $x = 40$.

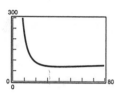

61. $C = \dfrac{3t^2 + t}{t^3 + 50}$, $0 \le t$

(a) Horizontal asymptote is $C = 0$ which means that the concentration tends to 0 as time goes on.

(b)

C is a maximum when $t = 4.5$ hours.

Section 4.3   Partial Fractions

■ You should know how to decompose a rational function $N(x)/D(x)$ into partial fractions.

(a) If the fraction is improper, divide to obtain
$$\frac{N(x)}{D(x)} = p(x) + \frac{N_1(x)}{D(x)}$$
where $p(x)$ is a polynomial.

(b) Factor the denominator completely into linear and irreducible (over the reals) quadratic factors.

(c) For each factor of the form $(px+q)^m$, the partial fraction decomposition includes the terms
$$\frac{A_1}{(px+q)} + \frac{A_2}{(px+q)^2} + \cdots + \frac{A_m}{(px+q)^m}.$$

(d) For each irreducible factor of the form $(ax^2+bx+c)^n$, the partial fraction decomposition includes the terms
$$\frac{B_1 x + C_1}{ax^2+bx+c} + \frac{B_2 x + C_2}{(ax^2+bx+c)^2} + \cdots + \frac{B_n x + C_n}{(ax^2+bx+c)^n}.$$

■ You should know how to determine the values of the constants in the numerators.

(a) Set $\dfrac{N_1(x)}{D(x)}$ = partial fraction decomposition.

(b) Multiply both sides by $D(x)$. This is called the basic equation.

(c) For distinct linear factors, substitute the roots of the distinct linear factors into the basic equation.

(d) For repeated linear factors, use the coefficients found in part (c) to rewrite the basic equation. Then use other values of x to solve for the remaining coefficients.

(e) For quadratic factors, expand the basic equation, collect like terms, and then equate the coefficients of like powers.

■ You should know how to verify a partial fraction decomposition using a graphing utility.

1. $\dfrac{1}{x^2-1} = \dfrac{A}{x+1} + \dfrac{B}{x-1}$

$1 = A(x-1) + B(x+1)$

Let $x = -1$: $1 = -2A \Rightarrow A = -\frac{1}{2}$.

Let $x = 1$: $1 = 2B \Rightarrow B = \frac{1}{2}$.

$$\dfrac{1}{x^2-1} = \dfrac{1}{2}\left[\dfrac{1}{x-1} - \dfrac{1}{x+1}\right]$$

3. $\dfrac{1}{x^2+x} = \dfrac{A}{x} + \dfrac{B}{x+1}$

$1 = A(x+1) + Bx$

Let $x = 0$: $1 = A$.

Let $x = -1$: $1 = -B \Rightarrow B = -1$.

$$\dfrac{1}{x^2+x} = \dfrac{1}{x} - \dfrac{1}{x+1}$$

5. $\dfrac{1}{2x^2+x} = \dfrac{A}{2x+1} + \dfrac{B}{x}$

$1 = Ax + B(2x+1)$

Let $x = -\frac{1}{2}$: $1 = -\frac{1}{2}A \Rightarrow A = -2$.

Let $x = 0$: $1 = B$.

$$\dfrac{1}{2x^2+x} = \dfrac{1}{x} - \dfrac{2}{2x+1}$$

7. $\dfrac{3}{x^2+x-2} = \dfrac{A}{x-1} + \dfrac{B}{x+2}$

$3 = A(x+2) + B(x-1)$

Let $x = 1$: $3 = 3A \Rightarrow A = 1$.

Let $x = -2$: $3 = -3B \Rightarrow B = -1$.

$$\dfrac{3}{x^2+x-2} = \dfrac{1}{x-1} - \dfrac{1}{x+2}$$

9. $\dfrac{5-x}{2x^2+x-1} = \dfrac{A}{2x-1} + \dfrac{B}{x+1}$

$-x+5 = A(x+1) + B(2x-1)$

Let $x = \frac{1}{2}$: $\frac{9}{2} = \frac{3}{2}A \Rightarrow A = 3$.

Let $x = -1$: $6 = -3B \Rightarrow B = -2$.

$$\dfrac{5-x}{2x^2+x-1} = \dfrac{3}{2x-1} - \dfrac{2}{x+1}$$

11. $\dfrac{x^2+12x+12}{x^3-4x} = \dfrac{A}{x} + \dfrac{B}{x+2} + \dfrac{C}{x-2}$

$x^2+12x+12 = A(x+2)(x-2) + Bx(x-2) + Cx(x+2)$

Let $x = 0$: $12 = -4A \Rightarrow A = -3$.

Let $x = -2$: $-8 = 8B \Rightarrow B = -1$.

Let $x = 2$: $40 = 8C \Rightarrow C = 5$.

$$\dfrac{x^2+12x+12}{x^3-4x} = -\dfrac{3}{x} - \dfrac{1}{x+2} + \dfrac{5}{x-2}$$

13. $\dfrac{4x^2 + 2x - 1}{x^2(x+1)} = \dfrac{A}{x} + \dfrac{B}{x^2} + \dfrac{C}{x+1}$

$4x^2 + 2x - 1 = Ax(x+1) + B(x+1) + Cx^2$

Let $x = 0$: $-1 = B$.

Let $x = -1$: $1 = C$.

Let $x = 1$: $5 = 2A + 2B + C$

$$5 = 2A - 2 + 1$$

$$6 = 2A$$

$$3 = A$$

$$\dfrac{4x^2 + 2x - 1}{x^2(x+1)} = \dfrac{3}{x} - \dfrac{1}{x^2} + \dfrac{1}{x+1}$$

15. $\dfrac{x-1}{x^3 + x^2} = \dfrac{A}{x} + \dfrac{B}{x^2} + \dfrac{C}{x+1}$

$x - 1 = Ax(x+1) + B(x+1) + Cx^2$

Let $x = -1$: $-2 = C$.

Let $x = 0$: $-1 = B$.

Let $x = 1$: $0 = 2A + 2B + C$

$$0 = 2A - 2 - 2$$

$$2 = A$$

$$\dfrac{x-1}{x^3 + x^2} = \dfrac{2}{x} - \dfrac{1}{x^2} - \dfrac{2}{x+1}$$

17. $\dfrac{3x}{(x-3)^2} = \dfrac{A}{x-3} + \dfrac{B}{(x-3)^2}$

$3x = A(x-3) + B$

Let $x = 3$: $9 = B$.

Let $x = 0$: $0 = -3A + B$

$$0 = -3A + 9$$

$$3 = A$$

$$\dfrac{3x}{(x-3)^2} = \dfrac{3}{x-3} + \dfrac{9}{(x-3)^2}$$

19. $\dfrac{x^2 - 1}{x(x^2+1)} = \dfrac{A}{x} + \dfrac{Bx + C}{x^2+1}$

$x^2 - 1 = A(x^2+1) + (Bx+C)x$

Let $x = 0$: $-1 = A$.

$$x^2 - 1 = Ax^2 + A + Bx^2 + Cx$$

$$= -x^2 - 1 + Bx^2 + Cx$$

$$= x^2(B-1) + Cx - 1$$

Equating coefficients of like powers:

$$1 = B - 1$$

$$2 = B \quad \text{and} \quad 0 = C$$

$$\dfrac{x^2 - 1}{x(x^2+1)} = -\dfrac{1}{x} + \dfrac{2x}{x^2+1}$$

21. $\dfrac{x^2}{x^4 - 2x^2 - 8} = \dfrac{x^2}{(x^2 - 4)(x^2 + 2)} = \dfrac{A}{x + 2} + \dfrac{B}{x - 2} + \dfrac{Cx + D}{x^2 + 2}$

$x^2 = A(x - 2)(x^2 + 2) + B(x + 2)(x^2 + 2) + (Cx + D)(x^2 - 4)$

Let $x = -2$: $4 = -24A \Rightarrow A = -\frac{1}{6}$.

Let $x = 2$: $4 = 24B \Rightarrow B = \frac{1}{6}$.

$$x^2 = -\frac{1}{6}(x - 2)(x^2 + 2) + \frac{1}{6}(x + 2)(x^2 + 2) + (Cx + D)(x^2 - 4)$$

$$x^2 = -\frac{1}{6}x^3 + \frac{1}{3}x^2 - \frac{1}{3}x + \frac{2}{3} + \frac{1}{6}x^3 + \frac{1}{3}x^2 + \frac{1}{3}x + \frac{2}{3} + Cx^3 + Dx^2 - 4Cx - 4D$$

$$x^2 = Cx^3 + \left(\frac{2}{3} + D\right)x^2 - 4Cx + \left(\frac{4}{3} - 4D\right)$$

Equating coefficients of like powers:

$$C \Rightarrow 0$$

$$1 = \frac{2}{3} + D \Rightarrow D = \frac{1}{3}$$

$$\frac{x^2}{x^4 - 2x^2 - 8} = \frac{1}{6(x - 2)} - \frac{1}{6(x + 2)} + \frac{1}{3(x^2 + 2)}$$

23. $\dfrac{x}{16x^4 - 1} = \dfrac{A}{2x + 1} + \dfrac{B}{2x - 1} + \dfrac{Cx + D}{4x^2 + 1}$

$x = A(2x - 1)(4x^2 + 1) + B(2x + 1)(4x^2 + 1) + (Cx + D)(2x + 1)(2x - 1)$

Let $x = -\frac{1}{2}$: $-\frac{1}{2} = -4A \Rightarrow A = \frac{1}{8}$.

Let $x = \frac{1}{2}$: $\frac{1}{2} = 4B \Rightarrow B = \frac{1}{8}$.

Let $x = 0$: $0 = -A + B - D$

$$0 = -\tfrac{1}{8} + \tfrac{1}{8} - D$$

$$0 = D$$

Let $x = 1$: $1 = 5A + 15B + 3C + 3D$

$$1 = \tfrac{5}{8} + \tfrac{15}{8} + 3C + 0$$

$$-\tfrac{1}{2} = C$$

$$\frac{x}{16x^4 - 1} = \frac{1/8}{2x + 1} + \frac{1/8}{2x - 1} - \frac{x/2}{4x^2 + 1} = \frac{1}{8}\left[\frac{1}{2x + 1} + \frac{1}{2x - 1} - \frac{4x}{4x^2 + 1}\right]$$

25. $\dfrac{x^2 + x + 2}{(x^2 + 2)^2} = \dfrac{Ax + B}{x^2 + 2} + \dfrac{Cx + D}{(x^2 + 2)^2}$

$x^2 + x + 2 = (Ax + B)(x^2 + 2) + Cx + D$

$x^2 + x + 2 = Ax^3 + Bx^2 + (2A + C)x + (2B + D)$

Equating coefficient of like powers:

$0 = A$

$1 = B$

$1 = 2A + C \Rightarrow C = 1$

$2 = 2B + D \Rightarrow D = 0$

$\dfrac{x^2 + x + 2}{(x^2 + 2)^2} = \dfrac{1}{x^2 + 2} + \dfrac{x}{(x^2 + 2)^2}$

27. $\dfrac{x^2 + 5}{(x + 1)(x^2 - 2x + 3)} = \dfrac{A}{x + 1} + \dfrac{Bx + C}{x^2 - 2x + 3}$

$x^2 + 5 = A(x^2 - 2x + 3) + (Bx + C)(x + 1)$

Let $x = -1$: $6 = 6A \Rightarrow A = 1$.

$x^2 + 5 = x^2 - 2x + 3 + Bx^2 + Bx + Cx + C = x^2(1 + B) + x(-2 + B + C) + (3 + C)$

Equating coefficients of like powers:

$1 = 1 + B, \qquad 0 = -2 + B + C, \qquad$ and $5 = 3 + C$

$0 = B \qquad\qquad 0 = -2 + 0 + C \qquad\qquad 2 = C$

$\qquad\qquad\qquad 2 = C$

$\dfrac{x^2 + 5}{(x + 1)(x^2 - 2x + 3)} = \dfrac{1}{x + 1} + \dfrac{2}{x^2 - 2x + 3}$

29. $\dfrac{2x^3 - 4x^2 - 15x + 5}{x^2 - 2x - 8} = 2x + \dfrac{x + 5}{(x + 2)(x - 4)}$

$\dfrac{x + 5}{(x + 2)(x - 4)} = \dfrac{A}{x + 2} + \dfrac{B}{x - 4}$

$x + 5 = A(x - 4) + B(x + 2)$

Let $x = -2$: $3 = -6A \Rightarrow A = -\frac{1}{2}$.

Let $x = 4 : 9 = 6B \Rightarrow B = \frac{3}{2}$.

$\dfrac{2x^3 - 4x^2 - 15x + 5}{x^2 - 2x - 8} = 2x + \dfrac{1}{2}\left[\dfrac{3}{x - 4} - \dfrac{1}{x + 2}\right]$

31.
$$\frac{x^4}{(x-1)^3} = \frac{x^4}{x^3 - 3x^2 + 3x - 1} = x + 3 + \frac{6x^2 - 8x + 3}{(x-1)^3}$$

$$\frac{6x^2 - 8x + 3}{(x-1)^3} = \frac{A}{x-1} + \frac{B}{(x-1)^2} + \frac{C}{(x-1)^3}$$

$$6x^2 - 8x + 3 = A(x-1)^2 + B(x-1) + C$$

Let $x = 1$: $1 = C$. $6x^2 - 8x + 3 = Ax^2 - 2Ax + A + Bx - B + 1$

$$6x^2 - 8x + 3 = Ax^2 + (-2A + B)x + (A - B + 1)$$

Equating coefficients of like powers:

$$6 = A, \quad -8 = -2A + B \quad \text{and} \quad 3 = A - B + 1$$

$$-8 = -12 + B \qquad 3 = 6 - B + 1$$

$$4 = \qquad B \qquad 4 = \qquad B$$

$$\frac{x^4}{(x-1)^3} = x + 3 + \frac{6}{x-1} + \frac{4}{(x-1)^2} + \frac{1}{(x-1)^3}$$

33. $\dfrac{1}{a^2 - x^2} = \dfrac{A}{a + x} + \dfrac{B}{a - x}$, a is a constant.

$$1 = A(a - x) + B(a + x)$$

Let $x = -a$: $1 = 2aA \Rightarrow A = \dfrac{1}{2a}$.

Let $x = a$: $1 = 2aB \Rightarrow B = \dfrac{1}{2a}$.

$$\frac{1}{a^2 - x^2} = \frac{1}{2a}\left[\frac{1}{a + x} + \frac{1}{a - x}\right]$$

To check this result graphically, let $a = 1$ and graph

$$y_1 = \frac{1}{1 - x^2}$$

$$y_2 = \frac{1}{2}\left[\frac{1}{1 + x} + \frac{1}{1 - x}\right]$$

on the same viewing rectangle.

35. $\dfrac{1}{x(a - x)} = \dfrac{A}{x} + \dfrac{B}{a - x}$

$$1 = A(a - x) + Bx$$

Let $x = 0$: $1 = aA \Rightarrow A = \dfrac{1}{a}$.

Let $x = a$: $1 = aB \Rightarrow B = \dfrac{1}{a}$.

$$\frac{1}{x(a - x)} = \frac{1}{a}\left(\frac{1}{x} + \frac{1}{a - x}\right)$$

To check this result graphically, let $a = 1$ and graph

$$y_1 = \frac{1}{x(1 - x)}$$

$$y_2 = \left(\frac{1}{x} + \frac{1}{1 - x}\right)$$

on the same viewing rectangle.

Section 4.4   Conic Sections and Graphs

You should know the following basic definitions of conic sections.

■ A circle is the set of all points $(x,\ y)$ that are equidistant from a fixed point $(h,\ k)$.

(a) Standard equation: $(x-h)^2 + (y-k)^2 = r^2$

(b) Center: $(h,\ k)$

(c) Radius: r

■ A parabola is the set of all points $(x,\ y)$ that are equidistant from a fixed line (directrix) and a fixed point (focus) not on the line.

(a) Standard equation with vertex $(0, 0)$ and directrix $y = -p$ (vertical axis): $x^2 = 4py$

(b) Standard equation with vertex $(0, 0)$ and directrix $x = -p$ (horizontal axis):
$y^2 = 4px$

(c) The focus lies on the axis p units (directed distance) from the vertex.

■ An ellipse is the set of all points $(x,\ y)$ the sum of whose distances from two distinct fixed points (foci) is constant.

(a) Standard equation of an ellipse with center $(0, 0)$, major axis length $2a$, and minor axis length $2b$:

1. Horizontal major axis: $\dfrac{x^2}{a^2} + \dfrac{y^2}{b^2} = 1,\ \ 0 < b < a$

2. Vertical major axis: $\dfrac{x^2}{b^2} + \dfrac{y^2}{a^2} = 1,\ \ 0 < b < a$

(b) The foci lie on the major axis, c units from the center, where a, b, and c are related by the equation $c^2 = a^2 - b^2$.

(c) The vertices and endpoints of the minor axis are:

1. Horizontal axis: $(\pm a,\ 0)$ and $(0,\ \pm b)$

2. Vertical axis: $(0,\ \pm a)$ and $(\pm b,\ 0)$

■ A hyperbola is the set of all points (x, y) the difference of whose distances from two distinct fixed points (foci) is constant.

(a) Standard equation of a hyperbola with center $(0, 0)$

    1. Horizontal transverse axis: $\dfrac{x^2}{a^2} - \dfrac{y^2}{b^2} = 1$

    2. Vertical transverse axis: $\dfrac{y^2}{a^2} - \dfrac{x^2}{b^2} = 1$

(b) The vertices and foci are a and c units from the center and $b^2 = c^2 - a^2$.

(c) The asymptotes of the hyperbola are:

    1. Horizontal transverse axis: $y = \pm \dfrac{b}{a} x$

    2. Vertical transverse axis: $y = \pm \dfrac{a}{b} x$

■ You should be able to graph conic sections using your graphing utility.

---

1. $x^2 = 4y$

Upward opening parabola

Graph (a)

```
RANGE
Xmin=-7
Xmax=7
Xscl=1
Ymin=-2
Ymax=8
Yscl=1
```

3. $y^2 = 4x$

Parabola opening to the right

Graph (d)

```
RANGE
Xmin=-2
Xmax=9
Xscl=1
Ymin=-4
Ymax=4
Yscl=1
```

5. $\dfrac{x^2}{1} + \dfrac{y^2}{4} = 1$

Ellipse with vertical major axis

Graph (g)

```
RANGE
Xmin=-4
Xmax=4
Xscl=1
Ymin=-3
Ymax=3
Yscl=1
```

7. $\dfrac{x^2}{1} - \dfrac{y^2}{4} = 1$

Hyperbola with horizontal transverse axis

Graph (e)

```
RANGE
Xmin=-4
Xmax=4
Xscl=1
Ymin=-3
Ymax=3
Yscl=1
```

9. $y = 4x^2$

$\frac{1}{4}y = x^2$

$4\left(\frac{1}{16}\right)y = x^2; \quad p = \frac{1}{16}$

Vertex: $(0, 0)$

Focus: $\left(0, \frac{1}{16}\right)$

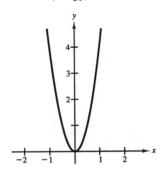

11. $y^2 = -6x$

$y^2 = 4\left(-\frac{3}{2}\right)x; \quad p = -\frac{3}{2}$

Vertex: $(0, 0)$

Focus: $\left(-\frac{3}{2}, 0\right)$

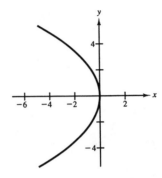

13. $x^2 + 8y = 0$

$x^2 = 4(-2)y; \quad p = -2$

Vertex: $(0, 0)$

Focus: $(0, -2)$

15. $y^2 - 8x = 0 \Rightarrow y_1 = \sqrt{8x}$

$y_2 = -\sqrt{8x}$

$x - y + 2 = 0 \Rightarrow y = x + 2$

17. Focus: $\left(0, -\frac{3}{2}\right)$

$x^2 = 4\left(-\frac{3}{2}\right)y$

$x^2 = -6y$

19. Focus: $(-2, 0)$

$y^2 = 4(-2)x$

$y^2 = -8x$

21. Directrix: $y = -1$

$x^2 = 4(1)y$

$x^2 = 4y$

23. Directrix: $y = 2$

$x^2 = 4(-2)y$

$x^2 = -8y$

25. $y^2 = 4px$

$6^2 = 4p(4)$

$36 = 16p$

$p = \frac{9}{4}$

$y^2 = 4\left(\frac{9}{4}\right)x$

$y^2 = 9x$

27. Focus: $(0, 3)$, $p = 3$

$x^2 = 4(3)y$

$x^2 = 12y$

29. $\dfrac{x^2}{25} + \dfrac{y^2}{16} = 1$

Horizontal major axis

$a = 5$, $b = 4$

Center: $(0, 0)$

Vertices: $(\pm 5, 0)$

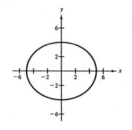

31. $\dfrac{x^2}{16} + \dfrac{y^2}{25} = 1$

Vertical major axis

$a = 5$, $b = 4$

Center: $(0, 0)$

Vertices: $(0, \pm 5)$

33. $\dfrac{x^2}{9} + \dfrac{y^2}{5} = 1$

Horizontal major axis

$a = 3$, $b = \sqrt{5}$

Center: $(0, 0)$

Vertices: $(\pm 3, 0)$

35. $5x^2 + 3y^2 = 15$

$$3y^2 = 15 - 5x^2$$

$$y^2 = 5 - \tfrac{5}{3}x^2$$

$$y_1 = \sqrt{5 - \tfrac{5}{3}x^2}$$

$$y_2 = -\sqrt{5 - \tfrac{5}{3}x^2}$$

37. Vertices: $(0, \pm 2) \Rightarrow a = 2$
Minor axis of length $2 \Rightarrow b = 1$
Vertical major axis

$$\frac{x^2}{b^2} + \frac{y^2}{a^2} = 1$$

$$\frac{x^2}{1} + \frac{y^2}{4} = 1$$

39. Vertices: $(\pm 5, 0) \Rightarrow a = 5$
Foci: $(\pm 2, 0) \Rightarrow b = \sqrt{5^2 - 2^2} = \sqrt{21}$
Horizontal major axis

$$\frac{x^2}{a^2} + \frac{y^2}{b^2} = 1$$

$$\frac{x^2}{25} + \frac{y^2}{21} = 1$$

41. Foci: $(\pm 5, 0) \Rightarrow c = 5$
Major axis of length $12 \Rightarrow a = 6$
$$b = \sqrt{6^2 - 5^2} = \sqrt{11}$$
Horizontal major axis

$$\frac{x^2}{a^2} + \frac{y^2}{b^2} = 1$$

$$\frac{x^2}{36} + \frac{y^2}{11} = 1$$

43. Vertices:
$(0, \pm 5) \Rightarrow a = 5$
Vertical major axis

$$\frac{x^2}{b^2} + \frac{y^2}{25} = 1$$

$$\frac{(4)^2}{b^2} + \frac{(2)^2}{25} = 1$$

$$\frac{400}{21} = b^2$$

$$\frac{21x^2}{400} + \frac{y^2}{25} = 1$$

45. $2a = 5 \Rightarrow a = 2.5$

$$b = 2$$

$$c^2 = (2.5)^2 - (2)^2$$

$$c = \sqrt{2.25} = 1.5$$

The tacks should be placed at $(\pm 1.5, 0)$.
The length of the string should be $2a = 5$
feet.

47.

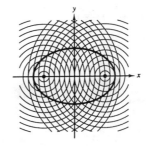

49. $\dfrac{x^2}{4} + \dfrac{y^2}{1} = 1$

$a = 2, \ b = 1, \ c = \sqrt{3}$

Points on the ellipse: $(\pm 2, \ 0), \ (0, \pm 1)$

Length of latus recta: $\dfrac{2b^2}{a} = \dfrac{2(1)^2}{2} = 1$

Additional points:

$\left(-\sqrt{3}, \ \pm\dfrac{1}{2}\right), \ \left(\sqrt{3}, \ \pm\dfrac{1}{2}\right)$

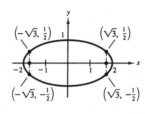

51. $9x^2 + 4y^2 = 36$

$\dfrac{x^2}{4} + \dfrac{y^2}{9} = 1$

$a = 3, \ b = 2, \ c = \sqrt{5}$

Points on the ellipse: $(\pm 2, \ 0), \ (0, \ \pm 3)$

Length of latus recta: $\dfrac{2b^2}{a} = \dfrac{2 \cdot 2^2}{3} = \dfrac{8}{3}$

Additional points:

$\left(\pm\dfrac{4}{3}, \ -\sqrt{5}\right), \ \left(\pm\dfrac{4}{3}, \ \sqrt{5}\right)$

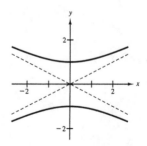

53. $x^2 - y^2 = 1$

$a = 1, \ b = 1$

Center: $(0, \ 0)$

Vertices: $(\pm 1, \ 0)$

Asymptotes: $y = \pm x$

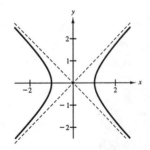

55. $\dfrac{y^2}{1} - \dfrac{x^2}{4} = 1$

$a = 1, \ b = 2$

Center: $(0, \ 0)$

Vertices: $(0, \ \pm 1)$

Asymptotes: $y = \pm\dfrac{1}{2}x$

57. $\dfrac{y^2}{25} - \dfrac{x^2}{144} = 1$

$a = 5, \; b = 12$

Center: $(0, 0)$

Vertices: $(0, \pm 5)$

Asymptotes: $y = \pm \dfrac{5}{12} x$

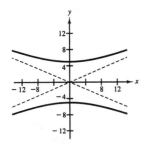

59. $2x^2 - 3y^2 = 6$

$3y^2 = 2x^2 - 6$

$y_1 = \sqrt{\dfrac{2}{3} x^2 - 2}$

$y_2 = -\sqrt{\dfrac{2}{3} x^2 - 2}$

Asymptotes: $y = \pm \dfrac{\sqrt{6}}{3} x$

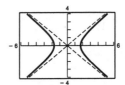

61. Vertices: $(0, \pm 2) \Rightarrow a = 2$

Foci: $(0, \pm 4) \Rightarrow c = 4$

$b^2 = c^2 - a^2 = 12$

Vertical transverse axis

$\dfrac{y^2}{a^2} - \dfrac{x^2}{b^2} = 1$

$\dfrac{y^2}{4} - \dfrac{x^2}{12} = 1$

63. Vertices: $(\pm 1, 0) \Rightarrow a = 1$

Asymptotes: $y = \pm 3x$

Horizontal transverse axis

$3 = \dfrac{b}{a} = \dfrac{b}{1} \Rightarrow b = 3$

$\dfrac{x^2}{a^2} - \dfrac{y^2}{b^2} = 1$

$\dfrac{x^2}{1} - \dfrac{y^2}{9} = 1$

65. Foci: $(0, \pm 8) \Rightarrow c = 8$

Asymptotes: $y = \pm 4x$

Vertical transverse axis

$4 = \dfrac{a}{b} \Rightarrow a = 4b$

$16b^2 + b^2 = (8)^2$

$b^2 = \dfrac{64}{17} \Rightarrow a^2 = \dfrac{1024}{17}$

$\dfrac{y^2}{a^2} - \dfrac{x^2}{b^2} = 1$

$\dfrac{17y^2}{1024} - \dfrac{17x^2}{64} = 1$

67. Vertices: $(0, \pm 3) \Rightarrow a = 3$

Vertical transverse axis

$\dfrac{y^2}{9} - \dfrac{x^2}{b^2} = 1$

$\dfrac{5^2}{9} - \dfrac{(-2)^2}{b^2} = 1$

$b^2 = \dfrac{9}{4}$

$\dfrac{y^2}{9} - \dfrac{4x^2}{9} = 1$

69. Foci: $(\pm 150,\ 0) \Rightarrow C = 150$

Center: $(0,\ 0) = (h,\ k)$

$$\frac{d_2}{186,000} - \frac{d_1}{186,000} = 0.001 \Rightarrow 2a = 186, \quad a = 93$$

$$b^2 = c^2 - a^2 = 150^2 - 93^2 = 13,851$$

$$\frac{x^2}{93^2} - \frac{y^2}{13,851} = 1$$

For $y = 75$, we have

$$x^2 = 93^2 \left(1 + \frac{75^2}{13,851}\right) \approx 12,161$$

$$x \approx 110.3 \text{ miles.}$$

71. Let $(x,\ y)$ be such that the sum of the distance from $(c,\ 0)$ and $(-c,\ 0)$ is $2a$. (Note that this is only deriving the standard form for the ellipse with horizontal major axis.)

$$2a = \sqrt{(x - c)^2 + y^2} + \sqrt{(x + c)^2 + y^2}$$

$$2a - \sqrt{(x + c)^2 + y^2} = \sqrt{(x - c)^2 + y^2}$$

$$4a^2 - 4a\sqrt{(x + c)^2 + y^2} + (x + c)^2 + y^2 = (x - c)^2 + y^2$$

$$4a^2 + 4cx = 4a\sqrt{(x + c)^2 + y^2}$$

$$a^2 + cx = a\sqrt{(x + c)^2 + y^2}$$

$$a^4 + 2a^2cx + c^2x^2 = a^2(x^2 + 2cx + c^2 + y^2)$$

$$a^4 + c^2x^2 = a^2x^2 + a^2c^2 + a^2y^2$$

$$a^2(a^2 - c^2) = (a^2 - c^2)x^2 + a^2y^2$$

Let $b^2 = a^2 - c^2$. Then we have

$$a^2b^2 = b^2x^2 + a^2y^2 \Rightarrow 1 = \frac{x^2}{a^2} + \frac{y^2}{b^2}.$$

73. The shape continuously changes from an ellipse with a vertical major axis of length 8 and a minor axis of length 2 to a circle with a diameter of 8 and then to an ellipse with a horizontal major axis of length 16 and a minor axis of length 8.

Section 4.5   Conic Sections and Translations

You should know the following basic facts about conic sections.

■ Parabola with vertex $(h,\ k)$

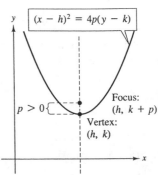

(a) Vertical axis
   1. Standard equation: $(x - h)^2 = 4p(y - k)$
   2. Focus: $(h,\ k + p)$
   3. Directrix: $y = k - p$

(b) Horizontal axis
   1. Standard equation: $(y - k)^2 = 4p(x - h)$
   2. Focus: $(h + p,\ k)$
   3. Directrix: $x = h - p$

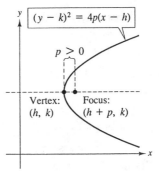

■ Circle with center $(h,\ k)$ and radius r
   Standard equation: $(x - h)^2 + (y - k)^2 = r^2$

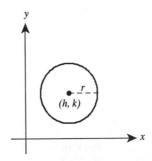

■ Ellipse with center (h, k)

  (a) Horizontal major axis:

    1. Standard equation:
$$\frac{(x - h)^2}{a^2} + \frac{(y - k)^2}{b^2} = 1$$

    2. Vertices: $(h \pm a, \ k)$

    3. Foci: $(h \pm c, \ k)$

    4. Eccentricity: $e = \dfrac{c}{a}$

    5. $c^2 = a^2 - b^2$

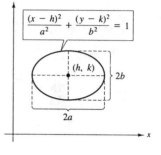

  (b) Vertical major axis:

    1. Standard equation:
$$\frac{(x - h)^2}{b^2} + \frac{(y - k)^2}{a^2} = 1$$

    2. Vertices: $(h, \ k \pm a)$

    3. Foci: $(h, \ k \pm c)$

    4. Eccentricity: $e = \dfrac{c}{a}$

    5. $c^2 = a^2 - b^2$

■ Hyperbola with center (h, k)

  (a) Horizontal transverse axis:

    1. Standard equation:
$$\frac{(x - h)^2}{a^2} - \frac{(y - k)^2}{b^2} = 1$$

    2. Vertices: $(h \pm a, \ k)$

    3. Foci: $(h \pm c, \ k)$

    4. Asymptotes: $y - k = \pm\dfrac{b}{a}(x - h)$

    5. $c^2 = a^2 + b^2$

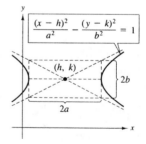

  (b) Vertical transverse axis:

    1. Standard equation:
$$\frac{(y - k)^2}{a^2} - \frac{(x - h)^2}{b^2} = 1$$

    2. Vertices: $(h, \ k \pm a)$

    3. Foci: $(h, \ k \pm c)$

    4. Asymptotes: $y - k = \pm\dfrac{a}{b}(x - h)$

    5. $c^2 = a^2 + b^2$

1. $(x-1)^2 + 8(y+2) = 0$

$(x-1)^2 = 4(-2)(y+2); \quad p = -2$

Vertex: $(1, -2)$

Focus: $(1, -4)$

Directrix: $y = 0$

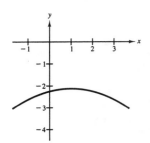

3. $\left(y + \dfrac{1}{2}\right)^2 = 2(x - 5)$

$\left(y + \dfrac{1}{2}\right)^2 = 4\left(\dfrac{1}{2}\right)(x - 5); \quad p = \dfrac{1}{2}$

Vertex: $\left(5, -\frac{1}{2}\right)$

Focus: $\left(\frac{11}{2}, -\frac{1}{2}\right)$

Directrix: $x = \frac{9}{2}$

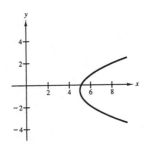

5. $y = \frac{1}{4}(x^2 - 2x + 5)$

$y = \frac{1}{4}(x-1)^2 + 1$

$4(y-1) = (x-1)^2; \quad p = 1$

Vertex: $(1, 1)$

Focus: $(1, 2)$

Directrix: $y = 0$

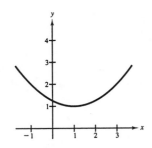

7. $y^2 + 6y + 8x + 25 = 0$

$(y+3)^2 = 4(-2)(x+2); \quad p = -2$

Vertex: $(-2, -3)$

Focus: $(-4, -3)$

Directrix: $x = 0$

9. $y = -\frac{1}{6}(x^2 + 4x - 2)$

$y = -\frac{1}{6}(x + 2)^2 + 1$

$4\left(-\frac{3}{2}\right)(y - 1) = (x + 2)^2; \quad p = -\frac{3}{2}$

Vertex: $(-2,\ 1)$

Focus: $\left(-2,\ -\frac{1}{2}\right)$

Directrix: $y = \frac{5}{2}$

11. $y^2 + x + y = 0$

$$\left(y + \frac{1}{2}\right)^2 = 4\left(-\frac{1}{4}\right)\left(x - \frac{1}{4}\right); \quad p = -\frac{1}{4}$$

Vertex: $\left(\frac{1}{4},\ -\frac{1}{2}\right)$

Focus: $\left(0,\ -\frac{1}{2}\right)$

Directrix: $x = \frac{1}{2}$

To graph this parabola, note that

$$\left(y + \frac{1}{2}\right)^2 = \frac{1}{4} - x$$

$$\left(y + \frac{1}{2}\right) = \pm\sqrt{(1/4) - x}.$$

Hence, we use

$$y_1 = -\frac{1}{2} + \sqrt{(1/4) - x}$$

$$y_2 = -\frac{1}{2} - \sqrt{(1/4) - x}.$$

13. Vertex: $(3, 2)$

Focus: $(1, 2)$

Horizontal axis

$p = 1 - 3 = -2$

$(y - 2)^2 = 4(-2)(x - 3)$

$(y - 2)^2 = -8(x - 3)$

15. Vertex: $(0, 4)$

Directrix: $y = 2$

Vertical axis

$p = 4 - 2 = 2$

$(x - 0)^2 = 4(2)(y - 4)$

$x^2 = 8(y - 4)$

17. Focus: $(2, 2)$

Directrix: $x = -2$

Horizontal axis

Vertex: $(0, 2)$

$p = 2 - 0 = 2$

$(y - 2)^2 = 4(2)(x - 0)$

$(y - 2)^2 = 8x$

19. Vertex: $(0, 4)$

Opens downward and passes through $(\pm 2, 0)$

$$(x - 0)^2 = 4p(y - 4)$$
$$x^2 = 4p(y - 4)$$
$$2^2 = 4p(0 - 4)$$
$$p = -\tfrac{1}{4}$$
$$x^2 = 4(-\tfrac{1}{4})(y - 4)$$
$$x^2 = -(y - 4)$$

21. (a) $V = 17{,}500\sqrt{2}$ mi/hr

$\approx 24{,}750$ mi/hr

(b) $p = -4100$, $(h, k) = (0, 4100)$

$$(x - 0)^2 = 4(-4100)(y - 4100)$$
$$x^2 = -16{,}400(y - 4100)$$

23. $y = -0.08x^2 + x + 4$

Highest point: 7.125 feet

Range $(y = 0)$: 15.69 feet

25. $\dfrac{(x - 1)^2}{9} + \dfrac{(y - 5)^2}{25} = 1$

$a = 5$, $b = 3$, $c = \sqrt{a^2 - b^2} = 4$

Center: $(1, 5)$

Foci: $(1, 1)$, $(1, 9)$

Vertices: $(1, 0)$, $(1, 10)$

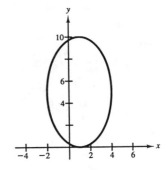

27. $9x^2 + 4y^2 + 36x - 24y + 36 = 0$

$$9(x^2 + 4x + 4) + 4(y^2 - 6y + 9) = 36$$
$$\dfrac{(x + 2)^2}{4} + \dfrac{(y - 3)^2}{9} = 1$$

$a = 3$, $b = 2$, $c = \sqrt{a^2 - b^2} = \sqrt{5}$

Vertical major axis

Center: $(-2, 3)$

Foci: $(-2, 3 - \sqrt{5})$, $(-2, 3 + \sqrt{5})$

Vertices: $(-2, 0)$, $(-2, 6)$

29. $16x^2 + 25y^2 - 32x + 50y + 16 = 0$

$16(x^2 - 2x + 1) + 25(y^2 + 2y + 1) = 25$

$$\frac{(x-1)^2}{25/16} + (y+1)^2 = 1$$

$a = \dfrac{5}{4}, \quad b = 1, \quad c = \sqrt{a^2 - b^2} = \dfrac{3}{4}$

Horizontal major axis

Center: $(1, -1)$

Foci: $\left(\frac{1}{4}, -1\right), \left(\frac{7}{4}, -1\right)$

Vertices: $\left(-\frac{1}{4}, -1\right), \left(\frac{9}{4}, -1\right)$

31. $12x^2 + 20y^2 - 12x + 40y - 37 = 0$

$12\left(x^2 - x + \dfrac{1}{4}\right) + 20(y^2 + 2y + 1) = 60$

$$\frac{\left(x-\frac{1}{2}\right)^2}{5} + \frac{(y+1)^2}{3} = 1$$

$a = \sqrt{5}, \quad b = \sqrt{3}, \quad c = \sqrt{a^2 - b^2} = \sqrt{2}$

Horizontal major axis

Center: $\left(\frac{1}{2}, -1\right)$

Foci: $\left(\frac{1}{2} - \sqrt{2}, -1\right), \left(\frac{1}{2} + \sqrt{2}, -1\right)$

Vertices: $\left(\frac{1}{2} - \sqrt{5}, -1\right), \left(\frac{1}{2} - \sqrt{5}, -1\right)$

To graph this ellipse, note that

$$\frac{(y+1)^2}{3} = 1 - \frac{\left(x-\frac{1}{2}\right)^2}{5}$$

$$y + 1 = \pm\sqrt{3 - \tfrac{3}{5}\left(x - \tfrac{1}{2}\right)^2}$$

$$y_1 = -1 + \sqrt{3 - \tfrac{3}{5}\left(x - \tfrac{1}{2}\right)^2}$$

$$y_2 = -1 - \sqrt{3 - \tfrac{3}{5}\left(x - \tfrac{1}{2}\right)^2}.$$

33. Vertices: $(0, 2), (4, 2)$
Minor axis of length 2

$a = \dfrac{4 - 0}{2} = 2, \quad b = \dfrac{2}{2} = 1$

Center: $(2, 2)$
Horizontal major axis

$$\frac{(x-2)^2}{4} + (y-2)^2 = 1$$

35. Foci: $(0, 0), (0, 8)$
Major axis of length 16
$a = 8, \; c = 4, \; b^2 = 48$
Center: $(0, 4)$
Vertical major axis

$$\frac{x^2}{48} + \frac{(y-4)^2}{64} = 1$$

37. Vertices: $(3, 1), (3, 9)$
Minor axis of length 6
$a = 4, \quad b = 3$
Center: $(3, 5)$
Vertical major axis
$$\frac{(x - 3)^2}{9} + \frac{(y - 5)^2}{16} = 1$$

39. Center: $(0, 4)$
$a = 2c$
Vertices: $(-4, 4), (4, 4)$
$a = 4, \quad c = 2, \quad b^2 = 12$
Horizontal major axis
$$\frac{x^2}{16} + \frac{(y - 4)^2}{12} = 1$$

41. Vertices: $(\pm 5, 0)$
$$e = \frac{c}{a} = \frac{3}{5}$$
$a = 5, \quad c = 3,$
$b = \sqrt{a^2 - c^2}$
$\quad = \sqrt{25 - 9} = 4$
$$\frac{x^2}{25} + \frac{y^2}{16} = 1$$

43. $a = 3.666 \times 10^9$
$$e = \frac{c}{a} = 0.248$$
$c = 909,168,000$
Least distance: $a - c = 2,756,832,000$
Greatest distance: $a + c = 4,575,168,000$

45. Least distance: $a - c = 4000 + 132$
Greatest distance: $a + c = 4000 + 583$
$$a = 4132 + c$$
$$(4132 + c) + c = 4583$$
$$2c = 451$$
$$c = 225.5$$
$$a = 4132 + 225.5$$
$$a = 4357.5$$
$$e = \frac{c}{a} = \frac{225.5}{4357.5} \approx 0.052$$

47. $\dfrac{(x - 1)^2}{4} - \dfrac{(y + 2)^2}{1} = 1$
$a = 2, \quad b = 1, \quad c = \sqrt{a^2 + b^2} = \sqrt{5}$
Center: $(1, -2)$
Horizontal transverse axis
Vertices: $(-1, -2), (3, -2)$
Foci: $(1 \pm \sqrt{5}, -2)$
Asymptotes: $y = \pm \frac{1}{2}(x - 1) - 2$

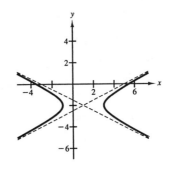

49. $(y+6)^2 - (x-2)^2 = 1$

$a = 1$, $b = 1$, $c = \sqrt{a^2 + b^2} = \sqrt{2}$

Center: $(2, -6)$

Vertical transverse axis

Vertices: $(2, -5)$, $(2, -7)$

Foci: $(2, -6 \pm \sqrt{2})$

Asymptotes: $y = \pm(x-2) - 6$

51. $9x^2 - y^2 - 36x - 6y + 18 = 0$

$9(x^2 - 4x + 4) - (y^2 + 6y + 9) = 9$

$$(x-2)^2 - \frac{(y+3)^2}{9} = 1$$

$a = 1$, $b = 3$, $c = \sqrt{a^2 + b^2} = \sqrt{10}$

Center: $(2, -3)$

Horizontal transverse axis

Vertices: $(1, -3)$, $(3, -3)$

Foci: $(2 \pm \sqrt{10}, -3)$

Asymptotes: $y = \pm 3(x-2) - 3$

53. $x^2 - 9y^2 + 2x - 54y - 80 = 0$

$(x^2 + 2x + 1) - 9(y^2 + 6y + 9) = 0$

$$9(y+3)^2 = (x+1)^2$$

$$y = \pm \tfrac{1}{3}(x+1) - 3$$

The graph of this equation is two lines intersecting at $(-1, -3)$.

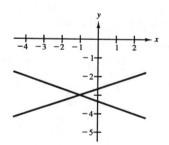

55.
$$9y^2 - x^2 + 2x + 54y + 62 = 0$$
$$9(y^2 + 6y + 9) - (x^2 - 2x + 1) = 18$$
$$\frac{(y+3)^2}{2} - \frac{(x-1)^2}{18} = 1$$
$a = \sqrt{2}, \quad b = 3\sqrt{2}, \quad c = \sqrt{a^2 + b^2} = 2\sqrt{5}$

Center: $(1, -3)$

Vertical transverse axis

Vertices: $(1, -3 \pm \sqrt{2})$

Foci: $(1, -3 \pm 2\sqrt{5})$

Asymptotes: $y = \pm\frac{1}{3}(x - 1) - 3$

To graph this hyperbola, note that

$$\frac{(y+3)^2}{2} = 1 + \frac{(x-1)^2}{18}$$

$$y + 3 = \pm\sqrt{2 + \frac{(x-1)^2}{9}}$$

$$y_1 = -3 + \sqrt{2 + \frac{(x-1)^2}{9}}$$

$$y_2 = -3 - \sqrt{2 + \frac{(x-1)^2}{9}}.$$

You can also graph the asymptotes

$$y_3 = \frac{1}{3}(x - 1) - 3$$

$$y_4 = -\frac{1}{3}(x - 1) - 3.$$

57. Vertices: $(2, 0), (6, 0)$

Foci: $(0, 0), (8, 0)$

Center: $(4, 0)$

Horizontal transverse axis

$a = 2, \quad c = 4, \quad b^2 = c^2 - a^2 = 12$

$$\frac{(x-4)^2}{4} - \frac{y^2}{12} = 1$$

59. Vertices: $(4, 1), (4, 9)$

Foci: $(4, 0), (4, 10)$

Center: $(4, 5)$

Vertical transverse axis

$a = 4, \quad c = 5, \quad b^2 = c^2 - a^2 = 9$

$$\frac{(y-5)^2}{16} - \frac{(x-4)^2}{9} = 1$$

61. Vertices: $(2, 3), (2, -3)$

Passes through the point $(0, 5)$

Center: $(2, 0)$

Vertical transverse axis

$a = 3$

$$\frac{y^2}{9} - \frac{(x-2)^2}{b^2} = 1$$

$$\frac{5^2}{9} - \frac{(0-2)^2}{b^2} = 1$$

$$b^2 = \frac{9}{4}$$

$$\frac{y^2}{9} - \frac{4(x-2)^2}{9} = 1$$

63. Vertices: $(0, 2), (6, 2)$

Asymptotes: $y = \frac{2}{3}x, \quad y = 4 - \frac{2}{3}x$

Center: $(3, 2)$

Horizontal transverse axis

$a = 3, \quad b = 2$

$$\frac{(x-3)^2}{9} - \frac{(y-2)^2}{4} = 1$$

65. $x^2 + y^2 - 6x + 4y + 9 = 0$

$$(x-3)^2 + (y+2)^2 = 4$$

Circle

67. $4x^2 - y^2 - 4x - 3 = 0$

$$4\left(x - \frac{1}{2}\right)^2 - y^2 = 4$$

$$\left(x - \frac{1}{2}\right)^2 - \frac{y^2}{4} = 1$$

Hyperbola

69. $4x^2 + 3y^2 + 8x - 24y + 51 = 0$

$$4(x+1)^2 + 3(y-4)^2 = 1$$

$$\frac{(x+1)^2}{1/4} + \frac{(y-4)^2}{1/3} = 1$$

Ellipse

71. $25x^2 - 10x - 200y - 119 = 0$

$$25\left(x - \tfrac{1}{5}\right)^2 = 200\left(y + \tfrac{3}{5}\right)$$

$$\left(x - \tfrac{1}{5}\right)^2 = 8\left(y + \tfrac{3}{5}\right)$$

Parabola

Chapter 4   Review Exercises

1. $f(x) = \dfrac{4}{x+3}$

  Domain: All real numbers except -3

  Vertical asymptote: $x = -3$

  Horizontal asymptote: $y = 0$

3. $g(x) = \dfrac{x^2}{x^2 - 4}$

  Domain: All real numbers except ± 2

  Vertical asymptotes: $x = -2$, $x = 2$

  Horizontal asymptote: $y = 1$

5. $f(x) = \dfrac{-5}{x^2}$

  y-axis symmetry

  Vertical asymptote: $x = 0$

  Horizontal asymptote: $y = 0$

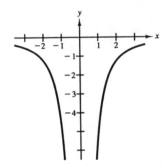

7. $g(x) = \dfrac{2+x}{1-x} = -\dfrac{x+2}{x-1}$

  x-intercept: $(-2,\ 0)$

  y-intercept: $(0,\ 2)$

  Vertical asymptote: $x = 1$

  Horizontal asymptote: $y = -1$

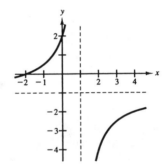

9. $P(x) = \dfrac{x^2}{x^2 + 1}$

  Intercept: $(0, 0)$

  y-axis symmetry

  Horizontal asymptote: $y = 1$

11. $y = \dfrac{x}{x^2 - 1}$

  Intercept: $(0, 0)$

  Origin symmetry

  Vertical asymptotes: $x = -1$, $x = 1$

  Horizontal asymptote: $y = 0$

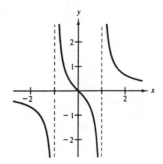

13. $f(x) = \dfrac{2x^3}{x^2+1}$

$$= 2x - \dfrac{2x}{x^2+1}$$

Intercept: $(0,\ 0)$
Origin symmetry
Slant asymptote: $y = 2x$

15. $s(x) = \dfrac{8x^2}{x^2+4}$

17. $g(x) = \dfrac{x^2+1}{x+1}$

19. $\overline{C} = \dfrac{C}{x} = \dfrac{0.5x+500}{x},\quad 0 < x$

$$= 0.5 + \dfrac{500}{x}$$

As x increases, the cost approaches the horizontal asymptote, $\overline{C} = 0.5$.

21. (a) When $p = 25$, $C = \dfrac{528(25)}{100-25} = \$176$ million.

(b) When $p = 50$, $C = \dfrac{528(50)}{100-50} = \$528$ million.

(c) When $p = 75$, $C = \dfrac{528(75)}{100-75} = \$1584$ million.

(d) As $p \Rightarrow 100$, C tends to infinity. No, it is not possible.

23. $y = \left(\dfrac{0.80 - 0.54x}{1 + 2.72x}\right)^2, \quad 0 < x$

For $y = 0.1, \quad x = 0.35$ inches.

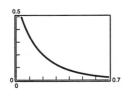

25. $\dfrac{4 - x}{x^2 + 6x + 8} = \dfrac{A}{x + 2} + \dfrac{B}{x + 4}$

$4 - x = A(x + 4) + B(x + 2)$

Let $x = -2$: $6 = 2A \ \Rightarrow \ A = 3.$

Let $x = -4$: $8 = -2B \ \Rightarrow \ B = -4.$

$\dfrac{4 - x}{x^2 + 6x + 8} = \dfrac{3}{x + 2} - \dfrac{4}{x + 4}$

27. $\dfrac{x^2}{x^2 + 2x - 15} = 1 - \dfrac{2x - 15}{x^2 + 2x - 15} = 1 + \dfrac{A}{x + 5} + \dfrac{B}{x - 3}$

$-2x + 15 = A(x - 3) + B(x + 5)$

Let $x = -5$: $25 = -8A \ \Rightarrow \ A = -\frac{25}{8}.$

Let $x = 3$: $9 = 8B \ \Rightarrow \ B = \frac{9}{8}.$

$\dfrac{x^2}{x^2 + 2x - 15} = 1 + \dfrac{9}{8(x - 3)} - \dfrac{25}{8(x + 5)}$

29. $\dfrac{x^2 + 2x}{x^3 - x^2 + x - 1} = \dfrac{A}{x - 1} + \dfrac{Bx + C}{x^2 + 1}$

$x^2 + 2x = A(x^2 + 1) + (Bx + C)(x - 1)$

Let $x = 1$: $3 = 2A \ \Rightarrow \ A = \frac{3}{2}.$

Let $x = 0$: $0 = A - C \ \Rightarrow \ C = \frac{3}{2}.$

Let $x = 2$: $8 = 5A + 2B + C$

$\qquad 8 = \left(\frac{15}{2}\right) + 2B + \left(\frac{3}{2}\right) \ \Rightarrow \ B = -\frac{1}{2}.$

$\dfrac{x^2 + 2x}{x^3 - x^2 + x - 1} = \dfrac{3/2}{x - 1} + \dfrac{-(1/2)x + 3/2}{x^2 + 1} = \dfrac{1}{2}\left(\dfrac{3}{x - 1} - \dfrac{x - 3}{x^2 + 1}\right)$

31. $\dfrac{3x^3 + 4x}{(x^2 + 1)^2} = \dfrac{Ax + B}{x^2 + 1} + \dfrac{Cx + D}{(x^2 + 1)^2}$

$3x^3 + 4x = (Ax + B)(x^2 + 1) + Cx + D = Ax^3 + Bx^2 + (A + C)x + B + D$

Equating coefficients of like powers:

$3 = A$

$0 = B$

$4 = 3 + C \;\Rightarrow\; C = 1$

$0 = B + D \;\Rightarrow\; D = 0$

$\dfrac{3x^3 + 4x}{(x^2 + 1)^2} = \dfrac{3x}{x^2 + 1} + \dfrac{x}{(x^2 + 1)^2}$

33. $4x = y^2$

Parabola

Vertex: $(0, 0)$

Horizontal axis

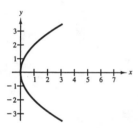

35. $x^2 - 6x + 2y + 9 = 0$

$(x - 3)^2 = -2y$

Parabola

Vertex: $(3, 0)$

Focus: $\left(3, -\tfrac{1}{2}\right)$

37. $\qquad x^2 + y^2 - 2x - 4y + 5 = 0$

$(x^2 - 2x + 1) + (y^2 - 4y + 4) = -5 + 1 + 4$

$(x - 1)^2 + (y - 2)^2 = 0$

Point: $(1, 2)$

Note: This is a degenerate conic–a circle of radius zero.

39. $4x^2 + y^2 = 16$

$$\frac{x^2}{4} + \frac{y^2}{16} = 1$$

Ellipse
Center: $(0, \ 0)$
Vertices: $(0, \ -4), \ (0, \ 4)$

41. $x^2 + 9y^2 + 10x - 18y + 25 = 0$

$$(x + 5)^2 + 9(y - 1)^2 = 9$$

$$\frac{(x + 5)^2}{9} + (y - 1)^2 = 1$$

Ellipse
Center: $(-5, \ 1)$
Vertices: $(-8, \ 1), \ (-2, \ 1)$

43. $5y^2 - 4x^2 = 20$

$$\frac{y^2}{4} - \frac{x^2}{5} = 1$$

Hyperbola
Vertical transverse axis
Center: $(0, 0)$
Vertices: $(0, \pm 2)$

Asymptotes: $y = \pm \dfrac{2\sqrt{5}}{5} x$

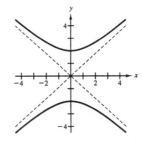

45. $x^2 - 10xy + y^2 + 1 = 0$

$$y^2 - 10xy + (x^2 + 1) = 0$$

$$y = \frac{10x \pm \sqrt{100x^2 - 4(x^2 + 1)}}{2}$$

$$y = 5x + \sqrt{24x^2 - 1}$$

$$y = 5x - \sqrt{24x^2 - 1}$$

Hyperbola

47. Vertical axis, $p = -2$

$$(x - h)^2 = 4p(y - k)$$

$$(x - 4)^2 = 4(-2)(y - 2)$$

$$(x - 4)^2 = -8(y - 2)$$

49. $(y - k)^2 = 4p(x - h)$

$$(0 - 2)^2 = 4p(-1 - 0)$$

$$p = -1$$

$$(y - 2)^2 = 4(-1)(x - 0)$$

$$(y - 2)^2 = -4x$$

51. Horizontal major axis

Center: $(2, 0)$

$a = 5$, $c = 2$,

$b = \sqrt{25 - 4} = \sqrt{21}$

$$\frac{(x - h)^2}{a^2} + \frac{(y - k)^2}{b^2} = 1$$

$$\frac{(x - 2)^2}{25} + \frac{y^2}{21} = 1$$

53. Vertical major axis

Center: $(0, 0)$

$a = 6$

$$\frac{(x - h)^2}{b^2} + \frac{(y - k)^2}{a^2} = 1$$

$$\frac{(2 - 0)^2}{b^2} + \frac{(2 - 0)^2}{6^2} = 1$$

$$b^2 = \frac{9}{2}$$

$$\frac{2x^2}{9} + \frac{y^2}{36} = 1$$

55. Vertical transverse axis

Center: $(0, 0)$

$a = 1$, $c = 3$,

$b = \sqrt{9 - 1} = \sqrt{8}$

$$\frac{y^2}{1} - \frac{x^2}{8} = 1$$

57. Horizontal transverse axis

Center: $(4, 0)$ $\Rightarrow$ $C = 4$

$$\frac{b}{a} = 2 \quad \Rightarrow \quad b = 2a$$

$$a^2 + b^2 = c^2$$

$$a^2 + (2a)^2 = 4^2$$

$$a^2 = \frac{16}{5}$$

$$b^2 = \frac{64}{5}$$

$$\frac{(x - h)^2}{a^2} - \frac{(y - k)^2}{b^2} = 1$$

$$\frac{5(x - 4)^2}{16} - \frac{5y^2}{64} = 1$$

59. $y = \dfrac{x^2}{200}$, $0 \le x \le 100$

Vertex: $(0, 0)$

$x^2 = 200y$

$4p = 200$

$p = 50$

Focus: $(0, 50)$

CHAPTER 5

Exponential and Logarithmic Functions

Section 5.1   **Exponential Functions and Their Graphs**

- You should know that a function of the form $y = a^x$, where $a > 0$, $a \neq 1$, is called an exponential function with base a.

- You should be able to graph exponential functions by hand and with a graphing utility.

- You should know the basic properties of exponential functions where $a > 0$ and $a \neq 1$.
  - (a) If $a^x = a^y$, then $x = y$.
  - (b) If $a^x = b^x$ and $x \neq 0$, then $a = b$.
  - (c) Domain: $(-\infty, \infty)$
  - (d) Range: $(0, \infty)$

- You should be familiar with the number e and the function e^x.

- You should know formulas for compound interest.
  - (a) For n compoundings per year: $A = P\left(1 + \dfrac{r}{n}\right)^{nt}$.
  - (b) For continuous compoundings: $A = Pe^{rt}$.

- You should be able to use exponential functions in applications like radioactive decay and population growth.

---

1. $(3.4)^{5.6} \approx 946.852$

3. $1000(1.06)^{-5} \approx 747.258$

5. $5^{-\pi} \approx 0.006$

7. $100^{\sqrt{2}} \approx 673.639$

9. $e^{-3/4} \approx 0.472$

11. $f(x) = 3^x$

y-intercept: $(0, 1)$

3^x increases as x increases.

Matches graph (g)

```
RANGE
Xmin=-3
Xmax=3
Xscl=1
Ymin=-1
Ymax=3
Yscl=1
```

13. $f(x) = 3^{-x}$

y-intercept: $(0, 1)$

3^{-x} decreases as x increases.

Matches graph (b)

```
RANGE
Xmin=-3
Xmax=3
Xscl=1
Ymin=-1
Ymax=3
Yscl=1
```

15. $f(x) = 3^x - 4$

y-intercept: $(0, -3)$

$3^x - 4$ increases as x increases.

Matches graph (d)

```
RANGE
Xmin=-3
Xmax=3
Xscl=1
Ymin=-5
Ymax=1
Yscl=1
```

17. $f(x) = -3^{x-2}$

y-intercept: $\left(0, -\frac{1}{9}\right)$

-3^{x-2} decreases as x increases.

Point: $(2, -1)$

Matches graph (f)

```
RANGE
Xmin=-1
Xmax=5
Xscl=1
Ymin=-5
Ymax=1
Yscl=1
```

19. $4^x < 3^x$ for $x < 0$

21. $g(x) = 5^x$

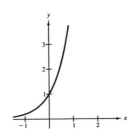

23. $f(x) = \left(\dfrac{1}{5}\right)^x = 5^{-x}$

25. $h(x) = 5^{x-2}$

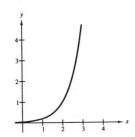

27. $g(x) = 5^{-x} - 3$

29. $f(x) = 3^{x-2} + 1$

31. $y = 1.08^{-5x}$

33. $s(t) = 2e^{0.12t}$

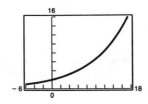

35. $g(x) = 1 + e^{-x}$

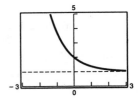

37. (a) $f(x) = 3^x$
(b) $g(x) = 3^{x-2}$
(c) $h(x) = -\frac{1}{2}(3^x)$
(d) $q(x) = 3^{-x} + 3$

39. (a) $f(x) = x^2 e^{-x}$

Increasing: $(0, 2)$
Decreasing: $(-\infty, 0)$, $(2, \infty)$
Relative maximum: $(2, 0.54)$
Relative minimum: $(0, 0)$

(b) $g(x) = x2^{3-x}$

Increasing: $(-\infty, 1.44)$
Decreasing: $(1.44, \infty)$
Relative maximum: $(1.44, 4.25)$

41. $P = \$2500$, $r = 12\%$, $t = 10$ years

Compounded n times per year: $A = 2500\left(1 + \dfrac{0.12}{n}\right)^{10n}$

Compounded continuously: $A = 2500e^{0.12(10)}$

n	1	2	4	12	365	Continuous compounding
A	\$7,764.62	\$8,017.84	\$8,155.09	\$8,250.97	\$8,298.66	\$8,300.29

43. $P = \$2500$, $r = 12\%$, $t = 20$ years

Compounded n times per year: $A = 2500 \left(1 + \dfrac{0.12}{n}\right)^{20n}$

Compounded continuously: $A = 2500e^{0.12(20)}$

n	1	2	4	12	365	Continuous compounding
A	\$24,115.73	\$25,714.29	\$26,602.23	\$27,231.38	\$27,547.07	\$27,557.94

45. $P = 100,000e^{-0.09t}$

t	1	10	20	30	40	50
P	\$91,393.12	\$40,656.97	\$16,529.89	\$6,720.55	\$2,732.37	\$1,110.90

47. $P = 100,000 \left(1 + \dfrac{0.10}{12}\right)^{-12t}$

t	1	10	20	30	40	50
P	\$90,521.24	\$36,940.70	\$13,646.15	\$5,040.98	\$1,862.17	\$687.90

49. $A = 25,000e^{(0.0875)(25)} \approx \$222,822.57$

51. $p(x) = 500 - 0.5e^{0.004x}$

(a) $x = 1000$

$p = 500 - 0.5e^4 \approx \$472.70$

(b) $x = 1500$

$p = 500 - 0.5e^6 \approx \$298.29$

The graph of p is a decreasing function. Since $p \geq 0$, we see from graphing p that the domain is $(0, 1726.94)$ and the range is $(0, 499.50)$.

53. $P(t) = 100e^{0.2197t}$

(a) $P(0) = 100e^{(0.2197)(0)} = 100$

(b) $P(5) = 100e^{(0.2197)(5)} \approx 300$

(c) $P(10) = 100e^{(0.2197)(10)} \approx 900$

55. $Q = 25 \left(\dfrac{1}{2}\right)^{t/1620}$

(a) When $t = 0$,

$$Q = 25 \left(\frac{1}{2}\right)^{0/1620}$$

$$= 25(1)$$

$$= 25 \text{ units.}$$

(b) When $t = 1000$,

$$Q = 25 \left(\frac{1}{2}\right)^{1000/1620}$$

$$\approx 16.297 \text{ units.}$$

(c)

57. $y = \dfrac{300}{3 + 17e^{-1.57x}}$

(a)

(b) If $x = 2$, $y = 80.3\%$.

(c) If $y = 66.67\%$, $x = 1.55$
(1550 egg masses).

59. $V(t) = 20{,}000 \left(\dfrac{3}{4}\right)^{t}$

$$V(2) = 20{,}000 \left(\frac{3}{4}\right)^{2} = \$11{,}250$$

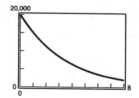

Section 5.2   Logarithmic Functions and Their Graphs

- You should know that a function of the form $y = \log_a M$, where $a > 0$, $a \neq 1$, and $M > 0$, is called a logarithm of M to base a.

- You should be able to convert from logarithmic form to exponential form and vice versa.

  $y = \log_a M \iff a^y = M$

- You should know the following properties of logarithms.
  - (a) $\log_a 1 = 0$
  - (b) $\log_a a = 1$
  - (c) $\log_a a^x = x$
  - (d) Domain: $(0, \infty)$
  - (e) Range: $(-\infty, \infty)$

- You should know the definition of the natural logarithmic function.

  $\log_e x = \ln x, \quad x > 0$

- You should know the properties of the natural logarithmic function.
  - (a) $\ln 1 = 0$
  - (b) $\ln e = 1$
  - (c) $\ln e^x = x$
  - (d) Domain: $(0, \infty)$
  - (e) Range: $(-\infty, \infty)$

- You should be able to graph logarithmic functions by hand and with a graphing utility.

---

1. $\log_2 16 = \log_2 2^4 = 4$

3. $\log_{16} 4 = \log_{16} 16^{1/2} = \frac{1}{2}$

5. $\log_7 1 = \log_7 7^0 = 0$

7. $\log_{10} 0.01 = \log_{10} 10^{-2} = -2$

9. $\ln e^3 = 3$

11. $\log_a a^2 = 2$

13. $5^3 = 125$

$3 = \log_5 125$

15. $81^{1/4} = 3$

$\frac{1}{4} = \log_{81} 3$

17. $6^{-2} = \frac{1}{36}$

$-2 = \log_6 \left(\frac{1}{36} \right)$

19. $e^3 = 20.0855\ldots$

$3 = \ln 20.0855\ldots$

21. $\log_{10} 345 \approx 2.538$

23. $\log_{10}(0.48) \approx -0.319$

25. $\ln 18.42 \approx 2.913$

27. $f(x) = 3^x, \quad g(x) = \log_3 x$

29. $f(x) = e^x, \quad g(x) = \ln x$

Notice that the graphs are symmetric with respect to the line $y = x$.

Notice that the graphs are symmetric with respect to the line $y = x$.

31. $f(x) = \ln x + 2$
Rises to the right
Vertical asymptote:
   $x = 0$
Point on graph: $(1, 2)$
Graph (d)

```
RANGE
Xmin=-1
Xmax=4
Xscl=1
Ymin=-1
Ymax=3
Yscl=1
```

33. $f(x) = -\ln(x + 2)$
Falls to the right
Vertical asymptote:
   $x = -2$
Intercepts:
   $(-1, 0), (0, -\ln 2)$
Graph (a)

```
RANGE
Xmin=-3
Xmax=3
Xscl=1
Ymin=-2
Ymax=2
Yscl=1
```

35. $f(x) = \ln(1 - x)$
Rises to the left
Vertical asymptote:
   $x = 1$
Intercept: $(0, 0)$
Graph (f)

```
RANGE
Xmin=-3
Xmax=2
Xscl=1
Ymin=-2
Ymax=2
Yscl=1
```

37. $f(x) = \log_4 x$
Domain: $(0, \infty)$
Vertical asymptote: $x = 0$
Intercept: $(1, 0)$

39. $y = -\log_3(x + 2)$
Domain: $x + 2 > 0 \Rightarrow x > -2$
Vertical asymptote: $x = -2$
x-intercept: $(-1, 0)$

41. $f(x) = \ln(x - 2)$

Domain: $(2, \infty)$

Vertical asymptote: $x = 2$

Intercept: $(3, 0)$

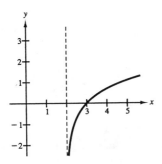

43. $f(x) = \dfrac{x}{2} - \ln\left(\dfrac{x}{4}\right)$

Increasing: $(2, \infty)$

Decreasing: $(0, 2)$

Relative minimum: $(2, \ 1.693)$

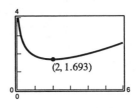

45. (a) $f(x) = \ln x$

$g(x) = \sqrt{x}$

$\sqrt{x}$ increases more rapidly than $\ln x$.

(b) $f(x) = \ln x$

$g(x) = \sqrt[4]{x}$

$\sqrt[4]{x}$ increases more rapidly than $\ln x$.

(The graphs of $\ln x$ and $\sqrt[4]{x}$ cross at approximately $x = 5504$.) The rate of growth of $\ln x$ is less than $\sqrt{x}$ and $\sqrt[4]{x}$ (and $\sqrt[n]{x}$) for large x.

47. $f(t) = 80 - 17 \log_{10}(t + 1), \quad 0 \le t \le 12$

(a) $f(0) = 80 - 17 \log_{10}(0 + 1) = 80 - 17(0) = 80$

(b) $f(4) = 80 - 17 \log_{10}(4 + 1) = 80 - 17(0.699) \approx 68.1$

(c) $f(10) = 80 - 17 \log_{10}(10 + 1) = 80 - 17(1.041) \approx 62.3$

49. $t = \dfrac{\ln 2}{r}$

r	0.005	0.010	0.015	0.020	0.025	0.030
t	138.6	69.3	46.2	34.7	27.7	23.1

51. $y = 80.4 - 11 \ln x = 80.4 - 11 \ln 300$

$y \approx 17.658$ cubic feet per minute

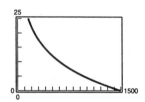

53. $t = \dfrac{5.315}{-6.7968 + \ln x}$, $1000 < x$

$= \dfrac{5.315}{-6.7968 + \ln 1167.41}$

$t \approx 20$

The length of the mortgage will be about 20 years.

55. From Exercise 53, we know the length of the mortgage will be about 20 years. Thus, the total amount paid will be $12(20)(1167.41) = \$280{,}178.40$.

57. $W = 19{,}440(\ln 9 - \ln 3) \approx 21{,}357.023$ ft-lb

59. $f(x) = \dfrac{\ln x}{x}$

(a)

x	1	5	10	10^2	10^4	10^6
$f(x)$	0	0.322	0.230	0.046	0.00092	0.0000138

(b) As $x \Rightarrow \infty$, $f(x) \Rightarrow 0$.

(c)

61. $y = 2 \ln x$ and $y = \ln x^2$ are not identical since the domain of the former is $(0, \infty)$, whereas, that of $y = \ln x^2$ is all $x \neq 0$. They are identical on $(0, \infty)$. You can verify this by graphing the two functions on the same viewing rectangle.

Section 5.3   Properties of Logarithms

- You should know the following properties of logarithms.
  - (a) $\log_a(uv) = \log_a u + \log_a v$
  - (b) $\log_a(u/v) = \log_a u - \log_a v$
  - (c) $\log_a u^n = n \log_a u$
  - (d) $\log_a x = \dfrac{\log_b x}{\log_b a}$
    Change of base
- You should be able to rewrite logarithmic expressions.

---

1. $\log_3 5 = \dfrac{\log_{10} 5}{\log_{10} 3}$

3. $\log_2 x = \dfrac{\log_{10} x}{\log_{10} 2}$

5. $\log_3 5 = \dfrac{\ln 5}{\ln 3}$

7. $\log_2 x = \dfrac{\ln x}{\ln 2}$

9. $\log_3 7 = \dfrac{\log_{10} 7}{\log_{10} 3}$
$= \dfrac{\ln 7}{\ln 3}$
≈ 1.771

11. $\log_{1/2} 4 = \dfrac{\log_{10} 4}{\log_{10} \frac{1}{2}}$
$= \dfrac{\ln 4}{\ln \frac{1}{2}}$
$= -2.000$

13. $\log_9(0.4) = \dfrac{\log_{10} 0.4}{\log_{10} 9} = \dfrac{\ln 0.4}{\ln 9} \approx -0.417$

15. $\log_{15} 1250 = \dfrac{\log_{10} 1250}{\log_{10} 15} = \dfrac{\ln 1250}{\ln 15} \approx 2.633$

17. $\log_{10} 5x = \log_{10} 5 + \log_{10} x$

19. $\log_{10} \dfrac{5}{x} = \log_{10} 5 - \log_{10} x$

21. $\log_8 x^4 = 4 \log_8 x$

23. $\ln \sqrt{z} = \ln z^{1/2} = \frac{1}{2} \ln z$

25. $\ln xyz = \ln x + \ln y + \ln z$

27. $\ln \sqrt{a-1} = \ln(a-1)^{1/2}$
$= \frac{1}{2} \ln(a-1)$

29. $\ln z(z-1)^2 = \ln z + \ln(z-1)^2$
$= \ln z + 2\ln(z-1)$

31. $\ln \sqrt[3]{\dfrac{x}{y}} = \ln \left(\dfrac{x}{y}\right)^{1/3} = \dfrac{1}{3}\ln\dfrac{x}{y} = \dfrac{1}{3}(\ln x - \ln y) = \dfrac{1}{3}\ln x - \dfrac{1}{3}\ln y$

33. $\ln \dfrac{x^4 \sqrt{y}}{z^5} = \ln x^4 + \ln \sqrt{y} - \ln z^5$
$= 4\ln x + \dfrac{1}{2}\ln y - 5\ln z$

35. $\log_b \dfrac{x^2}{y^2 z^3} = \log_b x^2 - (\log_b y^2 + \log_b z^3)$
$= 2\log_b x - 2\log_b y - 3\log_b z$

37. $\ln x + \ln 2 = \ln 2x$

39. $\log_4 z - \log_4 y = \log_4 \dfrac{z}{y}$

41. $2\log_2(x+4) = \log_2(x+4)^2$

43. $\frac{1}{3}\log_3 5x = \log_3(5x)^{1/3} = \log_3 \sqrt[3]{5x}$

45. $\ln x - 3\ln(x+1) = \ln x - \ln(x+1)^3$

$$= \ln \dfrac{x}{(x+1)^3}$$

47. $\ln(x-2) - \ln(x+2) = \ln \dfrac{x-2}{x+2}$

49. $\ln x - 2[\ln(x+2) + \ln(x-2)] = \ln x - 2\ln(x^2-4) = \ln x - \ln(x^2-4)^2 = \ln \dfrac{x}{(x^2-4)^2}$

51. $\dfrac{1}{3}[2\ln(x+3) + \ln x - \ln(x^2-1)] = \dfrac{1}{3}\ln \dfrac{x(x+3)^2}{x^2-1} = \ln \sqrt[3]{\dfrac{x(x+3)^2}{x^2-1}}$

53. $\dfrac{1}{3}[\ln y + 2\ln(y+4)] - \ln(y-1) = \dfrac{1}{3}\ln y(y+4)^2 - \ln(y-1) = \ln \dfrac{\sqrt[3]{y(y+4)^2}}{y-1}$

55. $2\ln 3 - \dfrac{1}{2}\ln(x^2+1) = \ln 3^2 - \ln \sqrt{x^2+1} = \ln \dfrac{9}{\sqrt{x^2+1}}$

57. $\log_b 6 = \log_b(2 \cdot 3)$

$\quad = \log_b 2 + \log_b 3$

$\quad \approx 0.3562 + 0.5646$

$\quad = 0.9208$

59. $\log_b 40 = \log_b(2^3 \cdot 5)$

$\quad = 3\log_b 2 + \log_b 5$

$\quad = 3(0.3562) + 0.8271$

$\quad = 1.8957$

61. $\log_b\left(\dfrac{\sqrt{2}}{2}\right) = \log_b 2^{1/2} - \log_b 2$

$$= \dfrac{1}{2}\log_b 2 - \log_b 2$$

$$= -\dfrac{1}{2}\log_b 2$$

$$= -\dfrac{1}{2}(0.3562)$$

$$= -0.1781$$

63. $\log_b \sqrt{5b} = \frac{1}{2}[\log_b 5 + \log_b b]$

$\quad \approx \frac{1}{2}(0.8271 + 1)$

$\quad = 0.9136$

65. $\log_b \dfrac{(4.5)^3}{\sqrt{3}} = 3\log_b \dfrac{9}{2} - \dfrac{1}{2}\log_b 3 = 3(\log_b 3^2 - \log_b 2) - \dfrac{1}{2}\log_b 3$

$$= 3(2\log_b 3 - \log_b 2) - \dfrac{1}{2}\log_b 3 \approx 3[2(0.5646) - 0.3562] - \dfrac{1}{2}(0.5646) = 2.0367$$

67. $\log_3 9 = \log_3 3^2$

$\quad = 2\log_3 3$

$\quad = 2(1)$

$\quad = 2$

69. $\log_4 16^{1.2} = 1.2\log_4 16$

$\quad = 1.2\log_4 4^2$

$\quad = 1.2(2)\log_4 4$

$\quad = 1.2(2)(1)$

$\quad = 2.4$

71. $\ln e^{4.5} = 4.5\ln e$

$\quad = 4.5(1)$

$\quad = 4.5$

73. $\log_4 8 = \log_4 2^3$

$\quad = 3\log_4 2$

$\quad = 3\log_4 \sqrt{4}$

$\quad = 3\log_4 4^{1/2}$

$\quad = 3\left(\frac{1}{2}\right)\log_4 4 = \frac{3}{2}$

75. $\log_7 \sqrt{70} = \frac{1}{2}\log_7(7\cdot 10)$

$\quad = \frac{1}{2}(\log_7 7 + \log_7 10)$

$\quad = \frac{1}{2} + \frac{1}{2}\log_7 10$

77. $\log_5 \frac{1}{250} = \log_5 1 - \log_5 250$

$\quad = 0 - \log_5(125\cdot 2)$

$\quad = -\log_5(5^3 \cdot 2)$

$\quad = -[\log_5 5^3 + \log_5 2]$

$\quad = -[3\log_5 5 + \log_5 2]$

$\quad = -3 - \log_5 2$

79. $\ln(5e^6) = \ln 5 + \ln e^6 = 6 + \ln 5$

81. $\beta = 10\log_{10}\left(\dfrac{I}{10^{-16}}\right) = 10\left[\log_{10} I - \log_{10} 10^{-16}\right] = 10[\log_{10} I + 16] = 160 + 10\log_{10} I$

When $I = 10^{-10}$, we have $\beta = 160 + 10\log_{10} 10^{-10} = 160 + 10(-10) = 60$ decibels.

83. $f(x) = \ln\left(\dfrac{x}{2}\right)$

$g(x) = \dfrac{\ln x}{\ln 2}$

$h(x) = \ln x - \ln 2$

From the graphs, we see that $f(x) = h(x)$ and $f(x) \neq g(x)$!

85. Let $x = \log_b u$, then $u = b^x$ and $u^n = (b^x)^n = b^{nx}$ and $\log_b u^n = \log_b b^{nx} = nx = n\log_b u$.

Section 5.4   Solving Exponential and Logarithmic Equations

■ You should be able to solve exponential and logarithmic equations graphically and algebraically.

■ To solve an exponential equation, take the logarithm of both sides.

■ To solve a logarithmic equation, rewrite it in exponential form.

■ Your graphing utility is especially helpful for checking answers.

1. $4^x = 16$

$4^x = 4^2$

$x = 2$

3. $7^x = \frac{1}{49}$

$7^x = 7^{-2}$

$x = -2$

5. $\left(\frac{3}{4}\right)^x = \frac{27}{64}$

$\left(\frac{3}{4}\right)^x = \left(\frac{3}{4}\right)^3$

$x = 3$

7. $\log_4 x = 3$

$x = 4^3 = 64$

9. $\log_{10} x = -1$

$x = 10^{-1} = \frac{1}{10}$

11. $\ln e^{x^2} = x^2$

13. $e^{\ln(5x+2)} = 5x + 2$

15. $e^{\ln x^2} = x^2$

17. $e^x = 10$

$x = \ln 10 \approx 2.303$

19. $7 - 2e^x = 5$

$-2e^x = -2$

$e^x = 1$

$x = \ln 1 = 0$

21. $e^{3x} = 12$

$3x = \ln 12$

$x = \frac{1}{3} \ln 12$

≈ 0.828

23. $500e^{-x} = 300$

$e^{-x} = \frac{3}{5}$

$-x = \ln \frac{3}{5}$

$x = -\ln \frac{3}{5}$

$= \ln \frac{5}{3} \approx 0.511$

25. $e^{2x} - 4e^x - 5 = 0$

$(e^x + 1)(e^x - 5) = 0$

$e^x + 1 = 0$ or $e^x - 5 = 0$

    $e^x = -1$ $e^x x = 5$

No solution $x = \ln 5$

                   ≈ 1.609

Checking with a graphing utility, the only
x-intercept is $x = 1.61$.

27. $20(100 - e^{x/2}) = 500$

    $100 - e^{x/2} = 25$

       $e^{x/2} = 75$

      $\dfrac{x}{2} = \ln 75$

      $x = 2\ln 75 \approx 8.635$

29. $10^x = 42$

    $x = \log_{10} 42$

      ≈ 1.623

31. $3^{2x} = 80$

    $\ln 3^{2x} = \ln 80$

    $2x \ln 3 = \ln 80$

       $x = \dfrac{\ln 80}{2 \ln 3}$

        ≈ 1.994

33. $5^{-t/2} = 0.20$

   $5^{-t/2} = \dfrac{1}{5}$

   $5^{-t/2} = 5^{-1}$

    $-\dfrac{t}{2} = -1$

      $t = 2$

35. $\left(1 + \dfrac{0.10}{12}\right)^{12t} = 2$

$\ln \left(1 + \dfrac{0.10}{12}\right)^{12t} = \ln 2$

$12t \ln \left(1 + \dfrac{0.10}{12}\right) = \ln 2$

       $t = \dfrac{\ln 2}{12 \ln \left(1 + \dfrac{0.10}{12}\right)} \approx 6.960$

37. $3e^{3x/2} = 962$

    $f(x) = 3e^{3x/2} - 962$

      $x = 3.847$

39. $e^{0.09t} = 3$

    $f(t) = e^{0.09t} - 3$

      $t = 12.207$

41. $8(10^{3x}) = 12$

    $f(x) = 8(10^{3x}) - 12$

      $x = 0.059$

43. $\left(1 + \dfrac{0.065}{365}\right)^{365t} = 4$

$$f(t) = \left(1 + \dfrac{0.065}{365}\right)^{365t} - 4$$

$$t = 21.330$$

45. $\ln x = -3 \Rightarrow e^{-3} = x \Rightarrow x \approx 0.050$

47. $\ln 2x = 2.4$

$2x = e^{2.4}$

$x = \dfrac{e^{2.4}}{2} \approx 5.512$

49. $\ln \sqrt{x+2} = 1$

$\sqrt{x+2} = e^1$

$x + 2 = e^2$

$x = -2 + e^2 \approx 5.389$

51. $\ln x + \ln(x-2) = 1$

$\ln x(x-2) = 1$

$x(x-2) = e^1$

$x^2 - 2x - e = 0$

$$x = \dfrac{-(-2) \pm \sqrt{(-2)^2 - 4(1)(-e)}}{2(1)} = \dfrac{2 \pm 2\sqrt{1+e}}{2} = 1 \pm \sqrt{1+e}$$

$x = 1 + \sqrt{1+e} \approx 2.928$

$x = 1 - \sqrt{1+e} \approx -0.928$ extraneous

Checking with a graphing utility, the only solution to $y = \ln x + \ln(x-2) - 1 = 0$ is $x = 2.93$.

53. $\log_{10}(z-3) = 2$

$z - 3 = 10^2$

$z = 10^2 + 3 = 103$

55. $\log_{10}(x+4) - \log_{10} x = \log_{10}(x+2)$

$$\log_{10}\left(\frac{x+4}{x}\right) = \log_{10}(x+2)$$

$$\frac{x+4}{x} = x+2$$

$$x + 4 = x^2 + 2x$$

$$0 = x^2 + x - 4$$

$$x = \frac{-1 \pm \sqrt{17}}{2} = -\frac{1}{2} \pm \frac{\sqrt{17}}{2}$$

$$x = -\frac{1}{2} + \frac{\sqrt{17}}{2} \approx 1.562$$

$$x = -\frac{1}{2} - \frac{\sqrt{17}}{2} \approx -2.562 \text{ extraneous}$$

Checking with a graphing utility, the only solution to $y = \log_{10}(x+4) - \log_{10} x - \log_{10}(x+2)$ is $x = 1.56$.

57. $\log_3 x + \log_3(x^2 - 8) = \log_3 8x$

$$\log_3 x(x^2 - 8) = \log_3 8x$$

$$x(x^2 - 8) = 8x$$

$$x^3 - 16x = 0$$

$$x(x+4)(x-4) = 0$$

$$x = 0 \text{ extraneous}$$

$$x + 4 = 0 \Rightarrow x = -4 \text{ extraneous}$$

$$x - 4 = 0 \Rightarrow x = 4$$

59. $\ln(x+5) = \ln(x-1) - \ln(x+1)$

$$\ln(x+5) = \ln\left(\frac{x-1}{x+1}\right)$$

$$x + 5 = \frac{x-1}{x+1}$$

$$(x+5)(x+1) = x - 1$$

$$x^2 + 6x + 5 = x - 1$$

$$x^2 + 5x + 6 = 0$$

$$(x+2)(x+3) = 0$$

$$x = -2 \text{ or } x = -3$$

Both of these solutions are extraneous, so the equation has no solution. The graph of $y = \ln(x+5) - \ln(x-1) + \ln(x+1)$ confirms that there are no solutions.

61. $2\ln x = 7$

$$f(x) = 2\ln x - 7$$

$$x = 33.115$$

63. $\ln x + \ln(x^2 + 1) = 8$

$$f(x) = \ln x + \ln(x^2 + 1) - 8$$

$$x = 14.369$$

65.
$$A = Pe^{rt}$$
$$2000 = 1000e^{0.085t}$$
$$2 = e^{0.085t}$$
$$\ln 2 = 0.085t$$
$$\frac{\ln 2}{0.085} = t$$
$$t \approx 8.2 \text{ years}$$

67.
$$A = Pe^{rt}$$
$$3000 = 1000e^{0.085t}$$
$$3 = e^{0.085t}$$
$$\ln 3 = 0.085t$$
$$\frac{\ln 3}{0.085} = t$$
$$t \approx 12.9 \text{ years}$$

69. $p = 500 - 0.5(e^{0.004x})$

(a)
$$350 = 500 - 0.5(e^{0.004x})$$
$$-150 = -0.5(e^{0.004x})$$
$$300 = e^{0.004x}$$
$$0.004x = \ln 300$$
$$x = \frac{\ln 300}{0.004} \approx 1426 \text{ units}$$

(b)
$$300 = 500 - 0.5(e^{0.004x})$$
$$-200 = -0.5(e^{0.004x})$$
$$400 = e^{0.004x}$$
$$0.004x = \ln 400$$
$$x = \frac{\ln 400}{0.004} \approx 1498 \text{ units}$$

71. $V = 6.7e^{-48.1/t}$

(a)

(b) The horizontal asymptote is $V = 6.7$. The horizontal asymptote represents the limiting yield per acre.

(c)
$$1.3 = 6.7e^{-48.1/t}$$
$$\frac{1.3}{6.7} = e^{-48.1/t}$$
$$\ln\frac{1.3}{6.7} = -\frac{48.1}{t}$$
$$t = -\frac{48.1}{\ln(1.3/6.7)}$$
$$\approx 29.33 \text{ years}$$

Or, graphing
$$V - 1.3 = 6.7e^{-48.1/t} - 1.3,$$
we see that the t-intercept is $t = 29.33$.

73. (a)

(b) The horizontal asymptote is $y = 100$ for each function.

(c) For males: For females:

$$50 = \frac{100}{1 + e^{-0.6114(x-69.71)}} \qquad\qquad 50 = \frac{100}{1 + e^{-0.66607(x-64.51)}}$$

$$1 + e^{-0.6114(x-69.71)} = \frac{100}{50} \qquad\qquad 1 + e^{-0.66607(x-64.51)} = \frac{100}{50}$$

$$e^{-0.6114(x-69.71)} = 1 \qquad\qquad e^{-0.66607(x-64.51)} = 1$$

$$-0.6114(x - 69.71) = \ln 1 \qquad\qquad -0.66607(x - 64.51) = \ln 1$$

$$x - 69.71 = 0 \qquad\qquad\qquad x - 64.51 = 0$$

$$x = 69.71 \text{ in. for males} \qquad\qquad x = 64.51 \text{ in. for females}$$

Or, you can determine the average height by using a graping utility to find the intersection of $m(x)$ (or $f(x)$) and $y = 50$.

Section 5.5   Applications of Exponential and Logarithmic Functions

---

■ You should be able to solve compound interest problems.

(a) Compound interest formulas:

    1. $A = P\left(1 + \dfrac{r}{n}\right)^{nt}$ 2. $A = Pe^{rt}$

(b) Effective yield:

    1. Effective yield $= \left(1 + \dfrac{r}{n}\right)^{n} - 1$, n compoundings per year

    2. Effective yield $= e^{r} - 1$, continuous compounding

■ You should be able to solve growth and decay problems: $Q(t) = Ce^{kt}$

(a) If $k > 0$, the population grows.

(b) If $k < 0$, the population decays.

■ You should be able to solve logistics model problems: $y = \dfrac{a}{1 + be^{-(x-c)/d}}$

■ You should be able to solve intensity model problems: $S = K \log_{10} \dfrac{I}{I_0}$

	Initial investment	Annual % rate	Effective yield	Time to double	Amount after 10 yrs
1.	1000	12%	12.75%	5.78 yrs	3,320.12
3.	750	8.94%	9.35%	7.75 yrs	1,833.67
5.	500	9.5%	9.97%	7.30 yrs	1,292.85
7.	6392.79	11%	11.63%	6.30 yrs	19,205.00
9.	5000	8%	8.33%	8.66 yrs	11,127.70

Formulas used in Exercises 1–9:

Initial investment: $P = Ae^{-rt}$ Annual % rate: $r = \dfrac{\ln(A/P)}{t}$ or $r = \ln(1 + \text{effective yield})$

Effective yield $= e^{r} - 1$ Time to double $= \dfrac{\ln 2}{r}$

Amount after ten years $= Pe^{10r}$

11. $500{,}000 = P\left(1 + \dfrac{0.075}{12}\right)^{12(20)}$

$500{,}000 = P(1.00625)^{240}$

$P \approx \$112{,}087.09$

13. $P = 1000, \ r = 11\%$

(a) $n = 1$

$t = \dfrac{\ln 2}{\ln(1 + 0.11)} \approx 6.642$ years

(b) $n = 12$

$t = \dfrac{\ln 2}{12\ln\left(1 + \dfrac{0.11}{12}\right)} \approx 6.330$ years

(c) $n = 365$

$t = \dfrac{\ln 2}{365\ln\left(1 + \dfrac{0.11}{365}\right)} \approx 6.302$ years

(d) Continuously

$t = \dfrac{\ln 2}{0.11} \approx 6.301$ years

15. $3P = Pe^{rt}$

$3 = e^{rt}$

$rt = \ln 3$

$t = \dfrac{\ln 3}{r}$

r	2%	4%	6%	8%	10%	12%
t	54.93	27.47	18.31	13.73	10.99	9.16

17. $A = 1 + 0.075t$ (simple interest)

$A = e^{0.07t}$ (continuous compound interest)

Continuous compounding at 7% grows faster.

Isotope	Half-life	Initial quantity	Amt. after 1000 yrs	Amt. after 10,000 yrs
19. ^{226}Ra	1620	10 grams	6.52 grams	0.14 grams
21. ^{14}C	5730	6.70 grams	5.95 grams	2 grams
23. ^{230}Pu	24,360	2.16 grams	2.1 grams	1.62 grams

Formula used in Exercises 19–23:

$$Q(t) = Ce^{-(\ln 2/T)t}$$
$$Q(t) = \text{amount}, \ C = \text{initial amount}, \ T = \text{half-life}, \ t = \text{time}$$

25. $y = e^{kt}$

$10 = e^{4k}$

$4k = \ln 10$

$k = \frac{1}{4}\ln 10 \approx 0.5756$

27. $y = e^{kt}$

$\frac{1}{4} = e^{4k}$

$4k = \ln\frac{1}{4}$

$k = \frac{1}{4}\ln\frac{1}{4} \approx -0.3466$

29. (a) If $t = 0$, $P = 105{,}300$.

(b) $150{,}000 = 105{,}300e^{0.015t}$

$0.015t = \ln\left(\dfrac{150{,}000}{105{,}300}\right)$

$t = \dfrac{1}{0.015}\ln\left(\dfrac{150{,}000}{105{,}300}\right)$

≈ 23.588 years

$1990 + 23 = 2013$

The city will have a population of 150,000 in the year 2013.

31. $1350 = 2500e^{k(-45)}$

$-45k = \ln\left(\dfrac{1350}{2500}\right)$

$k = \left(-\dfrac{1}{45}\right)\ln\left(\dfrac{1350}{2500}\right) \approx 0.0137$

$P = 2500e^{0.0137(20)} \approx 3288$

33. $P = Ce^{kt}$

$4.22 = Ce^{k(0)} \Rightarrow C = 4.22$

$6.49 = 4.22e^{10k}$

$\dfrac{6.49}{4.22} = e^{10k}$

$k = \dfrac{1}{10}\ln\left(\dfrac{6.49}{4.22}\right) \approx 0.0430$

$P = 4.22e^{0.0430}$

When $t = 20$, $P \approx 9.97$ million.

35. $N = 100e^{kt}$

$300 = 100e^{5k}$

$k = \dfrac{\ln 3}{5} \approx 0.2197$

$N = 100e^{0.2197t}$

$200 = 100e^{0.2197t}$

$t = \dfrac{\ln 2}{0.2197}$

≈ 3.15 hours

37. $Q(t) = Ce^{kt}$

$\tfrac{1}{2}C = Ce^{k(1620)}$

$\tfrac{1}{2} = e^{1620k}$

$k = \dfrac{1}{1620}\ln(\tfrac{1}{2}) \approx -0.000428$

$Q(t) = Ce^{-0.000428t}$

When $t = 100$,

$Q(100) \approx 0.958C$

$= 95.8\%$ of C.

39. $16{,}500 = 22{,}000e^{k(1)}$

$\dfrac{16{,}500}{22{,}000} = e^k$

$\ln\tfrac{3}{4} = k$

$k \approx -0.2877$

$y = 22{,}000e^{-0.2877(3)}$

$y \approx \$9{,}281$

41. $S(t) = 100(1 - e^{kt})$

(a) $15 = 100(1 - e^{k(1)})$

$-85 = -100e^k$

$k = \ln 0.85$

$k \approx -0.1625$

$S(t) = 100(1 - e^{-0.1625t})$

(b) $S(5) = 100(1 - e^{-0.1625(5)})$

$\approx 55.625 = 55{,}625$ units

43. $p = 0.166e^{-(x-64.5)^2/11.5}$

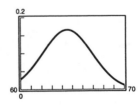

The average height is 64.5, the highest point on the graph.

45. $p(t) = \dfrac{10{,}000}{1 + 19e^{-t/5}}$

(a)

The larger horizontal asymptote is $p = 10{,}000$, which represents the carrying capacity of the lake for this species of fish.

(b) $p(5) = \dfrac{10{,}000}{1 + 19e^{-1}} \approx 1252$ fish

(c) $\quad 2000 = \dfrac{10{,}000}{1 + 19e^{-t/5}}$

$$1 + 19e^{-t/5} = 5$$

$$e^{-t/5} = \frac{4}{19}$$

$$-\frac{t}{5} = \ln\left(\frac{4}{19}\right)$$

$$t = -5\ln\left(\frac{4}{19}\right)$$

$$\approx 7.8 \text{ months}$$

Or, using a graphing utility to graph

$$y = \frac{10{,}000}{1 + 19e^{-t/5}} - 2000,$$

we see that the x-intercept is 7.79.

47. $S = 10(1 - e^{kx})$

(a) $2.5 = 10(1 - e^{k(5)})$

$$\tfrac{1}{4} = 1 - e^{5k}$$

$$5k = \ln \tfrac{3}{4}$$

$$k = \tfrac{1}{5}\ln\tfrac{3}{4} \approx -0.0575$$

$$S = 10(1 - e^{-0.0575x})$$

(b) $S = 10\left(1 - e^{-0.0575(7)}\right)$

$$\approx 3.314 \text{ or } 3314 \text{ units}$$

49. $R = \log_{10}\dfrac{I}{I_0} = \log_{10} I$ since $I_0 = 1$

(a) $R = \log_{10} 80{,}500{,}000 \approx 7.9$

(b) $R = \log_{10} 48{,}275{,}000 \approx 7.7$

51. $\beta(I) = 10 \log_{10} \dfrac{I}{I_0}$ where $I_0 = 10^{-16}$ watt/cm^2

    (a) $\beta(10^{-14}) = 10 \log_{10} \dfrac{10^{-14}}{10^{-16}} = 10 \log_{10} 10^2 = 20$ decibels

    (b) $\beta(10^{-9}) = 10 \log_{10} \dfrac{10^{-9}}{10^{-16}} = 10 \log_{10} 10^7 = 70$ decibels

    (c) $\beta(10^{-6.5}) = 10 \log_{10} \dfrac{10^{-6.5}}{10^{-16}} = 10 \log_{10} 10^{9.5} = 95$ decibels

    (d) $\beta(10^{-4}) = 10 \log_{10} \dfrac{10^{-4}}{10^{-16}} = 10 \log_{10} 10^{12} = 120$ decibels

53. $\qquad \beta = 10 \log_{10} \dfrac{I}{I_0}$

$\qquad \dfrac{\beta}{10} = \log_{10} \dfrac{I}{I_0}$

$\qquad 10^{\beta/10} = \dfrac{I}{I_0}$

$\qquad\quad I = I_0 10^{\beta/10}$

$\text{\% decrease} = \dfrac{I_0 10^{93/10} - I_0 10^{80/10}}{I_0 10^{93/10}} \times 100 \approx 95\%$

55. $\text{pH} = -\log_{10}[\text{H}^+]$

$\qquad = -\log_{10}[2.3 \times 10^{-5}]$

$\qquad \approx 4.64$

57. $\quad \text{pH} = -\log[\text{H}^+]$

$\qquad 5.8 = -\log[\text{H}^+]$

$\qquad [\text{H}^+] = 10^{-5.8} \approx 1.6 \times 10^{-6}$

59. $\qquad \text{pH} = -\log_{10}[\text{H}^+]$

$\qquad -\text{pH} = \log_{10}[\text{H}^+]$

$\qquad 10^{-\text{pH}} = [\text{H}^+]$

$\dfrac{\text{Hydrogen ion concentration of fruit}}{\text{Hydrogen ion concentration of tablet}} = \dfrac{10^{-2.5}}{10^{-9.5}} = 10^7$

61. (a)

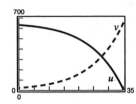

(b) In the early years of the mortgage, the larger part of the monthly payment goes for interest payments $(u > v)$. Using the zoom feature, $u = v$ when $t = 27.7$ years.

63. $t = -2.5 \ln \left(\dfrac{T - 70}{98.6 - 70} \right)$

At 9:00 A.M. we have:

$$t = -2.5 \ln \left(\frac{85.7 - 70}{98.6 - 70} \right) \approx 1.5 \text{ hours.}$$

From this we can conclude that the person died at 7:30 A.M.

Chapter 5   Review Exercises

1. $f(x) = 2^x$

    Horizontal asymptote: $y = 0$

    y-intercept: $(0, 1)$

    As x increases, $f(x)$ increases.

    Matches (d)

```
RANGE
Xmin=-4
Xmax=3
Xscl=1
Ymin=-1
Ymax=4
Yscl=1
```

3. $f(x) = -2^x$

    Horizontal asymptote: $y = 0$

    y-intercept: $(0, -1)$

    As x increases, $f(x)$ decreases.

    Matches (a)

```
RANGE
Xmin=-4
Xmax=4
Xscl=1
Ymin=-5
Ymax=1
Yscl=1
```

5. $f(x) = \log_2 x$

    Vertical asymptote: $x = 0$

    x-intercept: $(1, 0)$

    As x increases, $f(x)$ increases.

    Matches (c)

```
RANGE
Xmin=-3
Xmax=6
Xscl=1
Ymin=-3
Ymax=3
Yscl=1
```

7. $f(x) = 6^x$

9. $g(x) = 6^{-x}$

11. $h(x) = e^{-x/2}$

13. $f(x) = e^{x+2}$

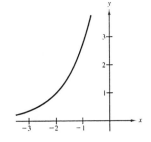

15. $n = 1:$ $A = 3500(1 + 0.105)^{10}$ $\approx \$9,499.28$

   $n = 2:$ $A = 3500\left(1 + \dfrac{0.105}{2}\right)^{20}$ $\approx \$9,738.91$

   $n = 4:$ $A = 3500\left(1 + \dfrac{0.105}{4}\right)^{40}$ $\approx \$9,867.22$

   $n = 12:$ $A = 3500\left(1 + \dfrac{0.105}{12}\right)^{120}$ $\approx \$9,956.20$

   $n = 365:$ $A = 3500\left(1 + \dfrac{0.105}{365}\right)^{3650}$ $\approx \$10,000.27$

   Continuous: $A = 3500e^{(0.105)(10)} \approx \$10,001.78$

17. $A = Pe^{rt}$

   $P = Ae^{-rt} = 200,000e^{-0.08t}$

   $t = 1:$ $P = 200,000e^{-0.08} \approx \$184,623.27$

   $t = 10:$ $P = 200,000e^{-0.8} \approx \$89,865.79$

   $t = 20:$ $P = 200,000e^{-1.6} \approx \$40,379.30$

   $t = 30:$ $P = 200,000e^{-2.4} \approx \$18,143.59$

   $t = 40:$ $P = 200,000e^{-3.2} \approx \$8,152.44$

   $t = 50:$ $P = 200,000e^{-4.0} \approx \$3,663.13$

19. $A = 50,000e^{0.0875(35)}$

   $\approx \$1,069,047.14$

21. $A = 500e^{-0.013t}$

   $A = 500e^{-0.013(60)}$

   ≈ 229.2 units per milliliter
   The algebraic solution is easier.

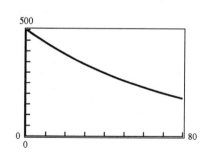

23. $y = 28e^{0.6-0.012s}, \ s \geq 50$

When $s = 50$, $y = 28e^{0.6-0.012(50)} = 28$ miles per gallon.

When $s = 55$, $y = 28e^{0.6-0.012(55)} \approx 26.4$ miles per gallon.

When $s = 60$, $y = 28e^{0.6-0.012(60)} \approx 24.8$ miles per gallon.

When $s = 65$, $y = 28e^{0.6-0.012(65)} \approx 23.4$ miles per gallon.

When $s = 70$, $y = 28e^{0.6-0.012(70)} \approx 22.0$ miles per gallon.

25. $g(x) = \log_3 x$

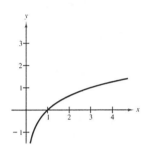

27. $f(x) = \ln x + 3$

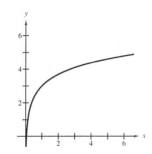

29. $h(x) = \ln(e^{x-1}) = x - 1$

31. $4^3 = 64$

$\quad 3 = \log_4 64$

33. $\log_{10} 1000 = \log_{10} 10^3$

$\qquad\qquad\quad = 3$

35. $\log_3 \frac{1}{9} = \log_3 3^{-2}$

$\qquad\quad = -2$

37. $\ln e^7 = 7 \ln e$

$\qquad\ = 7(1)$

$\qquad\ = 7$

39. $\ln 1 = \ln e^0$

$\qquad = 0 \cdot \ln e$

$\qquad = 0$

41. $\log_4 9 = \dfrac{\log_{10} 9}{\log_{10} 4}$

$\qquad\quad = \dfrac{\ln 9}{\ln 4}$

$\qquad\quad \approx 1.585$

43. $\log_{12} 200 = \dfrac{\log_{10} 200}{\log_{10} 12}$

$\qquad\qquad\ = \dfrac{\ln 200}{\ln 12} \approx 2.132$

45. $\log_5 5x^2 = \log_5 5 + \log_5 x^2$

$\qquad\qquad = 1 + 2\log_5 x$

47. $\log_{10} \dfrac{5\sqrt{y}}{x^2} = \log_{10} 5 + \log_{10} y^{1/2} - \log_{10} x^2 = \log_{10} 5 + \dfrac{1}{2}\log_{10} y - 2\log_{10} x$

49. $\ln[(x^2+1)(x-1)] = \ln(x^2+1) + \ln(x-1)$

51. $\log_2 5 + \log_2 x = \log_2 5x$

53. $\frac{1}{2}\ln|2x-1| - 2\ln|x+1| = \ln\sqrt{|2x-1|} - \ln(x+1)^2 = \ln\dfrac{\sqrt{|2x-1|}}{(x+1)^2}$

55. $\ln 3 + \frac{1}{3}\ln(4-x^2) - \ln x = \ln 3 + \ln\sqrt[3]{4-x^2} - \ln x = \ln\dfrac{3\sqrt[3]{4-x^2}}{x}$

57. False. The domain is all $x > 0$. Try using your graphing utility to graph $f(x) = \ln x$.

59. False

$\ln(x+2) \neq \ln x + \ln 2$

Try graphing $y_1 = \ln(x+2)$ and $y_2 = \ln x + \ln 2$. In fact, $\ln x + \ln 2 = \ln 2x$.

61. $\log_b 25 = \log_b 5^2$

$= 2\log_b 5$

$\approx 2(0.8271)$

$= 1.6542$

63. $\log_b \sqrt{3} = \log_b 3^{1/2}$

$= \frac{1}{2}\log_b 3$

$\approx \frac{1}{2}(0.5646)$

$= 0.2823$

65. $s = 25 - \dfrac{13\ln\left(\frac{10}{12}\right)}{\ln 3}$

≈ 27.16 miles

67. $e^x = 12$

$x = \ln 12 \approx 2.485$

69. $3e^{-5x} = 132$

$e^{-5x} = 44$

$-5x = \ln 44$

$x = -\frac{1}{5}\ln 44 \approx -0.757$

71. $e^{2x} - 7e^x + 10 = 0$

$(e^x - 5)(e^x - 2) = 0$

$e^x - 5 = 0 \qquad$ or $\quad e^x - 2 = 0$

$x = \ln 5 \qquad\qquad x = \ln 2$

$\approx 1.609 \qquad\qquad \approx 0.693$

73. $\ln 3x = 8.2$

$3x = e^{8.2}$

$x = \frac{1}{3}e^{8.2}$

≈ 1213.650

75. $\ln x - \ln 3 = 2$

$\ln\dfrac{x}{3} = 2$

$\dfrac{x}{3} = e^2$

$x = 3e^2$

≈ 22.167

77. $2 = Ce^{k(0)}$

$2 = Ce^0 = C$

$3 = 2e^{k(4)}$

$\frac{3}{2} = e^{4k}$

$4k = \ln\frac{3}{2}$

$k = \frac{1}{4}\ln\frac{3}{2}$

≈ 0.1014

$y = 2e^{0.1014t}$

79. $4 = Ce^{k(0)}$

$4 = Ce^0 = C$

$\frac{1}{2} = 4e^{k(5)}$

$\frac{1}{8} = e^{5k}$

$5k = \ln\frac{1}{8}$

$k = \frac{1}{5}\ln\frac{1}{8}$

≈ -0.4159

$y = 4e^{-0.4159t}$

81. $p = 500 - 0.5e^{0.004x}$

   (a) $p = 450$

$$450 = 500 - 0.5e^{0.004x}$$

$$0.5e^{0.004x} = 50$$

$$e^{0.004x} = 100$$

$$0.004x = \ln 100$$

$$x \approx 1151 \text{ units}$$

   (b) $p = 400$

$$400 = 500 - 0.5e^{0.004x}$$

$$0.5e^{0.004x} = 100$$

$$e^{0.004x} = 200$$

$$0.004x = \ln 200$$

$$x \approx 1325 \text{ units}$$

83. (a) $\quad t = \dfrac{\ln 2}{r}$

$$7.75 = \frac{\ln 2}{r}$$

$$r = \frac{\ln 2}{7.75}$$

$$\approx 0.0894$$

$$\text{or } 8.94\%$$

(b) $A = Pe^{rt}$

$$A = 750e^{[(\ln 2)/7.75](10)}$$

$$\approx \$1834.37$$

(c) $A = Pe^{[(\ln 2)/7.75](1)}$

$$\approx P(1.0936)$$

$$= P(1 + 0.0936)$$

$$\text{Effective yield } \approx 0.0936$$

$$= 9.36\%$$

85.

$$\beta = 10 \log_{10}\left(\frac{I}{10^{-16}}\right)$$

$$125 = 10 \log_{10}\left(\frac{I}{10^{-16}}\right)$$

$$\frac{125}{10} = \log_{10}\left(\frac{I}{10^{-16}}\right)$$

$$10^{12.5} = \frac{I}{10^{-16}}$$

$$10^{12.5} = 10^{16}I$$

$$10^{12.5}10^{-16} = I$$

$$10^{-3.5} = I$$

CHAPTER 6
Trigonometry

Section 6.1 Angles and Their Measure

You should know the following basic facts about angles, their measurement, and their applications.

■ Types of Angles:
 (a) Acute: Measure between $0°$ and $90°$
 (b) Right: Measure $90°$
 (c) Obtuse: Measure between $90°$ and $180°$

■ α and β are complementary if $\alpha + \beta = 90°$. They are supplementary if $\alpha + \beta = 180°$.

■ Two angles in standard position that have the same terminal side are called coterminal angles.

■ To convert degrees to radians, use $1° = \pi/180$ radians.

■ To convert radians to degrees, use 1 radian $= (180/\pi)°$.

■ $1' =$ one minute $= 1/60$ of $1°$.

■ $1'' =$ one second $= 1/60$ of $1' = 1/3600$ of $1°$.

■ The length of a circular arc is $s = r\theta$ where θ is measured in radians.

■ Speed = distance/time

■ Angular speed $= \theta/t = s/rt$

---

1. (a) $130°$ Quadrant II
   (b) $285°$ Quadrant IV

3. (a) $-132°50'$ Quadrant III
   (b) $-336°$ Quadrant I

5. (a) $\dfrac{\pi}{5}$ Quadrant I
   (b) $\dfrac{7\pi}{5}$ Quadrant III

7. (a) $-\dfrac{\pi}{12}$ Quadrant IV
   (b) $-\dfrac{11\pi}{9}$ Quadrant II

9. (a) 3.5 Quadrant III
   (b) 2.25 Quadrant II

11. (a)

(b)

13. (a)

(b)

15. (a)

(b)

17. (a) $36° + 360° = 396°$

$36° - 360° = -324°$

(b) $-45° + 360° = 315°$

$-45° - 360° = -405°$

21. (a) $\dfrac{\pi}{9} + 2\pi = \dfrac{19\pi}{9}$

$\dfrac{\pi}{9} - 2\pi = -\dfrac{17\pi}{9}$

19. (a) $300° + 360° = 660°$

$300° - 360° = -60°$

(b) $740° - 720° = 20°$

$740° - 1080° = -340°$

(b) $\dfrac{4\pi}{3} + 2\pi = \dfrac{10\pi}{3}$

$\dfrac{4\pi}{3} - 2\pi = -\dfrac{2\pi}{3}$

23. (a) $-\dfrac{9\pi}{4} + 4\pi = \dfrac{7\pi}{4}$

$-\dfrac{9\pi}{4} + 2\pi = -\dfrac{\pi}{4}$

(b) $-\dfrac{2\pi}{15} + 2\pi = \dfrac{28\pi}{15}$

$-\dfrac{2\pi}{15} - 2\pi = -\dfrac{32\pi}{15}$

25. (a) Complement: $90° - 18° = 72°$
Supplement: $180° - 18° = 162°$
(b) Complement: None
Supplement: $180° - 115° = 65°$

27. (a) Complement: $\dfrac{\pi}{2} - \dfrac{\pi}{3} = \dfrac{\pi}{6}$
Supplement: $\pi - \dfrac{\pi}{3} = \dfrac{2\pi}{3}$
(b) Complement: None
Supplement: $\pi - \dfrac{3\pi}{4} = \dfrac{\pi}{4}$

29. (a) $30° = 30\left(\dfrac{\pi}{180}\right)$

$= \dfrac{\pi}{6}$ radians

(b) $150° = 150\left(\dfrac{\pi}{180}\right)$

$= \dfrac{5\pi}{6}$ radians

31. (a) $-20° = -20\left(\dfrac{\pi}{180}\right)$

$= -\dfrac{\pi}{9}$ radians

(b) $-240° = -240\left(\dfrac{\pi}{180}\right)$

$= -\dfrac{4\pi}{3}$ radians

33. (a) $\dfrac{3\pi}{2} = \dfrac{3\pi}{2}\left(\dfrac{180}{\pi}\right) = 270°$

(b) $\dfrac{7\pi}{6} = \dfrac{7\pi}{6}\left(\dfrac{180}{\pi}\right) = 210°$

35. (a) $\dfrac{7\pi}{3} = \dfrac{7\pi}{3}\left(\dfrac{180}{\pi}\right) = 420°$

(b) $-\dfrac{11\pi}{30}\left(\dfrac{180}{\pi}\right) = -66°$

37. $115° = 115\left(\dfrac{\pi}{180}\right) \approx 2.007$ radians

39. $-216.35° = -216.35\left(\dfrac{\pi}{180}\right)$

≈ -3.776 radians

41. $532° = 532\left(\dfrac{\pi}{180}\right) \approx 9.285$ radians

43. $-0.83° = -0.83\left(\dfrac{\pi}{180}\right)$

≈ -0.014 radians

45. $\dfrac{\pi}{7} = \dfrac{\pi}{7}\left(\dfrac{180}{\pi}\right) \approx 25.714°$

47. $\dfrac{15\pi}{8} = \dfrac{15\pi}{8}\left(\dfrac{180}{\pi}\right) \approx 337.500°$

49. $-4.2\pi = -4.2\pi\left(\dfrac{180}{\pi}\right) \approx -756.000°$

51. $-2 = -2\left(\dfrac{180}{\pi}\right) \approx -114.592°$

53. (a) $54°45' = 54\frac{45}{60} = 54.75°$
(b) $-128°30' = -128.5°$

55. (a) $85°18'30'' = 85 + \frac{18}{60} + \frac{30}{3600} \approx 85.308°$
(b) $330°25'' = 330\frac{25}{3600} \approx 330.007°$

57. (a) $240.6° = 240° + (0.6)(60') = 240°36'$

(b) $-145.8° = -(145° + (0.8)(60'))$
$$= -145°48'$$

59. (a) $2.5 = 2.5 \left(\dfrac{180}{\pi}\right)^{°}$

$\approx 143.23945°$

$= 143° + (0.23945)(60')$

$\approx 143°14' + (0.367)(60'')$

$= 143°14'22''$

(b) $-3.58 = -3.58 \left(\dfrac{180}{\pi}\right)^{°}$

$\approx -205.1189°$

$= -(205° + (0.1189)(60'))$

$\approx -(205°7' + 0.1334(60''))$

$= -205°7'8''$

61. $\theta = \dfrac{s}{r} = \dfrac{4}{15}$

63. $r = 14.5$ cm, $s = 25$ cm
$$\theta = \dfrac{s}{r} = \dfrac{25}{14.5} \approx 1.724$$

65. $\theta = 180° \left(\dfrac{\pi}{180°}\right) = \pi$

$s = r\theta = 15(\pi) = 15\pi$ in.

≈ 47.12 in.

67. $s = r\theta = 6(2) = 12$ m

69. $\theta = 41°15'42'' - 32°47'9''$

$= 8°28'33'' \approx 0.1479$

$s \approx 4000(0.1479) \approx 591.72$ miles

71. $\theta = 42°7'15'' - 25°46'37''$

$= 16°20'38'' \approx 0.2853$

$s \approx 4000(0.2853) \approx 1141.02$ miles

73. $\theta = \frac{325}{4000} = 0.08125$ radian $\approx 4.655°$

75. $\theta = \dfrac{1/2}{2} = \dfrac{1}{4}$ radian $\approx 14.32°$

77. (a) 50 mi/hr $= \dfrac{50(5280)}{60} = 4400$ ft/min

Circumference $= 2.5\pi$ ft

$\dfrac{\text{Revolutions}}{\text{minute}} = \dfrac{4400}{2.5\pi} \approx 560.2$

(b) Angular speed $\approx 560.2(2\pi)$

≈ 3520 rad/min

79. (a) $\dfrac{\text{Revolutions}}{\text{Second}} = \dfrac{2400}{60} = 40$ rev/sec

Angular speed $= (2\pi)(40)$

$= 80\pi$ rad/sec

(b) Radius of saw blade $= \dfrac{7.5}{2} = 3.75$ in.

Radius in feet $= \dfrac{3.75 \text{ in.}}{12 \text{ in.}} = 0.3125$ ft

Speed $= \dfrac{s}{t} = \dfrac{r\theta}{t} = r\dfrac{\theta}{t}$

$= r(\text{angular speed})$

$= 0.3125(80\pi) = 78.54$ ft/sec

Section 6.2 Right Triangle Trigonometry

- You should know the right triangle definition of trigonometric functions.

  (a) $\sin \theta = \dfrac{\text{opp}}{\text{hyp}}$ (b) $\cos \theta = \dfrac{\text{adj}}{\text{hyp}}$

  (c) $\tan \theta = \dfrac{\text{opp}}{\text{adj}}$ (d) $\cot \theta = \dfrac{\text{adj}}{\text{opp}}$

  (e) $\sec \theta = \dfrac{\text{hyp}}{\text{adj}}$ (f) $\csc \theta = \dfrac{\text{hyp}}{\text{opp}}$

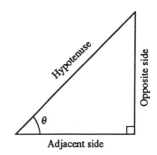

- You should know the following identities.

  (a) $\csc \theta = \dfrac{1}{\sin \theta}$ (b) $\sec \theta = \dfrac{1}{\cos \theta}$

  (c) $\cot \theta = \dfrac{1}{\tan \theta}$ (d) $\sin \theta = \dfrac{1}{\csc \theta}$

  (e) $\cos \theta = \dfrac{1}{\sec \theta}$ (f) $\tan \theta = \dfrac{1}{\cot \theta}$

  (g) $\tan \theta = \dfrac{\sin \theta}{\cos \theta}$ (h) $\cot \theta = \dfrac{\cos \theta}{\sin \theta}$

  (i) $\sin^2 \theta + \cos^2 \theta = 1$ (j) $1 + \tan^2 \theta = \sec^2 \theta$

  (k) $1 + \cot^2 \theta = \csc^2 \theta$

- You should know that two acute angles α and β are complementary if $\alpha + \beta = 90°$, and cofunctions of complementary angles are equal.

- You should know the function values of $30°$, $45°$, and $60°$, or be able to construct triangles from which you can determine them.

- You should be able to evaluate trigonometric functions with a calculator. Be sure your calculator is set in the appropriate mode—degree or radian.

1.

$$b = \sqrt{2^2 - 1^2} = \sqrt{3}$$

$$\sin \theta = \frac{1}{2} \qquad\qquad \csc \theta = 2$$

$$\cos \theta = \frac{\sqrt{3}}{2} \qquad\qquad \sec \theta = \frac{2}{\sqrt{3}} = \frac{2\sqrt{3}}{3}$$

$$\tan \theta = \frac{1}{\sqrt{3}} = \frac{\sqrt{3}}{3} \qquad \cot \theta = \frac{3}{\sqrt{3}} = \sqrt{3}$$

3.

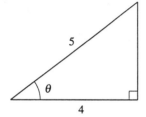

$$a = \sqrt{5^2 - 4^2} = 3$$

$$\sin \theta = \tfrac{3}{5} \qquad \csc \theta = \tfrac{5}{3}$$

$$\cos \theta = \tfrac{4}{5} \qquad \sec \theta = \tfrac{5}{4}$$

$$\tan \theta = \tfrac{3}{4} \qquad \cot \theta = \tfrac{4}{3}$$

5.

$$a = \sqrt{15^2 - 8^2} = \sqrt{161}$$

$$\sin \theta = \frac{\sqrt{161}}{15} \qquad \csc \theta = \frac{15}{\sqrt{161}} = \frac{15\sqrt{161}}{161}$$

$$\cos \theta = \frac{8}{15} \qquad \sec \theta = \frac{15}{8}$$

$$\tan \theta = \frac{\sqrt{161}}{8} \qquad \cot \theta = \frac{8}{\sqrt{161}} = \frac{8\sqrt{161}}{161}$$

7.

$$c = \sqrt{8^2 + 15^2} = 17$$

$$\sin \theta = \tfrac{15}{17} \qquad \csc \theta = \tfrac{17}{15}$$

$$\cos \theta = \tfrac{8}{17} \qquad \sec \theta = \tfrac{17}{8}$$

$$\tan \theta = \tfrac{15}{8} \qquad \cot \theta = \tfrac{8}{15}$$

9. Given: $\sin \theta = \dfrac{2}{3}$

$2^2 + (\text{adj})^2 = 3^2$

$\text{adj} = \sqrt{5}$

$\cos \theta = \dfrac{\sqrt{5}}{3}$

$\tan \theta = \dfrac{2\sqrt{5}}{5}$

$\cot \theta = \dfrac{\sqrt{5}}{2}$

$\sec \theta = \dfrac{3\sqrt{5}}{5}$

$\csc \theta = \dfrac{3}{2}$

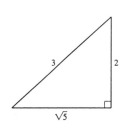

11. Given: $\sec \theta = 2$

$(\text{opp})^2 + 1^2 = 2^2$

$\text{opp} = \sqrt{3}$

$\sin \theta = \dfrac{\sqrt{3}}{2}$

$\cos \theta = \dfrac{1}{2}$

$\tan \theta = \sqrt{3}$

$\cot \theta = \dfrac{\sqrt{3}}{3}$

$\csc \theta = \dfrac{2\sqrt{3}}{3}$

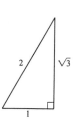

13. Given: $\tan \theta = 3$

$3^2 + 1^2 = (\text{hyp})^2$

$\text{hyp} = \sqrt{10}$

$\sin \theta = \dfrac{3\sqrt{10}}{10}$

$\cos \theta = \dfrac{\sqrt{10}}{10}$

$\cot \theta = \dfrac{1}{3}$

$\sec \theta = \sqrt{10}$

$\csc \theta = \dfrac{\sqrt{10}}{3}$

15. Given: $\cot \theta = \dfrac{3}{2}$

$$2^2 + 3^2 = (\text{hyp})^2$$

$$\text{hyp} = \sqrt{13}$$

$$\sin \theta = \frac{2}{\sqrt{13}} = \frac{2\sqrt{13}}{13}$$

$$\cos \theta = \frac{3}{\sqrt{13}} = \frac{3\sqrt{13}}{13}$$

$$\tan \theta = \frac{2}{3}$$

$$\csc \theta = \frac{\sqrt{13}}{2}$$

$$\sec \theta = \frac{\sqrt{13}}{3}$$

17. $\sin 60° = \dfrac{\sqrt{3}}{2}, \quad \cos 60° = \dfrac{1}{2}$

(a) $\tan 60° = \dfrac{\sin 60°}{\cos 60°} = \sqrt{3}$

(b) $\sin 30° = \cos 60° = \dfrac{1}{2}$

(c) $\cos 30° = \sin 60° = \dfrac{\sqrt{3}}{2}$

(d) $\cot 60° = \dfrac{\cos 60°}{\sin 60°} = \dfrac{1}{\sqrt{3}} = \dfrac{\sqrt{3}}{3}$

19. $\csc \theta = 3, \quad \sec \theta = \dfrac{3\sqrt{2}}{4}$

(a) $\sin \theta = \dfrac{1}{\csc \theta} = \dfrac{1}{3}$

(b) $\cos \theta = \dfrac{1}{\sec \theta} = \dfrac{2\sqrt{2}}{3}$

(c) $\tan \theta = \dfrac{\sin \theta}{\cos \theta} = \dfrac{1/3}{(2\sqrt{2})/3} = \dfrac{\sqrt{2}}{4}$

(d) $\sec(90° - \theta) = \csc \theta = 3$

21. (a) $\cos 60° = \dfrac{1}{2}$

(b) $\tan \dfrac{\pi}{4} = \dfrac{\sin 45°}{\cos 45°} = \dfrac{\sqrt{2}/2}{\sqrt{2}/2} = 1$

23. (a) $\cot 45° = 1$

(b) $\cos 45° = \dfrac{\sqrt{2}}{2}$

25. (a) $\sin 10° \approx 0.1736$

(b) $\cos 80° \approx 0.1736$

27. (a) $\sin 16.35° \approx 0.2815$

(b) $\csc 16.35° \approx 3.5523$

29. (a) $\sec 42°\,12' \approx 1.3499$

(b) $\csc 48°7' \approx 1.3432$

31. (a) $\cot \dfrac{\pi}{16} \approx 5.0273$

(b) $\tan \dfrac{\pi}{16} \approx 0.1989$

33. (a) $\csc 1 \approx 1.1884$

(b) $\sec\left(\dfrac{\pi}{2} - 1\right) = \csc 1 \approx 1.1884$

35. (a) $\sin \theta = \dfrac{1}{2} \Rightarrow \theta = 30° = \dfrac{\pi}{6}$

(b) $\csc \theta = 2 \Rightarrow \theta = 30° = \dfrac{\pi}{6}$

37. (a) $\sec\theta = 2 \Rightarrow \theta = 60° = \dfrac{\pi}{3}$

  (b) $\cot\theta = 1 \Rightarrow \theta = 45° = \dfrac{\pi}{4}$

39. (a) $\csc\theta = \dfrac{2\sqrt{3}}{3} \Rightarrow \theta = 60° = \dfrac{\pi}{3}$

  (b) $\sin\theta = \dfrac{\sqrt{2}}{2} \Rightarrow \theta = 45° = \dfrac{\pi}{4}$

41. (a) $\sin\theta = 0.8191 \Rightarrow$

$\theta \approx 55° \approx 0.96$ radians

  (b) $\cos\theta = 0.0175 \Rightarrow$

$\theta \approx 89° \approx 1.55$ radians

43. (a) $\tan\theta = 1.1920 \Rightarrow$

$\theta \approx 50° \approx 0.873$ radians

  (b) $\tan\theta = 0.4663 \Rightarrow$

$\theta \approx 25° \approx 0.436$ radians

45. $\tan 30° = \dfrac{y}{100}$

$y = 100\tan 30° \approx 57.74$

47. $\cot 60° = \dfrac{x}{25}$

$x = \dfrac{25}{\tan 60°} = \dfrac{25\sqrt{3}}{3} \approx 14.4$

49. $\csc 40° = \dfrac{r}{10}$

$r = \dfrac{10}{\sin 40°} \approx 15.56$

51. $\sin 50° = \dfrac{y}{12}$

$y \approx 12\sin 50 \approx 9.19$

53. $\tan\theta = \dfrac{6}{8} = \dfrac{h}{20}$

$h = 15$ ft

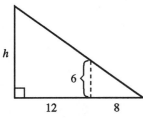

55. Let $h =$ the distance up the side of the house.

$$\sin 75° = \dfrac{h}{20}$$

$$h = 20\sin 75° \approx 19.32 \text{ ft}$$

57. Let $d =$ the distance from the shoreline.

$\cot 4° = \dfrac{d}{150}$

$d = 150\cot 4° \approx 2145.10$ ft

59.

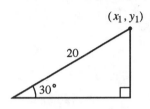

$$\sin 30° = \frac{y_1}{20}$$

$$y_1 = (\sin 30°)(20)$$

$$= \left(\frac{1}{2}\right)(20) = 10$$

$$\cos 30° = \frac{x_1}{20}$$

$$x_1 = \cos 30°(20)$$

$$= \frac{\sqrt{3}}{2}(20) = 10\sqrt{3}$$

$$(x_1,\ y_1) = (10\sqrt{3},\ 10)$$

$$\sin 60° = \frac{y_2}{20}$$

$$y_2 = \sin 60°(20)$$

$$= \left(\frac{\sqrt{3}}{2}\right)(20) = 10\sqrt{3}$$

$$\cos 60° = \frac{x_2}{20}$$

$$x_2 = (\cos 60°)(20)$$

$$= \left(\frac{1}{2}\right)(20) = 10$$

$$(x_2,\ y_2) = (10,\ 10\sqrt{3})$$

61. $\sin 25° \approx 0.42$

　　$\cos 25° \approx 0.91$

　　$\tan 25° \approx 0.47$

　　$\csc 25° \approx 2.37$

　　$\sec 25° \approx 1.10$

　　$\cot 25° \approx 2.14$

63. True

$$\csc x = \frac{1}{\sin x} \Rightarrow$$

$$\sin 60° \csc 60° = \sin 60° \frac{1}{\sin 60°} = 1$$

65. False, $\dfrac{\sqrt{2}}{2} + \dfrac{\sqrt{2}}{2} = \sqrt{2} \neq 1$

67. False

$$\frac{\sin 60°}{\sin 30°} = \frac{\cos 30°}{\sin 30°} = \cot 30°$$

$$\approx 1.7321$$

$$\neq \sin 2° = 0.0349$$

Section 6.3   Trigonometric Functions of Any Angle or Real Number

- You should know the signs of the trigonometric functions in each quadrant.
- You should know the trigonometric function values of the quadrant angles 0, $\pi/2$, π, and $3\pi/2$.
- You should be able to find reference angles.
- You should be able to evaluate trigonometric functions of any angle. (Use reference angles.)
- You should know that the period of sine and cosine is 2π.
- You should know which trigonometric functions are odd and even.

1. (a) $(x,\, y) = (3,\, 4)$

$$\theta = \sqrt{9 + 16} = 5$$

$$\sin\theta = \frac{y}{\theta} = \frac{4}{5} \qquad \csc\theta = \frac{\theta}{y} = \frac{5}{4}$$

$$\cos\theta = \frac{x}{\theta} = \frac{3}{5} \qquad \sec\theta = \frac{\theta}{x} = \frac{5}{3}$$

$$\tan\theta = \frac{y}{x} = \frac{4}{3} \qquad \cot\theta = \frac{x}{y} = \frac{3}{4}$$

(b) $(x,\, y) = (8,\, -15)$

$$\theta = \sqrt{64 + 225} = 17$$

$$\sin\theta = \frac{y}{\theta} = -\frac{15}{17} \qquad \csc\theta = \frac{\theta}{y} = -\frac{17}{15}$$

$$\cos\theta = \frac{x}{\theta} = \frac{8}{17} \qquad \sec\theta = \frac{\theta}{x} = \frac{17}{8}$$

$$\tan\theta = \frac{y}{x} = -\frac{15}{8} \qquad \cot\theta = \frac{x}{y} = -\frac{8}{15}$$

3. (a) $(x,\, y) = (-\sqrt{3},\, 1)$

$$\theta = \sqrt{3 + 1} = 2$$

$$\sin\theta = \frac{y}{\theta} = \frac{1}{2} \qquad \csc\theta = \frac{\theta}{y} = 2$$

$$\cos\theta = \frac{x}{\theta} = -\frac{\sqrt{3}}{2} \qquad \sec\theta = \frac{\theta}{x} = -\frac{2\sqrt{3}}{3}$$

$$\tan\theta = \frac{y}{x} = -\frac{\sqrt{3}}{3} \qquad \cot\theta = \frac{x}{y} = -\sqrt{3}$$

(b) $(x,\, y) = (-2,\, -2)$

$$\theta = \sqrt{4 + 4} = 2\sqrt{2}$$

$$\sin\theta = \frac{y}{\theta} = -\frac{\sqrt{2}}{2} \qquad \csc\theta = \frac{\theta}{y} = -\sqrt{2}$$

$$\cos\theta = \frac{x}{\theta} = -\frac{\sqrt{2}}{2} \qquad \sec\theta = \frac{\theta}{x} = -\sqrt{2}$$

$$\tan\theta = \frac{y}{x} = 1 \qquad \cot\theta = \frac{x}{y} = 1$$

5. (a) $(x,\, y) = (7,\, 24)$

$$\theta = \sqrt{49 + 576} = 25$$

$$\sin\theta = \frac{y}{\theta} = \frac{24}{25} \qquad \csc\theta = \frac{\theta}{y} = \frac{25}{24}$$

$$\cos\theta = \frac{x}{\theta} = \frac{7}{25} \qquad \sec\theta = \frac{\theta}{x} = \frac{25}{7}$$

$$\tan\theta = \frac{y}{x} = \frac{24}{7} \qquad \cot\theta = \frac{x}{y} = \frac{7}{24}$$

(b) $(x,\, y) = (7,\, -24)$

$$\theta = \sqrt{49 + 576} = 25$$

$$\sin\theta = \frac{y}{\theta} = -\frac{24}{25} \qquad \csc\theta = \frac{\theta}{y} = -\frac{25}{24}$$

$$\cos\theta = \frac{x}{\theta} = \frac{7}{25} \qquad \sec\theta = \frac{\theta}{x} = \frac{25}{7}$$

$$\tan\theta = \frac{y}{x} = -\frac{24}{7} \qquad \cot\theta = \frac{x}{y} = -\frac{7}{24}$$

7. (a) $(x, y) = (-4, 10)$

$$\theta = \sqrt{16 + 100} = 2\sqrt{29}$$

$$\sin\theta = \frac{y}{\theta} = \frac{5\sqrt{29}}{29} \qquad \csc\theta = \frac{\theta}{y} = \frac{\sqrt{29}}{5}$$

$$\cos\theta = \frac{x}{\theta} = -\frac{2\sqrt{29}}{29} \qquad \sec\theta = \frac{\theta}{x} = -\frac{\sqrt{29}}{2}$$

$$\tan\theta = \frac{y}{x} = -\frac{5}{2} \qquad \cot\theta = \frac{x}{y} = -\frac{2}{5}$$

(b) $(x, y) = (3, -5)$

$$\theta = \sqrt{9 + 25} = \sqrt{34}$$

$$\sin\theta = \frac{y}{\theta} = -\frac{5\sqrt{34}}{34} \qquad \csc\theta = \frac{\theta}{y} = -\frac{\sqrt{34}}{5}$$

$$\cos\theta = \frac{x}{\theta} = \frac{3\sqrt{34}}{34} \qquad \sec\theta = \frac{\theta}{x} = \frac{\sqrt{34}}{3}$$

$$\tan\theta = \frac{y}{x} = -\frac{5}{3} \qquad \cot\theta = \frac{x}{y} = -\frac{3}{5}$$

9. (a) $\sin\theta < 0$ and $\cos\theta < 0$
in Quadrant III

(b) $\sin\theta > 0$ and $\cos\theta < 0$
in Quadrant II

11. (a) $\sin\theta > 0$ and $\tan\theta < 0$
in Quadrant II

(b) $\cos\theta > 0$ and $\tan\theta < 0$
in Quadrant IV

13. $\sin\theta = \frac{y}{\theta} = \frac{3}{5} \Rightarrow |x| = 4$

θ in Quadrant II $\Rightarrow x = -4$

$$\sin\theta = \frac{y}{\theta} = \frac{3}{5} \qquad \csc\theta = \frac{\theta}{y} = \frac{5}{3}$$

$$\cos\theta = \frac{x}{\theta} = -\frac{4}{5} \qquad \sec\theta = \frac{\theta}{x} = -\frac{5}{4}$$

$$\tan\theta = \frac{y}{x} = -\frac{3}{4} \qquad \cot\theta = \frac{x}{y} = -\frac{4}{3}$$

15. $\sin\theta < 0 \Rightarrow y < 0$

$$\tan\theta = \frac{y}{x} = \frac{-15}{8} \Rightarrow \theta = 17$$

$$\sin\theta = \frac{y}{\theta} = -\frac{15}{17} \qquad \csc\theta = \frac{\theta}{y} = -\frac{17}{15}$$

$$\cos\theta = \frac{x}{\theta} = \frac{8}{17} \qquad \sec\theta = \frac{\theta}{x} = \frac{17}{8}$$

$$\tan\theta = \frac{y}{x} = -\frac{15}{8} \qquad \cot\theta = \frac{x}{y} = -\frac{8}{15}$$

17. $\sec\theta = \frac{\theta}{x} = \frac{2}{-1} \Rightarrow |y| = \sqrt{3}$

$\sin\theta > 0 \Rightarrow y = \sqrt{3}$

$$\sin\theta = \frac{y}{\theta} = \frac{\sqrt{3}}{2} \qquad \csc\theta = \frac{\theta}{y} = \frac{2\sqrt{3}}{3}$$

$$\cos\theta = \frac{x}{\theta} = -\frac{1}{2} \qquad \sec\theta = \frac{\theta}{x} = -2$$

$$\tan\theta = \frac{y}{x} = -\sqrt{3} \qquad \cot\theta = \frac{x}{y} = -\frac{\sqrt{3}}{3}$$

19. $\sin\theta = 0 \Rightarrow \theta = n\pi$

$\sec\theta = -1 \Rightarrow \theta = \pi$

$$\sin\theta = \frac{y}{\theta} = \frac{0}{\theta} = 0 \qquad \csc\theta = \frac{\theta}{y}, \text{ undefined}$$

$$\cos\theta = \frac{x}{\theta} = \frac{-\theta}{\theta} = -1 \qquad \sec\theta = \frac{\theta}{x} = -1$$

$$\tan\theta = \frac{y}{x} = \frac{0}{x} = 0 \qquad \cot\theta = \frac{x}{y}, \text{ undefined}$$

21. θ in Quadrant III and (x, y) satisfies $(x, 2x) \Rightarrow \theta^2 = x^2 + 4x^2$ and $x < 0$. Thus,
$\theta = \sqrt{5}|x| = -\sqrt{5}\,x$.

$$\sin\theta = \frac{y}{\theta} = -\frac{2x}{\sqrt{5}\,x} = -\frac{2\sqrt{5}}{5} \qquad \csc\theta = \frac{\theta}{y} = -\frac{\sqrt{5}}{2}$$

$$\cos\theta = \frac{x}{\theta} = -\frac{x}{\sqrt{5}\,x} = -\frac{\sqrt{5}}{5} \qquad \sec\theta = \frac{\theta}{x} = -\sqrt{5}$$

$$\tan\theta = \frac{y}{x} = \frac{2x}{x} = 2 \qquad \cot\theta = \frac{x}{y} = \frac{1}{2}$$

23. (a) $\theta = 203°$

$\theta' = 203° - 180° = 23°$

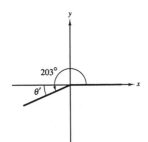

(b) $\theta = 127°$

$\theta' = 180° - 127° = 53°$

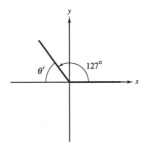

25. (a) $\theta = -245°$

$360° - 245° = 115°$

(coterminal angle)

$\theta' = 180° - 115° = 65°$

(b) $\theta = -72°$

$\theta' = 72°$

27. (a) $\theta = \dfrac{2\pi}{3}$

$\theta' = \pi - \dfrac{2\pi}{3} = \dfrac{\pi}{3}$

(b) $\theta = \dfrac{7\pi}{6}$

$\theta' = \dfrac{7\pi}{6} - \pi = \dfrac{\pi}{6}$

29. (a) $\theta = 3.5$

$\theta' = 3.5 - \pi \approx 0.3584$

(b) $\theta = 5.8$

$\theta' = 2\pi - 5.8 \approx 0.4832$

31. (a) $\theta = 225°$, $\theta' = 45°$, Quadrant III

$$\sin 225° = -\sin 45° = -\frac{\sqrt{2}}{2}$$

$$\cos 225° = -\cos 45° = -\frac{\sqrt{2}}{2}$$

$$\tan 225° = \tan 45° = 1$$

(b) $\theta = -225°$, $\theta' = 45°$, Quadrant II

$$\sin(-225°) = \sin 45° = \frac{\sqrt{2}}{2}$$

$$\cos(-225°) = -\cos 45° = -\frac{\sqrt{2}}{2}$$

$$\tan(-225°) = -\tan 45° = -1$$

33. (a) $\theta = 750°$, $\theta' = 30°$, Quadrant I

$$\sin 750° = \sin 30° = \frac{1}{2}$$

$$\cos 750° = \cos 30° = \frac{\sqrt{3}}{2}$$

$$\tan 750° = \tan 30° = \frac{\sqrt{3}}{3}$$

(b) $\theta = 510°$, $\theta' = 30°$, Quadrant II

$$\sin 510° = \sin 30° = \frac{1}{2}$$

$$\cos 510° = -\cos 30° = -\frac{\sqrt{3}}{2}$$

$$\tan 510° = -\tan 30° = -\frac{\sqrt{3}}{3}$$

35. (a) $\theta = \dfrac{4\pi}{3}$, $\theta' = \dfrac{\pi}{3}$, Quadrant III

$$\sin \frac{4\pi}{3} = -\sin \frac{\pi}{3} = -\frac{\sqrt{3}}{2}$$

$$\cos \frac{4\pi}{3} = -\cos \frac{\pi}{3} = -\frac{1}{2}$$

$$\tan \frac{4\pi}{3} = \tan \frac{\pi}{3} = \sqrt{3}$$

(b) $\theta = \dfrac{2\pi}{3}$, $\theta' = \dfrac{\pi}{3}$, Quadrant II

$$\sin \frac{2\pi}{3} = \sin \frac{\pi}{3} = \frac{\sqrt{3}}{2}$$

$$\cos \frac{2\pi}{3} = -\cos \frac{\pi}{3} = -\frac{1}{2}$$

$$\tan \frac{2\pi}{3} = -\tan \frac{\pi}{3} = -\sqrt{3}$$

37. (a) $\theta = -\dfrac{\pi}{6}$, $\theta' = \dfrac{\pi}{6}$, Quadrant IV

$$\sin\left(-\frac{\pi}{6}\right) = -\sin\frac{\pi}{6} = -\frac{1}{2}$$

$$\cos\left(-\frac{\pi}{6}\right) = \cos\frac{\pi}{6} = \frac{\sqrt{3}}{2}$$

$$\tan\left(-\frac{\pi}{6}\right) = -\tan\frac{\pi}{6} = -\frac{\sqrt{3}}{3}$$

(b) $\theta = \dfrac{5\pi}{6}$, $\theta' = \dfrac{\pi}{6}$, Quadrant II

$$\sin\frac{5\pi}{6} = \sin\frac{\pi}{6} = \frac{1}{2}$$

$$\cos\frac{5\pi}{6} = -\cos\frac{\pi}{6} = -\frac{\sqrt{3}}{2}$$

$$\tan\frac{5\pi}{6} = -\tan\frac{\pi}{6} = -\frac{\sqrt{3}}{3}$$

39. (a) $\theta = \dfrac{11\pi}{4}$, $\theta' = \dfrac{\pi}{4}$, Quadrant II

$$\sin\frac{11\pi}{4} = \sin\frac{\pi}{4} = \frac{\sqrt{2}}{2}$$

$$\cos\frac{11\pi}{4} = -\cos\frac{\pi}{4} = -\frac{\sqrt{2}}{2}$$

$$\tan\frac{11\pi}{4} = -\tan\frac{\pi}{4} = -1$$

(b) $\theta = -\dfrac{13\pi}{6}$, $\theta' = \dfrac{\pi}{6}$, Quadrant IV

$$\sin\left(-\frac{13\pi}{6}\right) = -\sin\frac{\pi}{6} = -\frac{1}{2}$$

$$\cos\left(-\frac{13\pi}{6}\right) = \cos\frac{\pi}{6} = \frac{\sqrt{3}}{2}$$

$$\tan\left(-\frac{13\pi}{6}\right) = -\tan\frac{\pi}{6} = -\frac{\sqrt{3}}{3}$$

41. (a) $\sin 10° \approx 0.1736$
  (b) $\csc 10° \approx 5.7588$

43. (a) $\cos(-110°) \approx -0.3420$
  (b) $\cos 250° \approx -0.3420$

45. (a) $\tan 240° \approx 1.7321$
  (b) $\cot 210° \approx 1.7321$

47. (a) $\tan \dfrac{\pi}{9} \approx 0.3640$

  (b) $\tan \dfrac{10\pi}{9} \approx 0.3640$

49. (a) $\sin\theta = \dfrac{1}{2} \Rightarrow$ reference angle is $30°$ or $\dfrac{\pi}{6}$ and θ is in Quadrant I or Quadrant II.

  Values in degrees: $30°$, $150°$

  Values in radian: $\dfrac{\pi}{6}$, $\dfrac{5\pi}{6}$

  (b) $\sin\theta = -\dfrac{1}{2} \Rightarrow$ reference angle is $30°$ or $\dfrac{\pi}{6}$ and θ is in Quadrant III or IV.

  Values in degrees: $210°$, $330°$

  Values in radians: $\dfrac{7\pi}{6}$, $\dfrac{11\pi}{6}$

51. (a) $\csc \theta = \dfrac{2\sqrt{3}}{3} \Rightarrow$ reference angle is 60° or $\dfrac{\pi}{3}$ and θ is in Quadrant I or II.

Values in degrees: 60°, 120°

Values in radians: $\dfrac{\pi}{3}, \dfrac{2\pi}{3}$

(b) $\cot \theta = -1 \Rightarrow$ reference angle is 45° or $\dfrac{\pi}{4}$ and θ is in Quadrant II or IV.

Values in degrees: 135°, 315°

Values in radians: $\dfrac{3\pi}{4}, \dfrac{7\pi}{4}$

53. (a) $\tan \theta = 1 \Rightarrow$ reference angle is 45° or $\dfrac{\pi}{4}$ and θ is in Quadrant I or III.

Values in degrees: 45°, 225°

Values in radians: $\dfrac{\pi}{4}, \dfrac{5\pi}{4}$

(b) $\cot \theta = -\sqrt{3} \Rightarrow$ reference angle is 30° or $\dfrac{\pi}{6}$ and θ is in Quadrant II or IV.

Values in degrees: 150°, 330°

Values in radians: $\dfrac{5\pi}{6}, \dfrac{11\pi}{6}$

55. (a) $\sin \theta = 0.8191$

Quadrant I:
$\theta = \sin^{-1} 0.8191 \approx 54.99°$

Quadrant II:
$\theta = 180° - \sin^{-1} 0.8191 \approx 125.01°$

(b) $\sin \theta = -0.2589 \Rightarrow \theta' \approx 15.00°$

Quadrant III:
$\theta = 180° + \theta' \approx 195.00°$

Quadrant IV:
$\theta = 360° - \theta' \approx 345.00°$

57. (a) $\cos \theta = 0.9848 \Rightarrow \theta' \approx 0.175$

Quadrant I:
$\theta = \cos^{-1}(0.9848) \approx 0.175$

Quadrant IV:
$\theta = 2\pi - \theta' \approx 6.109$

(b) $\cos \theta = -0.5890 \Rightarrow \theta' \approx 0.941$

Quadrant II:
$\theta = \cos^{-1}(-0.5890) \approx 2.201$

Quadrant III:
$\theta = \pi + \theta' \approx 4.083$

59. (a) $\tan \theta = 1.192 \Rightarrow \theta' \approx 0.873$

Quadrant I: $\theta = \tan^{-1} 1.192 \approx 0.873$

Quadrant III: $\theta = \pi + \theta' \approx 4.014$

(b) $\tan \theta = -8.144 \Rightarrow \theta' \approx 1.449$

Quadrant II: $\theta = \pi - \theta' \approx 1.693$

Quadrant IV: $\theta = 2\pi - \theta' \approx 4.835$

61.
$$\sin \theta = -\tfrac{3}{5}$$
$$\sin^2 \theta + \cos^2 \theta = 1$$
$$\cos^2 \theta = 1 - \sin^2 \theta$$
$$\cos^2 \theta = 1 - \left(-\frac{3}{5}\right)^2$$
$$\cos^2 \theta = 1 - \frac{9}{25}$$
$$\cos^2 \theta = \frac{16}{25}$$
$\cos \theta > 0$ in Quadrant IV.
$$\cos \theta = \frac{4}{5}$$

63. $\tan \theta = \dfrac{3}{2}$
$$\sec^2 \theta = 1 + \tan^2 \theta$$
$$\sec^2 \theta = 1 + \left(\frac{3}{2}\right)^2$$
$$\sec^2 \theta = 1 + \frac{9}{4} = \frac{13}{4}$$
$\sec \theta < 0$ in Quadrant III.
$$\sec \theta = -\frac{\sqrt{13}}{2}$$

65. $\cos \theta = \dfrac{5}{8}$
$$\cos \theta = \frac{1}{\sec \theta} \Rightarrow \sec \theta = \frac{1}{\cos \theta}$$
$$\sec \theta = \frac{1}{5/8} = \frac{8}{5}$$

67. $T = 45 - 23 \cos\left[\dfrac{2\pi}{365}(t - 32)\right]$

(a) $T = 45 - 23 \cos\left[\dfrac{2\pi}{365}(1 - 32)\right]$
$$\approx 25.2°$$

(b) $T = 45 - 23 \cos\left[\dfrac{2\pi}{365}(185 - 32)\right]$
$$\approx 65.1°$$

(c) $T = 45 - 23 \cos\left[\dfrac{2\pi}{365}(291 - 32)\right]$
$$\approx 50.8°$$

69. $y(t) = \tfrac{1}{4} \cos 6t$

(a) $y(0) = \tfrac{1}{4} \cos(6 \cdot 0) = 0.2500$ ft

(b) $y\left(\tfrac{1}{4}\right) = \tfrac{1}{4} \cos\left(6 \cdot \tfrac{1}{4}\right) \approx 0.0177$ ft

(c) $y\left(\tfrac{1}{2}\right) = \tfrac{1}{4} \cos\left(6 \cdot \tfrac{1}{2}\right) \approx -0.2475$ ft

71. (a) $\sin 30° = \dfrac{5}{d}$
$$d = \frac{5}{\sin 30°} = \frac{5}{1/2} = 10 \text{ mi}$$

(b) $\sin 90° = \dfrac{5}{d}$
$$d = \frac{5}{\sin 90°} = \frac{5}{1} = 5 \text{ mi}$$

(c) $\sin 120° = \dfrac{5}{d}$
$$d = \frac{5}{\sin 120°} = \frac{5}{0.866} = 5.77 \text{ mi}$$

Section 6.4   Graphs of Sine and Cosine Functions

- You should be able to graph sine and cosine functions with your graphing utility. Be sure you have set the calculator in radian mode.

- You should be able to graph $y = a\sin(bx - c)$ and $y = a\cos(bx - c)$.

- Amplitude: $|a|$

- Period: $\dfrac{2\pi}{|b|}$

- Shift: Solve $bx - c = 0$ and $bx - c = 2\pi$.

---

1. $y = 2\sin 2x$

  Amplitude: $|2| = 2$

  Period: $\dfrac{2\pi}{|2|} = \pi$

```
RANGE
Xmin=0
Xmax=3π
Xscl=π/2
Ymin=-3
Ymax=3
Yscl=1
```

3. $y = \dfrac{3}{2}\cos\dfrac{x}{2}$

  Amplitude: $\left|\dfrac{3}{2}\right| = \dfrac{3}{2}$

  Period: $\dfrac{2\pi}{|1/2|} = 4\pi$

```
RANGE
Xmin=0
Xmax=4π
Xscl=π
Ymin=-2
Ymax=2
Yscl=1
```

5. $y = \dfrac{1}{2}\sin \pi x$

  Amplitude: $\left|\dfrac{1}{2}\right| = \dfrac{1}{2}$

  Period: $\dfrac{2\pi}{|\pi|} = 2$

```
RANGE
Xmin=0
Xmax=6
Xscl=1
Ymin=-2
Ymax=2
Yscl=0.5
```

7. $y = -3\sin 10x$

  Amplitude: $|-3| = 3$

  Period: $\dfrac{2\pi}{|10|} = \dfrac{\pi}{5}$

9. $y = 3\sin 4\pi x$

  Amplitude: $|3| = 3$

  Period: $\dfrac{2\pi}{|4\pi|} = \dfrac{1}{2}$

11. $f(x) = \sin x$

  $g(x) = \sin(x - \pi)$

  The graph of g is a horizontal shift to the right π units of the graph of f (a phase shift). Verify this by graphing f and g on the same viewing rectangle.

13. $f(x) = \cos 2x$

$g(x) = -\cos 2x$

The graph of g is a reflection in the x-axis of the graph of f. Verify this by graphing f and g on the same viewing rectangle.

15. $f(x) = \sin x$

$g(x) = 2 + \sin x$

The graph of g is a vertical shift upward of 2 units of the graph of f. Verify this by graphing f and g on the same viewing rectangle.

17. $f(x) = -2\sin x$

$g(x) = 4\sin x$

19. $f(x) = \cos x$

$g(x) = 1 + \cos x$

21. $f(x) = -\dfrac{1}{2}\sin\dfrac{x}{2}$

$g(x) = 3 - \dfrac{1}{2}\sin\dfrac{x}{2}$

23. $f(x) = 2\cos x$

$g(x) = 2\cos(x + \pi)$

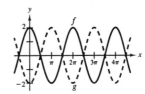

25. $f(x) = \sin x$

$g(x) = \cos\left(x - \dfrac{\pi}{2}\right)$

27. $f(x) = \cos x$

$g(x) = -\sin\left(x - \dfrac{\pi}{2}\right)$

29. $y = -2\sin 6x$

31. $y = \cos 2\pi x$

33. $y = -\sin\dfrac{2\pi x}{3}$

35. $y = 2 - \sin\dfrac{2\pi x}{3}$

37. $y = \sin\left(x - \dfrac{\pi}{4}\right)$

39. $y = 3\cos(x + \pi)$

41. $y = \dfrac{1}{10}\cos(60\pi x)$

43. $y = 3\cos(x + \pi) - 3$

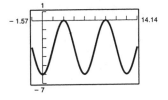

45. $y = \dfrac{2}{3}\cos\left(\dfrac{x}{2} - \dfrac{\pi}{4}\right)$

47. $y = -2\sin(4x + \pi)$

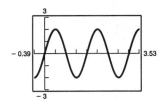

49. $y = \cos\left(2\pi x - \dfrac{\pi}{2}\right) + 1$

51. $y = -0.1\sin\left(\dfrac{\pi x}{10} + \pi\right)$

53. $y = 5\cos(\pi - 2x) + 2$

55. $f(x) = \sin x$

$\sin x = -\dfrac{1}{2}$ for

$x = -\dfrac{5\pi}{6},\ -\dfrac{\pi}{6},\ \dfrac{7\pi}{6},\ \dfrac{11\pi}{6}$

57.

$\cos x = \dfrac{\sqrt{2}}{2}$ for

$x = -\dfrac{7\pi}{4},\ -\dfrac{\pi}{4},\ \dfrac{\pi}{4},\ \dfrac{7\pi}{4}$

59. $f(x) = a\cos x + d$
Amplitude: $a = 2$
Vertical shift upwards 2 units: $d = 2$
$f(x) = 2\cos x + 2$
Verify this result using your graphing utility.

61. $y = a\sin(bx - c)$

Amplitude: $a = 2$

Period: $\dfrac{\pi}{2} = \dfrac{2\pi}{4} \Rightarrow b = 4$

Phase shift: $c = 0$

$y = 2\sin 4x$

Verify this result using your graphing utility.

63. $y = a\cos(bx - c)$

Amplitude: $a = 1$

Period: $\pi = \dfrac{2\pi}{2} \Rightarrow b = 2$

Phase shift: $-\dfrac{\pi}{4} = \dfrac{c}{b} \Rightarrow c = -\dfrac{\pi}{2}$

$y = \cos\left(2x + \dfrac{\pi}{2}\right)$

Verify using your graphing utility.

65. $f(x) = 2e^x$, $g(x) = 5\cos x$

There are two points of intersection. Using the zoom and trace features, we obtain $(-1.480, 0.455)$ and $(0.672, 3.914)$.

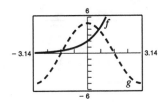

67. $v = 0.85\sin\dfrac{\pi t}{3}$

(a) Period: $\dfrac{2\pi}{\pi/3} = 6$

(b) $\dfrac{60}{6} = 10$ cycles/min

(c)

69. $y = 0.001\sin 880\pi t$

(a) Period: $\dfrac{2\pi}{880\pi} = \dfrac{1}{440}$

(b) Frequency:

$\dfrac{1}{1/440} = 440$

(c)

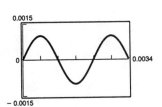

71. $S = 22.3 - 3.4\cos\dfrac{\pi t}{6}$

The maximum sales occur in June $(t = 6)$ and the minimum sales in December $(t = 12)$.

73. $g(x) = 2f(x)$

75. $g(x) = f(x - \pi)$

Section 6.5   Graphs of Other Trigonometric Functions

■ You should be able to obtain all the graphs of the trigonometric functions with your graphing utility.

■ You should be able to graph:

$$y = a\tan(bx - c) \qquad y = a\cot(bx - c)$$

$$y = a\sec(bx - c) \qquad y = a\csc(bx - c)$$

■ When graphing $y = a\sec(bx - c)$ or $y = a\csc(bx - c)$ you should know to first graph $y = a\cos(bx - c)$ or $y = a\sin(bx - c)$ since

(a) The intercepts of sine and cosine are vertical asymptotes of cosecant and secant.

(b) The maximums of sine and cosine are local minimums of cosecant and secant.

(c) The minimums of sine and cosine are local maximums of cosecant and secant.

---

1. $y = \sec 2x$ matches graph (c)

```
RANGE
Xmin=-π/2
Xmax=3π/2
Xscl=π/4
Ymin=-3
Ymax=3
Yscl=1
```

3. $y = \tan \dfrac{x}{2}$ matches graph (e)

```
RANGE
Xmin=-2π
Xmax=2π
Xscl=π/2
Ymin=-3
Ymax=3
Yscl=1
```

5. $y = \cot \pi x$ matches graph (d)

```
RANGE
Xmin=-1
Xmax=4
Xscl=1
Ymin=-2
Ymax=2
Yscl=1
```

7. $y = -\sec x$ matches graph (b)

```
RANGE
Xmin=-π
Xmax=2π
Xscl=π/2
Ymin=-3
Ymax=3
Yscl=1
```

9. $y = \frac{1}{3} \tan x$

11. $y = \tan 2x$

13. $y = -\frac{1}{2} \sec x$

15. $y = -\sec \pi x$

17. $y = \sec \pi x - 1$

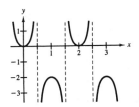

19. $y = \csc \dfrac{x}{2}$

21. $y = \cot \dfrac{x}{2}$

23. $y = \frac{1}{2} \sec 2x$

25. $y = \tan \dfrac{\pi x}{4}$

27. $y = \csc(\pi - x)$

29. $y = \dfrac{1}{4} \csc \left(x + \dfrac{\pi}{4} \right)$

31. $y = \tan \dfrac{x}{3}$

33. $y = -2\sec 4x$

35. $y = \tan\left(x - \dfrac{\pi}{4}\right)$

37. $y = \dfrac{1}{4}\cot\left(x - \dfrac{\pi}{2}\right)$

39. $y = 2\sec(2x - \pi)$

41. $f(x) = \tan x$

$\tan x = 1$ for

$$x = -\frac{7\pi}{4}, \; -\frac{3\pi}{4}, \; \frac{\pi}{4}, \; \frac{5\pi}{4}$$

43. $f(x) = \sec x$

$\sec x = -2$ for

$$x = -\frac{4\pi}{3}, \; -\frac{2\pi}{3}, \; \frac{2\pi}{3}, \; \frac{4\pi}{3}$$

45. The function $f(x) = \sec x = 1/\cos x$ is even since its graph is symmetric about the y-axis.

47. $f(x) = 2\sin x$ and $g(x) = \frac{1}{2}\csc x, \quad 0 < x < \pi$

(a)

(b) $f > g$ on the interval (0.524, 2.618).

(c) As x approaches π, f approaches 0 and g increases without bound. g is the reciprocal of f:

$$g(x) = \frac{1}{2}\csc x = \frac{1}{2\sin x} = \frac{1}{f(x)}$$

49. $\tan x = \dfrac{6}{d}$

$d = \dfrac{6}{\tan x}$

$d = 6\cot x$

Section 6.6 Advanced Graphing Techniques

■ You should be able to graph by addition of ordinates.

■ You should be able to graph vertical translations.

■ You should be able to graph using a damping factor.

---

1. $y = 2 - 2\sin\dfrac{x}{2}$

3. $y = 4 - 2\cos \pi x$

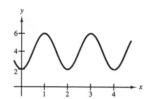

5. $y = 1 + \csc x$

7. $y = \sin x + \cos x$
Period: 2π
Relative maximum: $(0.785,\ 1.414)$
Relative minimum: $(3.927,\ -1.414)$

9. $f(x) = 2\sin x + \sin 2x$
Period: 2π
Relative maximum: $(1.047,\ 2.598)$
Relative minimum: $(5.236,\ -2.598)$

11. $g(x) = \cos x - \cos \dfrac{x}{2}$

Period: 4π

Relative maximum: $(0, 0)$, $(2\pi, 2)$

Relative minimum:

$(2.636, -1.125)$, $(9.930, -1.125)$

13. $h(x) = \sin x + \frac{1}{3} \sin 5x$

15. $y = -3 + \cos x + 2 \sin 2x$

17. $y_1 = x + \sin x$

$y_2 = x$

19. $y_1 = \frac{1}{2}x - 2 \cos x$

$y_2 = \frac{1}{2}x$

21. $y_1 = -t + \sin \dfrac{\pi t}{2}$

$y_2 = -t$

23. $y_1 = \dfrac{x^2}{8} + \sin\left(\dfrac{\pi x}{2}\right)$

$\quad y_2 = \dfrac{x^2}{8}$

25. $y_1 = 2^{-x/4} \cos \pi x$

$\quad y_2 = 2^{-x/4}, \quad y_3 = -2^{-x/4}$

The functional values approach 0 as x increases without bound.

27. $y_1 = e^{-x^2/2} \sin x$

$\quad y_2 = e^{-x^2/2}, \quad y_3 = -e^{-x^2/2}$

The functional values approach 0 as x increases without bound.

29. $y_1 = x \cos x$

$\quad y_2 = x$

$\quad y_3 = -x$

The functional values approach 0 as x approaches 0.

31. $y_1 = |x| \sin x$

$y_2 = x$

$y_3 = -x$

The functional values approach 0 as x approaches 0.

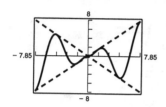

33. $y = \dfrac{6}{x} + \cos x, \ x > 0$

y increases without bound as x approaches 0.

35. $g(x) = \dfrac{\sin x}{x}$

g approaches the value of 1 as x approaches 0.

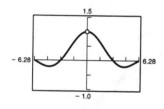

37. $f(x) = \sin\left(\dfrac{1}{x}\right)$

f oscillates between -1 and 1 as x approaches 0.

39. $f(x) = \sin x + \cos\left(x + \dfrac{\pi}{2}\right)$

$g(x) = 0$

$f = g$

(The functions are identically 0.)

41. $f(x) = \sin^2 x$

$g(x) = \frac{1}{2}(1 - \cos 2x)$

$f = g$

(The functions are equal.)

43. $f(t) = t^2 \sin t, \; [0, \; 2\pi]$

45. $f(x) = \sin x - \frac{1}{3}\sin 3x + \frac{1}{5}\sin 5x, \;\; [0, \; \pi]$

47. $S = 74 + 3t + 40\sin\dfrac{\pi t}{6}$

49. $P = 10{,}000 + 3000 \sin \dfrac{2\pi t}{24}$

$p = 15{,}000 + 5000 \cos \dfrac{2\pi t}{24}$

We can explain the cycles of this predator-prey population by noting the following cause and effect pattern:

51. $y = \frac{1}{2} e^{-t/4} \cos 4t$

Section 6.7   Inverse Trigonometric Functions

■ You should know the definitions, domains, and ranges of $y = \arcsin x$, $y = \arccos x$, and $y = \arctan x$.

■ You should know the inverse properties of the inverse trigonometric functions.

■ You should be able to use the triangle technique to convert trigonometric expressions into algebraic expressions.

■ You should be able to produce the graphs of the inverse trigonometric functions with your graphing utility.

---

1. $y = \arcsin \dfrac{1}{2} \Rightarrow \sin y = \dfrac{1}{2}$ for $-\dfrac{\pi}{2} \le y \le \dfrac{\pi}{2} \Rightarrow y = \dfrac{\pi}{6}$

3. $y = \arccos \dfrac{1}{2} \Rightarrow \cos y = \dfrac{1}{2}$ for $0 \le y \le \pi \Rightarrow y = \dfrac{\pi}{3}$

5. $y = \arctan \dfrac{\sqrt{3}}{3} \Rightarrow \tan y = \dfrac{\sqrt{3}}{3}$ for $-\dfrac{\pi}{2} < y < \dfrac{\pi}{2} \Rightarrow y = \dfrac{\pi}{6}$

7. $y = \arccos\left(-\dfrac{\sqrt{3}}{2}\right) \Rightarrow \cos y = -\dfrac{\sqrt{3}}{2}$ for $0 \le y \le \pi \Rightarrow y = \dfrac{5\pi}{6}$

9. $y = \arctan(-\sqrt{3}) \Rightarrow \tan y = -\sqrt{3}$ for $-\dfrac{\pi}{2} < y < \dfrac{\pi}{2} \Rightarrow y = -\dfrac{\pi}{3}$

11. $y = \arccos\left(-\dfrac{1}{2}\right) \Rightarrow \cos y = -\dfrac{1}{2}$ for $0 \le y \le \pi \Rightarrow y = \dfrac{2\pi}{3}$

13. $y = \arcsin \dfrac{\sqrt{3}}{2} \Rightarrow \sin y = \dfrac{\sqrt{3}}{2}$ for $-\dfrac{\pi}{2} \le y \le \dfrac{\pi}{2} \Rightarrow y = \dfrac{\pi}{3}$

15. $y = \arctan 0 \Rightarrow \tan y = 0$ for $-\dfrac{\pi}{2} < y < \dfrac{\pi}{2} \Rightarrow y = 0$

17. $\arccos 0.28 \approx 1.29$ **19.** $\arcsin(-0.75) \approx -0.85$ **21.** $\arctan(-2) \approx -1.11$

23. $\arcsin 0.31 \approx 0.32$ **25.** $\arccos(-0.41) \approx 1.99$ **27.** $\arctan 0.92 \approx 0.74$

29. $f(x) = \tan x, \ -\dfrac{\pi}{2} < x < \dfrac{\pi}{2}$

$g(x) = \arctan x$

$y = x$

31. $y = \sin(\arcsin 0.3) = 0.3$

33. $\cos[\arccos(-0.1)] = -0.1$

35. $\arcsin(\sin 3\pi) = \arcsin 0 = 0$

37. $\qquad y = \arctan \dfrac{3}{4}$

$\sin y = \sin\left(\arctan \dfrac{3}{4}\right)$

$\qquad\quad = \dfrac{3}{5}$

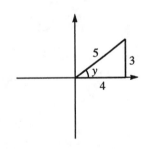

39. $\qquad y = \arctan 2$

$\cos y = \cos(\arctan 2)$

$\qquad\quad = \dfrac{1}{\sqrt{5}} = \dfrac{\sqrt{5}}{5}$

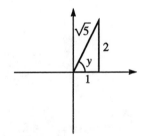

41. $y = \arcsin \frac{5}{13}$

$\cos y = \cos \left(\arcsin \frac{5}{13} \right)$

$= \frac{12}{13}$

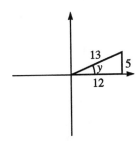

43. $y = \arctan \left(-\frac{3}{5} \right)$

$\sec y = \sec \left[\arctan \left(-\frac{3}{5} \right) \right] = \frac{\sqrt{34}}{5}$

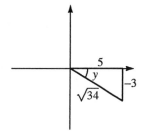

45. $f(x) = \sin(\arctan 2x)$

$g(x) = \dfrac{2x}{\sqrt{1 + 4x^2}}$

Asymptotes: $y = \pm 1$

47. $y = \arctan x$

$\cot y = \cot(\arctan x) = \frac{1}{x}$

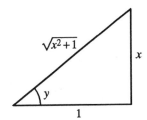

49. $y = \arcsin 2x$

$\cos y = \cos(\arcsin 2x) = \sqrt{1 - 4x^2}$

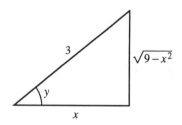

51. $y = \arccos x$

$\sin y = \sin(\arccos x) = \sqrt{1 - x^2}$

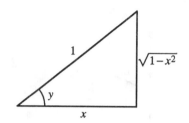

53. $y = \arccos \dfrac{x}{3}$

$\tan y = \tan\left(\arccos \dfrac{x}{3}\right) = \dfrac{\sqrt{9 - x^2}}{x}$

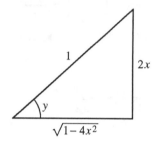

55. $y = \arccos \dfrac{x}{\sqrt{2}}$

$\csc y = \csc\left(\arccos \dfrac{x}{\sqrt{2}}\right) = \dfrac{\sqrt{2}}{\sqrt{2 - x^2}}$

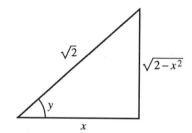

57. $\arctan \dfrac{9}{x} = \arcsin \dfrac{9}{\sqrt{x^2 + 81}}$

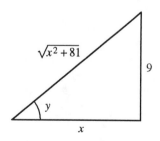

59. $\arccos \dfrac{3}{\sqrt{x^2 - 2x + 10}}$

$= \arcsin \dfrac{|x - 1|}{\sqrt{x^2 - 2x + 10}}$

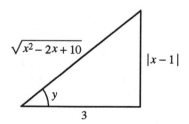

61. $f(x) = \arcsin(x - 1)$

63. $f(x) = \arctan 2x$

65. $f(t) = 3\cos 2t + 3\sin 2t$

$w = 2, \ A = 3, \ B = 3$

$= \sqrt{9 + 9}\sin\left(2t + \arctan\left(\dfrac{3}{3}\right)\right)$

$= 3\sqrt{2}\sin\left(2t + \dfrac{\pi}{4}\right)$

67. $\beta = \arctan\dfrac{4x}{x^2 + 5}$

(a)

(b) When $x = 2.236$, β is a maximum (0.730).

(c) $\beta = 0$ is a horizontal asymptote. As the distance from the picture increases without bound, the angle β approaches 0.

69. $\theta = \arcsin\left(\dfrac{12}{s}\right)$

(a) $\theta = \arcsin\left(\dfrac{12}{48}\right) \Rightarrow$

$\sin\theta = \dfrac{1}{4} \Rightarrow \theta = 14.5°$

(b) $\theta = \arcsin\left(\dfrac{12}{24}\right) \Rightarrow$

$\sin\theta = \dfrac{1}{2} \Rightarrow \theta = 30.0°$

71. $y = \text{arccot } x$ if and only if $\cot y = x$ where $-\infty < x < \infty$ and $0 < y < \pi$. The domain of $y = \text{arccot } x$ is $(-\infty, \infty)$ and the range is $(0, \pi)$.

73. $y = \text{arccsc } x$ if and only if $\csc y = x$ where $x \le -1 \cup x \ge 1$ and $-\pi/2 \le y < 0$ and $0 < y \le \pi/2$. The domain of $y = \text{arccsc } x$ is $(-\infty, -1] \cup [1, \infty)$ and the range is $[-\pi/2, 0) \cup (0, \pi/2]$.

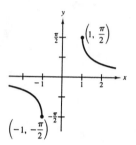

75.
$$y = \arcsin(-x), \quad -1 \le x \le 1$$
$$\sin y = -x, \quad -\frac{\pi}{2} \le y \le \frac{\pi}{2}$$
$$-\sin y = x$$
$$\sin(-y) = x$$
(The sine function is odd.)
$$-y = \arcsin x$$
$$y = -\arcsin x$$

77. $y = \pi - \arccos x$
$$\cos y = \cos(\pi - \arccos x)$$
$$\cos y = \cos \pi \cos(\arccos x) + \sin \pi \sin(\arccos x)$$
$$\cos y = -x$$
$$y = \arccos(-x)$$

79. $y_2 = \dfrac{\pi}{2} - y_1$

$\arcsin x + \arccos x = y_1 + y_2$
$$= y_1 + \left(\frac{\pi}{2} - y_1\right)$$
$$= \frac{\pi}{2}$$

Section 6.8 Applications of Trigonometry

- You should be able to solve right triangles.
- You should be able to solve right triangle applications.
- You should be able to solve applications of simple harmonic motion.

1. Given: $A = 20°$, $b = 10$

$$\tan A = \frac{a}{b} \Rightarrow a = b \tan A = 10 \tan 20°$$
$$\approx 3.6397$$

$$\cos A = \frac{a}{c} \Rightarrow c = \frac{a}{\cos A} = \frac{10}{\cos 20°}$$
$$\approx 10.642$$

$$B = 90° - 20° = 70°$$

3. Given: $B = 71°$, $b = 24$

$$\tan B = \frac{b}{a} \Rightarrow a = \frac{b}{\tan B} = \frac{24}{\tan 71°}$$
$$\approx 8.2639$$

$$\sin B = \frac{b}{c} \Rightarrow c = \frac{b}{\sin B} = \frac{24}{\sin 71°}$$
$$\approx 25.383$$

$$A = 90° - 71° = 19°$$

5. Given: $A = 12°15'$, $c = 430.5$

$$\sin A = \frac{a}{c} \Rightarrow a = c \sin A$$
$$= 430.5 \sin 12.25°$$
$$\approx 91.342$$

$$\cos A = \frac{b}{c} \Rightarrow b = c \cos A$$
$$= 430.5 \cos 12.25°$$
$$\approx 420.70$$

$$B = 90° - 12°15' = 77°45'$$

7. Given: $a = 6$, $b = 10$

$$c^2 = a^2 + b^2 \Rightarrow$$
$$c = \sqrt{36 + 100} = 2\sqrt{34} \approx 11.662$$

$$\tan A = \frac{a}{b} = \frac{6}{10} \Rightarrow$$

$$A = \arctan \frac{3}{5} \approx 30.96°$$
$$B \approx 90° - 30.964° = 59.04°$$

9. Given: $b = 16$, $c = 52$

$$a^2 = c^2 - b^2 \Rightarrow a = \sqrt{2704 - 256} = 12\sqrt{17} \approx 49.477$$

$$\cos A = \frac{b}{c} = \frac{16}{52} \Rightarrow A = \arccos \frac{4}{13} \approx 72.08°$$

$$B \approx 90° - 72.080° = 17.92°$$

11. $\tan\theta = \dfrac{h}{\frac{1}{2}b} \Rightarrow h = \dfrac{1}{2}b\tan\theta$

$\qquad h = \dfrac{1}{2}b\tan\theta$

$\qquad h = \dfrac{1}{2}(4)\tan 52° \approx 2.56$ in.

13. $\tan 30° = \dfrac{70}{x}$

$\qquad x = \dfrac{70}{\tan 30°}$

$\qquad \approx 121.2$ ft

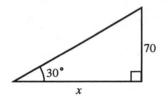

15. $\sin 74° = \dfrac{h}{16}$

$\qquad h = 16\sin 74°$

$\qquad \approx 15.4$ ft

17. $\tan\theta = \frac{75}{50} = 1.5$

$\qquad \theta = \arctan 1.5$

$\qquad \approx 0.9828$ radians

$\qquad \approx 56.3°$

19. $\cos\theta = \frac{4000}{4100} = \frac{40}{41}$

$\qquad \theta = \arccos\frac{40}{41}$

$\qquad \approx 0.2213$ radians

$\qquad \approx 12.7°$

21. Since the airplane speed is

$$\left(275\frac{\text{ft}}{\text{sec}}\right)\left(60\frac{\text{sec}}{\text{min}}\right) = 16{,}500\frac{\text{ft}}{\text{min}},$$

after one minute its distance travelled is
16,500 feet.

$$\sin 18° = \frac{a}{16{,}500}$$

$$a = 16{,}500 \sin 18°$$

$$\approx 5099 \text{ ft}$$

23. $\tan 47°40' = \dfrac{b}{50}$

$$b = 50 \tan 47°40'$$

$$\tan 35° = \frac{a}{50}$$

$$a = 50 \tan 35°$$

Height of steeple $= b - a$

$$= 50 \tan 47°40' - 50 \tan 35°$$

$$\approx 19.9 \text{ ft}$$

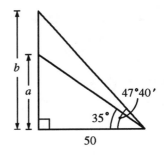

25. 550 mph for 1.5 hours takes the plane 825
miles from its point of departure.

$$\sin 38° = \frac{a}{825} \Rightarrow a \approx 508 \text{ miles north}$$

$$\cos 38° = \frac{b}{825} \Rightarrow b \approx 650 \text{ miles east}$$

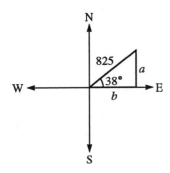

27. $\tan\theta = \frac{45}{30} \Rightarrow \theta \approx 56.3°$

Bearing: N 56.3° W

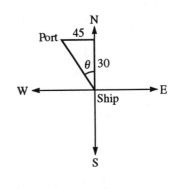

29. $\theta = 32°$, $\phi = 68°$

(a) $\alpha = 90° - 32° = 58°$

Bearing from A to C: N 58° E

(b) $\beta = \theta = 32°$

$\gamma = 90° - \phi = 22°$

$C = \beta + \gamma = 54°$

$\tan C = \dfrac{d}{50} \Rightarrow$

$\tan 54° = \dfrac{d}{50} \Rightarrow d \approx 68.8$ yd

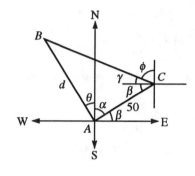

31. $\cot 6.5° = \dfrac{d}{300} \Rightarrow d \approx 2633.07$ ft

$\cot 4° = \dfrac{D}{300} \Rightarrow D \approx 4290.20$ ft

Distance between ships:

$D - d \approx 4290.20 - 2633.07$

$= 1657.13$ ft

33. $\tan 57° = \dfrac{a}{x} \Rightarrow x = a \cot 57°$

$\tan 16° = \dfrac{a}{x + (55/6)}$

$\tan 16° = \dfrac{a}{a \cot 57° + (55/6)}$

$\cot 16° = \dfrac{a \cot 57° + (55/6)}{a}$

$a \cot 16° - a \cot 57° = \dfrac{55}{6}$

$a \approx 3.23$ miles

$\approx 17{,}054$ ft

35. $\sin 36° = \dfrac{d}{25} \Rightarrow d \approx 14.6946$

Length of side: $2d \approx 29.389$ inches

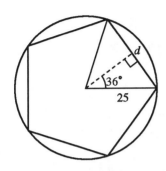

37. $\cos 30° = \dfrac{b}{r}$

$b = \cos 30° r$

$b = \dfrac{\sqrt{3}\,r}{2}$

$y = 2b = 2\left(\dfrac{\sqrt{3}\,r}{2}\right) = \sqrt{3}\,r$

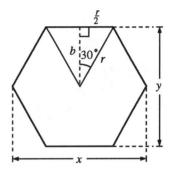

39. $\tan 35° = \dfrac{a}{10}$

$a = 10\tan 35° \approx 7$

$\cos 35° = \dfrac{10}{c}$

$c = \dfrac{10}{\cos 35°} \approx 12.2$

41. $d = 4\cos 8\pi t$

(a) Maximum displacement = amplitude = 4

(b) Frequency $= \dfrac{1}{\text{period}} = \dfrac{1}{1/4} = 4$ cycles/unit of time

(c) $8\pi t = \dfrac{\pi}{2} \Rightarrow t = \dfrac{1}{16}$

43. $d = \dfrac{1}{16} \sin 120\pi t$

    (a) Maximum displacement = amplitude = $\dfrac{1}{16}$

    (b) Frequency $= \dfrac{1}{\text{period}} = \dfrac{1}{1/60} = 60$ cycles/unit of time

    (c) $120\pi t = \pi \Rightarrow t = \dfrac{1}{120}$

45. $d = a \sin \omega t$

    Period $= \dfrac{2\pi}{\omega} = \dfrac{1}{\text{frequency}}$

            $\dfrac{2\pi}{\omega} = \dfrac{1}{264}$

                $\omega = 2\pi(264) = 528\pi$

Chapter 6 Review Exercises

1. $\theta = \dfrac{11\pi}{4}$

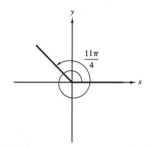

Coterminal angles: $\dfrac{3\pi}{4}, \ -\dfrac{5\pi}{4}$

3. $\theta = -110°$

Coterminal angles: $250°, \ -470°$

5. $135°16'45'' = 135 + \frac{16}{60} + \frac{45}{3600} \approx 135.28°$

7. $5°22'53'' = 5 + \frac{22}{60} + \frac{53}{3600} \approx 5.38°$

9. $135.27 = 135° + (0.27)(60)$

$\qquad = 135° + 16' + 0.2(60)$

$\qquad = 135°16'12''$

11. $-85.15° = -[85° + (0.15)(60)] = -85°9'$

13. $\dfrac{5\pi \text{ rad}}{7} = \dfrac{5\pi \text{ rad}}{7} \cdot \dfrac{180°}{\pi \text{ rad}} \approx 128.57°$

15. $-3.5 \text{ rad} = -3.5 \text{ rad} \cdot \dfrac{180°}{\pi \text{ rad}} \approx -200.54°$

17. $480° = 480° \cdot \dfrac{\pi \text{ rad}}{180°}$

$\qquad = \dfrac{8\pi}{3} \text{ rad}$

$\qquad \approx 8.3776 \text{ rad}$

19. $-33°45' = -33.75°$

$\qquad = -33.75° \cdot \dfrac{\pi \text{ rad}}{180°}$

$\qquad = -\dfrac{3\pi}{16} \text{ rad}$

$\qquad \approx -0.5890 \text{ rad}$

21. $252°$ is in Quadrant III.

$\qquad$ Reference angle: $252° - 180° = 72°$

23. $-\dfrac{6\pi}{5}$ is in Quadrant II; coterminal to $\dfrac{4\pi}{5}$

$\qquad$ Reference angle: $\pi - \dfrac{4\pi}{5} = \dfrac{\pi}{5}$

25. $x = 12, \; y = 16$

$$r = \sqrt{144 + 256} = \sqrt{400} = 20$$

$\sin \theta = \frac{4}{5}$ $\csc \theta = \frac{5}{4}$

$\cos \theta = \frac{3}{5}$ $\sec \theta = \frac{5}{3}$

$\tan \theta = \frac{4}{3}$ $\cot \theta = \frac{3}{4}$

27. $x = -7, \; y = 2, \; r = \sqrt{49 + 4} = \sqrt{53}$

$\sin \theta = \dfrac{y}{r} = \dfrac{2}{\sqrt{53}} = \dfrac{2\sqrt{53}}{53}$ $\csc \theta = \dfrac{\sqrt{53}}{2}$

$\cos \theta = \dfrac{x}{r} = -\dfrac{7}{\sqrt{53}} = -\dfrac{7\sqrt{53}}{53}$ $\sec \theta = -\dfrac{\sqrt{53}}{7}$

$\tan \theta = \dfrac{y}{x} = -\dfrac{2}{7}$ $\cot \theta = -\dfrac{7}{2}$

29. $x = -4, \; y = -6, \; r = \sqrt{16 + 36} = 2\sqrt{13}$

$\sin \theta = \dfrac{y}{r} = \dfrac{-6}{2\sqrt{13}} = -\dfrac{3\sqrt{13}}{13}$ $\csc \theta = -\dfrac{\sqrt{13}}{3}$

$\cos \theta = \dfrac{x}{r} = \dfrac{-4}{2\sqrt{13}} = -\dfrac{2\sqrt{13}}{13}$ $\sec \theta = -\dfrac{\sqrt{13}}{2}$

$\tan \theta = \dfrac{y}{x} = \dfrac{-6}{-4} = \dfrac{3}{2}$ $\cot \theta = \dfrac{2}{3}$

31. $\sec \theta = \dfrac{6}{5}, \quad \tan \theta < 0 \Rightarrow \theta$ is in Quadrant IV.

$r = 6, \quad x = 5, \quad y = -\sqrt{36 - 25} = -\sqrt{11}$

$\sin \theta = \dfrac{y}{r} = -\dfrac{\sqrt{11}}{6}$ $\csc \theta = -\dfrac{6\sqrt{11}}{11}$

$\cos \theta = \dfrac{x}{r} = \dfrac{5}{6}$ $\sec \theta = \dfrac{6}{5}$

$\tan \theta = \dfrac{y}{x} = -\dfrac{\sqrt{11}}{5}$ $\cot \theta = -\dfrac{5\sqrt{11}}{11}$

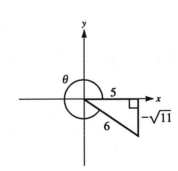

33. $\sin\theta = \dfrac{3}{8}$, $\cos\theta < 0 \Rightarrow \theta$ is in Quadrant II.

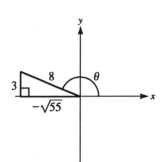

$y = 3,\ \ r = 8,\ \ x = -\sqrt{55}$

$\sin\theta = \dfrac{y}{r} = \dfrac{3}{8}$ $\qquad\qquad$ $\csc\theta = \dfrac{8}{3}$

$\cos\theta = \dfrac{x}{r} = -\dfrac{\sqrt{55}}{8}$ $\qquad$ $\sec\theta = -\dfrac{8}{\sqrt{55}} = -\dfrac{8\sqrt{55}}{55}$

$\tan\theta = \dfrac{y}{x} = -\dfrac{3}{\sqrt{55}} = -\dfrac{3\sqrt{55}}{55}$ $\qquad$ $\cot\theta = -\dfrac{\sqrt{55}}{3}$

35. $\tan\dfrac{\pi}{3} = \sqrt{3}$

37. $\sin\dfrac{5\pi}{3} = -\sin\dfrac{\pi}{3}$
$= -\dfrac{\sqrt{3}}{2}$

39. $\cos 495° = -\cos 45°$
$= -\dfrac{\sqrt{2}}{2}$

41. $\tan 33° \approx 0.65$

43. $\sec\dfrac{12\pi}{5} \approx 3.24$

45. $\cos\theta = -\dfrac{\sqrt{2}}{2} \Rightarrow \theta$ is in Quadrant II or III.

Reference angle: $\dfrac{\pi}{4}$

$\theta = \dfrac{3\pi}{4},\ \dfrac{5\pi}{4}$ or $\theta = 135°,\ 225°$

47. $\csc\theta = -2 \Rightarrow \theta$ is in Quadrant III or IV.

Reference angle: $\dfrac{\pi}{6}$

$\theta = \dfrac{7\pi}{6},\ \dfrac{11\pi}{6}$ or $\theta = 210°,\ 330°$

49. $\sin\theta = 0.8387 \Rightarrow \theta$ is in Quadrant I or II.

$= \arcsin 0.8387$

$\theta \approx 0.9949$ rad or $0.9949 \cdot \dfrac{180}{\pi} = 57.0°$

$\theta \approx \pi - 0.9949 \approx 2.1467$ rad or

$2.1467 \cdot \dfrac{180}{\pi} = 123.0°$

51. $\sec\theta = -1.0353$, θ is in Quadrant II or III.

Reference angle: $15.0°$

$\theta = 165.0°$ or $165° \cdot \dfrac{\pi}{180°} \approx 2.8798$ rad

$\theta = 195.0°$ or $195° \cdot \dfrac{\pi}{180°} \approx 3.4034$ rad

53. $\sec[\arcsin(x-1)] = \sec\theta$

$$= \frac{1}{\sqrt{-x^2+2x}}$$

$$= \frac{\sqrt{-x^2+2x}}{-x^2+2x}$$

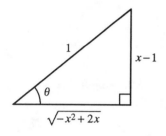

55. $\sin\left(\arccos\dfrac{x^2}{4-x^2}\right) = \sin\theta$

$$= \frac{2\sqrt{4-2x^2}}{4-x^2}$$

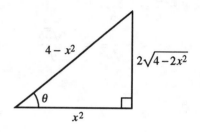

57. $y = 3\cos 2\pi x$

59. $f(x) = 5\sin\dfrac{2x}{5}$

61. $f(x) = -\dfrac{1}{4}\cos\dfrac{\pi x}{4}$

63. $g(t) = \dfrac{5}{2}\sin(t-\pi)$

65. $h(t) = \tan\left(t - \dfrac{\pi}{4}\right)$

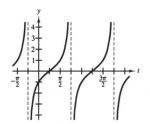

67. $f(t) = \csc\left(3t - \dfrac{\pi}{2}\right)$

69. $f(\theta) = \cot \dfrac{\pi\theta}{8}$

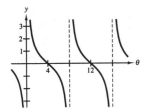

71. $f(x) = \dfrac{x}{4} - \sin x$

73. $y = \dfrac{x}{3} + \cos \pi x$

75. $h(\theta) = \theta \sin \pi\theta$

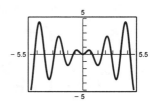

77. $y = \arcsin \dfrac{x}{2}$

79. $f(x) = \dfrac{\pi}{2} + \arctan x$

81. $f(x) = e^{\sin x}$

The function is periodic with period 2π.
Relative maximum: (1.571, 2.718)
Relative minimum: (4.712, 0.368)

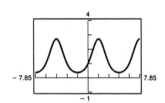

83. $g(x) = 2 \sin x \cos^2 x$

The function is periodic with period 2π.
Relative maxima:
(0.615, 0.770), (2.526, 0.770), (4.712, 0)
Relative minima:
(1.571, 0), (3.757, −0.770), (5.668, −0.770)

85. $\sin 50° = \dfrac{h}{10} \Rightarrow h = 10 \sin 50°$

≈ 7.66 m

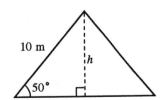

87. $\tan 28° = \dfrac{h}{2.5}$

$h = 2.5 \tan 28° \approx 1.33$ mi

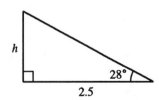

89. $\tan 1°10' = \dfrac{a}{2.5}$

$a = 2.5 \tan(1.167°)$

$a \approx 0.051$ miles ≈ 268.8 feet

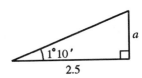

91. (a) $\sin x \approx x - \dfrac{x^3}{3!} + \dfrac{x^5}{5!} - \dfrac{x^7}{7!}$

$\cos x \approx 1 - \dfrac{x^2}{2!} + \dfrac{x^4}{4!} - \dfrac{x^6}{6!}$

(b)

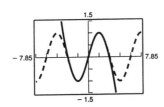

(c) The next term for $\sin x$ is $x^9/9!$, while that for $\cos x$ is $x^8/8!$. The accuracy increases with additional terms.

CHAPTER 7

Analytic Trigonometry

Section 7.1   Applications of Fundamental Identities

■ You should know the fundamental trigonometric identities.

(a) Reciprocal Identities

$$\sin u = \frac{1}{\csc u} \qquad\qquad \csc u = \frac{1}{\sin u}$$

$$\cos u = \frac{1}{\sec u} \qquad\qquad \sec u = \frac{1}{\cos u}$$

$$\tan u = \frac{1}{\cot u} = \frac{\sin u}{\cos u} \qquad \cot u = \frac{1}{\tan u} = \frac{\cos u}{\sin u}$$

(b) Pythagorean Identities

$$\sin^2 u + \cos^2 u = 1$$

$$1 + \tan^2 u = \sec^2 u$$

$$1 + \cot^2 u = \csc^2 u$$

(c) Cofunction Identities

$$\sin\left(\frac{\pi}{2} - u\right) = \cos u \qquad \cos\left(\frac{\pi}{2} - u\right) = \sin u$$

$$\tan\left(\frac{\pi}{2} - u\right) = \cot u \qquad \cot\left(\frac{\pi}{2} - u\right) = \tan u$$

$$\sec\left(\frac{\pi}{2} - u\right) = \csc u \qquad \csc\left(\frac{\pi}{2} - u\right) = \sec u$$

(d) Even–Odd Identities

$$\sin(-x) = -\sin x \qquad \csc(-x) = -\csc x$$

$$\cos(-x) = \cos x \qquad \sec(-x) = \sec x$$

$$\tan(-x) = -\tan x \qquad \cot(-x) = -\cot x$$

■ You should be able to use these fundamental identities to find function values.

■ You should be able to convert trigonometric expressions to equivalent forms by factoring and using the fundamental identities.

■ You should be able to verify trigonometric identities using your graphing utilities.

1. $\sin x = \dfrac{1}{2}$

$\cos x = \dfrac{\sqrt{3}}{2} \Rightarrow x$ is in Quadrant I.

$\tan x = \dfrac{\sin x}{\cos x} = \dfrac{1/2}{\sqrt{3}/2} = \dfrac{1}{\sqrt{3}} = \dfrac{\sqrt{3}}{3}$

$\cot x = \dfrac{1}{\tan x} = \sqrt{3}$

$\sec x = \dfrac{1}{\cos x} = \dfrac{2}{\sqrt{3}} = \dfrac{2\sqrt{3}}{3}$

$\csc x = \dfrac{1}{\sin x} = 2$

5. $\sin(-x) = -\sin x = -\dfrac{2}{3} \Rightarrow \sin x = \dfrac{2}{3}$

$\sin x = \dfrac{2}{3}$

$\tan x = -\dfrac{2\sqrt{5}}{5} \Rightarrow x$ is in Quadrant II.

$\cos x = -\sqrt{1 - \sin^2 x}$

$\qquad = -\sqrt{1 - \dfrac{4}{9}} = -\dfrac{\sqrt{5}}{3}$

$\cot x = \dfrac{1}{\tan x} = -\dfrac{\sqrt{5}}{2}$

$\sec x = \dfrac{1}{\cos x} = -\dfrac{3\sqrt{5}}{5}$

$\csc x = \dfrac{1}{\sin x} = \dfrac{3}{2}$

9. $\sin\theta = -1, \quad \cot\theta = 0 \Rightarrow \theta = \dfrac{3\pi}{2}$

$\cos\theta = \sqrt{1 - \sin^2\theta} = 0$

$\sec\theta$ is undefined.

$\tan\theta$ is undefined.

$\csc\theta = -1$

13. $\tan^2 x - \sec^2 x = \tan^2 x - (\tan^2 x + 1) = -1$

The expression is matched with (a).

3. $\sec\theta = \sqrt{2}$

$\sin\theta = -\dfrac{\sqrt{2}}{2} \Rightarrow \theta$ is in Quadrant IV.

$\cos\theta = \dfrac{1}{\sec\theta} = \dfrac{1}{\sqrt{2}} = \dfrac{\sqrt{2}}{2}$

$\tan\theta = \dfrac{\sin\theta}{\cos\theta} = \dfrac{-\sqrt{2}/2}{\sqrt{2}/2} = -1$

$\cot\theta = \dfrac{1}{\tan\theta} = -1$

$\csc\theta = -\sqrt{2}$

7. $\tan\theta = 2$

$\sin\theta < 0 \Rightarrow \theta$ is in Quadrant III.

$\sec\theta = -\sqrt{\tan^2\theta + 1}$

$\qquad = -\sqrt{4 + 1} = -\sqrt{5}$

$\cos\theta = \dfrac{1}{\sec\theta} = -\dfrac{1}{\sqrt{5}} = -\dfrac{\sqrt{5}}{5}$

$\sin\theta = -\sqrt{1 - \cos^2\theta}$

$\qquad = -\sqrt{1 - \dfrac{1}{5}} = -\dfrac{2}{\sqrt{5}} = -\dfrac{2\sqrt{5}}{5}$

$\csc\theta = \dfrac{1}{\sin\theta} = -\dfrac{\sqrt{5}}{2}$

$\cot\theta = \dfrac{1}{\tan\theta} = \dfrac{1}{2}$

11. $\sec x \cos x = \sec x \cdot \dfrac{1}{\sec x} = 1$

The expression is matched with (d).

15. $\cot x \sin x = \dfrac{\cos x}{\sin x} \cdot \sin x = \cos x$

The expression is matched with (b).

17. $\sin x \sec x = \sin x \cdot \dfrac{1}{\cos x} = \tan x$

The expression is matched with (b).

19. $\dfrac{\sec^2 x - 1}{\sin^2 x} = \dfrac{\tan^2 x}{\sin^2 x}$

$\qquad = \dfrac{\sin^2 x}{\cos^2 x} \cdot \dfrac{1}{\sin^2 x} = \sec^2 x$

The expression is matched with (e).

21. $\sec^4 x - \tan^4 x = (\sec^2 + \tan^2 x)(\sec^2 x - \tan^2 x) = (\sec^2 + \tan^2 x)(1) = \sec^2 x + \tan^2 x$

The expression is matched with (f).

23. $\tan \phi \csc \phi = \dfrac{\sin \phi}{\cos \phi} \cdot \dfrac{1}{\sin \phi}$

$\qquad = \dfrac{1}{\cos \phi} = \sec \phi$

25. $\cos \beta \tan \beta = \cos \beta \left(\dfrac{\sin \beta}{\cos \beta} \right)$

$\qquad = \sin \beta$

27. $\dfrac{\cot x}{\csc x} = \dfrac{\cos x / \sin x}{1 / \sin x}$

$\qquad = \dfrac{\cos x}{\sin x} \cdot \dfrac{\sin x}{1} = \cos x$

29. $\sec^2 x(1 - \sin^2 x) = \sec^2 x \cdot \cos^2 x$

$\qquad = \dfrac{1}{\cos^2 x} \cdot \cos^2 x$

$\qquad = 1$

31. $\dfrac{\sin(-x)}{\cos x} = -\dfrac{\sin x}{\cos x} = -\tan x$

33. $\cos \left(\dfrac{\pi}{2} - x \right) \sec x = (\sin x)(\sec x)$

$\qquad = (\sin x) \left(\dfrac{1}{\cos x} \right)$

$\qquad = \dfrac{\sin x}{\cos x}$

$\qquad = \tan x$

35. $\dfrac{\cos^2 y}{1 - \sin y} = \dfrac{1 - \sin^2 y}{1 - \sin y} = \dfrac{(1 + \sin y)(1 - \sin y)}{1 - \sin y} = 1 + \sin y$

37. $\tan^2 x - \tan^2 x \sin^2 x = \tan^2 x(1 - \sin^2 x) = \tan^2 x \cos^2 x = \dfrac{\sin^2 x}{\cos^2 x} \cdot \cos^2 x = \sin^2 x$

39. $\sin^2 x \sec^2 x - \sin^2 x = \sin^2 x(\sec^2 x - 1)$

$\qquad = \sin^2 x \tan^2 x$

41. $\tan^4 x + 2 \tan^2 x + 1 = (\tan^2 x + 1)^2$

$\qquad = (\sec^2 x)^2$

$\qquad = \sec^4 x$

43. $\sin^4 x - \cos^4 x = (\sin^2 x + \cos^2 x)(\sin^2 x - \cos^2 x) = (1)(\sin^2 x - \cos^2 x) = \sin^2 x - \cos^2 x$

45. $(\sin x + \cos x)^2 = \sin^2 x + 2\sin x \cos x + \cos^2 x$
$$= (\sin^2 x + \cos^2 x) + 2\sin x \cos x = 1 + 2\sin x \cos x$$

47. $(\sec x + 1)(\sec x - 1) = \sec^2 x - 1 = \tan^2 x$

49. $\dfrac{1}{1+\cos x} + \dfrac{1}{1-\cos x} = \dfrac{1-\cos x + 1 + \cos x}{(1+\cos x)(1-\cos x)} = \dfrac{2}{1-\cos^2 x} = \dfrac{2}{\sin^2 x} = 2\csc^2 x$

51. $\dfrac{\cos x}{1+\sin x} + \dfrac{1+\sin x}{\cos x} = \dfrac{\cos^2 x + (1+\sin x)^2}{\cos x(1+\sin x)}$
$$= \dfrac{2+2\sin x}{\cos x(1+\sin x)} = \dfrac{2(1+\sin x)}{\cos x(1+\sin x)} = \dfrac{2}{\cos x} = 2\sec x$$

53. $\dfrac{\sin^2 y}{1-\cos y} = \dfrac{1-\cos^2 y}{1-\cos y} = \dfrac{(1+\cos y)(1-\cos y)}{1-\cos y} = 1 + \cos y$

55. $\dfrac{3}{\sec x - \tan x} \cdot \dfrac{\sec x + \tan x}{\sec x + \tan x} = \dfrac{3(\sec x + \tan x)}{\sec^2 x - \tan^2 x} = \dfrac{3(\sec x + \tan x)}{1} = 3(\sec x + \tan x)$

57. $y_1 = \csc x$

$y_2 = \cot \dfrac{x}{2} - \cot x$

The graphs of y_1 and y_2 appear to be equal. The equation is an identity.

59. $y_1 = \sin 2x$

$y_2 = 2\sin x$

The graphs of y_1 and y_2 are different. The equation is not an identity.

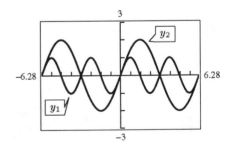

61. $y_1 = \cos x$

$y_2 = \sqrt{1-\sin^2 x}$

(a) The graphs of y_1 and y_2 coincide on $[0, \pi/2]$ and $[3\pi/2, 2\pi]$. The graphs of $y_1 = \cos x$ and $y_2 = -\sqrt{1-\sin^2 x}$ coincide on $[\pi/2, 3\pi/2]$.

63. $\sqrt{25 - x^2} = \sqrt{25 - (5\sin\theta)^2}$, $x = 5\sin\theta$
$$= \sqrt{25 - 25\sin^2\theta}$$
$$= \sqrt{25(1 - \sin^2\theta)}$$
$$= \sqrt{25\cos^2\theta}$$
$$= 5\cos\theta$$

65. $\sqrt{x^2 - 9} = \sqrt{(3\sec\theta)^2 - 9}, \quad x = 3\sec\theta$

$\qquad = \sqrt{9\sec^2\theta - 9}$

$\qquad = \sqrt{9(\sec^2\theta - 1)}$

$\qquad = \sqrt{9\tan^2\theta}$

$\qquad = 3\tan\theta$

67. $\sqrt{x^2 + 25} = \sqrt{(5\tan\theta)^2 + 25}, \quad x = 5\tan\theta$

$\qquad = \sqrt{25\tan^2\theta + 25}$

$\qquad = \sqrt{25(\tan^2\theta + 1)}$

$\qquad = \sqrt{25\sec^2\theta}$

$\qquad = 5\sec\theta$

69. $\sqrt{1 - (x-1)^2} = \sqrt{1 - (\sin\theta)^2}, \quad x - 1 = \sin\theta$

$\qquad = \sqrt{\cos^2\theta}$

$\qquad = \cos\theta$

71. $\sqrt{(9 + x^2)^3} = \sqrt{[9 + (3\tan\theta)^2]^3}, \quad x = 3\tan\theta$

$\qquad = \sqrt{(9 + 9\tan^2\theta)^3} = \sqrt{[9(1 + \tan^2\theta)]^3}$

$\qquad = \sqrt{(9\sec^2\theta)^3} = \left(\sqrt{9\sec^2\theta}\right)^3$

$\qquad = (3\sec\theta)^2 = 27\sec^3\theta$

73. $\sec\theta = \sqrt{1 + \tan^2\theta}$ is valid for θ in Quadrant I, $0 \le \theta < \pi/2$, and Quadrant IV, $3\pi/2 < \theta \le 2\pi$.

75. $\ln|\cos\theta| - \ln|\sin\theta| = \ln\left|\dfrac{\cos\theta}{\sin\theta}\right|$

$\qquad = \ln|\cot\theta|$

77. False, $\dfrac{\sin k\theta}{\cos k\theta} = \tan k\theta \ne \tan\theta$ in general.

79. True; $\sin\theta\csc\theta = \sin\theta\left(\dfrac{1}{\sin\theta}\right) = 1$, provided $\sin\theta \ne 0$.

81. $\csc^2 - \cot^2\theta = 1$

(a) $\theta = 132°$

$\qquad \csc^2 132° - \cot^2 132° \approx 1.8107 - 0.8107 = 1$

(b) $\theta = \dfrac{2\pi}{7}$

$\qquad \csc^2\dfrac{2\pi}{7} - \cot^2\dfrac{2\pi}{7} \approx 1.6360 - 0.6360 = 1$

83. $\cos\left(\dfrac{\pi}{2} - \theta\right) = \sin\theta$

    (a) $\theta = 80°$

$$\cos(90° - 80°) = \sin 80°$$

$$0.9848 = 0.9848$$

    (b) $\theta = 0.8$

$$\cos\left(\dfrac{\pi}{2} - 0.8\right) = \sin 0.8$$

$$0.7174 = 0.7174$$

85. $\cos\theta = \pm\sqrt{1 - \sin^2\theta}$

$$\tan\theta = \dfrac{\sin\theta}{\cos\theta} = \pm\dfrac{\sin\theta}{\sqrt{1 - \sin^2\theta}}$$

$$\cot\theta = \dfrac{\cos\theta}{\sin\theta} = \pm\dfrac{\sqrt{1 - \sin^2\theta}}{\sin\theta}$$

$$\sec\theta = \dfrac{1}{\cos\theta} = \pm\dfrac{1}{\sqrt{1 - \sin^2\theta}}$$

$$\csc\theta = \dfrac{1}{\sin\theta}$$

Section 7.2   Verifying Trigonometric Identities

- You should know the difference between an expression, a conditional equation, and an identity.

- You should be able to solve trigonometric identities, using the following techniques.
  (a) Work with *one* side at a time. Do not "cross" the equal sign.
  (b) Use algebraic techniques such as combining fractions, factoring expressions, rationalizing denominators, and squaring binomials.
  (c) Use the fundamental identities.
  (d) Convert all the terms into sines and cosines.

- You can verify trigonometric identities by graphing both sides with your graphing utility.

---

1. $\sin t \csc t = \sin t \left(\dfrac{1}{\sin t} \right) = 1$

3. $(1 + \sin \alpha)(1 - \sin \alpha) = (1 - \sin^2 \alpha)$
$$= \cos^2 \alpha$$

5. $\cos^2 \beta - \sin^2 \beta = (1 - \sin^2 \beta) - \sin^2 \beta$
$$= 1 - 2\sin^2 \beta$$

7. $\tan^2 \theta + 4 = (\sec^2 \theta - 1) + 4$
$$= \sec^2 \theta + 3$$

9. $\sin^2 \alpha - \sin^4 \alpha = (1 - \cos^2 \alpha) - (1 - \cos^2 \alpha)^2$
$$= 1 - \cos^2 \alpha - 1 + 2\cos^2 \alpha - \cos^4 \alpha = \cos^2 \alpha - \cos^4 \alpha$$

11. $\dfrac{\sec^2 x}{\tan x} = \dfrac{1}{\cos^2 x} \cdot \dfrac{\cos x}{\sin x}$

$$= \dfrac{1}{\cos x} \cdot \dfrac{1}{\sin x}$$

$$= \sec x \csc x$$

13. $\dfrac{\cot^2 t}{\csc t} = \dfrac{\cos^2 t}{\sin^2 t} \cdot \sin t$

$$= \dfrac{\cos^2 t}{\sin t}$$

$$= \dfrac{1 - \sin^2 t}{\sin t}$$

$$= \csc t - \sin t$$

15. $\sin^{1/2} x \cos x - \sin^{5/2} x \cos x = \sin^{1/2} x \cos x (1 - \sin^2 x) = \sin^{1/2} x \cos x \cdot \cos^2 x = \cos^3 x \sqrt{\sin x}$

17. $\dfrac{1}{\sec x \tan x} = \cos x \cdot \dfrac{\cos x}{\sin x}$

$\qquad = \dfrac{\cos^2 x}{\sin x}$

$\qquad = \dfrac{1 - \sin^2 x}{\sin x}$

$\qquad = \dfrac{1}{\sin x} - \sin x$

$\qquad = \csc x - \sin x$

19. $\csc x - \sin x = \dfrac{1}{\sin x} - \sin x$

$\qquad = \dfrac{1 - \sin^2 x}{\sin x}$

$\qquad = \dfrac{\cos^2 x}{\sin x}$

$\qquad = \cos x \cdot \dfrac{\cos x}{\sin x}$

$\qquad = \cos x \cot x$

21. $\dfrac{1}{\tan x} + \dfrac{1}{\cot x} = \dfrac{\cot x + \tan x}{\tan x \cot x}$

$\qquad = \dfrac{\cot x + \tan x}{1}$

$\qquad = \tan x + \cot x$

23. $\dfrac{\cos \theta \cot \theta}{1 - \sin \theta} - 1 = \dfrac{\cos \theta \cot \theta - (1 - \sin \theta)}{1 - \sin \theta}$

$\qquad = \dfrac{\cos \theta (\cos \theta / \sin \theta) - 1 + \sin \theta}{1 - \sin \theta}$

$\qquad = \dfrac{\cos^2 \theta - \sin \theta + \sin^2 \theta}{\sin \theta (1 - \sin \theta)}$

$\qquad = \dfrac{1 - \sin \theta}{\sin \theta (1 - \sin \theta)}$

$\qquad = \dfrac{1}{\sin \theta}$

$\qquad = \csc \theta$

25. $2\sec^2 x - 2\sec^2 x \sin^2 x - \sin^2 x - \cos^2 x = 2\sec^2 x(1 - \sin^2 x) - (\sin^2 x + \cos^2 x)$

$\qquad = 2\sec^2 x(\cos^2 x) - 1$

$\qquad = 2 \cdot \dfrac{1}{\cos^2 x} \cdot \cos^2 x - 1$

$\qquad = 2 - 1$

$\qquad = 1$

27. $2 + \cos^2 x - 3\cos^4 x = (1 - \cos^2 x)(2 + 3\cos^2 x) = \sin^2 x(2 + 3\cos^2 x)$

29. $\sec^4 \theta - \tan^4 \theta = (\sec^2 \theta + \tan^2 \theta)(\sec^2 \theta - \tan^2 \theta)$

$\qquad = (1 + \tan^2 \theta + \tan^2 \theta)(1) = 1 + 2\tan^2 \theta$

31. $\dfrac{\sin \beta}{1 - \cos \beta} \cdot \dfrac{1 + \cos \beta}{1 + \cos \beta} = \dfrac{\sin \beta(1 + \cos \beta)}{1 - \cos^2 \beta}$

$\qquad = \dfrac{1 + \cos \beta}{\sin \beta}$

33. $\cos\left(\dfrac{\pi}{2} - x\right) \csc x = \sin x \csc x$

$\qquad = \dfrac{1}{\csc x} \cdot \csc x = 1$

35.
$$\frac{\csc(-x)}{\sec(-x)} = \frac{1/\sin(-x)}{1/\cos(-x)}$$
$$= \frac{\cos(-x)}{\sin(-x)}$$
$$= \frac{\cos x}{-\sin x}$$
$$= -\cot x$$

37.
$$\frac{\cos(-\theta)}{1+\sin(-\theta)} = \frac{\cos\theta}{1-\sin\theta} \cdot \frac{1+\sin\theta}{1+\sin\theta}$$
$$= \frac{\cos\theta(1+\sin\theta)}{1-\sin^2\theta}$$
$$= \frac{\cos\theta(1+\sin\theta)}{\cos^2\theta}$$
$$= \frac{1+\sin\theta}{\cos\theta}$$
$$= \frac{1}{\cos\theta} + \frac{\sin\theta}{\cos\theta}$$
$$= \sec\theta + \tan\theta$$

39. $\sin^2 x + \sin^2\left(\dfrac{\pi}{2} - x\right) = \sin^2 x + \cos^2 x$
$$= 1$$

41.
$$\sqrt{\frac{1+\sin\theta}{1-\sin\theta}} = \sqrt{\frac{1+\sin\theta}{1-\sin\theta} \cdot \frac{1+\sin\theta}{1+\sin\theta}}$$
$$= \sqrt{\frac{(1+\sin\theta)^2}{1-\sin^2\theta}}$$
$$= \sqrt{\frac{(1+\sin\theta)^2}{\cos^2\theta}}$$
$$= \frac{1+\sin\theta}{|\cos\theta|}$$

43.
$$\frac{\sin x\cos y + \cos x\sin y}{\cos x\cos y - \sin x\sin y} = \frac{\dfrac{\sin x\cos y}{\cos x\cos y} + \dfrac{\cos x\sin y}{\cos x\cos y}}{\dfrac{\cos x\cos y}{\cos x\cos y} - \dfrac{\sin x\sin y}{\cos x\cos y}} = \frac{\tan x + \tan y}{1 - \tan x\tan y}$$

45.
$$\frac{\tan x + \cot y}{\tan x\cot y} = \frac{\dfrac{1}{\cot x} + \dfrac{1}{\tan y}}{\dfrac{1}{\cot x} \cdot \dfrac{1}{\tan y}} \cdot \frac{\cot x\tan y}{\cot x\tan y} = \tan y + \cot x$$

47. $\ln|\tan\theta| = \ln\left|\dfrac{\sin\theta}{\cos\theta}\right| = \ln|\sin\theta| - \ln|\cos\theta|$

49. $\ln(1 - \cos\theta) - 2\ln|\sin\theta| = \ln(1 - \cos\theta) - \ln(\sin^2\theta) = \ln\left(\dfrac{1-\cos\theta}{\sin^2\theta}\right) = \ln\left(\dfrac{1-\cos\theta}{1-\cos^2\theta}\right)$
$$= \ln\left(\frac{1-\cos\theta}{(1-\cos\theta)(1+\cos\theta)}\right) = \ln\left(\frac{1}{1+\cos\theta}\right) = -\ln(1+\cos\theta)$$

51. True Identity: $\sin\theta = \pm\sqrt{1 - \cos^2\theta}$

$\sin\theta = \sqrt{1 - \cos^2\theta}$ is not true for $\pi < \theta < 2\pi$. For instance, let $\theta = 7\pi/4$.

53. True Identity: $\pm\sqrt{\tan^2 x} = \tan x$

$\sqrt{\tan^2 x} = \tan x$ is not true for $\pi/2 < \theta < \pi$ or $3\pi/2 < \theta < 2\pi$. For instance, let $\theta = 3\pi/4$.

55. $\mu W \cos\theta = W \sin\theta$

$$\mu = \frac{W \sin\theta}{W \cos\theta} = \frac{\sin\theta}{\cos\theta} = \tan\theta$$

Section 7.3   Solving Trigonometric Equations

- You should be able to identify and solve trigonometric equations. Use your graphing utility to check your answers.

- A trigonometric equation is a conditional equation. It is true for a specific set of values.

- To solve trigonometric equations, use algebraic techniques such as collecting like terms, taking square roots, factoring, squaring, converting to quadratic form, and using formulas.

- Your graphing utility is especially useful in solving trigonometric equations.

1. $2\cos x - 1 = 0$

(a) $2\cos\dfrac{\pi}{3} - 1 = 2\left(\dfrac{1}{2}\right) - 1 = 0$

(b) $2\cos\dfrac{5\pi}{3} - 1 = 2\left(\dfrac{1}{2}\right) - 1 = 0$

3. $3\tan^2 2x - 1 = 0$

(a) $3\left[\tan 2\left(\dfrac{\pi}{12}\right)\right]^2 - 1 = 3\tan^2\dfrac{\pi}{6} - 1 = 3\left(\dfrac{1}{\sqrt{3}}\right)^2 - 1 = 0$

(b) $3\left[\tan 2\left(\dfrac{5\pi}{12}\right)\right]^2 - 1 = 3\tan^2\dfrac{5\pi}{6} - 1 = 3\left(-\dfrac{1}{\sqrt{3}}\right)^2 - 1 = 0$

5. $2\sin^2 x - \sin x - 1 = 0$

(a) $2\sin^2\dfrac{\pi}{2} - \sin\dfrac{\pi}{2} - 1 = 2(1)^2 - 1 - 1 = 0$

(b) $2\sin^2\dfrac{7\pi}{6} - \sin\dfrac{7\pi}{6} - 1 = 2\left(-\dfrac{1}{2}\right)^2 - \left(-\dfrac{1}{2}\right) - 1 = \dfrac{1}{2} + \dfrac{1}{2} - 1 = 0$

7. $2\cos x + 1 = 0$

$2\cos x = -1$

$\cos x = -\dfrac{1}{2}$

$x = \dfrac{2\pi}{3} + 2n\pi$

or $x = \dfrac{4\pi}{3} + 2n\pi$

9. $\sqrt{3}\csc x - 2 = 0$

$\sqrt{3}\csc x = 2$

$\csc x = \dfrac{2}{\sqrt{3}}$

$x = \dfrac{\pi}{3} + 2n\pi$

or $x = \dfrac{2\pi}{3} + 2n\pi$

11. $2\sin^2 x = 1$

$$\sin x = \pm\frac{\sqrt{2}}{2}$$

$$x = \frac{\pi}{4} + \frac{n\pi}{2}$$

13. $3\sec^2 x - 4 = 0$

$$\sec x = \pm\frac{2}{\sqrt{3}}$$

$$x = \frac{\pi}{6} + n\pi$$

$$\text{or } x = \frac{5\pi}{6} + n\pi$$

15. $\tan x(\tan x - 1) = 0$

$\tan x = 0$ or $\tan x - 1 = 0$

$\quad x = n\pi \qquad\qquad \tan x = 1$

$$x = \frac{\pi}{4} + n\pi$$

17. $\sin x(\sin x + 1) = 0$

$\sin x = 0$ or $\sin x = -1$

$\quad x = n\pi \qquad\qquad x = \frac{3\pi}{2} + 2n\pi$

19. $\qquad\qquad \sin^2 x = 3\cos^2 x$

$\quad \sin^2 x - 3(1 - \sin^2 x) = 0$

$\qquad\qquad 4\sin^2 x = 3$

$$\sin x = \pm\frac{\sqrt{3}}{2}$$

$$x = \frac{\pi}{3} + n\pi$$

$$\text{or } x = \frac{2\pi}{3} + n\pi$$

21. $\sec x \csc x - 2\csc x = 0$

$\qquad \csc x(\sec x - 2) = 0$

$\csc x = 0$ or $\sec x - 2 = 0$

No solution $\qquad\quad \sec x = 2$

$$x = \frac{\pi}{3}, \frac{5\pi}{3}$$

23. $\quad 2\sin^2 x + 3\sin x + 1 = 0$

$\quad (2\sin x + 1)(\sin x + 1) = 0$

$2\sin x + 1 = 0 \qquad\quad$ or $\sin x + 1 = 0$

$$\sin x = -\frac{1}{2} \qquad\qquad \sin x = -1$$

$$x = \frac{7\pi}{6}, \frac{11\pi}{6} \qquad\qquad x = \frac{3\pi}{2}$$

25. $\quad 2\sec^2 x + \tan^2 x - 3 = 0$

$\quad 2(\tan^2 x + 1) + \tan^2 x - 3 = 0$

$\qquad\qquad 3\tan^2 x - 1 = 0$

$$\tan x = \pm\frac{\sqrt{3}}{3}$$

$$x = \frac{\pi}{6}, \frac{5\pi}{6}, \frac{7\pi}{6}, \frac{11\pi}{6}$$

27. $2\sin x + \csc x = 0$

$2\sin x + \dfrac{1}{\sin x} = 0$

$2\sin^2 x + 1 = 0$

Since $2\sin^2 x + 1 > 0$, there are no solutions.

29. $\sin 2x = -\dfrac{\sqrt{3}}{2}$

$2x = \dfrac{4\pi}{3} + 2n\pi \quad$ or $\quad 2x = \dfrac{5\pi}{3} + 2n\pi$

$x = \dfrac{2\pi}{3} + n\pi \qquad\qquad x = \dfrac{5\pi}{6} + n\pi$

$x = \dfrac{2\pi}{3}, \dfrac{5\pi}{3} \qquad\qquad x = \dfrac{5\pi}{6}, \dfrac{11\pi}{6}$

31. $\cos\left(\dfrac{x}{2}\right) = \dfrac{\sqrt{2}}{2}$

$\dfrac{x}{2} = \dfrac{\pi}{4} + 2n\pi$

$x = \dfrac{\pi}{2} + 4n\pi$

$x = \dfrac{\pi}{2}$

33.

$6y^2 - 13y + 6 = 0$

$(3y - 2)(2y - 3) = 0$

$3y - 2 = 0 \quad$ or $\quad 2y - 3 = 0$

$y = \dfrac{2}{3} \qquad\qquad y = \dfrac{3}{2}$

$6\cos^2 x - 13\cos x + 6 = 0$

$(3\cos x - 2)(2\cos x - 3) = 0$

$3\cos x - 2 = 0 \qquad\qquad$ or $\qquad 2\cos x - 3 = 0$

$\cos x = \dfrac{2}{3} \qquad\qquad\qquad\qquad \cos x = \dfrac{3}{2}$

$x \approx 0.8411,\ 5.4421 \qquad\qquad$ (No solution)

35. $y^2 - 8y + 13 = 0$

$y = \dfrac{8 \pm \sqrt{64 - 52}}{2}$

$= \dfrac{8 \pm \sqrt{12}}{2}$

$= \dfrac{8 \pm 2\sqrt{3}}{2}$

$= 4 \pm \sqrt{3}$

$\tan^2 x - 8\tan x + 13 = 0$

$\tan x = \dfrac{8 \pm \sqrt{64 - 52}}{2} \approx 5.73205,\ 2.26795$

$\tan x = 5.73205 \qquad$ or $\qquad \tan x = 2.26795$

$x \approx 1.3981,\ 4.5397 \qquad\qquad x \approx 1.1555,\ 4.2971$

37. The graph of $y = 2\cos x - \sin x$ has two x-intercepts: $x = 1.107$ and $x = 4.249$.

39. The graph of

$$y = \frac{1 + \sin x}{\cos x} + \frac{\cos x}{1 + \sin x} - 4$$

has two x-intercepts: $x = 1.047$ and $x = 5.236$.

41. The graph of $y = 2\sin x - x$ has two x-intercepts: $x = 0$ and $x = 1.895$.

43. The graph of $y = \sec^2 x + 0.5\tan x - 1$ has five x-intercepts:
$x = 0$, $x = 2.678$, $x = 3.142$, $x = 5.820$, and $x = 6.283$.

45. The graph of $y = 2\tan^2 x + 7\tan x - 15$ has four x-intercepts:
$x = 0.983$, $x = 1.768$, $x = 4.124$, and $x = 4.910$.

47. The graph of $y = 12\sin^2 x - 13\sin x + 3$ has four x-intercepts:
$x = 0.340$, $x = 0.848$, $x = 2.294$, and $x = 2.802$.

49. The graph of $\sin^2 x + 2\sin x - 1$ has two x-intercepts: $x = 0.427$ and $x = 2.715$.

51. (a) $f(x) = \sin x + \cos x$

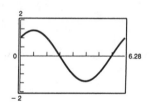

Maximum at $(0.785, 1.414)$
Minimum at $(3.927, -1.414)$

(b) The graph of $y = \cos x - \sin x$ has the same two x-intercepts:
$x = 0.785$, $x = 3.927$.

53.
$$\cos x = x$$

$$\cos 0.5 = 0.8775825619$$

$$\cos(0.8775825619) = 0.6390124942$$

$$\cos(0.6390124942) = 0.8026851007$$

$$\vdots$$

$$\cos(0.7390851332) = 0.7390851332$$

You could also solve the equation $\cos x = x$ by finding the solution to $\cos x - x = 0$ using a graphing utility.

55. $A = 2x \cos x, \quad -\dfrac{\pi}{2} < x < \dfrac{\pi}{2}$

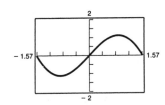

The area of the largest rectangle is 1.122, corresponding to $x = 0.860$.

57.
$$y = \frac{1}{4}(\cos 8t - 3 \sin 8t)$$

$$\frac{1}{4}(\cos 8t - 3 \sin 8t) = 0$$

$$\cos 8t = 3 \sin 8t$$

$$\frac{1}{3} = \tan 8t$$

$$8t = 0.32175 + n\pi$$

$$t = 0.04 + \frac{n\pi}{8}$$

In the interval $0 \le t \le 1$, $t = 0.04$, 0.43, and 0.83.

59. $r = \frac{1}{32} v_0{}^2 \sin 2\theta, \quad r = 300, \quad v_0 = 100$

$$300 = \tfrac{1}{32}(100)^2 \sin 2\theta$$

$$\sin 2\theta = 0.96$$

$$2\theta \approx 1.287 \qquad \text{or} \quad 2\theta = \pi - 1.287 \approx 1.855$$

$$\theta \approx 0.6435 \approx 37° \qquad \theta \approx 0.928 \approx 53°$$

61. $f(x) = \tan\left(\dfrac{\pi x}{4}\right) = x$

Solving $\tan(\pi x/4) - x = 0$, we see that $x = 1.0$.

63. $f(x) = \dfrac{4x - x^2 + 2}{4} = x$

Solving

$$\frac{4x - x^2 + 2}{4} - x = 0$$

we see that $x = 1.414$ or $x = \sqrt{2}$.

Section 7.4   Sum and Difference Formulas

■ You should memorize the sum and difference formulas.

$\sin(u \pm v) = \sin u \cos v \pm \cos u \sin v$

$\cos(u \pm v) = \cos u \cos v \mp \sin u \sin v$

$\tan(u \pm v) = \dfrac{\tan u \pm \tan v}{1 \mp \tan u \tan v}$

■ You should be able to use these formulas to find the values of the trigonometric functions of angles whose sums or differences are special angles.

■ You should be able to use these formulas to solve trigonometric equations.

---

1. $\sin 75° = \sin(30° + 45°)$

$$= \sin 30° \cos 45° + \sin 45° \cos 30° = \frac{1}{2} \cdot \frac{\sqrt{2}}{2} + \frac{\sqrt{2}}{2} \cdot \frac{\sqrt{3}}{2} = \frac{\sqrt{2}}{4}(1 + \sqrt{3})$$

$\cos 75° = \cos(30° + 45°)$

$$= \cos 30° \cos 45° - \sin 30° \sin 45° = \frac{\sqrt{3}}{2} \cdot \frac{\sqrt{2}}{2} - \frac{1}{2} \cdot \frac{\sqrt{2}}{2} = \frac{\sqrt{2}}{4}(\sqrt{3} - 1)$$

$\tan 75° = \tan(30° + 45°)$

$$= \frac{\tan 30° + \tan 45°}{1 - \tan 30° \tan 45°} = \frac{(\sqrt{3}/3) + 1}{1 - (\sqrt{3}/3)} = \sqrt{3} + 2$$

3. $\sin 105° = \sin(60° + 45°)$

$$= \sin 60° \cos 45° + \sin 45° \cos 60° = \frac{\sqrt{3}}{2} \cdot \frac{\sqrt{2}}{2} + \frac{\sqrt{2}}{2} \cdot \frac{1}{2} = \frac{\sqrt{2}}{4}(\sqrt{3} + 1)$$

$\cos 105° = \cos(60° + 45°)$

$$= \cos 60° \cos 45° - \sin 60° \sin 45° = \frac{1}{2} \cdot \frac{\sqrt{2}}{2} - \frac{\sqrt{3}}{2} \cdot \frac{\sqrt{2}}{2} = \frac{\sqrt{2}}{4}(1 - \sqrt{3})$$

$\tan 105° = \tan(60° + 45°)$

$$= \frac{\tan 60° + \tan 45°}{1 - \tan 60° \tan 45°} = \frac{\sqrt{3} + 1}{1 - \sqrt{3}} = -2 - \sqrt{3}$$

5. $\sin 195° = \sin(225° - 30°) = \sin 225° \cos 30° - \sin 30° \cos 225°$

$$= -\sin 45° \cos 30° + \sin 30° \cos 45° = -\frac{\sqrt{2}}{2} \cdot \frac{\sqrt{3}}{2} + \frac{1}{2} \cdot \frac{\sqrt{2}}{2} = \frac{\sqrt{2}}{4}(1 - \sqrt{3})$$

$\cos 195° = \cos(225° - 30°) = \cos 225° \cos 30° + \sin 225° \sin 30°$

$$= -\cos 45° \cos 30° - \sin 45° \sin 30° = -\frac{\sqrt{2}}{2} \cdot \frac{\sqrt{3}}{2} - \frac{\sqrt{2}}{2} \cdot \frac{1}{2} = -\frac{\sqrt{2}}{4}(\sqrt{3} + 1)$$

$\tan 195° = \tan(225° - 30°)$

$$= \frac{\tan 225° - \tan 30°}{1 + \tan 225° \tan 30°} = \frac{\tan 45° - \tan 30°}{1 + \tan 45° \tan 30°} = \frac{1 - (\sqrt{3}/3)}{1 + (\sqrt{3}/3)} = 2 - \sqrt{3}$$

7. $\sin \frac{11\pi}{12} = \sin\left(\frac{3\pi}{4} + \frac{\pi}{6}\right)$

$$= \sin \frac{3\pi}{4} \cos \frac{\pi}{6} + \sin \frac{\pi}{6} \cos \frac{3\pi}{4} = \frac{\sqrt{2}}{2} \cdot \frac{\sqrt{3}}{2} + \frac{1}{2}\left(-\frac{\sqrt{2}}{2}\right) = \frac{\sqrt{2}}{4}(\sqrt{3} - 1)$$

$\cos \frac{11\pi}{12} = \cos\left(\frac{3\pi}{4} + \frac{\pi}{6}\right)$

$$= \cos \frac{3\pi}{4} \cos \frac{\pi}{6} - \sin \frac{3\pi}{4} \sin \frac{\pi}{6} = -\frac{\sqrt{2}}{2} \cdot \frac{\sqrt{3}}{2} - \frac{\sqrt{2}}{2} \cdot \frac{1}{2} = -\frac{\sqrt{2}}{4}(\sqrt{3} + 1)$$

$\tan \frac{11\pi}{12} = \tan\left(\frac{3\pi}{4} + \frac{\pi}{6}\right)$

$$= \frac{\tan(3\pi/4) + \tan(\pi/6)}{1 - \tan(3\pi/4) \tan(\pi/6)} = \frac{-1 + (\sqrt{3}/3)}{1 - (-1)(\sqrt{3}/3)} = -2 + \sqrt{3}$$

9. $\sin \frac{17\pi}{12} = \sin\left(\frac{9\pi}{4} - \frac{5\pi}{6}\right)$

$$= \sin \frac{9\pi}{4} \cos \frac{5\pi}{6} - \sin \frac{5\pi}{6} \cos \frac{9\pi}{4} = \frac{\sqrt{2}}{2}\left(-\frac{\sqrt{3}}{2}\right) - \left(\frac{1}{2}\right)\left(\frac{\sqrt{2}}{2}\right) = -\frac{\sqrt{2}}{4}(\sqrt{3} + 1)$$

$\cos \frac{17\pi}{12} = \cos\left(\frac{9\pi}{4} - \frac{5\pi}{6}\right)$

$$= \cos \frac{9\pi}{4} \cos \frac{5\pi}{6} + \sin \frac{9\pi}{4} \sin \frac{5\pi}{6} = \frac{\sqrt{2}}{2}\left(-\frac{\sqrt{3}}{2}\right) + \frac{\sqrt{2}}{2}\left(\frac{1}{2}\right) = \frac{\sqrt{2}}{4}(1 - \sqrt{3})$$

$\tan \frac{17\pi}{12} = \tan\left(\frac{9\pi}{4} - \frac{5\pi}{6}\right)$

$$= \frac{\tan(9\pi/4) - \tan(5\pi/6)}{1 + \tan(9\pi/4) \tan(5\pi/6)} = \frac{1 - (-\sqrt{3}/3)}{1 + (-\sqrt{3}/3)} = 2 + \sqrt{3}$$

11. $\cos 25° \cos 15° - \sin 25° \sin 15° = \cos(25° + 15°) = \cos 40°$

13. $\sin 230° \cos 30° - \cos 230° \sin 30° = \sin(230° - 30°) = \sin 200°$

15. $\dfrac{\tan 325° - \tan 86°}{1 + \tan 325° \tan 86°} = \tan(325° - 86°) = \tan 239°$

17. $\sin 3 \cos 1.2 - \cos 3 \sin 1.2 = \sin(3 - 1.2) = \sin 1.8$

19. $\dfrac{\tan 2x + \tan x}{1 - \tan 2x \tan x} = \tan(2x + x) = \tan 3x$

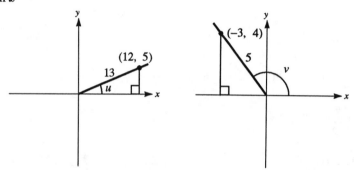

FIGURES FOR EXERCISES 21 AND 23

21. $\sin(u + v) = \sin u \cos v + \cos u \sin v$

$= \left(\tfrac{5}{13}\right)\left(-\tfrac{3}{5}\right) + \left(\tfrac{12}{13}\right)\left(\tfrac{4}{5}\right)$

$= \tfrac{-15}{65} + \tfrac{48}{65}$

$= \tfrac{33}{65}$

23. $\cos(v + u) = \cos v \cos u - \sin v \sin u$

$= \left(-\tfrac{3}{5}\right)\left(\tfrac{12}{13}\right) - \left(\tfrac{4}{5}\right)\left(\tfrac{5}{13}\right)$

$= \tfrac{-36}{65} - \tfrac{20}{65}$

$= -\tfrac{56}{65}$

FIGURES FOR EXERCISES 25 AND 27

25. $\cos(u+v) = \cos u \cos v - \sin u \sin v$

$\qquad = \left(-\frac{24}{25}\right)\left(\frac{4}{5}\right) = \left(\frac{7}{25}\right)\left(\frac{-3}{5}\right)$

$\qquad = -\frac{96}{125} + \frac{21}{125}$

$\qquad = -\frac{75}{125}$

$\qquad = -\frac{3}{5}$

27. $\sin(v-u) = \sin v \cos u - \cos v \sin u$

$\qquad = \left(-\frac{3}{5}\right)\left(-\frac{24}{25}\right) - \left(\frac{4}{5}\right)\left(\frac{7}{25}\right)$

$\qquad = \frac{72}{125} - \frac{28}{125}$

$\qquad = \frac{44}{125}$

29. $\sin\left(\dfrac{\pi}{2}+x\right) = \sin\dfrac{\pi}{2}\cos x + \sin x \cos\dfrac{\pi}{2} = (1)(\cos x) + (\sin x)(0) = \cos x$

31. $\sin\left(\dfrac{\pi}{6}+x\right) = \sin\dfrac{\pi}{6}\cos x + \sin x \cos\dfrac{\pi}{6} = \dfrac{1}{2}(\cos x + \sqrt{3}\sin x)$

33. $\cos(\pi-\theta) + \sin\left(\dfrac{\pi}{2}+\theta\right) = \cos\pi\cos\theta + \sin\pi\sin\theta + \sin\dfrac{\pi}{2}\cos\theta + \sin\theta\cos\dfrac{\pi}{2}$

$\qquad\qquad = (-1)(\cos\theta) + (0)(\sin\theta) + (1)(\cos\theta) + (\sin\theta)(0)$

$\qquad\qquad = -\cos\theta + \cos\theta$

$\qquad\qquad = 0$

35. $\cos(x+y)\cos(x-y) = (\cos x \cos y - \sin x \sin y)(\cos x \cos y + \sin x \sin y)$

$\qquad\qquad = \cos^2 x \cos^2 y - \sin^2 x \sin^2 y$

$\qquad\qquad = \cos^2 x(1-\sin^2 y) - \sin^2 x \sin^2 y$

$\qquad\qquad = \cos^2 x - \cos^2 x \sin^2 y - \sin^2 x \sin^2 y$

$\qquad\qquad = \cos^2 x - \sin^2 y(\cos^2 x + \sin^2 x)$

$\qquad\qquad = \cos^2 x - \sin^2 y$

37. $\sin(x+y) + \sin(x-y) = \sin x \cos y + \sin y \cos x + \sin x \cos y - \sin y \cos x$

$\qquad\qquad = 2\sin x \cos y$

39. $\cos(n\pi+\theta) = \cos n\pi \cos\theta - \sin n\pi \sin\theta$

$\qquad = (-1)^n(\cos\theta) - (0)(\sin\theta) = (-1)^n(\cos\theta)$, where n is an integer

41. $C = \arctan\dfrac{b}{a} \Rightarrow \sin C = \dfrac{b}{\sqrt{a^2+b^2}}, \quad \cos C \dfrac{a}{\sqrt{a^2+b^2}}$

$\qquad \sqrt{a^2+b^2}\sin(B\theta+C) = \sqrt{a^2+b^2}\left(\sin B\theta \cdot \dfrac{a}{\sqrt{a^2+b^2}} + \dfrac{b}{\sqrt{a^2+b^2}} \cdot \cos B\theta\right)$

$\qquad\qquad = a\sin B\theta + b\cos B\theta$

43. $y_1 = \cos\left(\dfrac{3\pi}{2} - x\right)$

$y_2 = -\sin x$

The graphs of y_1 and y_2 coincide.

45. $y_1 = \sin\left(\dfrac{3\pi}{2} + \theta\right) + \sin(\pi - \theta)$

$y_2 = \sin\theta - \cos\theta$

The graphs of y_1 and y_2 coincide.

47. $\sin\theta + \cos\theta$

$a = 1, \quad b = 1, \quad B = 1$

(a) $C = \arctan\dfrac{b}{a} = \arctan 1 = \dfrac{\pi}{4}$

$\sin\theta + \cos\theta = \sqrt{a^2 + b^2}\,\sin(B\theta + C) = \sqrt{2}\sin\left(\theta + \dfrac{\pi}{4}\right)$

(b) $C = \arctan\dfrac{a}{b} = \arctan 1 = \dfrac{\pi}{4}$

$\sin\theta + \cos\theta = \sqrt{a^2 + b^2}\,\cos(B\theta - C) = \sqrt{2}\cos\left(\theta - \dfrac{\pi}{4}\right)$

49. $12\sin 3\theta + 5\cos 3\theta$

$a = 12, \quad b = 5, \quad B = 3$

(a) $C = \arctan\dfrac{b}{a} = \arctan\dfrac{5}{12} \approx 0.3948$

$12\sin 3\theta + 5\cos 3\theta = \sqrt{a^2 + b^2}\,\sin(B\theta + C) \approx 13\sin(3\theta + 0.3948)$

(b) $C = \arctan\dfrac{a}{b} = \arctan\dfrac{12}{5} \approx 1.1760$

$12\sin 3\theta + 5\cos 3\theta = \sqrt{a^2 + b^2}\,\cos(B\theta - C) \approx 13\cos(3\theta - 1.1760)$

51. $C = \arctan\dfrac{b}{a} = \dfrac{\pi}{4} \Rightarrow a = b$

$\sqrt{a^2 + b^2} = 2 \Rightarrow a = b = \sqrt{2}$

$B = 1$

$2\sin\left(\theta + \dfrac{\pi}{4}\right) = \sqrt{2}\sin\theta + \sqrt{2}\cos\theta$

53. $\sin(\arcsin x + \arccos x) = \sin(\arcsin x)\cos(\arccos x) + \sin(\arccos x)\cos(\arcsin x)$

$$= x \cdot x + \sqrt{1 - x^2} \cdot \sqrt{1 - x^2}$$

$$= x^2 + 1 - x^2$$

$$= 1$$

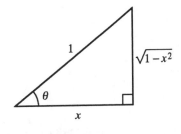

$\theta = \arcsin x$ $\theta = \arccos x$

55.
$$\sin\left(x + \frac{\pi}{3}\right) + \sin\left(x - \frac{\pi}{3}\right) = 1$$

$$\sin x \cos\frac{\pi}{3} + \cos x \sin\frac{\pi}{3} + \sin x \cos\frac{\pi}{3} - \cos x \sin\frac{\pi}{3} = 1$$

$$2\sin x(0.5) = 1$$

$$\sin x = 1$$

$$x = \frac{\pi}{2}$$

57.
$$\cos\left(x + \frac{\pi}{4}\right) + \cos\left(x - \frac{\pi}{4}\right) = 1$$

$$\cos x \cos\frac{\pi}{4} - \sin x \sin\frac{\pi}{4} + \cos x \cos\frac{\pi}{4} + \sin x \sin\frac{\pi}{4} = 1$$

$$2\cos x \left(\frac{\sqrt{2}}{2}\right) = 1$$

$$\sqrt{2}\cos x = 1$$

$$\cos x = \frac{1}{\sqrt{2}}$$

$$\cos x = \frac{\sqrt{2}}{2}$$

$$x = \frac{\pi}{4}, \frac{7\pi}{4}$$

59. $\cos\left(x + \dfrac{\pi}{4}\right) - \cos\left(x - \dfrac{\pi}{4}\right) = 1$

Graphing

$$y = \cos\left(x + \frac{\pi}{4}\right) - \cos\left(x - \frac{\pi}{4}\right) - 1$$

we see that there are two x-intercepts in the interval $[0,\ 2\pi)$: $x = 3.927$ and $x = 5.498$.

61. $y_1 = A\cos 2\pi\left(\dfrac{t}{T} - \dfrac{x}{\lambda}\right)$

$y_2 = A\cos 2\pi\left(\dfrac{t}{T} + \dfrac{x}{\lambda}\right)$

$y_1 + y_2 = A\cos 2\pi\left(\dfrac{t}{T} - \dfrac{x}{\lambda}\right) + A\cos 2\pi\left(\dfrac{t}{T} + \dfrac{x}{\lambda}\right)$

$y_1 + y_2 = A\left[\cos 2\pi\dfrac{t}{T}\cos 2\pi\dfrac{x}{\lambda} + \sin 2\pi\dfrac{t}{T}\sin 2\pi\dfrac{x}{\lambda}\right] + A\left[\cos 2\pi\dfrac{t}{T}\cos 2\pi\dfrac{x}{\lambda} - \sin 2\pi\dfrac{t}{T}\sin 2\pi\dfrac{x}{\lambda}\right]$

$\qquad = 2A\cos 2\pi\dfrac{t}{T}\cos 2\pi\dfrac{x}{\lambda}$

63. $\dfrac{\cos(x + h) - \cos x}{h} = \dfrac{\cos x \cdot \cos h - \sin x \cdot \sin h - \cos x}{h}$

$$= \cos x\left(\frac{\cos h - 1}{h}\right) - \sin x\left(\frac{\sin h}{h}\right)$$

Section 7.5   Multiple-Angle and Product-to-Sum Formulas

■ You should know the following double-angle formulas.

(a) $\sin 2u = 2 \sin u \cos u$ (b) $\cos 2u = \cos^2 u - \sin^2 u$ (c) $\tan 2u = \dfrac{2 \tan u}{1 - \tan^2 u}$

$$= 2 \cos^2 u - 1$$

$$= 1 - 2 \sin^2 u$$

■ You should be able to reduce the power of a trigonometric function.

(a) $\sin^2 u = \dfrac{1 - \cos 2u}{2}$ (b) $\cos^2 u = \dfrac{1 + \cos 2u}{2}$ (c) $\tan^2 u = \dfrac{1 - \cos 2u}{1 + \cos 2u}$

■ You should be able to use the half-angle formulas.

(a) $\sin \dfrac{u}{2} = \pm\sqrt{\dfrac{1 - \cos u}{2}}$ (b) $\cos \dfrac{u}{2} = \pm\sqrt{\dfrac{1 + \cos u}{2}}$ (c) $\tan \dfrac{u}{2} = \dfrac{1 - \cos u}{\sin u}$

$$= \dfrac{\sin u}{1 + \cos u}$$

■ You should be able to use the product-sum formulas.

(a) $\sin u \sin v = \dfrac{1}{2}[\cos(u - v) - \cos(u + v)]$

(b) $\cos u \cos v = \dfrac{1}{2}[\cos(u - v) + \cos(u + v)]$

(c) $\sin u \cos v = \dfrac{1}{2}[\sin(u + v) + \sin(u - v)]$

(d) $\cos u \sin v = \dfrac{1}{2}[\sin(u + v) - \sin(u - v)]$

■ You should be able to use the sum-product formulas.

(a) $\sin x + \sin y = 2 \sin \left(\dfrac{x + y}{2}\right) \cos \left(\dfrac{x - y}{2}\right)$

(b) $\sin x - \sin y = 2 \cos \left(\dfrac{x + y}{2}\right) \sin \left(\dfrac{x - y}{2}\right)$

(c) $\cos x + \cos y = 2 \cos \left(\dfrac{x + y}{2}\right) \cos \left(\dfrac{x - y}{2}\right)$

(d) $\cos x - \cos y = -2 \sin \left(\dfrac{x + y}{2}\right) \sin \left(\dfrac{x - y}{2}\right)$

1. $f(x) = \sin 2x - \sin x$

Graphing the function on the interval $[0, 2\pi)$, we find the zeros are $x = 0$, 1.047, 3.142, and 5.236. Algebraically:

$$\sin 2x - \sin x = 0$$

$$2 \sin x \cos x - \sin x = 0$$

$$\sin x(2 \cos x - 1) = 0$$

$$\sin x = 0 \qquad \text{or} \quad 2 \cos x - 1 = 0$$

$$x = 0, \ \pi \qquad\qquad \cos x = \frac{1}{2}$$

$$x = \frac{\pi}{3}, \ \frac{5\pi}{3}$$

3. $g(x) = 4 \sin x \cos x - 1$

Graphing the function on the interval $[0, 2\pi)$, we find the zeros are $x = 0.262$, 1.309, 3.403, and 4.451. Algebraically:

$$4 \sin x \cos x = 1$$

$$2 \sin 2x = 1$$

$$\sin 2x = \frac{1}{2}$$

$$2x = \frac{\pi}{6} + 2n\pi \quad \text{or} \quad 2x = \frac{5\pi}{6} + 2n\pi$$

$$x = \frac{\pi}{12} + n\pi \qquad\qquad x = \frac{5\pi}{12} + n\pi$$

$$x = \frac{\pi}{12}, \ \frac{13\pi}{12} \qquad\qquad x = \frac{5\pi}{12}, \ \frac{17\pi}{12}$$

5. $h(x) = \cos 2x - \cos x$

Graphing the function on the interval $[0, 2\pi)$, we find the zeros are $x = 0$, 2.094, and 4.189.

—CONTINUED ON NEXT PAGE—

5. —CONTINUED—

Algebraically:

$$\cos 2x = \cos x$$

$$\cos^2 x - \sin^2 x = \cos x$$

$$\cos^2 x - (1 - \cos^2 x) - \cos x = 0$$

$$2\cos^2 x - \cos x - 1 = 0$$

$$(2\cos x + 1)(\cos x - 1) = 0$$

$2\cos x + 1 = 0$ or $\cos x - 1 = 0$

$$\cos x = -\frac{1}{2} \qquad\qquad \cos x = 1$$

$$x = \frac{2\pi}{3},\ \frac{4\pi}{3} \qquad\qquad x = 0$$

7. $y = \tan 2x - \cot x$

Graphing the function on the interval $[0,\ 2\pi)$, we find the zeros are $x = 0.524,\ 1.571,\ 2.618,$ 3.665, 4.712, and 5.760. Algebraically:

$$\tan 2x - \cot x = 0$$

$$\frac{2\tan x}{1 - \tan^2 x} = \cot x$$

$$2\tan x = \cot x(1 - \tan^2 x)$$

$$2\tan x = \cot x - \cot x \tan^2 x$$

$$2\tan x = \cot x - \tan x$$

$$3\tan x = \cot x$$

$$3\tan x - \cot x = 0$$

$$3\tan x - \frac{1}{\tan x} = 0$$

$$\frac{3\tan^2 x - 1}{\tan x} = 0$$

$$\frac{1}{\tan x}(3\tan^2 x - 1) = 0$$

$$\cot x(3\tan^2 x - 1) = 0$$

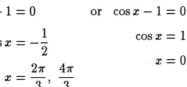

$\cot x = 0$ or $3\tan^2 x - 1 = 0$

$$x = \frac{\pi}{2},\ \frac{3\pi}{2} \qquad\qquad \tan^2 x = \frac{1}{3}$$

$$\tan x = \pm\frac{\sqrt{3}}{3}$$

$$x = \frac{\pi}{6},\ \frac{5\pi}{6},\ \frac{7\pi}{6},\ \frac{11\pi}{6}$$

9. $h(t) = \sin 4t + 2\sin 2t$

Graphing the function on the interval $[0,\ 2\pi)$, we find the zeros are $x = 0,\ 1.571,\ 3.142$, and 4.712. Algebraically:

$$\sin 4t + 2\sin 2t = 0$$

$$2\sin 2t \cos 2t + 2\sin 2t = 0$$

$$2\sin 2t(\cos 2t + 1) = 0$$

$2\sin 2t = 0 \qquad\qquad\text{or}\quad \cos 2t + 1 = 0$

$\sin 2t = 0 \qquad\qquad\qquad\quad \cos 2t = -1$

$2t = n\pi \qquad\qquad\qquad\quad 2t = \pi + 2n\pi$

$t = \dfrac{n}{2}\pi \qquad\qquad\qquad\quad t = \dfrac{\pi}{2} + n\pi$

$t = 0,\ \dfrac{\pi}{2},\ \pi,\ \dfrac{3\pi}{2} \qquad\qquad\quad t = \dfrac{\pi}{2},\ \dfrac{3\pi}{2}$

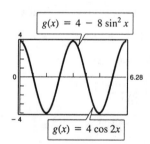

11. $f(x) = 6\sin x \cos x$

$\qquad = 3(2\sin x \cos x)$

$\qquad = 3\sin 2x$

Relative maxima: $(0.785,\ 3)$, $(3.927,\ 3)$
Relative minima:
$(2.356,\ -3)$, $(5.498,\ -3)$

13. $g(x) = 4 - 8\sin^2 x$

$\qquad = 4(1 - 2\sin^2 x)$

$\qquad = 4\cos 2x$

Relative maxima: $(0,\ 4)$, $(3.142,\ 4)$
Relative minima:
$(1.571,\ -4)$, $(4.712,\ -4)$

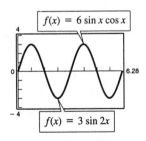

15. $\sin 2u = 2 \sin u \cos u$

$$= 2 \cdot \frac{3}{5} \cdot \frac{4}{5} = \frac{24}{25}$$

$\cos 2u = \cos^2 u - \sin^2 u$

$$= \frac{16}{25} - \frac{9}{25} = \frac{7}{25}$$

$\tan 2u = \dfrac{2 \tan u}{1 - \tan^2 u}$

$$= \frac{2(3/4)}{1 - (9/16)} = \frac{24}{7}$$

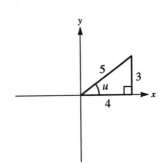

17. $\sin 2u = 2 \sin u \cos u$

$$= 2 \left(-\frac{1}{\sqrt{5}} \right) \left(-\frac{2}{\sqrt{5}} \right) = \frac{4}{5}$$

$\cos 2u = \cos^2 u - \sin^2 u$

$$= \left(-\frac{2}{\sqrt{5}} \right)^2 - \left(-\frac{1}{\sqrt{5}} \right)^2 = \frac{3}{5}$$

$\tan 2u = \dfrac{2 \tan u}{1 - \tan^2 u} = \dfrac{2(1/2)}{1 - (1/4)} = \dfrac{4}{3}$

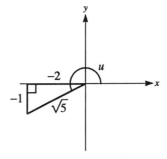

19. $\sin 2u = 2 \sin u \cos u$

$$= 2 \left(\frac{\sqrt{21}}{5} \right) \left(-\frac{2}{5} \right) = -\frac{4\sqrt{21}}{25}$$

$\cos 2u = \cos^2 u - \sin^2 u$

$$= \left(-\frac{2}{5} \right)^2 - \left(\frac{\sqrt{21}}{5} \right)^2 = -\frac{17}{25}$$

$\tan 2u = \dfrac{2 \tan u}{1 - \tan^2 u}$

$$= \frac{2(-\sqrt{21}/2)}{1 - (-\sqrt{21}/2)^2} = \frac{4\sqrt{21}}{17}$$

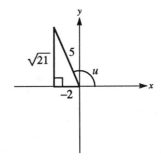

21. $\cos^4 x = (\cos^2 x)(\cos^2 x) = \left(\dfrac{1 + \cos 2x}{2} \right) \left(\dfrac{1 + \cos 2x}{2} \right) = \dfrac{1 + 2 \cos 2x + \cos^2 2x}{4}$

$$= \frac{1 + 2 \cos 2x + (1 + \cos 4x)/2}{4} = \frac{2 + 4 \cos 2x + 1 + \cos 4x}{8} = \frac{3 + 4 \cos 2x + \cos 4x}{8}$$

23. $\sin^2 x(\cos^2 x) = \dfrac{1 - \cos 2x}{2} \cdot \dfrac{1 + \cos 2x}{2}$

$$= \dfrac{1 - \cos^2 2x}{4} = \dfrac{1}{4}\left(1 - \dfrac{1 + \cos 4x}{2}\right) = \dfrac{1}{8}(2 - 1 - \cos 4x) = \dfrac{1}{8}(1 - \cos 4x)$$

25. $\sin^2 x \cos^4 x = \sin^2 x \cos^2 x \cos^2 x$

$$= \left(\dfrac{1 - \cos 2x}{2}\right)\left(\dfrac{1 + \cos 2x}{2}\right)\left(\dfrac{1 + \cos 2x}{2}\right)$$

$$= \dfrac{1}{8}(1 - \cos 2x)(1 + \cos 2x)(1 + \cos 2x)$$

$$= \dfrac{1}{8}(1 - \cos^2 2x)(1 + \cos 2x)$$

$$= \dfrac{1}{8}(1 + \cos 2x)\left(1 - \left(\dfrac{1 + \cos 4x}{2}\right)\right)$$

$$= \dfrac{1}{16}(1 + \cos 2x)(1 - \cos 4x)$$

27. $\sin 105° = \sin\left(\dfrac{1}{2} \cdot 210°\right) = \sqrt{\dfrac{1 - \cos 210°}{2}} = \sqrt{\dfrac{1 + (\sqrt{3}/2)}{2}} = \dfrac{1}{2}\sqrt{2 + \sqrt{3}}$

$\cos 105° = \cos\left(\dfrac{1}{2} \cdot 210°\right) = -\sqrt{\dfrac{1 + \cos 210°}{2}} = -\sqrt{\dfrac{1 - (\sqrt{3}/2)}{2}} = -\dfrac{1}{2}\sqrt{2 - \sqrt{3}}$

$\tan 105° = \tan\left(\dfrac{1}{2} \cdot 210°\right) = \dfrac{\sin 210°}{1 + \cos 210°} = \dfrac{-1/2}{1 - (\sqrt{3}/2)} = -2 - \sqrt{3}$

29. $\sin 112°30' = \sin\left(\dfrac{1}{2} \cdot 225°\right) = \sqrt{\dfrac{1 - \cos 225°}{2}} = \sqrt{\dfrac{1 + (\sqrt{2}/2)}{2}} = \dfrac{1}{2}\sqrt{2 + \sqrt{2}}$

$\cos 112°30' = \cos\left(\dfrac{1}{2} \cdot 225°\right) = -\sqrt{\dfrac{1 + \cos 225°}{2}} = -\sqrt{\dfrac{1 - (\sqrt{2}/2)}{2}} = -\dfrac{1}{2}\sqrt{2 - \sqrt{2}}$

$\tan 112°30' = \tan\left(\dfrac{1}{2} \cdot 225°\right) = \dfrac{\sin 225°}{1 + \cos 225°} = \dfrac{-\sqrt{2}/2}{1 - (\sqrt{2}/2)} = -1 - \sqrt{2}$

31. $\sin \dfrac{\pi}{8} = \sin\left[\dfrac{1}{2}\left(\dfrac{\pi}{4}\right)\right] = \sqrt{\dfrac{1 - \cos(\pi/4)}{2}} = \dfrac{1}{2}\sqrt{2 - \sqrt{2}}$

$\cos \dfrac{\pi}{8} = \cos\left[\dfrac{1}{2}\left(\dfrac{\pi}{4}\right)\right] = \sqrt{\dfrac{1 + \cos(\pi/4)}{2}} = \dfrac{1}{2}\sqrt{2 + \sqrt{2}}$

$\tan \dfrac{\pi}{8} = \tan\left[\dfrac{1}{2}\left(\dfrac{\pi}{4}\right)\right] = \dfrac{\sin(\pi/4)}{1 + \cos(\pi/4)} = \dfrac{\sqrt{2}/2}{1 + (\sqrt{2}/2)} = \sqrt{2} - 1$

33. $\sin\left(\dfrac{u}{2}\right) = \sqrt{\dfrac{1-\cos u}{2}} = \sqrt{\dfrac{1+(12/13)}{2}} = \dfrac{5\sqrt{26}}{26}$

$\cos\left(\dfrac{u}{2}\right) = \sqrt{\dfrac{1+\cos u}{2}} = \sqrt{\dfrac{1-(12/13)}{2}} = \dfrac{\sqrt{26}}{26}$

$\tan\left(\dfrac{u}{2}\right) = \dfrac{\sin u}{1+\cos u} = \dfrac{5/13}{1-(12/13)} = \dfrac{5}{1} = 5$

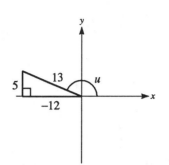

35. $\sin\left(\dfrac{u}{2}\right) = \sqrt{\dfrac{1-\cos u}{2}} = \sqrt{\dfrac{1-(8/\sqrt{89})}{2}}$

$\qquad = \sqrt{\dfrac{\sqrt{89}-8}{2\sqrt{89}}}$

$\cos\left(\dfrac{u}{2}\right) = -\sqrt{\dfrac{1+\cos u}{2}} = -\sqrt{\dfrac{1+(8/\sqrt{89})}{2}}$

$\qquad = -\sqrt{\dfrac{\sqrt{89}+8}{2\sqrt{89}}}$

$\tan\left(\dfrac{u}{2}\right) = \dfrac{1-\cos u}{\sin u} = \dfrac{1-(8/\sqrt{89})}{-5/\sqrt{89}}$

$\qquad = \dfrac{8-\sqrt{89}}{5}$

37. $\sin\left(\dfrac{u}{2}\right) = \sqrt{\dfrac{1-\cos u}{2}} = \sqrt{\dfrac{1+(4/5)}{2}} = \dfrac{3\sqrt{10}}{10}$

$\cos\left(\dfrac{u}{2}\right) = -\sqrt{\dfrac{1+\cos u}{2}} = -\sqrt{\dfrac{1-(4/5)}{2}} = -\dfrac{\sqrt{10}}{10}$

$\tan\left(\dfrac{u}{2}\right) = \dfrac{1-\cos u}{\sin u} = \dfrac{1+(4/5)}{-3/5} = -3$

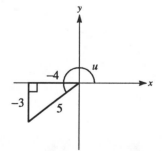

39. $\sqrt{\dfrac{1 - \cos 6x}{2}} = |\sin 3x|$

41. $-\sqrt{\dfrac{1 - \cos 8x}{1 + \cos 8x}} = -\dfrac{\sqrt{(1 - \cos 8x)/2}}{\sqrt{(1 + \cos 8x)/2}}$

$$= -\dfrac{\sin 4x}{\cos 4x}$$

$$= -|\tan 4x|$$

43. $f(x) = \sin \dfrac{x}{2} + \cos x$

Graphing the function on the interval $[0,\ 2\pi)$, we find the zero is $x = 3.142$. Algebraically:

$$\sin \dfrac{x}{2} + \cos x = 0$$

$$\sin \dfrac{x}{2} = -\cos x$$

$$\pm\sqrt{\dfrac{1 - \cos x}{2}} = -\cos x$$

$$\dfrac{1 - \cos x}{2} = \cos^2 x$$

$$1 - \cos x = 2\cos^2 x$$

$$2\cos^2 x + \cos x - 1 = 0$$

$$(2\cos x - 1)(\cos x + 1) = 0$$

$$2\cos x - 1 = 0 \qquad \text{or} \quad \cos x = -1$$

$$\cos x = \dfrac{1}{2} \qquad\qquad x = \pi$$

$$x = \dfrac{\pi}{3},\ \dfrac{5\pi}{3}$$

$\pi/3$ and $5\pi/3$ are extraneous solutions. π is the only solution.

45. $h(x) = \cos\dfrac{x}{2} - \sin x$

Graphing the function on the interval $[0,\ 2\pi)$, we find the zeros are $x = 1.047,\ 3.142,$ and 5.236. Algebraically:

$$\cos\dfrac{x}{2} - \sin x = 0$$

$$\pm\sqrt{\dfrac{1+\cos x}{2}} = \sin x$$

$$\dfrac{1+\cos x}{2} = \sin^2 x$$

$$1 + \cos x = 2\sin^2 x$$

$$1 + \cos x = 2 - 2\cos^2 x$$

$$2\cos^2 x + \cos x - 1 = 0$$

$$(2\cos x - 1)(\cos x + 1) = 0$$

$$2\cos x - 1 = 0 \qquad \text{or} \quad \cos x + 1 = 0$$

$$\cos x = \dfrac{1}{2} \qquad\qquad \cos x = -1$$

$$x = \pi$$

$$x = \dfrac{\pi}{3},\ \dfrac{5\pi}{3}$$

$\pi/3$, π, and $5\pi/3$ are all solutions to the equation.

47. $6\sin\dfrac{\pi}{4}\cos\dfrac{\pi}{4} = 6 \cdot \dfrac{1}{2}\left[\sin\left(\dfrac{\pi}{4}+\dfrac{\pi}{4}\right) + \sin\left(\dfrac{\pi}{4}-\dfrac{\pi}{4}\right)\right] = 3\left(\sin\dfrac{\pi}{2} + \sin 0\right)$

49. $\sin 5\theta \cos 3\theta = \dfrac{1}{2}[\sin(5\theta + 3\theta) + \sin(5\theta - 3\theta)] = \dfrac{1}{2}(\sin 8\theta + \sin 2\theta)$

51. $5\cos(-5\beta)\cos 3\beta = 5 \cdot \dfrac{1}{2}[\cos(-5\beta - 3\beta) + \cos(-5\beta + 3\beta)]$
$$= \dfrac{5}{2}[\cos(-8\beta) + \cos(-2\beta)] = \dfrac{5}{2}(\cos 8\beta + \cos 2\beta)$$

53. $\sin(x+y)\sin(x-y) = \dfrac{1}{2}(\cos 2y - \cos 2x)$ **55.** $\sin(\theta+\pi)\cos(\theta-\pi) = \dfrac{1}{2}(\sin 2\theta + \sin 2\pi)$

57. $\sin 60° + \sin 30° = 2\sin\left(\dfrac{60°+30°}{2}\right)\cos\left(\dfrac{60°-30°}{2}\right) = 2\sin 45° \cos 15°$

59. $\cos\dfrac{3\pi}{4} - \cos\dfrac{\pi}{4} = -2\sin\left(\dfrac{(3\pi/4)+(\pi/4)}{2}\right) + \left(\dfrac{(3\pi/4)-(\pi/4)}{2}\right) = -2\sin\dfrac{\pi}{2}\sin\dfrac{\pi}{4}$

61. $\cos 6x + \cos 2x = 2\cos\left(\dfrac{6x+2x}{2}\right)\cos\left(\dfrac{6x-2x}{2}\right) = 2\cos 4x \cos 2x$

63. $\sin(\alpha + \beta) - \sin(\alpha - \beta) = 2\cos\left(\dfrac{\alpha + \beta + \alpha - \beta}{2}\right)\sin\left(\dfrac{\alpha + \beta - \alpha + \beta}{2}\right) = 2\cos\alpha\sin\beta$

65. $\cos(\phi + 2\pi) + \cos\phi = 2\cos\left(\dfrac{\phi + 2\pi + \phi}{2}\right)\cos\left(\dfrac{\phi + 2\pi - \phi}{2}\right) = 2\cos(\phi + \pi)\cos\pi$

67. $g(x) = \sin 6x + \sin 2x$

Graphing the function on the interval $[0,\ 2\pi)$, we find the zeros are $x = 0, 0.785, 1.571, 2.356, 3.142, 3.927, 4.712,$ and 5.498. Algebraically:

$$\sin 6x + \sin 2x = 0$$

$$2\sin 4x \cos 2x = 0$$

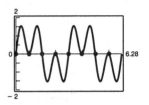

$\sin 4x = 0$	or	$\cos 2x = 0$

$$4x = n\pi \qquad\qquad\qquad 2x = \dfrac{\pi}{2} + n\pi$$

$$x = \dfrac{n\pi}{4} \qquad\qquad\qquad x = \dfrac{\pi}{4} + \dfrac{n\pi}{2}$$

$$x = 0, \dfrac{\pi}{4}, \dfrac{\pi}{2}, \dfrac{3\pi}{4}, \qquad\qquad x = \dfrac{\pi}{4}, \dfrac{3\pi}{4}, \dfrac{5\pi}{4}, \dfrac{7\pi}{4}$$

$$\pi, \dfrac{5\pi}{4}, \dfrac{3\pi}{2}, \dfrac{7\pi}{4}$$

69. $f(x) = \dfrac{\cos 2x}{\sin 3x - \sin x} - 1$

Graphing the function on the interval $[0,\ 2\pi)$, we find the zeros are $x = 0.524$ and 2.618. Algebraically:

$$\dfrac{\cos 2x}{\sin 3x - \sin x} = 1$$

$$\dfrac{\cos 2x}{2\cos 2x \sin x} = 1$$

$$2\sin x = 1$$

$$\sin x = \dfrac{1}{2}$$

$$x = \dfrac{\pi}{6}, \dfrac{5\pi}{6}$$

71. $\csc 2\theta = \dfrac{1}{\sin 2\theta}$

$$= \dfrac{1}{2\sin\theta\cos\theta}$$

$$= \dfrac{1}{\sin\theta} \cdot \dfrac{1}{2\cos\theta}$$

$$= \dfrac{\csc\theta}{2\cos\theta}$$

73. $\cos^2 2\alpha - \sin^2 2\alpha = \cos[2(2\alpha)]$

$$= \cos 4\alpha$$

75. $(\sin x + \cos x)^2 = \sin^2 x + 2\sin x \cos x + \cos^2 x$

$$= (\sin^2 x + \cos^2 x) + 2\sin x \cos x = 1 + \sin 2x$$

77. $\cos 3\beta = \cos(2\beta + \beta)$

$$= \cos 2\beta \cos \beta - \sin 2\beta \sin \beta$$

$$= (\cos^2 \beta - \sin^2 \beta)\cos \beta - 2\sin\beta\cos\beta\sin\beta$$

$$= \cos^3 \beta - \sin^2 \beta \cos \beta - 2\sin^2 \beta \cos \beta$$

$$= \cos^3 \beta - 3\sin^2 \beta \cos \beta$$

79. $1 + \cos 10y = 1 + \cos^2 5y - \sin^2 5y = 1 + \cos^2 5y - (1 - \cos^2 5y) = 2\cos^2 5y$

81. $\sec\dfrac{u}{2} = \pm\sqrt{\dfrac{1}{\cos(u/2)}} = \pm\sqrt{\dfrac{2}{1 + \cos u}} = \pm\sqrt{\dfrac{2\sin u}{\sin u(1 + \cos u)}} = \pm\sqrt{\dfrac{2\sin u}{\sin u + \sin u \cos u}}$

$$= \pm\sqrt{\dfrac{(2\sin u)/(\cos u)}{(\sin u)/(\cos u) + (\sin u \cos u)/(\cos u)}} = \pm\sqrt{\dfrac{2\tan u}{\tan u + \sin u}}$$

83. $\dfrac{\cos 4x + \cos 2x}{\sin 4x + \sin 2x} = \dfrac{2\cos\left(\dfrac{4x + 2x}{2}\right)\cos\left(\dfrac{4x - 2x}{2}\right)}{2\sin\left(\dfrac{4x + 2x}{2}\right)\cos\left(\dfrac{4x - 2x}{2}\right)} = \dfrac{2\cos 3x \cos x}{2\sin 3x \cos x} = \cot 3x$

85. $\dfrac{\cos 4x - \cos 2x}{2\sin 3x} = \dfrac{-2\sin\left(\dfrac{4x + 2x}{2}\right)\sin\left(\dfrac{4x - 2x}{2}\right)}{2\sin 3x} = \dfrac{-2\sin 3x \sin x}{2\sin 3x} = -\sin x$

87. $\dfrac{\cos t + \cos 3t}{\sin 3t - \sin t} = \dfrac{2\cos\left(\dfrac{4t}{2}\right)\cos\left(-\dfrac{2t}{2}\right)}{2\cos\left(\dfrac{4t}{2}\right)\sin\left(\dfrac{2t}{2}\right)}$

$\qquad\qquad = \dfrac{\cos(-t)}{\sin(t)}$

$\qquad\qquad = \dfrac{\cos(t)}{\sin(t)}$

$\qquad\qquad = \cot t$

89. $\sin^2 x = \dfrac{1 - \cos 2x}{2} = \dfrac{1}{2} - \dfrac{\cos 2x}{2}$

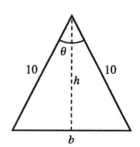

91. $\sin(2\arcsin x) = 2\sin(\arcsin x)\cos(\arcsin x) = 2x\sqrt{1 - x^2}$

93. $\frac{1}{2}[\sin(u + v) - \sin(u - v)] = \frac{1}{2}[\sin u \cos v + \sin v \cos u - (\sin u \cos v - \sin v \cos u)]$

$\qquad\qquad\qquad\qquad\qquad = \frac{1}{2}(2\sin v \cos u)$

$\qquad\qquad\qquad\qquad\qquad = \cos u \sin v$

95. (a) $A = \dfrac{1}{2}bh$

$\qquad \cos\dfrac{\theta}{2} = \dfrac{h}{10} \Rightarrow h = 10\cos\dfrac{\theta}{2}$

$\qquad \sin\dfrac{\theta}{2} = \dfrac{(1/2)b}{10} \Rightarrow \dfrac{1}{2}b = 10\sin\dfrac{\theta}{2}$

$\qquad A = 10\sin\dfrac{\theta}{2}10\cos\dfrac{\theta}{2} \Rightarrow A = 100\sin\dfrac{\theta}{2}\cos\dfrac{\theta}{2}$

(b) $A = 100\sin\dfrac{\theta}{2}\cos\dfrac{\theta}{2}$

$\qquad A = 50\left(2\sin\dfrac{\theta}{2}\cos\dfrac{\theta}{2}\right)$

$\qquad A = 50\sin\theta$

$\qquad$ When $\theta = \pi/2$, $\sin\theta = 1 \Rightarrow$ the area is a maximum.

$\qquad A = 50\sin\dfrac{\pi}{2} = 50(1) = 50$ square feet

Chapter 7   Review Exercises

1. $\dfrac{1}{\cos^2 x + 1} = \dfrac{1}{\csc^2 x} = \sin^2 x$

3. $\dfrac{\sin^2 \alpha - \cos^2 \alpha}{\sin^2 \alpha - \sin \alpha \cos \alpha} = \dfrac{(\sin \alpha + \cos \alpha)(\sin \alpha - \cos \alpha)}{\sin \alpha(\sin \alpha - \cos \alpha)} = \dfrac{\sin \alpha + \cos \alpha}{\sin \alpha} = 1 + \cot \alpha$

5. $\cos^2 \beta + \cos^2 \beta \tan^2 \beta = \cos^2 \beta(1 + \tan^2 \beta)$
$$= \cos^2 \beta \sec^2 \beta$$
$$= 1$$

7. $\tan^2 \theta(\csc^2 \theta - 1) = \tan^2 \theta \cot^2 \theta = 1$

9. $1 - 4\sin^2 x \cos^2 x = 1 - (2\sin x \cos x)^2$
$$= 1 - \sin^2 2x$$
$$= \cos^2 2x$$

11. $\tan x(1 - \sin^2 x) = \tan x \cos^2 x$
$$= \dfrac{\sin x}{\cos x} \cdot \cos^2 x$$
$$= \sin x \cos x$$
$$= \dfrac{1}{2}(2 \sin x \cos x)$$
$$= \dfrac{1}{2} \sin 2x$$

13. $\sec^2 x \cot x - \cot x = \cot x(\sec^2 x - 1) = \cot x \tan^2 x = \dfrac{1}{\tan x} \tan^2 x = \tan x$

15. $\sin^5 x \cos^2 x = \sin^4 x \cos^2 x \sin x$
$$= (1 - \cos^2 x)^2 \cos^2 x \sin x = (\cos^2 x - 2\cos^4 x + \cos^6 x) \sin x$$

17. Using a product-sum formula, we have
$$\sin 3\theta \sin \theta = \tfrac{1}{2}(\cos 2\theta - \cos 4\theta).$$

19. $\sqrt{\dfrac{1 - \sin \theta}{1 + \sin \theta}} = \sqrt{\dfrac{1 - \sin \theta}{1 + \sin \theta} \cdot \dfrac{1 - \sin \theta}{1 - \sin \theta}}$
$$= \dfrac{1 - \sin \theta}{|\cos \theta|}$$

21. $\cos 3x = \cos(2x + x) = \cos 2x \cos x - \sin 2x \sin x$
$$= (\cos^2 x - \sin^2 x) \cos x - 2 \sin x \cos x \sin x = \cos^3 x - 3\sin^2 x \cos x$$
$$= \cos^3 x - 3\cos x(1 - \cos^2 x) = \cos^3 x - 3\cos x + 3\cos^3 x = 4\cos^3 x - 3\cos x$$

23. $\cot\left(\dfrac{\pi}{2} - x\right) = \dfrac{\cos[(\pi/2) - x]}{\sin[(\pi/2) - x]} = \dfrac{\cos(\pi/2)\cos x + \sin(\pi/2)\sin x}{\sin(\pi/2)\cos x - \sin x \cos(\pi/2)} = \dfrac{\sin x}{\cos x} = \tan x$

25. $\dfrac{\sec x - 1}{\tan x} = \dfrac{(1/\cos x) - 1}{\sin x / \cos x}$

$\qquad = \dfrac{1 - \cos x}{\sin x} = \tan \dfrac{x}{2}$

27. $\dfrac{\cos 3x - \cos x}{\sin 3x - \sin x} = \dfrac{-2 \sin 2x \sin x}{2 \cos 2x \sin x} = -\tan 2x$

29. $2 \sin y \cos y \sec 2y = (\sin 2y)(\sec 2y) = \dfrac{\sin 2y}{\cos 2y} = \tan 2y$

31. $y_1 = \sin\left(x - \dfrac{3\pi}{2}\right)$

$y_2 = \cos x$

The graphs of y_1 and y_2 coincide.

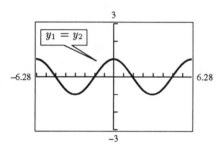

33. $y_1 = \tan^2 x$

$y_2 = \dfrac{1 - \cos 2x}{1 + \cos 2x}$

The graphs of y_1 and y_2 coincide.

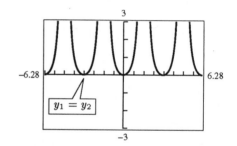

35. $y_1 = 1 + \cos 2x + \cos 4x + \cos 6x$

$y_2 = 4 \cos x \cos 2x \cos 3x$

The graphs of y_1 and y_2 coincide.

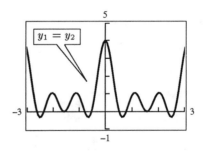

37. $\sin\dfrac{5\pi}{12} = \sin\left(\dfrac{2\pi}{3} - \dfrac{\pi}{4}\right)$

$\qquad = \sin\left(\dfrac{2\pi}{3}\right)\cos\left(\dfrac{\pi}{4}\right) - \cos\dfrac{2\pi}{3}\sin\left(\dfrac{\pi}{4}\right)$

$\qquad = \left(\dfrac{\sqrt{3}}{2}\right)\left(\dfrac{\sqrt{2}}{2}\right) - \left(-\dfrac{1}{2}\right)\left(\dfrac{\sqrt{2}}{2}\right)$

$\qquad = \dfrac{\sqrt{2}}{4}(\sqrt{3}+1)$

39. $\cos 157°30' = \cos\left(\dfrac{315°}{2}\right)$

$\qquad = -\sqrt{\dfrac{1 + \cos 315°}{2}}$

$\qquad = -\dfrac{\sqrt{2 + \sqrt{2}}}{2}$

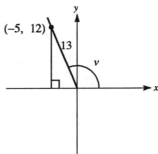

FIGURES FOR EXERCISES 37 AND 39

41. $\sin(u + v) = \sin u \cos v + \cos u \sin v$

$\qquad = \left(\dfrac{3}{4}\right)\left(-\dfrac{5}{13}\right) + \left(-\dfrac{\sqrt{7}}{4}\right)\left(\dfrac{12}{13}\right) = -\dfrac{15}{52} - \dfrac{12\sqrt{7}}{52} = \dfrac{-3(5 + 4\sqrt{7})}{52}$

43. $\cos(u - v) = \cos u \cos v + \sin u \sin v = \left(-\dfrac{\sqrt{7}}{4}\right)\left(-\dfrac{5}{13}\right) + \left(\dfrac{3}{4}\right)\left(\dfrac{12}{13}\right) = \dfrac{5\sqrt{7} + 36}{52}$

45. $\cos\dfrac{u}{2} = \sqrt{\dfrac{1 + \cos u}{2}}$

$\qquad = \sqrt{\dfrac{1 + (-\sqrt{7}/4)}{2}}$

$\qquad = \sqrt{\dfrac{4 - \sqrt{7}}{8}}$

$\qquad = \dfrac{1}{4}\sqrt{2(4 - \sqrt{7})}$

47. If $\dfrac{\pi}{2} < \theta < \pi$, then $\cos\dfrac{\theta}{2} < 0$. False, if

$\qquad \dfrac{\pi}{2} < \theta < \pi \Rightarrow \dfrac{\pi}{4} < \dfrac{\theta}{2} < \dfrac{\pi}{2}$,

which is in Quadrant I $\Rightarrow \cos(\theta/2) > 0$.
For example, let $\theta = 3\pi/4$. Then,

$\qquad \cos\dfrac{\theta}{2} = 0.3827 > 0.$

49. $4\sin(-x)\cos(-x) = -2\sin 2x$. True.

$\qquad 4\sin(-x)\cos(-x) = 4(-\sin x)(\cos x) = -4\sin x \cos x = -2(2\sin x \cos x) = -2\sin 2x$

51. $f(x) = \sin x - \tan x$

Graphing the function on the interval $[0,\ 2\pi)$, we find the zeros are $x = 0$ and 3.142.
Algebraically:

$$\sin x - \tan x = 0$$

$$\sin x - \frac{\sin x}{\cos x} = 0$$

$$\sin x \cos x - \sin x = 0$$

$$\sin x (\cos x - 1) = 0$$

$\sin x = 0 \qquad$ or $\ \cos x - 1 = 0$

$x = 0,\ \pi \qquad\qquad \cos x = 1$

$$x = 0$$

53. $g(x) = \sin 2x + \sqrt{2}\sin x$

Graphing the function on the interval $[0,\ 2\pi)$, we find the zeros are $x = 0$, 2.356, 3.142, and
3.927. Algebraically:

$$\sin 2x + \sqrt{2}\sin x = 0$$

$$2\sin x \cos x + \sqrt{2}\sin x = 0$$

$$\sin x (2\cos x + \sqrt{2}) = 0$$

$\sin x = 0 \qquad$ or $\quad 2\cos x + \sqrt{2} = 0$

$x = 0,\ \pi$

$$\cos x = -\frac{\sqrt{2}}{2}$$

$$x = \frac{3\pi}{4},\ \frac{5\pi}{4}$$

55. $h(x) = \cos^2 x + \sin x - 1$

Graphing the function on the interval $[0, \ 2\pi)$, we find the zeros are $x = 0, \ 1.571$ and 3.142.
Algebraically:

$$\cos^2 x + \sin x = 1$$

$$1 - \sin^2 x + \sin x = 1$$

$$\sin x(\sin x - 1) = 0$$

$$\sin x = 0 \qquad \text{or} \qquad \sin x = 1$$

$$x = 0, \ \pi \qquad\qquad x = \frac{\pi}{2}$$

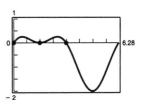

57. $y = \dfrac{1 + \sin x}{\cos x} + \dfrac{\cos x}{1 + \sin x} - 4$

Graphing the function on the interval $[0, \ 2\pi)$, we find the zeros are $x = 1.047$ and 5.236.
Algebraically:

$$\frac{1 + \sin x}{\cos x} + \frac{\cos x}{1 + \sin x} = 4$$

$$(1 + \sin x)^2 + \cos^2 x = 4 \cos x(1 + \sin x)$$

$$1 + 2 \sin x + \sin^2 x + \cos^2 x = 4 \cos x(1 + \sin x)$$

$$2 + 2 \sin x - 4 \cos x(1 + \sin x) = 0$$

$$2(1 + \sin x)(1 - 2 \cos x) = 0$$

$$1 + \sin x = 0 \qquad\qquad \text{or} \ \ 1 - 2 \cos x = 0$$

$$\sin x = -1 \qquad\qquad\qquad \cos x = \frac{1}{2}$$

$$x = \frac{3\pi}{2} \qquad\qquad\qquad x = \frac{\pi}{3}, \ \frac{5\pi}{3}$$

(extraneous solution)

59. $g(t) = \tan^3 t - \tan^2 t + 3\tan t - 3$

Graphing the function on the interval $[0,\ 2\pi)$, we find the zeros are $x = 0.785$ and 3.927. Algebraically:

$$\tan^3 t - \tan^2 t + 3\tan t - 3 = 0$$
$$\tan^2 t(\tan t - 1) + 3(\tan t - 1) = 0$$
$$(\tan^2 t + 3)(\tan t - 1) = 0$$

$\tan^2 t + 3 = 0 \quad$ or $\quad \tan t - 1 = 0$

(No solution) $\qquad\qquad \tan t = 1$

$$t = \frac{\pi}{4},\ \frac{5\pi}{4}$$

61. $\cos 3\theta + \cos 2\theta = 2\cos\dfrac{5\theta}{2}\cos\dfrac{\theta}{2}$

63. $\sin 3\alpha(\sin 2\alpha) = \frac{1}{2}[\cos(3\alpha - 2\alpha) - \cos(3\alpha + 2\alpha)] = \frac{1}{2}(\cos\alpha - \cos 5\alpha)$

65. $\cos(2\arccos 2x) = \cos 2\theta$

$= \cos^2\theta - \sin^2\theta$

$= (2x)^2 - (\sqrt{1-4x^2})^2$

$= 4x^2 - (1-4x^2)$

$= 8x^2 - 1$

67. $\sin^{-1/2}\cos x = \dfrac{\cos x}{\sin^{1/2} x}$

$= \dfrac{\cos x}{\sqrt{\sin x}}\cdot\dfrac{\sqrt{\sin x}}{\sqrt{\sin x}}$

$= \dfrac{\cos x}{\sin x}\sqrt{\sin x}$

$= \cot x\sqrt{\sin x}$

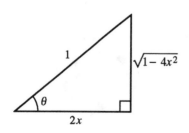

69. $y = 1.5 \sin 8t - 0.5 \cos 8t$

(a) $a = \dfrac{3}{2}$, $b = \dfrac{1}{2}$, $B = 8$, $C = \arctan\left(\dfrac{1/2}{3/2}\right)$

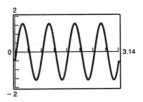

$$y = \sqrt{(3/2)^2 + (1/2)^2}\,\sin\left(8t + \arctan\dfrac{1}{3}\right)$$

$$y = \dfrac{1}{2}\sqrt{10}\,\sin\left(8t + \arctan\dfrac{1}{3}\right)$$

(c) Amplitude $= \sqrt{a^2 + b^2} = \dfrac{1}{2}\sqrt{10}$

(d) Frequency $= \dfrac{B}{\text{period}} = \dfrac{8}{2\pi} = \dfrac{4}{\pi}$

CHAPTER 8

Additional Topics in Trigonometry

Section 8.1 Law of Sines

- If ABC is any oblique triangle with sides a, b, and c, then
$$\frac{a}{\sin A} = \frac{b}{\sin B} = \frac{c}{\sin C}.$$

- You should be able to use the Law of Sines to solve an oblique triangle for the remaining three parts, given:
  (a) Two angles and any side (AAS or ASA)
  (b) Two sides and an angle opposite one of them (SSA)
    1. If A is acute and:
        (a) $a < h$, no triangle is possible.
        (b) $a = h$ or $a > b$, one triangle is possible.
        (c) $h < a < b$, two triangles are possible.
    2. If A is obtuse and:
        (a) $a \leq b$, no triangle is possible.
        (b) $a > b$, one triangle is possible.

- The area of any triangle equals one-half the product of the lengths of two sides times the sine of their included angle.
$$A = \tfrac{1}{2}ab \sin C = \tfrac{1}{2}ac \sin B = \tfrac{1}{2}bc \sin A$$

---

1. Given: $A = 30°$, $B = 45°$, $a = 10$

$C = 180° - A - B = 105°$

$$b = \frac{a}{\sin A}(\sin B) = \frac{10 \sin 45°}{\sin 30°} = 10\sqrt{2} \approx 14.14$$

$$c = \frac{a}{\sin A}(\sin C) = \frac{10 \sin 105°}{\sin 30°} \approx 19.32$$

3. Given: $A = 10°$, $B = 60°$, $a = 4.5$

$C = 180° - A - B = 110°$

$b = \dfrac{a}{\sin A}(\sin B) = \dfrac{4.5}{\sin 10°}(\sin 60°) \approx 22.44$

$c = \dfrac{a}{\sin A}(\sin C) = \dfrac{4.5}{\sin 10°}(\sin 110°) \approx 24.35$

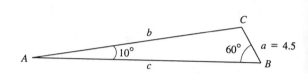

5. Given: $A = 36°$, $a = 8$, $b = 5$

$\sin B = \dfrac{b \sin A}{a} = \dfrac{5 \sin 36°}{8}$

$\approx 0.3674 \Rightarrow B \approx 21.6°$

$C = 180 - A - B$

$\approx 180° - 36° - 21.6° = 122.4°$

$c = \dfrac{a}{\sin A}(\sin C)$

$= \dfrac{8}{\sin 36°}(\sin 122.4°) \approx 11.49$

7. Given: $A = 150°$, $C = 20°$, $a = 200$

$B = 180° - A - C$

$= 180° - 150° - 20° = 10°$

$b = \dfrac{a}{\sin A}(\sin B)$

$= \dfrac{200}{\sin 150°}(\sin 10°) \approx 69.46$

$c = \dfrac{a}{\sin A}(\sin C)$

$= \dfrac{200}{\sin 150°}(\sin 20°) \approx 136.8$

9. Given: $A = 83°20'$, $C = 54.6°$, $c = 18.1$

$B = 180° - A - C$

$= 180° - 80°20' - 54°36' = 42°4'$

$a = \dfrac{c}{\sin C}(\sin A)$

$= \dfrac{18.1}{\sin 54.6°}(\sin 83°20') \approx 22.05$

$b = \dfrac{c}{\sin C}(\sin B)$

$= \dfrac{18.1}{\sin 54.6°}(\sin 42.1°) \approx 14.89$

11. Given: $B = 15°30'$, $a = 4.5$, $b = 6.8$

$\sin A = \dfrac{a \sin B}{b} = \dfrac{4.5 \sin 15°30'}{6.8}$

$\approx 0.1768 \Rightarrow A \approx 10.2°$

$C = 180° - A - B$

$\approx 180° - 10.2° - 15.5° = 154.3°$

$c = \dfrac{b}{\sin B}(\sin C)$

$\approx \dfrac{6.8}{\sin 15°30'}(\sin 154.3°) \approx 11.03$

13. Given: $C = 145°$, $b = 4$, $c = 14$

$$\sin B = \frac{b \sin C}{c}$$

$$= \frac{4 \sin 145°}{14} \approx 0.1639 \Rightarrow B \approx 9.43°$$

$$A = 180° - B - C$$

$$\approx 180° - 9.43° - 145° = 25.6°$$

$$a = \frac{c}{\sin C}(\sin A)$$

$$\approx \frac{14}{\sin 145°}(\sin 25.6°) \approx 10.53$$

15. Given: $A = 110°15'$, $a = 48$, $b = 16$

$$\sin B = \frac{b \sin A}{a} = \frac{16 \sin 110°15'}{48}$$

$$\approx 0.3127 \Rightarrow B = 18.22°$$

$$C = 180° - A - B$$

$$\approx 180° - 110.25° - 18.22° \approx 51.53°$$

$$c = \frac{a}{\sin A}(\sin C)$$

$$\approx \frac{48}{\sin 110°15'}(\sin 51.53°) \approx 40.05$$

17. Given: $a = 4.5$, $b = 12.8$, $A = 58°$

$h = 12.8 \sin 58° \approx 10.86$

Since $a < h$, no triangle is formed.

19. Given: $a = 4.5$, $b = 5$, $A = 58°$

$$\sin B = \frac{b \sin A}{a} = \frac{5 \sin 58°}{4.5} \approx 0.9423 \Rightarrow B = 70.4° \text{ or } B = 109.6°$$

Case 1	Case 2
$B \approx 70.4°$	$B \approx 109.6°$
$C \approx 180° - 70.4° - 58° = 51.6°$	$C \approx 180° - 109.6° - 58° = 12.4°$
$c \approx \dfrac{4.5}{\sin 58°}(\sin 51.6°) \approx 4.16$	$c \approx \dfrac{4.5}{\sin 58°}(\sin 12.4°) \approx 1.14$

21. Given: $a = 125$, $b = 200$, $A = 110°$

No triangle is formed because A is obtuse and $a < b$.

23. Given: $A = 36°$, $a = 5$

(a) One solution if $b \le 5$ or $b = \dfrac{5}{\sin 36°}$

(b) Two solutions if $5 < b < \dfrac{5}{\sin 36°}$

(c) No solution is $b > \dfrac{5}{\sin 36°}$

25. Area $= \frac{1}{2}ab \sin C$

$\quad = \frac{1}{2}(4)(6) \sin 120° \approx 10.39$

27. Area $= \frac{1}{2}bc \sin A$

$\quad = \frac{1}{2}(57)(85) \sin 43°45' \approx 1675$

29. Area $= \frac{1}{2}ac \sin B = \frac{1}{2}(62)(20) \sin 130° \approx 474.9$

31. $\sin B = \dfrac{5\sin 30°}{3} \approx 0.8333 \Rightarrow B \approx 56.4°$

$D \approx 180° - 30° - 56.4° = 93.6°$

$d \approx \dfrac{3}{\sin 30°}(\sin 93.6°) \approx 6 \text{ ft}$

33. Given: $A = 74° - 28° = 46°$,

$B = 180° - 41° - 74° = 65°$,

$c = 100$

$C = 180° - 46° - 65° = 69°$

$a = \dfrac{c}{\sin C}(\sin A) = \dfrac{100}{\sin 69°}(\sin 46°)$

$\approx 77 \text{ yds}$

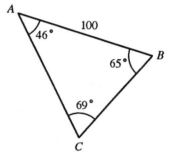

35. $C = 180° - 51° - 68° = 61°$

$a = \dfrac{c}{\sin C}(\sin A)$

$= \dfrac{6}{\sin 61°}(\sin 51°) \approx 5.33$

$h = a \sin B \approx 5.33(\sin 68°)$

$\approx 4.94 \approx 5 \text{ mi}$

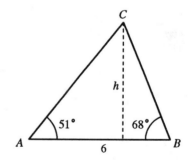

37. $A = 65° − 28° = 37°$

$\quad c = 18.5$

$\quad B = 180° − 16.5° − 65° = 98.5°$

$\quad C = 180° − 37° − 98.5° = 44.5°$

$\quad a = \dfrac{c}{\sin C}(\sin A) = \dfrac{18.5}{\sin 44.5°}(\sin 37°)$

$\qquad \approx 15.9$ miles to B

$\quad b = \dfrac{c}{\sin C}(\sin B) = \dfrac{18.5}{\sin 44.5°}(\sin 98.5°)$

$\qquad \approx 26.1$ miles to A

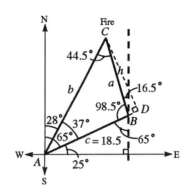

39. $A = 90° − 62° = 28°$,

$\quad B = 90° + 38° = 128°, \ c = 5$

$\quad C = 180° − 128° − 28° = 24°$

$\quad a = \dfrac{c}{\sin C}(\sin A)$

$\qquad = \dfrac{5}{\sin 24°}(\sin 28°) \approx 5.77$

$\quad d = a \sin(90° − 38°)$

$\qquad \approx 5.77 \sin 52° \approx 4.55$ miles

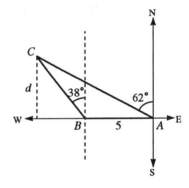

41. $h = b \sin A = 450 \sin 30° = 225$ ft

$\quad a = 120$ ft

Since $a < h$, no such triangle is possible.

Section 8.2   Law of Cosines

■ If ABC is any oblique triangle with sides a, b, and c, the following equations are valid.

(a) $a^2 = b^2 + c^2 - 2bc \cos A$ or $\cos A = \dfrac{b^2 + c^2 - a^2}{2bc}$

(b) $b^2 = a^2 + c^2 - 2ac \cos B$ or $\cos B = \dfrac{a^2 + c^2 - b^2}{2ac}$

(c) $c^2 = a^2 + b^2 - 2ab \cos C$ or $\cos C = \dfrac{a^2 + b^2 - c^2}{2ab}$

■ You should be able to use the Law of Cosines to solve an oblique triangle for the remaining three parts, given:
(a) Three sides (SSS)
(b) Two sides and their included angle (SAS)

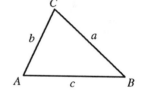

■ Given any triangle with sides of length a, b, and c, then the area of the triangle is

$$\text{Area} = \sqrt{s(s-a)(s-b)(s-c)}, \text{ where } s = \frac{a+b+c}{2}. \qquad \text{(Heron's Formula)}$$

1. Given: $a = 5$, $b = 7$, $c = 10$

$$\cos C = \frac{a^2 + b^2 - c^2}{2ab} = \frac{25 + 49 - 100}{2(5)(7)} \approx -0.3714 \Rightarrow C \approx 111.8°$$

$$\sin A = \frac{a \sin C}{c} \approx \frac{5 \sin 111.8°}{10} \approx 0.4642 \Rightarrow A \approx 27.7°$$

$$B \approx 180° - 111.8° - 27.7° = 40.5°$$

3. Given: $A = 30°$, $b = 10$, $c = 20$

$\qquad a^2 = b^2 + c^2 - 2bc \cos A$

$\qquad\qquad \approx 100 + 400 - 2(10)(20)(0.8660) \approx 153.6 \Rightarrow a \approx 12.39$

$\qquad \cos C = \dfrac{a^2 + b^2 - c^2}{2ab} = \dfrac{153.6 + 100 - 400}{2(12.39)(10)}$

$\qquad\qquad \approx -0.5907 \Rightarrow C \approx 126.2°$

$\qquad B \approx 180° - 30° - 126.2° = 23.8°$

5. Given: $a = 9$, $b = 12$, $c = 15$

$\qquad \cos C = \dfrac{a^2 + b^2 - c^2}{2ab} = \dfrac{81 + 144 - 225}{2(9)(12)} = 0 \Rightarrow C = 90°$

$\qquad \sin A = \dfrac{9}{15} = \dfrac{3}{5} \Rightarrow A \approx 36.9°$

$\qquad B \approx 180° - 90° - 36.9° = 53.13°$

7. Given: $a = 75.4$, $b = 52$, $c = 52$

$\qquad \cos A = \dfrac{b^2 + c^2 - a^2}{2bc} = \dfrac{52^2 + 52^2 - 75.4^2}{2(52)(52)} \approx -0.05125 \Rightarrow A \approx 92.9°$

$\qquad \sin B = \dfrac{b \sin A}{a} \approx \dfrac{52(0.9987)}{75.4} \approx 0.68875 \Rightarrow B \approx 43.5°$

$\qquad C = B \approx 43.5°$

9. Given: $A = 120°$, $b = 3$, $c = 10$

$\qquad a^2 = b^2 + c^2 - 2bc \cos A = 9 + 100 - 60 \cos 120° = 139 \Rightarrow a \approx 11.79$

$\qquad \sin B = \dfrac{b \sin A}{a} \approx \dfrac{3 \sin 120°}{11.79} \approx 0.2204 \Rightarrow B \approx 12.73°$

$\qquad C \approx 180° - 120° - 12.73° = 47.27°$

11. Given: $B = 8°45'$, $a = 25$, $c = 15$

$$b^2 = a^2 + c^2 - 2ac \cos B \approx 625 + 225 - 2(25)(15)(0.9884) \approx 108.7 \Rightarrow b \approx 10.43$$

$$\sin C = \frac{c \sin B}{b} = \frac{15(0.1521)}{10.43} \approx 0.2188 \Rightarrow C \approx 12.64°$$

$$A \approx 180° - 8.75° - 12.64° = 158.61°$$

13. Given: $C = 125°40'$, $a = 32$, $b = 32$

$$c^2 = a^2 + b^2 - 2ab \cos C \approx 32^2 + 32^2 - 2(32)(32)(-0.5831) \approx 3242.1 \Rightarrow c \approx 56.94$$

$$A = B \Rightarrow 2A = 180° - 125°40' = 54°20' \Rightarrow A = B = 27°10'$$

15.

$$d^2 = 4^2 + 6^2 - 2(4)(6) \cos 30°$$
$$d \approx 3.23$$
$$2\phi = 360° - 2(30°)$$
$$\phi = 150°$$
$$c^2 = 4^2 + 6^2 - 2(4)(6) \cos 150°$$
$$c \approx 9.67$$

17.

$$\cos \phi = \frac{10^2 + 14^2 - 20^2}{2(10)(14)}$$
$$\phi \approx 111.80°$$
$$2\theta \approx 360° - 2(111.80°)$$
$$\theta = 68.2°$$
$$d^2 = 10^2 + 14^2 - 2(10)(14) \cos 68.2°$$
$$d \approx 13.86$$

19.

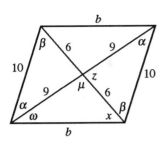

$$\cos\alpha = \frac{(9)^2 + (10)^2 - (6)^2}{2(9)(10)}$$

$$\alpha \approx 36.3°$$

$$\cos\beta = \frac{6^2 + 10^2 - 9^2}{2(6)(10)}$$

$$\beta \approx 62.7°$$

$$z = 180° - \alpha - \beta \approx 81.0°$$

$$\mu = 180° - z \approx 99.0°$$

$$b^2 = 9^2 + 6^2 - 2(9)(6)(\cos 99.0°)$$

$$b \approx 11.57$$

$$\cos\omega = \frac{9^2 + 11.57^2 - 6^2}{2(9)(11.57)}$$

$$\omega \approx 30.8°$$

$$\theta = \alpha + \omega \approx 67.1°$$

$$\cos x = \frac{6^2 + 11.57^2 - 9^2}{2(6)(11.57)}$$

$$x \approx 50.2°$$

$$\phi = \beta + x \approx 112.9°$$

21. $a = 5,\ b = 7,\ c = 10 \Rightarrow s = \dfrac{a+b+c}{2} = 11$

Area $= \sqrt{s(s-a)(s-b)(s-c)} = \sqrt{11(6)(4)(1)} \approx 16.25$

23. $a = 12,\ b = 15,\ c = 9 \Rightarrow s = \dfrac{12+15+9}{2} = 18$

Area $= \sqrt{18(6)(3)(9)} = 54$

25. $a = 20,\ b = 20,\ c = 10 \Rightarrow s = \dfrac{20+20+10}{2} = 25$

Area $= \sqrt{25(5)(5)(15)} \approx 96.82$

27. $a = 400,\ b = 500,\ c = 700 \Rightarrow s = \dfrac{a+b+c}{2} = 800$

Area $= \sqrt{s(s-a)(s-b)(s-c)} = \sqrt{800(400)(300)(100)} \approx 97{,}979.6 \text{ ft}^2$

29. $\cos B = \dfrac{3500^2 + 8000^2 - 6500^2}{2(3500)(8000)}$

$B = 52.62° \Rightarrow 52°37' \Rightarrow$ N 52°37′ E

$\cos C = \dfrac{3500^2 + 6500^2 - 8000^2}{2(3500)(6500)}$

$C = 102.05°$

$\alpha = 180° - 52.62° - 102.05° = 25.33°$

$\beta = 90° - \alpha = 64.67° \Rightarrow 64°40' \Rightarrow$ S 64°40′ E

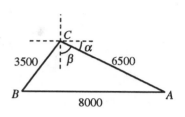

31. $C = 180° - 53° - 67° = 60°$

$c^2 = a^2 + b^2 - 2ab \cos C$

$= 36^2 + 48^2 - 2(36)(48)(0.5)$

$= 1872$

$c \approx 43.3$ mi

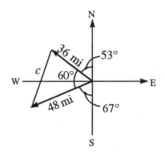

33. $\overline{AC} = \sqrt{800^2 + 950^2 - 2(800)(950)\cos 100°}$

$\approx \sqrt{1,806,445.23} \approx 1344$ ft

35. $4.25^2 = 2^2 + 3^2 - 2(2)(3)\cos\theta$

$\cos\theta = \dfrac{2^2 + 3^2 - 4.25^2}{2(2)(3)} \approx -0.4219$

$\theta \approx 114.95°$

37. $\overline{RS} = \sqrt{8^2 + 10^2} = \sqrt{164} = 2\sqrt{41} \approx 12.8$ ft

$\overline{PQ} = \frac{1}{2}\sqrt{16^2 + 10^2} = \frac{1}{2}\sqrt{356} = \sqrt{89} \approx 9.4$ ft

$\tan P = \frac{10}{16}$

$P = \arctan \frac{5}{8} \approx 32.0°$

$\overline{QS} = \sqrt{8^2 + 9.4^2 - 2(8)(9.4)\cos 32°} \approx \sqrt{24.82} \approx 5.0$ ft

39. Bearing from O to D: N θ W

Bearing from N to D: S ϕ W

$$\cos \phi = \frac{(9.25)^2 + 7^2 - (10.75)^2}{2(9.25)(7)} \approx 0.1467 \Rightarrow \phi \approx 81.6°$$

$$\cos \theta = 0.5249 \Rightarrow \theta \approx 58.3°$$

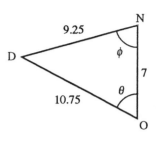

41. (a) $d^2 = 60^2 + 90^2 - 2(60)(90) \cos 45°$

$\approx 4063.25 \Rightarrow d \approx 63.74$ ft

(b) $\cos \alpha = \dfrac{d^2 + 60^2 - 90^2}{2d(60)} \approx -0.0571$

$\Rightarrow \alpha \approx 93.3°$

$\Rightarrow \angle HTP \approx 41.7°$

$\Rightarrow \angle STP \approx 48.3°$

$d_1{}^2 = 45^2 + 4063.25 - 2(45)(63.74) \cos 48.3°$

$\approx 2272 \Rightarrow d_1 \approx 47.7$ ft

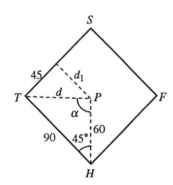

43. $A = 180° - 40° - 25° = 115°$

$$\frac{x}{\sin 25°} = \frac{7}{\sin 115°} \Rightarrow$$

$$x = \frac{7 \sin 25°}{\sin 115°} = 3.26 \text{ feet}$$

45. $a = 25, \ b = 55, \ c = 72 \Rightarrow s = \dfrac{25 + 55 + 72}{2} = 76$

(a) Area of triangle $= \sqrt{s(s - a)(s - b)(s - c)} = \sqrt{76(51)(21)(4)} \approx 570.6$

(b) $\cos C = \dfrac{a^2 + b^2 - c^2}{2ab} = \dfrac{25^2 + 55^2 - 72^2}{2(25)(55)} \approx -0.5578 \Rightarrow C \approx 123.9°$

$\quad 2R = \dfrac{c}{\sin C} = \dfrac{72}{0.8300} \approx 86.75 \Rightarrow R \approx 43.4$

Area of the circumscribed circle: $A = \pi R^2 \approx 5911$

(c) $r = \sqrt{\dfrac{(s - a)(s - b)(s - c)}{s}} = \sqrt{\dfrac{(51)(21)(4)}{76}} \approx 7.51$

Area of inscribed circle: $A = \pi r^2 \approx 177.1$

47.
$$a^2 = b^2 + c^2 - 2bc \cos A$$

$$\cos A = \dfrac{b^2 + c^2 - a^2}{2bc}$$

$$1 + \cos A = \dfrac{b^2 + 2bc + c^2 - a^2}{2bc}$$

$$\dfrac{1}{2}bc(1 + \cos A) = \dfrac{(b + c)^2 - a^2}{4} = \left(\dfrac{a + b + c}{2}\right)\left(\dfrac{-a + b + c}{2}\right)$$

Section 8.3   Vectors in the Plane

- A vector, **v**, is the collection of all directed line segments that are equivalent to a given directed line segment $\overrightarrow{PQ}$.

- You should be able to *geometrically* perform the operations of vector addition and scalar multiplication.

- The component form of the vector with initial point $P = (p_1, \, p_2)$ and terminal point $Q = (q_1, \, q_2)$ is $\overrightarrow{PQ} = \langle q_1 - p_1, \, q_2 - p_2 \rangle = \langle v_1, \, v_2 \rangle = \mathbf{v}$.

- The magnitude of $\mathbf{v} = \langle v_1, \, v_2 \rangle$ is given by $\|\mathbf{v}\| = \sqrt{v_1{}^2 + v_2{}^2}$.

- You should be able to perform the operations of scalar multiplication and vector addition in component form.

- You should know the following properties of vector addition and scalar multiplication.
  - (a) $\mathbf{u} + \mathbf{v} = \mathbf{v} + \mathbf{u}$
  - (b) $(\mathbf{u} + \mathbf{v}) + \mathbf{w} = \mathbf{u} + (\mathbf{v} + \mathbf{w})$
  - (c) $\mathbf{u} + \mathbf{O} = \mathbf{u}$
    ($\mathbf{O}$ is the zero vector.)
  - (d) $\mathbf{u} + (-\mathbf{u}) = \mathbf{O}$
  - (e) $c(d\mathbf{u}) = (cd)\mathbf{u}$
  - (f) $(c + d)\mathbf{u} = c\mathbf{u} + d\mathbf{u}$
  - (g) $c(\mathbf{u} + \mathbf{v}) = c\mathbf{u} + c\mathbf{v}$
  - (h) $1(\mathbf{u}) = \mathbf{u}, \; 0\mathbf{u} = \mathbf{O}$
  - (i) $\|c\mathbf{v}\| = |c| \, \|\mathbf{v}\|$

- A unit vector in the direction of **v** is given by $\mathbf{u} = \dfrac{\mathbf{v}}{\|\mathbf{v}\|}$.

- The standard unit vectors are $\mathbf{i} = \langle 1, \, 0 \rangle$ and $\mathbf{j} = \langle 0, \, 1 \rangle$. $\mathbf{v} = \langle v_1, \, v_2 \rangle$ can be written as $\mathbf{v} = v_1\mathbf{i} + v_2\mathbf{j}$.

- A vector, **v**, with magnitude $\|\mathbf{v}\|$ and direction θ can be written as $\mathbf{v} = a\mathbf{i} + b\mathbf{j} = \|\mathbf{v}\|(\cos \theta)\mathbf{i} + \|\mathbf{v}\|(\sin \theta)\mathbf{j}$ where $\tan \theta = b/a$.

1. $-\mathbf{u}$

3. $\mathbf{u} + \mathbf{v}$

5. $\mathbf{u} - \mathbf{v}$

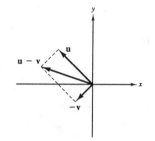

7. Initial point: $(0, 0)$
Terminal point: $(3, 4)$
$\mathbf{v} = \langle 3 - 0,\ 4 - 0 \rangle = \langle 3,\ 4 \rangle$
$\|\mathbf{v}\| = \sqrt{3^2 + 4^2} = 5$

9. Initial point: $(2, 1)$
Terminal point: $(-1, 3)$
$\mathbf{v} = \langle -1 - 2,\ 3 - 1 \rangle = \langle -3,\ 2 \rangle$
$\|\mathbf{v}\| = \sqrt{(-3)^2 + 2^2} = \sqrt{13}$

11. Initial point: $(2, -2)$
Terminal point: $(2, 3)$
$\mathbf{v} = \langle 2 - 2,\ 3 - (-2) \rangle = \langle 0,\ 5 \rangle$
$\|\mathbf{v}\| = \sqrt{0^2 + 5^2} = 5$

13. Initial point: $(-1, 5)$
Terminal point: $(15, 2)$
$\mathbf{v} = \langle 15 - (-1),\ 2 - 5 \rangle = \langle 16,\ -3 \rangle$
$\|\mathbf{v}\| = \sqrt{16^2 + (-3)^2} = \sqrt{265}$

15. Initial point: $(-3, -5)$
Terminal point: $(5, -1)$
$\mathbf{v} = \langle 5 - (-3),\ -1 - (-5) \rangle = \langle 8,\ 4 \rangle$
$\|\mathbf{v}\| = \sqrt{8^2 + 4^2} = 4\sqrt{5}$

17. $\mathbf{u} = \langle 1,\ 2 \rangle$, $\mathbf{v} = \langle 3,\ 1 \rangle$
(a) $\mathbf{u} + \mathbf{v} = \langle 4,\ 3 \rangle$
(b) $\mathbf{u} - \mathbf{v} = \langle -2,\ 1 \rangle$
(c) $2\mathbf{u} - 3\mathbf{v} = \langle -7,\ 1 \rangle$

19. $\mathbf{u} = \langle -2,\ 3 \rangle$, $\mathbf{v} = \langle -2,\ 1 \rangle$
(a) $\mathbf{u} + \mathbf{v} = \langle -4,\ 4 \rangle$
(b) $\mathbf{u} - \mathbf{v} = \langle 0,\ 2 \rangle$
(c) $2\mathbf{u} - 3\mathbf{v} = \langle 2,\ 3 \rangle$

21. $\mathbf{u} = \langle 4,\ -2 \rangle$, $\mathbf{v} = \langle 0,\ 0 \rangle$
(a) $\mathbf{u} + \mathbf{v} = \langle 4,\ -2 \rangle$
(b) $\mathbf{u} - \mathbf{v} = \langle 4,\ -2 \rangle$
(c) $2\mathbf{u} - 3\mathbf{v} = \langle 8,\ -4 \rangle$

23. $\mathbf{u} = \mathbf{i} + \mathbf{j}$, $\mathbf{v} = 2\mathbf{i} - 3\mathbf{j}$
(a) $\mathbf{u} + \mathbf{v} = 3\mathbf{i} - 2\mathbf{j}$
(b) $\mathbf{u} - \mathbf{v} = -\mathbf{i} + 4\mathbf{j}$
(c) $2\mathbf{u} - 3\mathbf{v} = -4\mathbf{i} + 11\mathbf{j}$

25. $\mathbf{u} = 2\mathbf{i}$, $\mathbf{v} = \mathbf{j}$
(a) $\mathbf{u} + \mathbf{v} = 2\mathbf{i} + \mathbf{j}$
(b) $\mathbf{u} - \mathbf{v} = 2\mathbf{i} - \mathbf{j}$
(c) $2\mathbf{u} - 3\mathbf{v} = 4\mathbf{i} - 3\mathbf{j}$

27. $\|\mathbf{v}\| = 5$, $\theta = 30°$

29. $\|\mathbf{v}\| = \sqrt{6^2 + (-6)^2} = \sqrt{72} = 6\sqrt{2}$

$$\tan \theta = \frac{-6}{6} = -1$$

Since $\mathbf{v}$ lies in Quadrant IV, $\theta = 315°$.

31. $\mathbf{v} = \langle 3\cos 0°,\ 3\sin 0° \rangle$

$\quad = \langle 3,\ 0 \rangle$

33. $\mathbf{v} = \langle \cos 150°,\ \sin 150° \rangle$

$\quad = \left\langle -\dfrac{\sqrt{3}}{2},\ \dfrac{1}{2} \right\rangle$

35. $\mathbf{v} = \langle 3\sqrt{2}\cos 150°,\ 3\sqrt{2}\sin 150° \rangle$

$\quad = \left\langle -\dfrac{3\sqrt{6}}{2},\ \dfrac{3\sqrt{2}}{2} \right\rangle$

37. $\mathbf{v} = 2\left(\dfrac{1}{\sqrt{3^2 + 1^2}}\right)(\mathbf{i} + 3\mathbf{j})$

$\quad = \dfrac{2}{\sqrt{10}}(\mathbf{i} + 3\mathbf{j})$

$\quad = \dfrac{\sqrt{10}}{5}\mathbf{i} + \dfrac{3\sqrt{10}}{5}\mathbf{j}$

39. $\mathbf{v} = \frac{3}{2}\mathbf{u}$

$\quad = \frac{3}{2}(2\mathbf{i} - \mathbf{j})$

$\quad = 3\mathbf{i} - \frac{3}{2}\mathbf{j}$

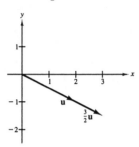

41. $\mathbf{v} = \mathbf{u} + 2\mathbf{w}$

$\quad = (2\mathbf{i} - \mathbf{j}) + 2(\mathbf{i} + 2\mathbf{j})$

$\quad = 4\mathbf{i} + 3\mathbf{j}$

43. $\mathbf{v} = \frac{1}{2}(3\mathbf{u} + \mathbf{w})$

$\quad = \frac{1}{2}(6\mathbf{i} - 3\mathbf{j} + \mathbf{i} + 2\mathbf{j})$

$\quad = \frac{7}{2}\mathbf{i} - \frac{1}{2}\mathbf{j}$

45. $\quad \mathbf{u} = \langle 5 \cos 0°, \ 5 \sin 0° \rangle = \langle 5, \ 0 \rangle$

$\quad \mathbf{v} = \langle 5 \cos 90°, \ 5 \sin 90° \rangle = \langle 0, \ 5 \rangle$

$\quad \mathbf{u} + \mathbf{v} = \langle 5, \ 5 \rangle$

47. $\quad \mathbf{u} = \langle 20 \cos 45°, \ 20 \sin 45° \rangle$

$\quad = \langle 10\sqrt{2}, \ 10\sqrt{2} \rangle$

$\quad \mathbf{v} = \langle 50 \cos 180°, \ 50 \sin 180° \rangle$

$\quad = \langle -50, \ 0 \rangle$

$\quad \mathbf{u} + \mathbf{v} = \langle 10\sqrt{2} - 50, \ 10\sqrt{2} \rangle$

49. $\mathbf{u} = \dfrac{1}{\|\mathbf{v}\|}\mathbf{v}$

$\quad = \dfrac{1}{\sqrt{16 + 9}}(4\mathbf{i} - 3\mathbf{j})$

$\quad = \dfrac{1}{5}(4\mathbf{i} - 3\mathbf{j}) = \dfrac{4}{5}\mathbf{i} - \dfrac{3}{5}\mathbf{j}$

51. $\mathbf{u} = \dfrac{1}{\|\mathbf{v}\|}\mathbf{v} = \dfrac{1}{2}(2\mathbf{j}) = \mathbf{j}$

53.
$$\mathbf{v} = \mathbf{i} + \mathbf{j}$$

$$\mathbf{w} = 2(\mathbf{i} - \mathbf{j})$$

$$\mathbf{u} = \mathbf{v} - \mathbf{w} = -\mathbf{i} + 3\mathbf{j}$$

$$\|\mathbf{v}\| = \sqrt{2}$$

$$\|\mathbf{w}\| = 2\sqrt{2}$$

$$\|\mathbf{v} - \mathbf{w}\| = \sqrt{10}$$

$$\cos \alpha = \frac{\|\mathbf{v}\|^2 + \|\mathbf{w}\|^2 - \|\mathbf{v} - \mathbf{w}\|^2}{2\|\mathbf{v}\|\,\|\mathbf{w}\|} = \frac{2 + 8 - 10}{2\sqrt{2} \cdot 2\sqrt{2}} = 0$$

$$\alpha = 90°$$

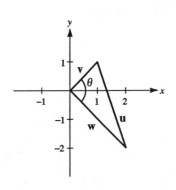

55.
$$\mathbf{v} = \mathbf{i} + \mathbf{j}$$

$$\mathbf{w} = 3\mathbf{i} - \mathbf{j}$$

$$\mathbf{u} = \mathbf{v} - \mathbf{w} = -2\mathbf{i} + 2\mathbf{j}$$

$$\cos \theta = \frac{\|\mathbf{v}\|^2 + \|\mathbf{w}\|^2 - \|\mathbf{v} - \mathbf{w}\|^2}{2\|\mathbf{v}\|\,\|\mathbf{w}\|} = \frac{2 + 10 - 8}{2\sqrt{2}\sqrt{10}} \approx 0.4472$$

$$\theta \approx 63.4°$$

57. Force One: $\mathbf{u} = 45\mathbf{i}$

Force Two: $\mathbf{v} = 60 \cos \theta \mathbf{i} + 60 \sin \theta \mathbf{j}$

Resultant Force: $\mathbf{u} + \mathbf{v} = (45 + 60 \cos \theta)\mathbf{i} + 60 \sin \theta \mathbf{j}$

$$\|\mathbf{u} + \mathbf{v}\| = \sqrt{(45 + 60 \cos \theta)^2 + (60 \sin \theta)^2} = 90$$

$$2025 + 5400 \cos \theta + 3600 = 8100$$

$$5400 \cos \theta = 2475$$

$$\cos \theta = \frac{2475}{5400} \approx 0.4583$$

$$\theta \approx 62.7°$$

59.
$$\mathbf{u} = 50\mathbf{i}$$

$$\mathbf{v} = 35\left(\frac{\sqrt{3}}{2}\mathbf{i} + \frac{1}{2}\mathbf{j}\right) = \frac{35\sqrt{3}}{2}\mathbf{i} + \frac{35}{2}\mathbf{j}$$

$$\mathbf{u} + \mathbf{v} = \left(50 + \frac{35\sqrt{3}}{2}\right)\mathbf{i} + \frac{35}{2}\mathbf{j}$$

$$\|\mathbf{u} + \mathbf{v}\| = \sqrt{\left(50 + \frac{35\sqrt{3}}{2}\right)^2 + \left(\frac{35}{2}\right)^2} \approx 82.2 \text{ pounds}$$

$$\tan\theta = \frac{35/2}{(100 + 35\sqrt{3})/2} = \frac{35}{100 + 35\sqrt{3}}$$

$$\theta \approx 12.3°$$

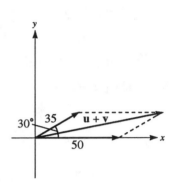

61.
$$\mathbf{u} = (75\cos 30°)\mathbf{i} + (75\sin 30°)\mathbf{j} \approx 64.95\mathbf{i} + 37.5\mathbf{j}$$

$$\mathbf{v} = (100\cos 45°)\mathbf{i} + (100\sin 45°)\mathbf{j} \approx 70.71\mathbf{i} + 70.71\mathbf{j}$$

$$\mathbf{w} = (125\cos 120°)\mathbf{i} + (125\sin 120°)\mathbf{j} \approx -62.5\mathbf{i} + 108.3\mathbf{j}$$

$$\mathbf{u} + \mathbf{v} + \mathbf{w} \approx 73.16\mathbf{i} + 216.5\mathbf{j}$$

$$\|\mathbf{u} + \mathbf{v} + \mathbf{w}\| \approx 228.5 \text{ pounds}$$

$$\tan\theta \approx \frac{216.5}{73.16} \approx 2.9592$$

$$\theta \approx 71.3°$$

63. Horizontal component of velocity:
$$80\cos 50° \approx 51.42 \text{ ft/sec}$$
Vertical component of velocity:
$$80\sin 50° \approx 61.28 \text{ ft/sec}$$

65. Rope $\overrightarrow{AC}$: $\mathbf{u} = \|\mathbf{u}\|(\cos 50°\mathbf{i} - \sin 50°\mathbf{j})$
Rope $\overrightarrow{BC}$: $\mathbf{v} = \|\mathbf{v}\|(-\cos 30°\mathbf{i} - \sin 30°\mathbf{j})$
Resultant: $\mathbf{u} + \mathbf{v} = -1000\mathbf{j}$

$$\|\mathbf{u}\|\cos 50° - \|\mathbf{v}\|\cos 30° = 0$$

$$-\|\mathbf{u}\|\sin 50° - \|\mathbf{v}\|\sin 30° = -1000$$

Solving this system of equations yields:

$$T_{AC} = \|\mathbf{u}\| \approx 879.4 \text{ pounds}$$

$$T_{BC} = \|\mathbf{v}\| \approx 652.7 \text{ pounds}$$

67. Towline 1: $\mathbf{u} = \|\mathbf{u}\|(\cos 20°\mathbf{i} + \sin 20°\mathbf{j})$
Towline 2: $\mathbf{v} = \|\mathbf{u}\|(\cos 20°\mathbf{i} - \sin 20°\mathbf{j})$
Resultant: $\mathbf{u} + \mathbf{v} = 6000\mathbf{i}$

$$\|\mathbf{u}\| \cos 20° + \|\mathbf{u}\| \cos 20° = 6000$$

$$\|\mathbf{u}\| \approx 3192.5$$

Therefore, the tension on each towline is $\|\mathbf{u}\| \approx 3192.5$ pounds.

69. Airspeed: $\mathbf{u} = (540 \cos 32°)\mathbf{i} - (540 \sin 32°)\mathbf{j} \approx 457.9\mathbf{i} - 286.2\mathbf{j}$
Groundspeed: $\mathbf{v} = (500 \cos 40°)\mathbf{i} - (500 \sin 40°)\mathbf{j} \approx 383.0\mathbf{i} - 321.4\mathbf{j}$
Wind: $\mathbf{w} = \mathbf{v} - \mathbf{u} \approx -74.9\mathbf{i} - 35.2\mathbf{j}$
Wind speed: $\|\mathbf{w}\| \approx \sqrt{(-74.9)^2 + (-35.2)^2} \approx 82.8$ miles/hour
Wind direction: $\tan \theta \approx \dfrac{-35.2}{-74.9} \approx 0.4700$

$$\theta \approx 25.2°$$

$$\text{N } 25.2° \text{ E}$$

71. $W = FD = (85 \cos 60°)(10) = 425$ ft-lb

85 lb

60°

10 ft

73. The program draws the parallelogram determined by the origin, (A, B) and (C, D). It also draws the vector sum $(A + C, B + D)$ as a diagonal of this parallelogram.

Section 8.4   Trigonometric Form of a Complex Number

- You should be able to graphically represent complex numbers and know the following facts about them.

- The absolute value of the complex number $z = a + bi$ is $|z| = \sqrt{a^2 + b^2}$.

- The trigonometric form of the complex number $z = a + bi$ is $z = r(\cos\theta + i\sin\theta)$ where
  (a) $a = r\cos\theta$.
  (b) $b = r\sin\theta$.
  (c) $r = \sqrt{a^2 + b^2}$; r is called the modulus of z.
  (d) $\tan\theta = b/a$; θ is called the argument of z.

- Given $z_1 = r_1(\cos\theta_1 + i\sin\theta_1)$ and $z_2 = r_2(\cos\theta_2 + i\sin\theta_2)$:
  (a) $z_1 z_2 = r_1 r_2[\cos(\theta_1 + \theta_2) + i\sin(\theta_1 + \theta_2)]$
  (b) $\dfrac{z_1}{z_2} = \dfrac{r_1}{r_2}[\cos(\theta_1 - \theta_2) + i\sin(\theta_1 - \theta_2)], \quad z_2 \neq 0$

1. $|-5i| = \sqrt{0^2 + (-5)^2}$
$= \sqrt{25} = 5$

3. $|-4 + 4i| = \sqrt{(-4)^2 + (4)^2}$
$= \sqrt{32} = 4\sqrt{2}$

5. $|6 - 7i| = \sqrt{6^2 + (-7)^2}$
$= \sqrt{85}$

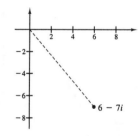

7. $z = 4i$

$r = \sqrt{0^2 + 4^2} = \sqrt{16} = 4$

$\tan\theta = \dfrac{4}{0}, \quad \text{undefined} \Rightarrow \theta = \dfrac{\pi}{2}$

$z = 4\left(\cos\dfrac{\pi}{2} + i\sin\dfrac{\pi}{2}\right)$

9. $z = -3 - 3i$

$r = \sqrt{(-3)^2 + (-3)^2} = \sqrt{18} = 3\sqrt{2}$

$\tan\theta = \dfrac{-3}{-3} = 1 \Rightarrow \theta = \dfrac{5\pi}{4}$

$z = 3\sqrt{2}\left(\cos\dfrac{5\pi}{4} + i\sin\dfrac{5\pi}{4}\right)$

11. $z = 3 - 3i$

$r = \sqrt{3^2 + (-3)^2} = \sqrt{18} = 3\sqrt{2}$

$\tan \theta = \dfrac{-3}{3} = -1 \Rightarrow \theta = \dfrac{7\pi}{4}$

$z = 3\sqrt{2}\left(\cos\dfrac{7\pi}{4} + i\sin\dfrac{7\pi}{4}\right)$

13. $z = \sqrt{3} + i$

$r = \sqrt{(\sqrt{3})^2 + 1^2} = \sqrt{4} = 2$

$\tan \theta = \dfrac{1}{\sqrt{3}} = \dfrac{\sqrt{3}}{3} \Rightarrow \theta = \dfrac{\pi}{6}$

$z = 2\left(\cos\dfrac{\pi}{6} + i\sin\dfrac{\pi}{6}\right)$

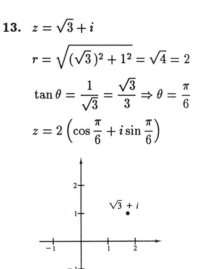

15. $z = -2(1 + \sqrt{3}\,i)$

$r = \sqrt{(-2)^2 + (-2\sqrt{3})^2} = \sqrt{16} = 4$

$\tan \theta = \dfrac{\sqrt{3}}{1} = \sqrt{3} \Rightarrow \theta = \dfrac{4\pi}{3}$

$z = 4\left(\cos\dfrac{4\pi}{3} + i\sin\dfrac{4\pi}{3}\right)$

17. $z = 0 + 6i$

$r = \sqrt{0^2 + (6)^2} = \sqrt{36} = 6$

$\tan \theta = \dfrac{6}{0}, \text{ undefined } \Rightarrow \theta = \dfrac{\pi}{2}$

$z = 6\left(\cos\dfrac{\pi}{2} + i\sin\dfrac{\pi}{2}\right)$

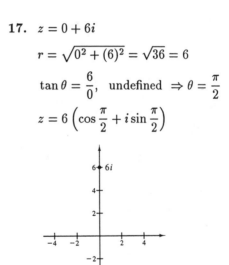

19. $z = -7 + 4i$

$r = \sqrt{(-7)^2 + (4)^2} = \sqrt{65}$

$\tan \theta = \dfrac{4}{-7} \Rightarrow \theta \approx 2.62$

$z \approx \sqrt{65}(\cos 2.62 + i \sin 2.62)$

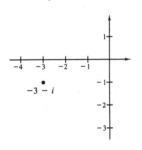

21. $z = 7 + 0i$

$r = \sqrt{(7)^2 + (0)^2}$

$= \sqrt{49} = 7$

$\tan \theta = \frac{0}{7} = 0 \Rightarrow \theta = 0$

$z = 7(\cos 0 + i \sin 0)$

23. $z = 1 + 6i$

$r = \sqrt{1^2 + (6)^2} = \sqrt{37}$

$\tan \theta = \dfrac{6}{1} = 6 \Rightarrow \theta \approx 1.41$

$z \approx \sqrt{37}(\cos 1.41 + i \sin 1.41)$

25. $z = -3 - i$

$r = \sqrt{(-3)^2 + (-1)^2} = \sqrt{10}$

$\tan \theta = \dfrac{-1}{-3} = \dfrac{1}{3} \Rightarrow \theta \approx 3.46$

$z \approx \sqrt{10}(\cos 3.46 + i \sin 3.46)$

27. $2(\cos 150° + i \sin 150°)$

$= 2\left[-\dfrac{\sqrt{3}}{2} + i\left(\dfrac{1}{2} \right) \right]$

$= -\sqrt{3} + i$

29. $\dfrac{3}{2}(\cos 300° + i\sin 300°)$

$$= \dfrac{3}{2}\left[\dfrac{1}{2} + i\left(-\dfrac{\sqrt{3}}{2}\right)\right]$$

$$= \dfrac{3}{4} - \dfrac{3\sqrt{3}}{4}i$$

31. $3.75\left(\cos\dfrac{3\pi}{4} + i\sin\dfrac{3\pi}{4}\right)$

$$= -\dfrac{15\sqrt{2}}{8} + \dfrac{15\sqrt{2}}{8}i$$

33. $4\left(\cos\dfrac{3\pi}{2} + i\sin\dfrac{3\pi}{2}\right) = 4(0 - i)$

$$= -4i$$

35. $3[\cos(18°\,45') + i\sin(18°\,45')]$

$$\approx 2.841 + 0.9643i$$

37. $\left[3\left(\cos\dfrac{\pi}{3} + i\sin\dfrac{\pi}{3}\right)\right]\left[4\left(\cos\dfrac{\pi}{6} + i\sin\dfrac{\pi}{6}\right)\right] = (3)(4)\left[\cos\left(\dfrac{\pi}{3} + \dfrac{\pi}{6}\right) + i\sin\left(\dfrac{\pi}{6} + \dfrac{\pi}{3}\right)\right]$

$$= 12\left(\cos\dfrac{\pi}{2} + i\sin\dfrac{\pi}{2}\right)$$

39. $\left[\tfrac{5}{3}(\cos 140° + i\sin 140°)\right]\left[\tfrac{2}{3}(\cos 60° + i\sin 60°)\right] = \left(\tfrac{5}{3}\right)\left(\tfrac{2}{3}\right)[\cos(140° + 60°) + i\sin(140° + 60°)]$

$$= \tfrac{10}{9}(\cos 200° + i\sin 200°)$$

41. $[0.45(\cos 310° + i \sin 310°)][0.60(\cos 200° + i \sin 200°)]$

$$= (0.45)(0.60)[\cos(310° + 200°) + i \sin(310° + 200°)]$$

$$= 0.27(\cos 510° + i \sin 510°)$$

$$= 0.27(\cos 150° + i \sin 150°)$$

43. $\dfrac{2(\cos 120° + i \sin 120°)}{4(\cos 40° + i \sin 40°)} = \dfrac{2}{4}[\cos(120° - 40°) + i \sin(120° - 40°)] = \dfrac{1}{2}(\cos 80° + i \sin 80°)$

45. $\dfrac{\cos(5\pi/3) + i \sin(5\pi/3)}{\cos \pi + i \sin \pi} = \cos\left(\dfrac{5\pi}{3} - \pi\right) + i \sin\left(\dfrac{5\pi}{3} - \pi\right) = \cos\left(\dfrac{2\pi}{3}\right) + i \sin\left(\dfrac{2\pi}{3}\right)$

47. $\dfrac{12(\cos 52° + i \sin 52°)}{3(\cos 110° + i \sin 110°)} = 4[\cos(52° - 110°) + i \sin(52° - 110°)]$

$$= 4[\cos(-58°) + i \sin(-58°)] = 4[\cos 302° + i \sin 302°]$$

49. (a) $2 + 2i = 2\sqrt{2}(\cos 45° + i \sin 45°)$

$\qquad 1 - i = \sqrt{2}[\cos(-45°) + i \sin(-45°)]$

(b) $(2 + 2i)(1 - i) = [2\sqrt{2}(\cos 45° + i \sin 45°)][\sqrt{2}(\cos(-45°) + i \sin(-45°))]$

$$= 4(\cos 0° + i \sin 0°) = 4$$

(c) $(2 + 2i)(1 - i) = 2 - 2i + 2i - 2i^2 = 2 + 2 = 4$

51. (a) $-2i = 2(\cos 270° + i \sin 270°)$

$\qquad 1 + i = \sqrt{2}(\cos 45° + i \sin 45°)$

(b) $-2(1 + i) = [2(\cos 270° + i \sin 270°)][\sqrt{2}(\cos 45° + i \sin 45°)]$

$$= 2\sqrt{2}(\cos 315° + i \sin 315°) = 2 - 2i$$

(c) $-2i(1 + i) = -2i - 2i^2 = -2i + 2 = 2 - 2i$

53. (a) $5 = 5(\cos 0° + i \sin 0°)$

$\qquad 2 + 3i = \sqrt{13}(\cos 56.31° + i \sin 56.31°)$

(b) $\dfrac{5}{2 + 3i} = \dfrac{5(\cos 0° + i \sin 0°)}{\sqrt{13}(\cos 56.3° + i \sin 56.3°)} = \dfrac{5\sqrt{13}}{13}(\cos 303.7° + i \sin 303.7°) \approx 0.7694 - 1.154i$

(c) $\dfrac{5}{2 + 3i} = \dfrac{5}{2 + 3i} \cdot \dfrac{2 - 3i}{2 - 3i} = \dfrac{10 - 15i}{13} = \dfrac{10}{13} - \dfrac{15}{13}i \approx 0.7694 - 1.154i$

55. $\dfrac{z_1}{z_2} = \dfrac{r_1(\cos\theta_1 + i\sin\theta_1)}{r_2(\cos\theta_2 + i\sin\theta_2)} \cdot \dfrac{\cos\theta_2 - i\sin\theta_2}{\cos\theta_2 - i\sin\theta_2}$

$\qquad = \dfrac{r_1}{r_2(\cos^2\theta_2 + \sin^2\theta_2)}[\cos\theta_1\cos\theta_2 + \sin\theta_1\sin\theta_2 + i(\sin\theta_1\cos\theta_2 - \sin\theta_2\cos\theta_1)]$

$\qquad = \dfrac{r_1}{r_2}[\cos(\theta_1 - \theta_2) + i\sin(\theta_1 - \theta_2)]$

57. (a) $z\bar{z} = [r(\cos\theta + i\sin\theta)][r(\cos(-\theta) + i\sin(-\theta)]$

$\qquad = r^2[\cos(\theta - \theta) + i\sin(\theta - \theta)] = r^2[\cos 0 + i\sin 0] = r^2$

(b) $\dfrac{z}{\bar{z}} = \dfrac{r(\cos\theta + i\sin\theta)}{r[\cos(-\theta) + i\sin(-\theta)]} = \dfrac{r}{r}[\cos(\theta - (-\theta)) + i\sin(\theta - (-\theta))] = \cos 2\theta + i\sin 2\theta$

59. Let $z = x + iy$ such that:

$\qquad |z| = 2 \Rightarrow 2 = \sqrt{x^2 + y^2}$

$\qquad\qquad \Rightarrow 4 = x^2 + y^2 :$

$\qquad$ circle with radius of 2

Section 8.5 DeMoivre's Theorem and nth Roots

■ You should know DeMoivre's Theorem: If $z = r(\cos\theta + i\sin\theta)$, then for any positive integer n, $z^n = r^n(\cos n\theta + i\sin n\theta)$.

■ You should know that for any positive integer n, $z = r(\cos\theta + i\sin\theta)$ has n distinct nth roots given by

$$\sqrt[n]{r}\left[\cos\left(\frac{\theta + 2\pi k}{n}\right) + i\sin\left(\frac{\theta + 2\pi k}{n}\right)\right]$$

where $k = 0, 1, 2, \ldots, n-1$.

---

1. $(1+i)^5 = \left[\sqrt{2}\left(\cos\dfrac{\pi}{4} + i\sin\dfrac{\pi}{4}\right)\right]^5$

$$= (\sqrt{2})^5\left(\cos\frac{5\pi}{4} + i\sin\frac{5\pi}{4}\right) = 4\sqrt{2}\left(-\frac{\sqrt{2}}{2} - \frac{\sqrt{2}}{2}i\right) = -4 - 4i$$

3. $(-1+i)^{10} = \left[\sqrt{2}\left(\cos\dfrac{3\pi}{4} + i\sin\dfrac{3\pi}{4}\right)\right]^{10}$

$$= (\sqrt{2})^{10}\left(\cos\frac{30\pi}{4} + i\sin\frac{30\pi}{4}\right) = 32\left[\cos\left(\frac{3\pi}{2} + 6\pi\right) + i\sin\left(\frac{3\pi}{2} + 6\pi\right)\right]$$

$$= 32\left(\cos\frac{3\pi}{2} + i\sin\frac{3\pi}{2}\right) = 32[0 + i(-1)] = -32i$$

5. $2(\sqrt{3}+i)^7 = 2\left[2\left(\cos\dfrac{\pi}{6} + i\sin\dfrac{\pi}{6}\right)\right]^7$

$$= 2\left[2^7\left(\cos\frac{7\pi}{6} + i\sin\frac{7\pi}{6}\right)\right]$$

$$= 256\left(-\frac{\sqrt{3}}{2} - \frac{1}{2}i\right)$$

$$= -128\sqrt{3} - 128i$$

7. $[5(\cos 20° + i\sin 20°)]^3 = 5^3(\cos 60° + i\sin 60°)$

$$= \frac{125}{2} + \frac{125\sqrt{3}}{2}i$$

9. $\left(\cos\dfrac{5\pi}{4} + i\sin\dfrac{5\pi}{4}\right)^{10} = \cos\dfrac{25\pi}{2} + i\sin\dfrac{25\pi}{2}$

$$= \cos\left(12\pi + \frac{\pi}{2}\right) + i\sin\left(12\pi + \frac{\pi}{2}\right) = \cos\frac{\pi}{2} + i\sin\frac{\pi}{2} = i$$

11. $[5(\cos 3.2 + i\sin 3.2)]^4 = 5^4(\cos 12.8 + i\sin 12.8)$

$$\approx 625(0.9728 + 0.2315i) \approx 608.0 + 144.7i$$

13. (a) Square roots of $9(\cos 120° + i\sin 120°)$:   (b)

$$\sqrt{9}\left[\cos\left(\frac{120° + 360°\,k}{2}\right) + i\sin\left(\frac{120° + 360°\,k}{2}\right)\right],\quad k = 0,\ 1$$

$$3(\cos 60° + i\sin 60°)$$

$$3(\cos 240° + i\sin 240°)$$

(c) $\dfrac{3}{2} + \dfrac{3\sqrt{3}}{2}i,\quad -\dfrac{3}{2} - \dfrac{3\sqrt{3}}{2}i$

15. (a) Fourth roots of $16\left(\cos\dfrac{4\pi}{3} + i\sin\dfrac{4\pi}{3}\right)$:

$$\sqrt[4]{16}\left[\cos\left(\frac{(4\pi/3) + 2k\pi}{4}\right) + i\sin\left(\frac{(4\pi/3) + 2k\pi}{4}\right)\right],\quad k = 0,\ 1,\ 2,\ 3$$

$$2\left(\cos\frac{\pi}{3} + i\sin\frac{\pi}{3}\right)$$ (b)

$$2\left(\cos\frac{5\pi}{6} + i\sin\frac{5\pi}{6}\right)$$

$$2\left(\cos\frac{4\pi}{3} + i\sin\frac{4\pi}{3}\right)$$

$$2\left(\cos\frac{11\pi}{6} + i\sin\frac{11\pi}{6}\right)$$

(c) $1 + \sqrt{3}\,i,\quad -\sqrt{3} + i,\quad -1 - \sqrt{3}\,i,\quad \sqrt{3} - i$

17. (a) Square roots of $-25i = 25\left(\cos\dfrac{3\pi}{2} + i\sin\dfrac{3\pi}{2}\right)$:

$$\sqrt{25}\left[\cos\left(\frac{(3\pi/2)+2k\pi}{2}\right) + i\sin\left(\frac{(3\pi/2)+2k\pi}{2}\right)\right], \quad k = 0,\ 1$$

$$5\left(\cos\frac{3\pi}{4} + i\sin\frac{3\pi}{4}\right)$$

(b)

$$5\left(\cos\frac{7\pi}{4} + i\sin\frac{7\pi}{4}\right)$$

(c) $-\dfrac{5\sqrt{2}}{2} + \dfrac{5\sqrt{2}}{2}i,\ \dfrac{5\sqrt{2}}{2} - \dfrac{5\sqrt{2}}{2}i$

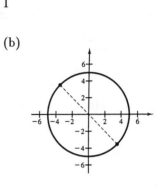

19. (a) Cube roots of $-\dfrac{125}{2}(1 + \sqrt{3}\,i) = 125\left(\cos\dfrac{4\pi}{3} + i\sin\dfrac{4\pi}{3}\right)$:

$$\sqrt[3]{125}\left[\cos\left(\frac{(4\pi/3)+2k\pi}{3}\right) + i\sin\left(\frac{(4\pi/3)+2k\pi}{3}\right)\right], \quad k = 0,\ 1,\ 2$$

$$5\left(\cos\frac{4\pi}{9} + i\sin\frac{4\pi}{9}\right)$$

(b)

$$5\left(\cos\frac{10\pi}{9} + i\sin\frac{10\pi}{9}\right)$$

$$5\left(\cos\frac{16\pi}{9} + i\sin\frac{16\pi}{9}\right)$$

(c) $0.8682 + 4.924i,\ -4.698 - 1.710i,\ 3.830 - 3.214i$

21. (a) Cube roots of $8 = 8(\cos 0 + i \sin 0)$:

$$\sqrt[3]{8}\left[\cos\left(\frac{2k\pi}{3}\right) + i\sin\left(\frac{2k\pi}{3}\right)\right], \ k = 0, \ 1, \ 2$$

$$2(\cos 0 + i\sin 0)$$

$$2\left(\cos\frac{2\pi}{3} + i\sin\frac{2\pi}{3}\right)$$

$$2\left(\cos\frac{4\pi}{3} + i\sin\frac{4\pi}{3}\right)$$

(c) $2, \ -1 + \sqrt{3}\,i, \ -1 - \sqrt{3}\,i$

(b)

23. (a) Fifth roots of $1 = \cos 0 + i\sin 0$:

$$\cos\frac{2k\pi}{5} + i\sin\frac{2k\pi}{5}, \ k = 0, \ 1, \ 2, \ 3, \ 4$$

$$\cos 0 + i\sin 0$$

$$\cos\frac{2\pi}{5} + i\sin\frac{2\pi}{5}$$

$$\cos\frac{4\pi}{5} + i\sin\frac{4\pi}{5}$$

$$\cos\frac{6\pi}{5} + i\sin\frac{6\pi}{5}$$

$$\cos\frac{8\pi}{5} + i\sin\frac{8\pi}{5}$$

(c) $1, \ 0.3090 + 0.9511i, \ -0.8090 + 0.5878i,$

$-0.8090 - 0.5878i, \ 0.3090 - 0.9511i$

(b)

25. $x^4 - i = 0$

$$x^4 = i$$

The solutions are the fourth roots of $i = \cos \dfrac{\pi}{2} + i \sin \dfrac{\pi}{2}$.

$$\sqrt[4]{1} \left[\cos \left(\dfrac{(\pi/2) + 2k\pi}{4} \right) + i \sin \left(\dfrac{(\pi/2) + 2k\pi}{4} \right) \right], \; k = 0,\, 1,\, 2,\, 3$$

$$\cos \dfrac{\pi}{8} + i \sin \dfrac{\pi}{8} \approx 0.9239 + 0.3827i$$

$$\cos \dfrac{5\pi}{8} + i \sin \dfrac{5\pi}{8} \approx -0.3827 + 0.9239i$$

$$\cos \dfrac{9\pi}{8} + i \sin \dfrac{9\pi}{8} \approx -0.9239 - 0.3827i$$

$$\cos \dfrac{13\pi}{8} + i \sin \dfrac{13\pi}{8} \approx 0.3827 - 0.9239i$$

27. $x^5 + 243 = 0$

$$x^5 = -243$$

The solutions are the fifth roots of -243:

$$\sqrt[5]{243} \left[\cos \left(\dfrac{\pi + 2k\pi}{5} \right) + i \sin \left(\dfrac{\pi + 2k\pi}{5} \right) \right], \; k = 0,\, 1,\, 2,\, 3,\, 4$$

$$3 \left(\cos \dfrac{\pi}{5} + i \sin \dfrac{\pi}{5} \right) \approx 2.427 + 1.763i$$

$$3 \left(\cos \dfrac{3\pi}{5} + i \sin \dfrac{3\pi}{5} \right) \approx -0.9271 + 2.853i$$

$$3 \left(\cos \pi + i \sin \pi \right) = -3$$

$$3 \left(\cos \dfrac{7\pi}{5} + i \sin \dfrac{7\pi}{5} \right) \approx -0.9271 - 2.853i$$

$$3 \left(\cos \dfrac{9\pi}{5} + i \sin \dfrac{9\pi}{5} \right) \approx 2.427 - 1.763i$$

29. $x^3 + 64i = 0$

$$x^3 = -64i$$

The solutions are the cube roots of $-64i$:

$$\sqrt[3]{64}\left[\cos\left(\frac{(3\pi/2) + 2k\pi}{3}\right) + i\sin\left(\frac{(3\pi/2) + 2k\pi}{3}\right)\right], \quad k = 0,\ 1,\ 2$$

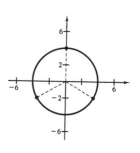

$$4\left(\cos\frac{\pi}{2} + i\sin\frac{\pi}{2}\right) = 4i$$

$$4\left(\cos\frac{7\pi}{6} + i\sin\frac{7\pi}{6}\right) = -2\sqrt{3} - 2i$$

$$4\left(\cos\frac{11\pi}{6} + i\sin\frac{11\pi}{6}\right) = 2\sqrt{3} - 2i$$

31. $x^3 - (1 - i) = 0$

$$x^3 = 1 - i = \sqrt{2}(\cos 315° + i\sin 315°)$$

The solutions are the cube roots of $1 - i$:

$$\sqrt[3]{\sqrt{2}}\left[\cos\left(\frac{315° + 360°k}{3}\right) + i\sin\left(\frac{315° + 360°k}{3}\right)\right], \quad k = 0,\ 1,\ 2$$

$$\sqrt[6]{2}(\cos 105° + i\sin 105°) \approx -0.2905 + 1.0842i$$

$$\sqrt[6]{2}(\cos 225° + i\sin 225°) \approx -0.7937 - 0.7937i$$

$$\sqrt[6]{2}(\cos 345° + i\sin 345°) \approx 1.0842 - 0.2905i$$

Chapter 8   Review Exercises

1. Given: $a = 5$, $b = 8$, $c = 10$

$$\cos C = \frac{a^2 + b^2 - c^2}{2ab} = \frac{25 + 64 - 100}{80} \approx -0.1375 \Rightarrow C \approx 97.9°$$

$$\sin A = \frac{a \sin C}{c} \approx \frac{5(0.9905)}{10} \approx 0.4953 \Rightarrow A \approx 29.7°$$

$$\sin B = \frac{b \sin C}{c} \approx \frac{8(0.9905)}{10} \approx 0.7924 \Rightarrow B \approx 52.4°$$

3. Given: $A = 12°$, $B = 58°$, $a = 5$

$$C = 180° - A - B = 180° - 12° - 58° = 110°$$

$$b = \frac{a \sin B}{\sin A} = \frac{5 \sin 58°}{\sin 12°} \approx \frac{5(0.8480)}{0.2079} \approx 20.4$$

$$c = \frac{a \sin C}{\sin A} = \frac{5 \sin 110°}{\sin 12°} \approx \frac{5(0.9397)}{0.2079} \approx 22.6$$

5. Given: $B = 110°$, $a = 4$, $c = 4$

$$b^2 = a^2 + c^2 - 2ac \cos B \approx 16 + 16 - 2(4)(4)(-0.3420) \approx 42.94 \Rightarrow b \approx 6.6$$

$$\sin A = \frac{a \sin B}{b} = \frac{4 \sin 110°}{6.6} \approx \frac{4(0.9397)}{6.6} \approx 0.5736 \Rightarrow A \approx 35°$$

$$c = a \Rightarrow C = A \approx 35°$$

7. Given: $A = 75°$, $a = 2.5$, $b = 16.5$

$$\sin B = \frac{b \sin A}{a} = \frac{16.5 \sin 75°}{2.5} \approx \frac{16.5(0.9659)}{2.5} \approx 6.375 \Rightarrow \text{ no triangle formed}$$

9. Given: $B = 115°$, $a = 7$, $b = 14.5$

$$\sin A = \frac{a \sin B}{b} = \frac{7 \sin 115°}{14.5} \approx \frac{7(0.9063)}{14.5} \approx 0.4375 \Rightarrow A \approx 25.9°$$

$$C \approx 180° - 115° - 25.9° = 39.1°$$

$$c^2 = a^2 + b^2 - 2ab \cos C \approx 7^2 + 14.5^2 - 2(7)(14.5)(0.7760) \approx 101.7 \Rightarrow c \approx 10.09$$

11. Given: $A = 15°$, $a = 5$, $b = 10$

$$\sin B = \frac{b \sin A}{a} = \frac{10 \sin 15°}{5} \approx \frac{10(0.2588)}{5} \approx 0.5176 \Rightarrow B \approx 31.2° \text{ or } 148.8°$$

$$\underline{\text{Case 1: } B \approx 31.2°} \qquad\qquad \underline{\text{Case 2: } B \approx 148.8°}$$

$$C \approx 180° - 15° - 31.2° = 133.8° \qquad C \approx 180° - 15° - 148.8° = 16.2°$$

$$c = \frac{a \sin C}{\sin A} \approx 13.94 \qquad\qquad c = \frac{a \sin C}{\sin A} \approx 5.390$$

13. Given: $B = 150°$, $a = 10$, $c = 20$

$$b^2 = a^2 + c^2 - 2ac \cos B \approx 100 + 400 - 400(-0.8660) \approx 846.4 \Rightarrow b \approx 29.09$$

$$\sin C = \frac{c \sin B}{b} \approx \frac{20(0.5)}{29.09} \approx 0.3437 \Rightarrow C \approx 20.1°$$

$$\sin A = \frac{a \sin B}{b} \approx \frac{10(0.5)}{29.09} \approx 0.1719 \Rightarrow A \approx 9.9°$$

15. Given: $B = 25°$, $a = 6.2$, $b = 4$

$$\sin A = \frac{a \sin B}{b} \approx 0.6551 \Rightarrow A \approx 40.9° \text{ or } 139.1°$$

$$\underline{\text{Case 1: } A \approx 40.9°} \qquad\qquad \underline{\text{Case 2: } A \approx 139.1°}$$

$$C \approx 180° - 25° - 40.9° = 114.1° \qquad C \approx 180° - 25° - 139.1° = 15.9°$$

$$c \approx 8.640 \qquad\qquad c \approx 2.593$$

17. $a = 4$, $b = 5$, $c = 7$

$$s = \frac{a + b + c}{2} = \frac{4 + 5 + 7}{2} = 8$$

$$\text{Area} = \sqrt{s(s - a)(s - b)(s - c)} = \sqrt{8(4)(3)(1)} \approx 9.798$$

19. $A = 27°$, $b = 5$, $c = 8$

$$\text{Area} = \tfrac{1}{2}bc \sin A = \tfrac{1}{2}(5)(8)(0.4540) = 9.080$$

21. Height of smaller triangle: $h = 75 \sin 32° \approx 39.74$ ft

Height of larger triangle: $H = b \tan 48° \approx 70.63$ ft

Height of tree: $H - h \approx 70.63 - 39.74 \approx 31$ ft

23. $\alpha = 180° - 31° = 149°$

$\phi = 180° - 149° - 17° = 14°$

$x = \dfrac{50 \sin 17°}{\sin \phi} = \dfrac{50 \sin 17°}{\sin 14°} \approx 60.43$

$h = x \sin 31°$

$\approx 60.43(0.5150) \approx 31.12$ meters

25. $d^2 = 850^2 + 1060^2 - 2(850)(1060) \cos 72°$

$\approx 1{,}289{,}251$

$d \approx 1135$ miles

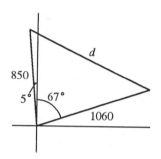

27. Initial point: $(0, 10)$

Terminal point: $(7, 3)$

$\mathbf{v} = \langle 7 - 0,\ 3 - 10 \rangle = \langle 7,\ -7 \rangle$

29. $\langle 8 \cos 120°,\ 8 \sin 120° \rangle = \langle -4,\ 4\sqrt{3} \rangle$

31. $\mathbf{u} = 6\mathbf{i} - 5\mathbf{j}$

$\dfrac{1}{\|\mathbf{u}\|}\mathbf{u} = \dfrac{1}{\sqrt{6^2 + 5^2}}(6\mathbf{i} - 5\mathbf{j})$

$= \dfrac{6}{\sqrt{61}}\mathbf{i} - \dfrac{5}{\sqrt{61}}\mathbf{j}$

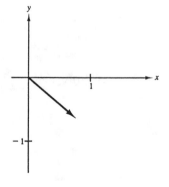

33. $\mathbf{u} = 6\mathbf{i} - 5\mathbf{j}, \quad \mathbf{v} = 10\mathbf{i} + 3\mathbf{j}$

$4\mathbf{u} - 5\mathbf{v} = (24\mathbf{i} - 20\mathbf{j}) - (50\mathbf{i} + 15\mathbf{j})$

$\qquad = -26\mathbf{i} - 35\mathbf{j}$

35. $\tan \alpha = \dfrac{12}{5} \Rightarrow \sin \alpha = \dfrac{12}{13}$ and $\cos \alpha = \dfrac{5}{13}$

$\tan \beta = \dfrac{3}{4} \Rightarrow \sin(180° - \beta) = \dfrac{3}{5}$ and $\cos(180° - \beta) = -\dfrac{4}{5}$

$\mathbf{u} = 300 \left(\dfrac{5}{13}\mathbf{i} + \dfrac{12}{13}\mathbf{j} \right)$

$\mathbf{v} = 150 \left(-\dfrac{4}{5}\mathbf{i} + \dfrac{3}{5}\mathbf{j} \right)$

$\mathbf{w} = 250(0\mathbf{i} - \mathbf{j})$

$\mathbf{r} = \mathbf{u} + \mathbf{v} + \mathbf{w} = \left(\dfrac{1500}{13} - 120 + 0 \right)\mathbf{i} + \left(\dfrac{3600}{13} + 90 - 250 \right)\mathbf{j} = -\dfrac{60}{13}\mathbf{i} + \dfrac{1520}{13}\mathbf{j}$

$\|\mathbf{r}\| = \sqrt{\left(-\dfrac{60}{13} \right)^2 + \left(\dfrac{1520}{13} \right)^2} \approx 117.0 \text{ lb}$

$\theta = 180° - \arctan \dfrac{1520}{60} \approx 92.3°$

37. Rope One: $\mathbf{u} = \|\mathbf{u}\|(\cos 30°\mathbf{i} - \sin 30°\mathbf{j}) = \|\mathbf{u}\| \left(\dfrac{\sqrt{3}}{2}\mathbf{i} - \dfrac{1}{2}\mathbf{j} \right)$

Rope Two: $\mathbf{v} = \|\mathbf{u}\|(- \cos 30°\mathbf{i} - \sin 30°\mathbf{j}) = \|\mathbf{u}\| \left(-\dfrac{\sqrt{3}}{2}\mathbf{i} - \dfrac{1}{2}\mathbf{j} \right)$

Resultant: $\mathbf{u} + \mathbf{v} = -\|\mathbf{u}\|\mathbf{j} = -100\mathbf{j}$

$\qquad\qquad \|\mathbf{u}\| = 100$

Therefore, the tension on each rope is $\|\mathbf{u}\| = 100$ lb.

39. Airspeed:

$$\mathbf{u} = 450\cos 60°\mathbf{i} + 450\sin 60°\mathbf{j} = 225\mathbf{i} + 225\sqrt{3}\,\mathbf{j}$$

Wind: $\mathbf{w} = 20\mathbf{i}$

Groundspeed: $\mathbf{u} + \mathbf{w} = 245\mathbf{i} + 225\sqrt{3}\,\mathbf{j}$

$$\|\mathbf{u} + \mathbf{w}\| = \sqrt{245^2 + (225\sqrt{3})^2} \approx 460.3 \text{ miles/hour}$$

$$\tan\theta = \frac{225\sqrt{3}}{245} \approx 1.5907$$

$$\theta \approx 57.8°$$

Bearing: N 32.2° E

41. $r = 5\sqrt{2},\;\; \theta = 315°$

$5 - 5i = 5\sqrt{2}(\cos 315° + i\sin 315°)$

43. $r = 13,\;\; \theta = 67.38°$

$5 + 12i = 13(\cos 67.38° + i\sin 67.38°)$

45. $100(\cos 240° + i\sin 240°) = 100\left(-\dfrac{1}{2} - \dfrac{\sqrt{3}}{2}i\right) = -50 - 50\sqrt{3}\,i$

47. $13(\cos 0 + i\sin 0) = 13(1 + 0i) = 13$

49. (a) $z_1 = 5(\cos\pi + i\sin\pi)$

$z_2 = 5\left(\cos\dfrac{\pi}{2} + i\sin\dfrac{\pi}{2}\right)$

(b) $z_1 z_2 = 25\left(\cos\dfrac{3\pi}{2} + i\sin\dfrac{3\pi}{2}\right) = -25i$

$\dfrac{z_1}{z_2} = \dfrac{5}{5}\left(\cos\dfrac{\pi}{2} + i\sin\dfrac{\pi}{2}\right) = i$

51. (a) $z_1 = -3(1 + i) = 3\sqrt{2}(\cos 225° + i\sin 225°)$

$z_2 = 2(\sqrt{3} + i) = 4(\cos 30° + i\sin 30°)$

(b) $z_1 z_2 = [3\sqrt{2}(\cos 225° + i\sin 225°)][4(\cos 30° + i\sin 30°)]$

$= 12\sqrt{2}(\cos 255° + i\sin 255°) \approx -4.392 - 16.39i$

$\dfrac{z_1}{z_2} = \dfrac{3\sqrt{2}(\cos 225° + i\sin 225°)}{4(\cos 30° + i\sin 30°)} = \dfrac{3\sqrt{2}}{4}(\cos 195° + i\sin 195°) \approx -1.025 - 0.2745i$

53. $\left[5\left(\cos\dfrac{\pi}{12}+i\sin\dfrac{\pi}{12}\right)\right]^4 = 5^4\left(\dfrac{4\pi}{12}+i\sin\dfrac{4\pi}{12}\right)$

$$= 625\left(\cos\dfrac{\pi}{3}+i\sin\dfrac{\pi}{3}\right)$$

$$= 625\left(\dfrac{1}{2}+\dfrac{\sqrt{3}}{2}i\right) = \dfrac{625}{2}+\dfrac{625\sqrt{3}}{2}i$$

55. $(2+3i)^6 = [\sqrt{13}(\cos 56.3° + i\sin 56.3°)]^6$

$$= 13^3(\cos 337.9° + i\sin 337.9°) \approx 13^3(0.9263 - 0.3769i) \approx 2035 - 828i$$

57. Sixth roots of $-729i = 729\left(\cos\dfrac{3\pi}{2}+i\sin\dfrac{3\pi}{2}\right)$:

$$\sqrt[6]{729}\left(\cos\dfrac{(3\pi/2)+2k\pi}{6}+i\sin\dfrac{(3\pi/2)+2k\pi}{6}\right),\ k=1,\ 2,\ 3,\ 4,\ 5$$

$$3\left(\cos\dfrac{\pi}{4}+i\sin\dfrac{\pi}{4}\right) \approx 2.121 + 2.121i$$

$$3\left(\cos\dfrac{7\pi}{12}+i\sin\dfrac{7\pi}{12}\right) \approx -0.7765 + 2.898i$$

$$3\left(\cos\dfrac{11\pi}{12}+i\sin\dfrac{11\pi}{12}\right) \approx -2.898 + 0.7765i$$

$$3\left(\cos\dfrac{5\pi}{4}+i\sin\dfrac{5\pi}{4}\right) \approx -2.121 - 2.121i$$

$$3\left(\cos\dfrac{19\pi}{12}+i\sin\dfrac{19\pi}{12}\right) \approx 0.7765 - 2.898i$$

$$3\left(\cos\dfrac{23\pi}{12}+i\sin\dfrac{23\pi}{12}\right) \approx 2.898 - 0.7765i$$

59. Cube roots of $-1 = \cos\pi + i\sin\pi$:

$$\cos\dfrac{\pi+2k\pi}{3}+i\sin\dfrac{\pi+2k\pi}{3},\ k=0,\ 1,\ 2$$

$$\cos\dfrac{\pi}{3}+i\sin\dfrac{\pi}{3} = \dfrac{1}{2}+\dfrac{\sqrt{3}}{2}i$$

$$\cos\pi + i\sin\pi = -1$$

$$\cos\dfrac{5\pi}{3}+i\sin\dfrac{5\pi}{3} = \dfrac{1}{2}-\dfrac{\sqrt{3}}{2}i$$

61. $x^4 + 81 = 0$

$$x^4 = -81$$

$$-81 = 81(\cos \pi + i \sin \pi)$$

$$\sqrt[4]{-81} = \sqrt[4]{81} \left[\cos \left(\frac{\pi + 2\pi k}{4} \right) + i \sin \left(\frac{\pi + 2\pi k}{4} \right) \right], \quad k = 0, 1, 2, 3$$

$$3 \left(\cos \frac{\pi}{4} + i \sin \frac{\pi}{4} \right) = \frac{3\sqrt{2}}{2} + \frac{3\sqrt{2}}{2} i$$

$$3 \left(\cos \frac{3\pi}{4} + i \sin \frac{3\pi}{4} \right) = -\frac{3\sqrt{2}}{2} + \frac{3\sqrt{2}}{2} i$$

$$3 \left(\cos \frac{5\pi}{4} + i \sin \frac{5\pi}{4} \right) = -\frac{3\sqrt{2}}{2} - \frac{3\sqrt{2}}{2} i$$

$$3 \left(\cos \frac{7\pi}{4} + i \sin \frac{7\pi}{4} \right) = \frac{3\sqrt{2}}{2} - \frac{3\sqrt{2}}{2} i$$

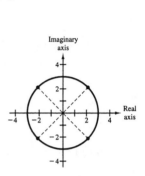

63. $(x^3 - 1)(x^2 + 1) = 0$

$$x^3 - 1 = 0 \qquad x^2 + 1 = 0$$

$$x^3 = 1$$

$$1 = 1(\cos 0 + i \sin 0)$$

$$\sqrt[3]{1} = \sqrt[3]{1} \left[\cos \left(\frac{0 + 2\pi k}{3} \right) + i \sin \left(\frac{0 + 2\pi k}{3} \right) \right], \quad k = 0, 1, 2$$

$$1(\cos 0 + i \sin 0) = 1$$

$$1 \left(\cos \frac{2\pi}{3} + i \sin \frac{2\pi}{3} \right) = -\frac{1}{2} + \frac{\sqrt{3}}{2} i$$

$$1 \left(\cos \frac{4\pi}{3} + i \sin \frac{4\pi}{3} \right) = -\frac{1}{2} - \frac{\sqrt{3}}{2} i$$

$$x^2 + 1 = 0$$

$$x^2 = -1$$

$$-1 = 1(\cos \pi + i \sin \pi)$$

$$\sqrt{-1} = \sqrt{1} \left[\cos \left(\frac{\pi + 2\pi k}{2} \right) + i \sin \left(\frac{\pi + 2\pi k}{2} \right) \right], \quad k = 0, 1$$

$$1 \left(\cos \frac{\pi}{2} + i \sin \frac{\pi}{2} \right) = i$$

$$1 \left(\cos \frac{3\pi}{2} + i \sin \frac{3\pi}{2} \right) = -i$$

CHAPTER 9

Linear Models and Systems of Equations

Section 9.1   Linear Modeling and Scatter Plots

> ■ You should be able to set up and analyze simple linear models.
>
> ■ The following statements are equivalent.
>   (a) y varies directly with x.
>   (b) y is directly proportional to x.
>   (c) $y = mx$ for some nonzero constant m.
>
> ■ You should be able to set up and analyze models that involve a known rate of change:
> $y = mx + b$.
>
> ■ You should know how to fit a line to a set of data represented by a scatter plot.

1. $y = 93{,}836.8 + 2{,}647.5t, \ 2 \le t \le 8$

Year	1982	1983	1984	1985	1986	1987	1988
Actual Number	99,526	100,834	105,005	107,150	109,597	112,440	114,968
Model Number	99,131.8	101,779.3	104,426.8	107,074.3	109,721.8	112,369.3	115,016.8

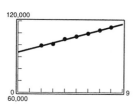

The model is a "good fit" for the actual data.

3. $y = mx$

$12 = m(5)$

$\frac{12}{5} = m$

$y = \frac{12}{5}x$

5. $y = mx$

$2050 = m(10)$

$205 = m$

$y = 205x$

7. $y = mx$

$1.75 = m(12)$

$\frac{7}{48} = m$

$y = \frac{7}{48}x$

9. $I = kP$

$187.59 = k(2500)$

$0.075 = k$

$I = 0.075P$

11. $y = kx$

$1840 = k(50,000)$

$0.0368 = k$

$y = 0.0368x$

When $x = 85,000$, we have

$y = 0.0368(85,000) = \$3128.$

13. $y = kx$

$33 = k(13)$

$\frac{33}{13} = k$

$y = \frac{33}{13}x$

Inches	5.00	10.00	20.00	25.00	30.00
Centimeters	12.69	25.38	50.77	63.46	76.15

15. $F = kx$

$50 = k(s) \Rightarrow k = 10 \Rightarrow F = 10x$

(a) $20 = 10(x) \Rightarrow x = 2$ inches

(b) $F = 10(1.5) = 15$ pounds

17. $F = kx$

$25 = k(1.9) \Rightarrow k = \dfrac{25}{1.9}$

$F = \dfrac{25}{1.9}(3)$

$= 39.47$ lbs is maximum height

19. $y = 20,500 + 460t$

21. $y = 1299 - 289t$

23. (a) $V = 1200 - 240t,\ 0 \le t \le 5$

(b)

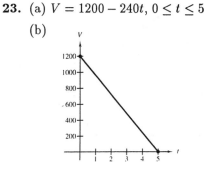

(c) Rate of change is -240 which
represents annual depreciation.

25. $S = L - 0.15L$

$= 0.85L$

27. $W = 9.25 + 1.10x$

29. 2 minutes = 120 seconds

$(0, 7000)$, $(120, 4600)$

$$h - 7000 = \frac{4600 - 7000}{120 - 0}(t - 0)$$

$$h = -20t + 7000$$

When the parachutist reaches the ground, we have

$$h = 0$$

$$0 = -20t + 7000$$

$$t = \frac{7000}{20} = 350 \text{ seconds} \approx 5.833 \text{ minutes.}$$

The time will be

$(2 \text{ hours} + 8 \text{ minutes}) + (5 \text{ minutes} + 50 \text{ seconds}) = 2\!:\!13\!:\!50 \text{ P.M.} \approx 2\!:\!14 \text{ P.M.}$

31. $N = 1200 + 50t$

To find the enrollment in the year 2000, let $t = 20$.

$N = 1200 + 50(20)$

$= 2200$ students

33. Yes, can be approximated by a linear model. The data seems to form a straight line pattern.

35. No, cannot be approximated by a linear model. The data does not seem to form a straight line pattern.

37.

39.

Two approximate points on the line are $(1, 3.4)$ and $(3, 4.25)$. Thus,

$$y - 3.4 = \frac{4.25 - 3.4}{3 - 1}(x - 1)$$

$$y - 3.4 = 0.425x - 0.425$$

$$y = 0.425x + 2.975.$$

Two approximate points on the line are $(2, 2)$ and $(4, 1)$. Thus,

$$y - 2 = \frac{1 - 2}{4 - 2}(x - 2)$$

$$y - 2 = -0.5x + 1$$

$$y = -0.5x + 3.$$

41.

43.

Two points on this line are approximately (0, 120) and (7.5, 350). Thus, the equation of the line is:

$$y - 120 = \frac{350 - 120}{7.5 - 0}(t - 0)$$

$$y \approx 30.67t + 120.$$

Two points on the line are approximately (0, 0) and (5, 8000). Thus, the equation of the line is $y = \frac{8000}{5}t = 1600t$.

Section 9.2   Solving Systems of Equations Algebraically and Graphically

---

■ You should be able to solve systems of equations by the method of substitution.
1. Solve one of the equations for one of the variables.
2. Substitute this expression into the other equation and solve.
3. Back substitute into the first equation to find the value of the other variable.
4. Check the solution in each of the original equations.

■ You should be able to find solutions graphically. (See Example 5 in the textbook.)

---

1. $2x + y = 4$ Equation 1

   $-x + y = 1$ Equation 2

Graphically, the lines $y = -2x + 4$ and $y = x + 1$ intersect at $(1, 2)$. Algebraically, we do the following.

Solve for y in Equation 1: $y = 4 - 2x$

Substitute for y in Equation 2: $-x + (4 - 2x) = 1$

Solve for x: $-3x = -3$ $\Rightarrow$ $x = 1$

Backsubstitute $x = 1$: $y = 4 - 2(x) = 4 - 2 = 2$

Solution: $(1, 2)$

3. $x - y = -3$ Equation 1

   $x^2 - y = -1$ Equation 2

Graphically, the line $y = x + 3$ intersects the parabola $y = x^2 + 1$ in two points, $(-1, 2)$ and $(2, 5)$. Algebraically, we do the following.

Solve for y in Equation 1: $y = x + 3$

Substitute for y in Equation 2: $x^2 - (x + 3) = -1$

Solve for x: $x^2 - x - 3 = -1$ $\Rightarrow$ $(x - 2)(x + 1) = 0$ $\Rightarrow$ $x = 2, -1$

Backsubstitute $x = 2$: $y = x + 3 = 2 + 3 = 5$

Backsubstitute $x = -1$: $y = x + 3 = -1 + 3 = 2$

Solutions: $(-1, 2)$, $(2, 5)$

5. $x + 3y = 15$ Equation 1

$x^2 + y^2 = 25$ Equation 2

Graphically, the line $y = \frac{1}{3}(-x + 15)$ intersects the circle $x^2 + y^2 = 25$ ($y_1 = \sqrt{25 - x^2}$, $y_2 = -\sqrt{25 - x^2}$) in two points (0, 5) and (3, 4). Algebraically, we do the following.
Solve for x in Equation 1: $x = -3y + 15$
Substitute for x in Equation 2: $(-3y + 15)^2 + y^2 = 25$
Solve for y: $10y^2 - 90y + 200 = 0$ $\Rightarrow$ $y^2 - 9y + 20 = 0$ $\Rightarrow$ $y = 5, 4$
Backsubstitute $y = 5$: $x = -3y + 15 = -3(5) + 15 = 0$
Backsubstitute $y = 4$: $x = -3y + 15 = -3(4) + 15 = 3$
Solutions: (0, 5), (3, 4)

7. $x^2 - y = 0$ Equation 1

$x^2 - 4x + y = 0$ Equation 2

Graphically, the parabolas $y = x^2$ and $y = -x^2 + 4x$ intersect in two points (0, 0) and (2, 4). Algebraically, we do the following.
Solve for y in Equation 1: $y = x^2$
Substitute for y in Equation 2: $x^2 - 4x + x^2 = 0$
Solve for x : $2x^2 - 4x = 0$ $\Rightarrow$ $2x(x - 2) = 0$ $\Rightarrow$ $x = 0, 2$
Backsubstitute $x = 0$: $y = x^2 = 0$
Backsubstitute $x = 2$: $y = x^2 = 4$
Solutions: (0, 0), (2, 4)

9. $x - 3y = -4$ Equation 1

$x^2 - y^3 = 0$ Equation 2

Graphically, the line $y = \frac{1}{3}(x + 4)$ intersects the curve $y = x^{2/3}$ in two points $(-1, 1)$ and (8, 4). Algebraically, we do the following.
Solve for x in Equation 1: $x = 3y - 4$
Substitute for x in Equation 2: $(3y - 4)^2 - y^3 = 0$
Solve for y: $-y^3 + 9y^2 - 24y + 16 = 0$ $\Rightarrow$ $(y - 1)(y - 4)^2 = 0$ $\Rightarrow$ $y = 1, 4$
Backsubstitute $y = 1$: $x = 3y - 4 = 3 - 4 = -1$
Backsubstitute $y = 4$: $x = 3y - 4 = 12 - 4 = 8$
Solutions: $(-1, 1)$, (8, 4)

11. $x - y = 0$ Equation 1

$5x - 3y = 10$ Equation 2

Solve for x in Equation 1: $y = x$
Substitute for y in Equation 2: $5x - 3x = 10$
Solve for x: $2x = 10$ $\Rightarrow$ $x = 5$
Backsubstitute in Equation 1: $y = x = 5$
Solution: $(5, 5)$

13. $2x - y + 2 = 0$ Equation 1

$4x + y - 5 = 0$ Equation 2

Solve for y in Equation 1: $y = 2x + 2$
Substitute for y in Equation 2 and solve for x: $4x + (2x + 2) - 5 = 0$ $\Rightarrow$ $x = \frac{1}{2}$
Backsubstitute $x = \frac{1}{2}$: $y = 2x + 2 = 2\left(\frac{1}{2}\right) + 2 = 3$
Solution: $\left(\frac{1}{2}, 3\right)$

15. $30x - 40y - 33 = 0$ Equation 1

$10x + 20y - 21 = 0$ Equation 2

Solve for x in Equation 2: $x = -2y + 2.1$
Substitute for x in Equation 1: $30(-2y + 2.1) - 40y - 33 = 0$
Solve for y: $-60y + 63 - 40y - 33 = 0$ $\Rightarrow$ $-100y + 30 = 0$ $\Rightarrow$ $y = 0.3$
Backsubstitute $y = 0.3$: $x = -2y + 2.1 = -2(0.3) + 2.1 = 1.5$
Solution: $(1.5,\ 0.3)$

17. $\frac{1}{5}x + \frac{1}{2}y = 8$ Equation 1

$x + y = 20$ Equation 2

Solve for x in Equation 2: $x = 20 - y$
Substitute for x in Equation 1: $\frac{1}{5}(20 - y) + \frac{1}{2}y = 8$
Solve for y: $4 - \frac{1}{5}y + \frac{1}{2}y = 8$ $\Rightarrow$ $\frac{3}{10}y = 4$ $\Rightarrow$ $y = \frac{40}{3}$
Backsubstitute $y = \frac{40}{3}$: $x = 20 - y = 20 - \frac{40}{3} = \frac{20}{3}$
Solution: $\left(\frac{20}{3}, \frac{40}{3}\right)$

19. $x - y = 0$ Equation 1

     $2x + y = 0$ Equation 2

Solve for y in Equation 1: $y = x$

Substitute for y in Equation 2:

     $2x + x = 0$

Solve for x: $3x = 0 \quad \Rightarrow \quad x = 0$

Backsubstitute $x = 0$: $y = x = 0$

Solution: $(0, 0)$

21. $y = 2x$ Equation 1

     $y = x^2 + 1$ Equation 2

Substitute for y in Equation 2:

     $2x = x^2 + 1$

Solve for x:

     $x^2 - 2x + 1 = (x - 1)^2 = 0 \quad \Rightarrow \quad x = 1$

Backsubstitute $x = 1$: $y = 2x = 2(1) = 2$

Solution: $(1, 2)$

23. $3x - 7y + 6 = 0$ Equation 1

     $x^2 - y^2 = 4$ Equation 2

Solve for y in Equation 1: $y = \dfrac{3x + 6}{7}$

Solve for x in Equation 2: $x^2 - \left(\dfrac{3x + 6}{7}\right)^2 = 4$

Solve for x: $x^2 - \dfrac{9x^2}{49} - \dfrac{36x}{49} - \dfrac{36}{49} - 4 = 0 \Rightarrow 10x^2 - 9x - 58 = 0$

$$\Rightarrow x = \frac{9 \pm \sqrt{81 + 40(58)}}{20} \Rightarrow x = \frac{29}{10}, -2$$

Backsubstitute $x = \dfrac{29}{10}$: $y = \dfrac{3x + 6}{7} = \dfrac{3(29/10) + 6}{7} = \dfrac{21}{10}$

Backsubstitute $x = -2$: $y = \dfrac{3x + 6}{7} = 0$

Solutions: $\left(\dfrac{29}{10}, \dfrac{21}{10}\right)$, $(-2, 0)$

25. $y - e^{-x} = 1 \Rightarrow y = e^{-x} + 1$

     $y - \ln x = 3 \Rightarrow y = \ln x + 3$

Graphing the two functions, you can use the zoom and trace features to obtain $(0.28, 1.75)$ as the only solution.

27. $y = x^4 - 2x^2 + 1$ Equation 1

$y = 1 - x^2$ Equation 2

Substitute for y in Equation 1: $1 - x^2 = x^4 - 2x^2 + 1$

Solve for x: $x^4 - x^2 = 0$ $\Rightarrow$ $x^2(x^2 - 1) = 0$ $\Rightarrow$ $x = 0, \pm 1$

Backsubstitute $x = 0$: $1 - x^2 = 1$

Backsubstitute $x = 1$: $1 - x^2 = 1 - 1^2 = 0$

Backsubstitute $x = -1$: $1 - x^2 = 1 - (-1)^2 = 0$

Solutions: $(0, 1), (\pm 1, 0)$

29. $xy - 1 = 0$ Equation 1

$2x - 4y + 7 = 0$ Equation 2

Solve for y in Equation 1: $y = \dfrac{1}{x}$

Substitute for y in Equation 2: $2x - 4\left(\dfrac{1}{x}\right) + 7 = 0$

Solve for x: $2x^2 - 4 + 7x = 0$ $\Rightarrow$ $(2x - 1)(x + 4) = 0$ $\Rightarrow$ $x = \dfrac{1}{2}, -4$

Backsubstitute $x = \dfrac{1}{2}$: $y = \dfrac{1}{x} = \dfrac{1}{1/2} = 2$

Backsubsitute $x = -4$: $y = \dfrac{1}{x} = \dfrac{1}{-4} = -\dfrac{1}{4}$

Solutions: $\left(\dfrac{1}{2}, 2\right), \left(-4, -\dfrac{1}{4}\right)$

31. $x + y = 4$

$x^2 + y^2 - 4x = 0 \Rightarrow (x - 2)^2 + y^2 = 4$

$y_1 = \sqrt{4x - x^2}$

$y_2 = -\sqrt{4x - x^2}$

Solution: $(2, 2), (4, 0)$

33. $2x - y + 3 = 0 \Rightarrow y = 2x + 3$

$x^2 + y^2 - 4x = 0 \Rightarrow (x - 2)^2 + y^2 = 4$

$y_1 = \sqrt{4x - x^2}$

$y_2 = -\sqrt{4x - x^2}$

No points of intersection

35. $x^2 + y^2 = 25, \quad (y = \pm\sqrt{25 - x^2})$

$(x - 8)^2 + y^2 = 41, \quad (y = \pm\sqrt{41 - (x - 8)^2})$

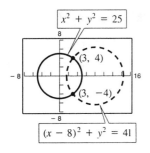

Solutions: $(3, -4), (3, 4)$

37. $y = e^x$

$x - y + 1 = 0 \quad \Rightarrow \quad y = x + 1$

Solution: $(0, 1)$

39. $y = \sqrt{x}$

$y = x$

Solutions: $(0, 0), (1, 1)$

41. $x^2 + y^2 = 169, \quad (y = \pm\sqrt{169 - x^2})$

$x^2 - 8y = 104, \quad (y = \tfrac{1}{8}(x^2 - 104))$

Solutions: $(0, -13), (\pm 12, 5)$

43. $C = 8650x + 250,000$, $R = 9950x$

$\qquad R = C$

$\qquad 9950x = 8650x + 250,000$

$\qquad 1300x = 250,000$

$\qquad\qquad x \approx 192.3 \text{ units}$

In order for the revenue to break even with the cost, 193 units must be sold.

45. $C = 2.65x + 350,000$, $R = 4.15x$

$\qquad R = C$

$\qquad 4.15x = 2.65x + 350,000$

$\qquad 1.5x = 350,000$

$\qquad\qquad x \approx 233,333.3$

In order for the revenue to break even with the cost, 233,334 units must be sold.

47. $C = 3.45x + 16,000$, $R = 5.95x$

$\qquad R = C$

$\qquad 5.95x = 3.45x + 16,000$

$\qquad 2.5x = 16,000$

$\qquad\qquad x = 6400 \text{ units}$

49. $x + y = 25,000 \quad \Rightarrow \quad y = 25,000 - x$

$\qquad 0.08x + 0.085y = 2060$

$\qquad 0.08x + 0.085(25,000 - x) = 2060$

$\qquad\qquad -0.005x + 2125 = 2060$

$\qquad\qquad 0.005x = 65$

$\qquad\qquad x = \$13,000 \text{ at } 8\%$

$\qquad\qquad y = 25,000 - 13,000$

$\qquad\qquad = \$12,000 \text{ at } 8.5\%$

51. $0.06x = 0.03x + 250$

$\qquad 0.03x = 250$

$\qquad\qquad x \approx \$8,333.33$

To make the straight commission offer better, you would have to sell more than $8,333.33 per week.

53. $V = (D-4)^2, \quad 5 \le D \le 40$

$V = 0.79D^2 - 2D - 4, \quad 5 \le D \le 40$

(a)

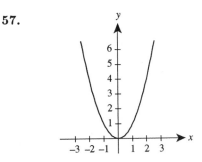

(b) The two graphs intersect at $D = 24.72$. Algebraically:

$$(D-4)^2 = 0.79D^2 - 2D - 4$$

$$D^2 - 8D + 16 = 0.79D^2 - 2D - 4$$

$$0.21D^2 - 6D + 20 = 0$$

$$D \approx 24.72, \; 3.9$$

Since $5 \le D \le 40$, the scales agree when $D \approx 24.72$ inches.

(c) V is larger using the Scribner Log Rule when $5 \le D \le 24.7$. V is larger using the Doyle Log Rule when $24.7 \le D \le 40$. Therefore, for large diameters, you would use the Doyle Log Rule.

55. $P = 2l + 2w = 40 \Rightarrow w = 20 - l$

$A = lw = l(20 - l) = 96$

$-l^2 + 20l - 96 = 0$

$l^2 - 20l + 96 = 0$

$(l - 8)(l - 12) = 0$

$l = 8 \quad \text{or} \quad l = 12$

$w = 12 \qquad w = 8$

The dimensions are 12 miles by 8 miles.

57.

(a) The line $y = 4$ intersects the graph of $y = x^2$ at two points, $(2, 4)$ and $(-2, 4)$.

(b) The line $x = 1$ intersects the graph of $y = x^2$ at one point, $(1, 1)$.

(c) The line $y = -1$ does not intersect the graph of $y = x^2$.

Section 9.3   Systems of Linear Equations in Two Variables

■ You should be able to solve a linear system by the method of elimination.

■ You should know that for a system of two linear equations, one of the following is true.
(a) There are infinitely many solutions; the lines are identical.
(b) There is no solution; the lines are parallel.
(c) There is one solution; the lines intersect at one point.

1. $2x + y = 4$

$\underline{\quad x - y = 2 \quad}$

$3x \qquad = 6$

$x = 2$

$y = 0$

Solution: $(2, 0)$

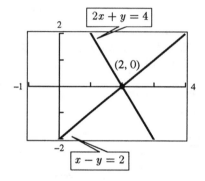

3. $\begin{aligned} x - y &= 0 \Rightarrow -2x + 2y = 0 \\ 3x - 2y &= -1 \Rightarrow \underline{\quad 3x - 2y = -1} \\ & \qquad\qquad\qquad x = -1 \\ & \qquad\qquad\qquad y = -1 \end{aligned}$

Solution: $(-1, -1)$

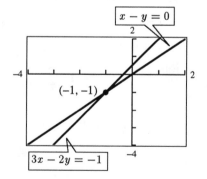

5.
$$x - y = 1 \Rightarrow 2x - 2y = 2$$
$$-2x + 2y = 5 \Rightarrow -2x + 2y = 5$$
$$\overline{\qquad\qquad\qquad 0 = 7}$$

Inconsistent; no solution

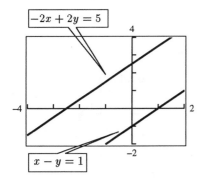

7.
$$3x - 2y = 6 \Rightarrow 6x - 4y = 12$$
$$-6x + 4y = -12 \Rightarrow -6x + 4y = -12$$
$$\overline{\qquad\qquad\qquad\qquad 0 = 0}$$

Solution: All points (x, y) lying on the line $3x - 2y = 6$, or any points of the form $(2a, \ 3a - 3)$.

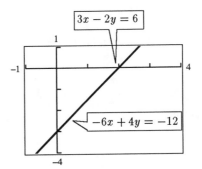

9.
$$9x - 3y = -1 \Rightarrow 18x - 6y = -2$$
$$3x + 6y = -5 \Rightarrow 3x + 6y = -5$$
$$\overline{\qquad\qquad\qquad 21x = -7}$$
$$x = -\tfrac{1}{3}$$
$$y = -\tfrac{2}{3}$$

Solution: $\left(-\tfrac{1}{3}, \ -\tfrac{2}{3}\right)$

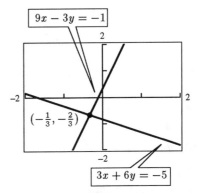

11.
$$x + 2y = 4$$
$$x - 2y = 1$$
$$\overline{2x = 5}$$
$$x = \tfrac{5}{2}$$
$$y = \tfrac{3}{4}$$

Solution: $\left(\tfrac{5}{2}, \ \tfrac{3}{4}\right)$

13.
$$2x + 3y = 18 \Rightarrow 2x + 3y = 18$$
$$5x - y = 11 \Rightarrow 15x - 3y = 33$$
$$\overline{\qquad\qquad\qquad 17x = 51}$$
$$x = 3$$
$$y = 4$$

Solution: $(3, 4)$

15. $\begin{aligned} 3x + 2y &= 10 \Rightarrow -6x - 4y = -20 \\ 2x + 5y &= 3 \Rightarrow \underline{6x + 15y = 9} \\ 11y &= -11 \\ y &= -1 \\ x &= 4 \end{aligned}$

Solution: $(4, -1)$

17. $\begin{aligned} 2u + v &= 120 \Rightarrow -4u - 2v = -240 \\ u + 2v &= 120 \Rightarrow \underline{u + 2v = 120} \\ -3u &= -120 \\ u &= 40 \\ v &= 40 \end{aligned}$

Solution: $(40, 40)$

19. $\begin{aligned} 6r - 5s &= 3 \Rightarrow 12r - 10s = 6 \\ 10s - 12r &= 5 \Rightarrow \underline{-12r + 10s = 5} \\ 0 &= 11 \end{aligned}$

Inconsistent; no solution

21. $\begin{aligned} \frac{x}{4} + \frac{y}{6} &= 1 \Rightarrow 6x + 4y = 24 \\ x - y &= 3 \Rightarrow \underline{4x - 4y = 12} \\ 10x &= 36 \\ x &= \tfrac{18}{5} \\ y &= \tfrac{3}{5} \end{aligned}$

Solution: $\left(\tfrac{18}{5}, \tfrac{3}{5}\right)$

23. $\begin{aligned} \frac{x+3}{4} + \frac{y-1}{3} &= 1 \Rightarrow 3(x+3) + 4(y-1) = 12 \Rightarrow 3x + 4y = 7 \\ 2x - y &= 12 \Rightarrow \underline{8x - 4y = 48} \\ & 11x = 55 \\ & x = 5 \\ & y = -2 \end{aligned}$

Solution: $(5, -2)$

25. $\begin{aligned} 2.5x - 3y &= 1.5 \Rightarrow 25x - 30y = 15 \Rightarrow 5x - 6y = 3 \\ 10x - 12y &= 6 \Rightarrow 5x - 6y = 3 \Rightarrow \underline{-5x + 6y = -3} \\ & 0 = 0 \end{aligned}$

Solution: All points (x, y) lying on the line $5x - 6y = 3$, or any points of the form $\left(a, \tfrac{5}{6}a - \tfrac{1}{2}\right)$.

27. $0.05x - 0.03y = 0.21 \Rightarrow 5x - 3y = 21 \Rightarrow 10x - 6y = 42$

 $0.07x + 0.02y = 0.16 \Rightarrow 7x + 2y = 16 \Rightarrow \underline{21x + 6y = 48}$

$$31x = 90$$

$$x = \tfrac{90}{31}$$

$$y = -\tfrac{67}{31}$$

Solution: $\left(\tfrac{90}{31}, \ -\tfrac{67}{31}\right)$

29. $4b + 3m = 3 \Rightarrow 44b + 33m = 33$

 $3b + 11m = 13 \Rightarrow \underline{-9b - 33m = -39}$

$$35b = -6$$

$$b = -\tfrac{6}{35}$$

$$m = \tfrac{43}{35}$$

Solution: $\left(-\tfrac{6}{35}, \ \tfrac{43}{35}\right)$

31. $200y - x = 200 \Rightarrow -200y + x = -200$

 $199y - x = -198 \Rightarrow \underline{199y - x = -198}$

$$-y = -398$$

$$y = 398$$

$$x = 199y + 198 = 79{,}400$$

Solution: $(79{,}400, \quad 398)$

Since $x = 79{,}400$ is so large, it is necessary to change the scale on the axis to see the point of intersection of the lines. Note that the slopes of the lines are nearly equal.

33. $3.6(g - w) = 1800 \Rightarrow g - w = 500$

 $3(g + w) = 1800 \Rightarrow \underline{g + w = 600}$

$$2g = 1100$$

$$g = 550$$

$$w = 50$$

Solution: Ground speed is 550 mph and wind speed is 50 mph.

35. $x + y = 10 \Rightarrow -2x - 2y = -20$

 $0.2x + 0.5y = 0.3(10) \Rightarrow \underline{2x + 5y = 30}$

$$3y = 10$$

$$y = \tfrac{10}{3}$$

$$x = \tfrac{20}{3}$$

Solution: $\tfrac{20}{3}$ gallons of 20% solution, $\tfrac{10}{3}$ gallons of 50% solution

37.

$$x + y = 12{,}000 \Rightarrow -120x - 120y = -1{,}440{,}000$$

$$0.105x + 0.12y = 1380 \Rightarrow \underline{105x + 120y = 1{,}380{,}000}$$

$$-15x = -60{,}000$$

$$x = 4000$$

$$y = 8000$$

Solution: $4000 is invested in 10.5% fund and $8000 is invested in 12% fund.

39.

$$x + y = 500 \Rightarrow -40x - 40y = -20{,}000$$

$$7.50x + 4.00y = 3312.50 \Rightarrow \underline{75x + 40y = 33{,}125}$$

$$35x = 13{,}125$$

$$x = 375$$

$$y = 125$$

Solution: 375 adult tickets and 125 child tickets sold

41. Supply = Demand

$$0.125x = 50 - 0.5x$$

$$0.625x = 50$$

$$x = 80$$

$$p = 10$$

Equilibrium point: $(80, 10)$

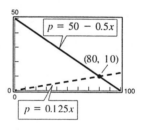

43. Supply = Demand

$$100 + x = 300 - x$$

$$2x = 200$$

$$x = 100$$

$$p = 200$$

Equilibrium point: $(100, 200)$

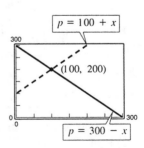

45.

$$\text{Supply} = \text{Demand}$$

$$80 + 0.00001x = 140 - 0.00002x$$

$$0.00003x = 60$$

$$x = 2{,}000{,}000$$

$$p = 100$$

Equilibrium point: $(2{,}000{,}000, \quad 100)$

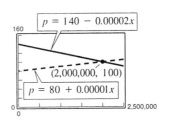

47. $x + y = 300 \Rightarrow -x - y = -300$

$ x = 3y \Rightarrow \quad x - 3y = \quad 0$

$$\overline{ -4y = -300}$$

$$y = \quad 75$$

$$x = \quad 225$$

Solution: One driver drives 75 miles and the other driver drives 225 miles.

49. $5b + 10a = 20.2 \Rightarrow -10b - 20a = -40.4$

$10b + 30a = 50.1 \Rightarrow \quad 10b + 30a = \quad 50.1$

$$\overline{ 10a = \quad 9.7}$$

$$a = \quad 0.97$$

$$b = \quad 2.10$$

$$y = ax + b$$

$$y = 0.97x + 2.10$$

51. $7b + 21a = \quad 35.1 \Rightarrow -21b - 63a = -105.3$

$21b + 91a = 114.2 \Rightarrow \quad 21b + 91a = \quad 114.2$

$$\overline{ 28a = \quad 8.9}$$

$$a = \quad \frac{8.9}{28} \approx 0.318$$

$$b = \quad \frac{1137}{280} \approx 4.061$$

$$y = ax + b$$

$$y = 0.318x + 4.061$$

53. $(-2, 0)$, $(0, 1)$, $(2, 3)$

$$n = 3, \quad \sum_{i=1}^{3} x_i = 0, \quad \sum_{i=1}^{3} y_i = 4,$$

$$\sum_{i=1}^{3} x_i^2 = 8, \quad \sum_{i=1}^{3} x_i y_i = 6$$

$$3b + 0 = 4$$
$$3b = 4$$
$$b = \tfrac{4}{3}$$
$$0 + 8a = 6$$
$$8a = 6$$
$$a = \tfrac{6}{8}$$
$$a = \tfrac{3}{4}$$
$$y = ax + b$$
$$y = \tfrac{3}{4}x + \tfrac{4}{3}$$

55. $(0, 4)$, $(1, 3)$, $(1, 1)$, $(2, 0)$

$$n = 4, \quad \sum_{i=1}^{4} x_i = 4, \quad \sum_{i=1}^{4} y_i = 8,$$

$$\sum_{i=1}^{4} x_i^2 = 6, \quad \sum_{i=1}^{4} x_i y_i = 4$$

$$4b + 4a = 8 \Rightarrow \quad 4b + 4a = \quad 8$$
$$4b + 6a = 4 \Rightarrow -4b - 6a = -4$$
$$\overline{}$$
$$-2a = \quad 4$$
$$a = -2$$
$$b = \quad 4$$
$$y = ax + b$$
$$y = -2x + 4$$

57. $(1.00, 450)$, $(1.25, 375)$, $(1.50, 330)$

$$n = 3, \quad \sum_{i=1}^{3} x_i = 3.75, \quad \sum_{i=1}^{3} y_i = 1155, \quad \sum_{i=1}^{3} x_i^2 = 4.8125, \quad \sum_{i=1}^{3} x_i y_i = 1413.75$$

$$3b + \quad 3.75a = 1155 \quad \Rightarrow \quad 11.25b + 14.0625a = \quad 4331.25$$
$$3.75b + 4.8125a = 1413.75 \Rightarrow -11.25b - 14.4375a = -4241.25$$
$$\overline{}$$
$$-0.375a = \quad 90$$
$$a = \quad -240$$
$$b = \quad 685$$

$$y = ax + b$$
$$y = -240x + 685$$

When $x = \$1.40$, $y = -240(1.40) + 685 = 349$ units.

59. Since $x = 3$ and $y = \tfrac{5}{2}$, one possible system of linear equations is

$$x + 2y = \quad 8$$
$$x + 4y = 13.$$

Section 9.4 Systems of Linear Equations in More Than Two Variables

- ■ You should know the operations that lead to equivalent systems of equations.
  - (a) Interchange any two equations.
  - (b) Multiply all terms of an equation by a nonzero constant.
  - (c) Replace an equation by the sum of itself and a constant multiple of any other equation in the system.

- ■ You should be able to use the method of Gaussian elimination.

- ■ A linear system can have:
  - (1) Exactly one solution
  - (2) No solution
  - (3) Infinitely many solutions.

- ■ You should be able to graphically interpret a system of linear equations in three variables.

1.
$$\begin{aligned} x + y + z &= 6 \\ 2x - y + z &= 3 \\ 3x \quad - z &= 0 \end{aligned}$$

$$\begin{aligned} x + y + z &= 6 \\ -3y - z &= -9 \\ -3y - 4z &= -18 \end{aligned}$$

$$\begin{aligned} x + y + z &= 6 \\ - 3y - z &= -9 \\ - 3z &= -9 \end{aligned}$$

$-3z = -9 \implies z = 3$

$-3y - 3 = -9 \implies y = 2$

$x + 2 + 3 = 6 \implies x = 1$

Solution: $(1, 2, 3)$

3.
$$\begin{aligned} x + y + z &= -3 \\ 4x + y - 3z &= 11 \\ 2x - 3y + 2z &= 9 \end{aligned}$$

$$\begin{aligned} x + y + z &= -3 \\ -3y - 7z &= 23 \\ -5y &= 15 \end{aligned}$$

$-5y = 15 \implies y = -3$

$-3(-3) - 7z = 23 \implies z = -2$

$x - 3 - 2 = -3 \implies x = 2$

Solution: $(2, -3, -2)$

5. $3x + 3y \qquad = \quad 9$

$\quad 2x \qquad - \quad 3z = \quad 10$

$\qquad 6y + \quad 4z = -12$

$\quad\; x + \quad y \qquad = \quad 3$

$\quad 2x \qquad - \quad 3z = \quad 10$

$\qquad 6y + \quad 4z = -12$

$\quad\; x + \quad y \qquad = \quad 3$

$\quad -2y - \quad 3z = \quad 4$

$\qquad 6y + \quad 4z = -12$

$\quad\; x + \quad y \qquad = \quad 3$

$\quad -2y - \quad 3z = \quad 4$

$\qquad\qquad -5z = \quad 0$

$-5z = 0 \quad \Rightarrow \quad z = 0$

$-2y - 3(0) = 4 \quad \Rightarrow \quad y = -2$

$x - 2 = 3 \quad \Rightarrow \quad x = 5$

Solution: $(5, -2, 0)$

7. $x + \quad y - \quad 2z = \quad 3$

$3x - \quad 2y + \quad 4z = \quad 1$

$2x - \quad 3y + \quad 6z = \quad 8$

$x + \quad y - \quad 2z = \quad 3$

$\quad -5y + 10z = -8$

$\quad -5y + 10z = \quad 2$

$x + \quad y - \quad 2z = \quad 3$

$\quad -5y + 10z = -8$

$\qquad\qquad 0 = \quad 10$

Inconsistent; no solution

9. $\begin{aligned} 3x + 3y + 5z &= 1 \\ 3x + 5y + 9z &= 0 \\ 5x + 9y + 17z &= 0 \end{aligned}$

$\begin{aligned} 6x + 6y + 10z &= 2 \\ 3x + 5y + 9z &= 0 \\ 5x + 9y + 17z &= 0 \end{aligned}$

$\begin{aligned} x - 3y - 7z &= 2 \\ 3x + 5y + 9z &= 0 \\ 5x + 9y + 17z &= 0 \end{aligned}$

$\begin{aligned} x - 3y - 7z &= 2 \\ 14y + 30z &= -6 \\ 24y + 52z &= -10 \end{aligned}$

$\begin{aligned} x - 3y - 7z &= 2 \\ 84y + 180z &= -36 \\ 84y + 182z &= -35 \end{aligned}$

$\begin{aligned} x - 3y - 7z &= 2 \\ 84y + 180z &= -36 \\ 2z &= 1 \end{aligned}$

$\begin{aligned} 2z = 1 &\Rightarrow z = \tfrac{1}{2} \\ 84y + 180\left(\tfrac{1}{2}\right) = -36 &\Rightarrow y = -\tfrac{3}{2} \\ x - 3\left(-\tfrac{3}{2}\right) - 7\left(\tfrac{1}{2}\right) = 2 &\Rightarrow x = 1 \end{aligned}$

Solution: $\left(1, -\tfrac{3}{2}, \tfrac{1}{2}\right)$

11. $\begin{aligned} x + 2y - 7z &= -4 \\ 2x + y + z &= 13 \\ 3x + 9y - 36z &= -33 \end{aligned}$

$\begin{aligned} x + 2y - 7z &= -4 \\ -3y + 15z &= 21 \\ 3y - 15z &= -21 \end{aligned}$

$\begin{aligned} x + 2y - 7z &= -4 \\ -3y + 15z &= 21 \end{aligned}$

$\begin{aligned} x + 2y - 7z &= -4 \\ y - 5z &= -7 \end{aligned}$

$\begin{aligned} x \qquad + 3z &= 10 \\ y - 5z &= -7 \end{aligned}$

$z = a$

$y = 5a - 7$

$x = -3a + 10$

Solution: $(-3a + 10, 5a - 7, a)$

13.
$$x \quad\quad + 4z = \quad 13$$
$$4x - 2y + \quad z = \quad 7$$
$$2x - 2y - 7z = -19$$

$$x \quad\quad + 4z = \quad 13$$
$$-2y - 15z = -45$$
$$-2y - 15z = -45$$

$$x \quad\quad + 4z = \quad 13$$
$$-2y - 15z = -45$$

$$z = a$$
$$y = -\frac{15}{2}a + \frac{45}{2}$$
$$x = -4a + 13$$
Solution: $\left(-4a + 13, \ -\frac{15}{2}a + \frac{45}{2}, \ a\right)$

15.
$$x - 2y + 5z = \quad 2$$
$$3x + 2y - \quad z = -2$$

$$x - 2y + 5z = \quad 2$$
$$8y - 16z = -8$$

$$x - 2y + 5z = \quad 2$$
$$y - 2z = -1$$

$$x \quad\quad + \quad z = \quad 0$$
$$y - 2z = -1$$

$$z = a$$
$$y = 2a - 1$$
$$x = -a$$
Solution: $(-a, \ 2a - 1, \ a)$

17.
$$2x - 3y + z = -2$$
$$-4x + 9y \quad\quad = \quad 7$$

$$2x - 3y + z = -2$$
$$3y + 2z = \quad 3$$

$$2x \quad\quad + 3z = \quad 1$$
$$3y + 2z = \quad 3$$

$$z = a$$
$$y = -\frac{2}{3}a + 1$$
$$x = -\frac{3}{2}a + \frac{1}{2}$$
Solution: $\left(-\frac{3}{2}a + \frac{1}{2}, \ -\frac{2}{3}a + 1, \ a\right)$

19.

$$\begin{aligned}
x \qquad\qquad + 3w &= 4 \\
2y - z - w &= 0 \\
3y \qquad - 2w &= 1 \\
2x - y + 4z \qquad &= 5
\end{aligned}$$

$$\begin{aligned}
x \qquad\qquad + 3w &= 4 \\
2y - z - w &= 0 \\
3y \qquad - 2w &= 1 \\
-y + 4z - 6w &= -3
\end{aligned}$$

$$\begin{aligned}
x \qquad\qquad + 3w &= 4 \\
y - 4z + 6w &= 3 \\
2y - z - w &= 0 \\
3y \qquad - 2w &= 1
\end{aligned}$$

$$\begin{aligned}
x \qquad\qquad + 3w &= 4 \\
y - 4z + 6w &= 3 \\
7z - 13w &= -6 \\
12z - 20w &= -8
\end{aligned}$$

$$\begin{aligned}
x \qquad\qquad + 3w &= 4 \\
y - 4z + 6w &= 3 \\
z - 3w &= -2 \\
12z - 20w &= -8
\end{aligned}$$

$$\begin{aligned}
x \qquad\qquad + 3w &= 4 \\
y - 4z + 6w &= 3 \\
z - 3w &= -2 \\
16w &= 16
\end{aligned}$$

$$\begin{aligned}
16w = 16 &\Rightarrow w = 1 \\
z - 3(1) = -2 &\Rightarrow z = 1 \\
y - 4(1) + 6(1) = 3 &\Rightarrow y = 1 \\
x + 3(1) = 4 &\Rightarrow x = 1
\end{aligned}$$

Solution: $(1, 1, 1, 1)$

21.

$$\begin{aligned}
x + \qquad 4z &= 1 \\
x + y + 10z &= 10 \\
2x - y + 2z &= -5
\end{aligned}$$

$$\begin{aligned}
x + \qquad 4z &= 1 \\
y + 6z &= 9 \\
-y - 6z &= -7
\end{aligned}$$

$$\begin{aligned}
x + \qquad 4z &= 1 \\
y + 6z &= 9 \\
0 &= 2
\end{aligned}$$

Inconsistent; no solution

23.
$$5x + 4y + 22z = 0$$
$$4x + 3y + 17z = 0$$
$$4x + 2y + 19z = 0$$

$$x + y + 5z = 0$$
$$4x + 3y + 17z = 0$$
$$4x + 2y + 19z = 0$$

$$x + y + 5z = 0$$
$$-y - 3z = 0$$
$$-2y - z = 0$$

$$x + y + 5z = 0$$
$$y + 3z = 0$$
$$5z = 0$$

$$5z = 0 \quad \Rightarrow \quad z = 0$$
$$y + 3(0) = 0 \quad \Rightarrow \quad y = 0$$
$$x + 0 + 5(0) \quad \Rightarrow \quad x = 0$$
Solution: $(0, 0, 0)$

25.
$$5x + 5y - z = 0$$
$$10x + 5y + 2z = 0$$
$$5x + 15y - 9z = 0$$

$$5x + 5y - z = 0$$
$$-5y + 4z = 0$$
$$10y - 8z = 0$$

$$5x + 3z = 0$$
$$-5y + 4z = 0$$

$$z = a$$
$$y = \tfrac{4}{5}a$$
$$x = -\tfrac{3}{5}a$$
Solution: $\left(-\tfrac{3}{5}a,\ \tfrac{4}{5}a,\ a\right)$

27. $y = ax^2 + bx + c$
Passing through $(0, -4)$, $(1, 1)$, and $(2, 10)$

$$-4 = \qquad\qquad c \qquad \text{Equation 1}$$
$$1 = a + b + c \qquad \text{Equation 2}$$
$$10 = 4a + 2b + c \qquad \text{Equation 3}$$

Solution: $a = 2,\ \ b = 3,\ \ c = -4$
The equation of the parabola is
$y = 2x^2 + 3x - 4$ which can be verified
with a graphing utility.

29. $y = ax^2 + bx + c$
Passing through $(1, 0)$, $(3, 0)$, and $(2, -1)$

$$0 = a + b + c \qquad \text{Equation 1}$$
$$0 = 9a + 3b + c \qquad \text{Equation 2}$$
$$-1 = 4a + 2b + c \qquad \text{Equation 3}$$

Solution: $a = 1,\ \ b = -4,\ \ c = 3$
The equation of the parabola is
$y = x^2 - 4x + 3$, which can be verified with
a graphing utility.

31. $x^2 + y^2 + Dx + Ey + F = 0$
Passing through $(0, 0)$, $(2, -2)$, and $(4, 0)$

$$F = 0 \qquad \text{Equation 1}$$
$$8 + 2D - 2E + F = 0 \qquad \text{Equation 2}$$
$$16 + 4D \qquad + F = 0 \qquad \text{Equation 3}$$

Solution: $D = -4$, $E = 0$, $F = 0$
The equation is $x^2 + y^2 - 4x = 0$.

33. $x^2 + y^2 + Dx + Ey + F = 0$
Passing through $(3, -1)$, $(-2, 4)$, and $(6, 8)$

$$10 + 3D - E + F = 0 \qquad \text{Equation 1}$$
$$20 - 2D + 4E + F = 0 \qquad \text{Equation 2}$$
$$100 + 6D + 8E + F = 0 \qquad \text{Equation 3}$$

Solution: $D = -6$, $E = -8$, $F = 0$
The equation is $x^2 + y^2 - 6x - 8y = 0$.

35. $s = \frac{1}{2}at^2 + v_0 t + s_0$
$(t, s) = (1, 128), (2, 80), (3, 0)$

$$128 = \frac{1}{2}a + v_0 + s_0 \qquad \text{Equation 1}$$
$$80 = 2a + 2v_0 + s_0 \qquad \text{Equation 2}$$
$$0 = \frac{9}{2}a + 3v_0 + s_0 \qquad \text{Equation 3}$$

$$s = \frac{1}{2}(-32)t^2 + 0t + 144$$
$$s = -16t^2 + 144$$

37. $s = \frac{1}{2}at^2 + v_0 t + s_0$
$(t, s) = (1, 452), (3, 260), (4, 116)$

$$452 = \frac{1}{2}a + v_0 + s_0 \qquad \text{Equation 1}$$
$$260 = \frac{9}{2}a + 3v_0 + s_0 \qquad \text{Equation 2}$$
$$116 = 8a + 4v_0 + s_0 \qquad \text{Equation 3}$$

$$s = \frac{1}{2}(-32)t^2 - 32t + 500$$
$$s = -16t^2 - 32t + 500$$

39.
$$x + y + z = 16{,}000$$
$$0.05x + 0.06y + 0.07z = 990$$
$$x = z - 3000$$
$$y = z - 2000$$
$$(z - 3000) + (z - 2000) + z = 16{,}000$$
$$3z = 21{,}000$$
$$z = 7000$$

$x = 4000$, $y = 5000$
Solution: $x = \$4000$ at 5%, $y = \$5000$ at 6%, $z = \$7000$ at 7%

41.
$$x + y + z = 775,000$$
$$0.08x + 0.09y + 0.10z = 67,500$$
$$x = 4z$$

$$y + \quad 5z = 775,000 \Rightarrow -9y - 45z = -6,975,000$$
$$\underline{0.09y + 0.42z = 67,500 \Rightarrow 9y + 42z = 6,750,000}$$
$$-3z = -225,000$$
$$z = 75,000$$

$y = 775,000 - 5z = 400,000, \quad x = 4z = 300,000$

Solution: $x = \$300,000$ at 8%, $\quad y = \$400,000$ at 9%, $\quad z = \$75,000$ at 10%

43.
$$C + M + B + G = 500,000$$
$$0.10C + 0.08M + 0.12B + 0.13G = 0.10(500,000)$$
$$B + G = \tfrac{1}{4}(500,000)$$

This system has infinitely many solutions.

Let $G = s$, then $B = 125,000 - s$, $\quad M = 125,000 + \tfrac{1}{2}s$, and $C = 250,000 - \tfrac{1}{2}s$.

Solution: $250,000 - \tfrac{1}{2}s$ in certificates of deposit, $125,000 + \tfrac{1}{2}s$ in municipal bonds, $125,000 - s$ in blue-chip stocks, and s in growth stocks

45. $\tfrac{1}{5}x + \quad \tfrac{1}{2}z = 12$

$\quad\; \tfrac{2}{5}x + \quad \tfrac{1}{2}z = 16$

$\quad\; \tfrac{2}{5}x + y \quad\quad = 26$

$\quad\; \tfrac{1}{5}x + \quad \tfrac{1}{2}z = 12$

$\quad\; \tfrac{1}{5}x \quad\quad\quad = 4$

$\quad\; \tfrac{2}{5}x + y \quad = 26$

$\quad\quad\quad \tfrac{1}{5}x = 4 \quad \Rightarrow \quad x = 20$

$\quad \tfrac{2}{5}(20) + y = 26 \quad \Rightarrow \quad 18$

$\quad \tfrac{1}{5}(20) + \tfrac{1}{2}z = 12 \quad \Rightarrow \quad z = 16$

Solution: 20 gallons of spray x

$\quad\quad\quad\quad\;$ 18 gallons of spray y

$\quad\quad\quad\quad\;$ 16 gallons of spray z

47. To haul 15 units of A and 16 units of B, some of the possible ways to use the trucks are:

(1) 4 medium trucks

(2) 2 large trucks, 1 medium truck, 2 small trucks.

49.
$$t_1 - 2t_2 \quad\quad = \quad 0$$
$$t_1 \quad\quad - 2a = 128$$
$$t_2 + \quad a = \quad 32$$

$$t_1 - 2t_2 \quad\quad = \quad 0$$
$$2t^2 - 2a = 128$$
$$t_2 + \quad a = \quad 32$$

$$t_1 - 2t_2 \quad\quad = \quad 0$$
$$2t_2 - 2a = 128$$
$$2a = -32$$

$$2a = -32 \quad \Rightarrow \quad a = -16$$
$$2t_2 - 2(-16) = 128 \quad \Rightarrow \quad t_2 = 48$$
$$t_1 - 2(48) = 0 \quad \Rightarrow \quad t_1 = 96$$

Solution: $a = -16$ ft/sec^2
$$t_1 = 96 \text{ lb}$$
$$t_2 = 48 \text{ lb}$$

51.
$$\frac{1}{x^3 - x} = \frac{1}{x(x-1)(x+1)} = \frac{A}{x} + \frac{B}{x-1} + \frac{C}{x+1}$$
$$1 = A(x-1)(x+1) + Bx(x+1) + Cx(x-1)$$
$$1 = Ax^2 - A + Bx^2 + Bx + Cx^2 - Cx$$
$$1 = (A + B + C)x^2 + (B - C)x - A$$

$$A + B + C = 0 \quad\quad \text{Equation 1}$$
$$B - C = 0 \quad\quad \text{Equation 2}$$
$$-A \quad\quad\quad = 1 \quad\quad \text{Equation 3}$$

Solution: $A = -1$, $B = \dfrac{1}{2}$, $C = \dfrac{1}{2}$

$$\frac{1}{x^3 - x} = -\frac{1}{x} + \frac{1}{2(x-1)} + \frac{1}{2(x+1)} = \frac{1}{2}\left(-\frac{2}{x} + \frac{1}{x-1} + \frac{1}{x+1} \right)$$

53. $$\frac{x^2 - 3x - 3}{x(x-2)(x+3)} = \frac{A}{x} + \frac{B}{x-2} + \frac{C}{x+3}$$

$$x^2 - 3x - 3 = A(x-2)(x+3) + B(x)(x+3) + C(x)(x-2)$$

$$x^2 - 3x - 3 = A(x^2 + x - 6) + B(x^2 + 3x) + C(x^2 - 2x)$$

$$x^2 - 3x - 3 = Ax^2 + Ax - 6A + Bx^2 + 3Bx + Cx^2 - 2Cx$$

$$x^2 - 3x - 3 = (A + B + C)x^2 + (A + 3B - 2C)x - 6A$$

$$\begin{array}{llll} A + & B + & C = & 1 & \text{Equation 1}\\ A + & 3B - & 2C = & -3 & \text{Equation 2}\\ -6A & & = & -3 & \text{Equation 3} \end{array}$$

Solution: $A = \dfrac{1}{2}, \quad B = -\dfrac{1}{2}, \quad C = 1$

$$\frac{x^2 - 3x - 3}{x(x-2)(x+3)} = \frac{1}{2x} - \frac{1}{2(x-2)} + \frac{1}{x+3} = \frac{1}{2}\left(\frac{1}{x} - \frac{1}{x-2} + \frac{2}{x+3}\right)$$

55.
$$\begin{array}{llll} 4c + & & 40a = & 19\\ & 40b & = & -12\\ 40c + & & 544a = & 160 \end{array}$$

$$\begin{array}{llll} 4c + & & 40a = & 19\\ & 40b & = & -12\\ & & 144a = & -30 \end{array}$$

$$144a = -30 \quad \Rightarrow \quad a = -\tfrac{5}{24}$$

$$40b = -12 \quad \Rightarrow \quad b = -\tfrac{3}{10}$$

$$4c + 40\left(-\tfrac{5}{24}\right) = 19 \quad \Rightarrow \quad c = \tfrac{41}{6}$$

$$y = ax^2 + bx + c$$

$$y = -\tfrac{5}{24}x^2 - \tfrac{3}{10}x + \tfrac{41}{6}$$

57.

$$4c + 9b + 29a = 20$$
$$9c + 29b + 99a = 70$$
$$29c + 99b + 353a = 254$$

$$1044c + 2349b + 7569a = 5220$$
$$1044c + 3364b + 11{,}484a = 8120$$
$$1044c + 3564b + 12{,}708a = 9144$$

$$1044c + 2349b + 7569a = 5220$$
$$1015b + 3915a = 2900$$
$$1215b + 5139a = 3924$$

$$1044c + 2349b + 7569a = 5220$$
$$7b + 27a = 20$$
$$135b + 571a = 436$$

$$1044c + 2349b + 7569a = 5220$$
$$945b + 3645a = 2700$$
$$945b + 3997a = 3052$$

$$1044c + 2349b + 7569a = 5220$$
$$945b + 3645a = 2700$$
$$352a = 352$$

$$352a = 352 \Rightarrow a = 1$$
$$945b + 3645(1) = 2700 \Rightarrow b = -1$$
$$1044c + 2349(-1) + 7569(1) = 5220 \Rightarrow c = 0$$
$$y = ax^2 + bx + c$$
$$y = x^2 - x$$

59. (a) and (b)

(b) $(20, 25)$, $(30, 55)$, $(40, 105)$, $(50, 188)$, $(60, 300)$

$n = 5$

$$\sum_{i=1}^{5} x_i = 200 \qquad \sum_{i=1}^{5} y_i = 673$$

$$\sum_{i=1}^{5} x_i^2 = 9000 \qquad \sum_{i=1}^{5} x_i y_i = 33{,}750$$

$$\sum_{i=1}^{5} x_i^3 = 440{,}000 \qquad \sum_{i=1}^{5} x_i^2 y_i = 1{,}777{,}500$$

$$\sum_{i=1}^{5} x_i^4 = 22{,}740{,}000$$

$$5c + 200b + 9000a = 673$$
$$200c + 9000b + 440{,}000a = 33{,}750$$
$$9000c + 440{,}000b + 22{,}740{,}000a = 1{,}777{,}500$$

Solving this system, we get $a \approx 0.141$, $b \approx -4.427$, and $c \approx 58.400$.

$$y = ax^2 + bx + c$$
$$y = 0.141x^2 - 4.427x + 58.400$$

61. Since $x = 4$, $y = -1$, and $z = 2$, one possible system of linear equations is

$$2x + 3y + z = 7$$
$$x - 2y + 4z = 14$$
$$x - 2y + 2z = 10.$$

Section 9.5   Matrices and Systems of Linear Equations

■ You should know the definition of a matrix.

■ You should know the three elementary row operations.
  (a) Interchange two rows.
  (b) Multiply a row by a nonzero constant.
  (c) Add a multiple of one row to another row.

■ You should be able to determine if a matrix is in row-echelon or reduced row-echelon form.

■ You should be able to solve a system of linear equations by Gaussian elimination with back substitution.

■ You should be able to solve a system of linear equations by Gauss-Jordan elimination.

1. 3×2 **3.** 5×1 **5.** 2×2

7. Reduced row-echelon form   **9.** Not in row-echelon form

11. $\begin{bmatrix} 1 & 4 & 3 \\ 2 & 10 & 5 \end{bmatrix}$ $\quad -2R_1 + R_2 \rightarrow \begin{bmatrix} 1 & 4 & 3 \\ 0 & 2 & -1 \end{bmatrix}$

13. $\begin{bmatrix} 1 & 1 & 4 & -1 \\ 3 & 8 & 10 & 3 \\ -2 & 1 & 12 & 6 \end{bmatrix}$ $\quad \begin{matrix} -3R_1 + R_2 \rightarrow \\ 2R_1 + R_3 \rightarrow \end{matrix} \begin{bmatrix} 1 & 1 & 4 & -1 \\ 0 & 5 & -2 & 6 \\ 0 & 3 & 20 & 4 \end{bmatrix}$

$$\frac{1}{5}R_2 \rightarrow \begin{bmatrix} 1 & 1 & 4 & -1 \\ 0 & 1 & -\frac{2}{5} & \frac{6}{5} \\ 0 & 3 & 20 & 4 \end{bmatrix}$$

15. $\begin{bmatrix} 1 & 2 & 3 \\ 2 & -1 & -4 \\ 3 & 1 & -1 \end{bmatrix}$

(a) $\begin{bmatrix} 1 & 2 & 3 \\ 0 & -5 & -10 \\ 3 & 1 & -1 \end{bmatrix}$ (b) $\begin{bmatrix} 1 & 2 & 3 \\ 0 & -5 & -10 \\ 0 & -5 & -10 \end{bmatrix}$ (c) $\begin{bmatrix} 1 & 2 & 3 \\ 0 & -5 & -10 \\ 0 & 0 & 0 \end{bmatrix}$

(d) $\begin{bmatrix} 1 & 2 & 3 \\ 0 & 1 & 2 \\ 0 & 0 & 0 \end{bmatrix}$ (e) $\begin{bmatrix} 1 & 0 & -1 \\ 0 & 1 & 2 \\ 0 & 0 & 0 \end{bmatrix}$

17. $\begin{bmatrix} 1 & 1 & 0 & 5 \\ -2 & -1 & 2 & -10 \\ 3 & 6 & 7 & 14 \end{bmatrix} \Rightarrow \begin{bmatrix} 1 & 1 & 0 & 5 \\ 0 & 1 & 2 & 0 \\ 0 & 3 & 7 & -1 \end{bmatrix} \Rightarrow \begin{bmatrix} 1 & 1 & 0 & 5 \\ 0 & 1 & 2 & 0 \\ 0 & 0 & 1 & -1 \end{bmatrix}$

19. $\begin{bmatrix} 1 & -1 & -1 & 1 \\ 5 & -4 & 1 & 8 \\ -6 & 8 & 18 & 0 \end{bmatrix} \Rightarrow \begin{bmatrix} 1 & -1 & -1 & 1 \\ 0 & 1 & 6 & 3 \\ 0 & 2 & 12 & 6 \end{bmatrix} \Rightarrow \begin{bmatrix} 1 & -1 & -1 & 1 \\ 0 & 1 & 6 & 3 \\ 0 & 0 & 0 & 0 \end{bmatrix}$

21. $\begin{bmatrix} 3 & 3 & 3 \\ -1 & 0 & -4 \\ 2 & 4 & -2 \end{bmatrix} \Rightarrow \begin{bmatrix} 1 & 1 & 1 \\ -1 & 0 & -4 \\ 2 & 4 & -2 \end{bmatrix} \Rightarrow \begin{bmatrix} 1 & 1 & 1 \\ 0 & 1 & -3 \\ 0 & 2 & -4 \end{bmatrix} \Rightarrow \begin{bmatrix} 1 & 0 & 4 \\ 0 & 1 & -3 \\ 0 & 0 & 2 \end{bmatrix}$

$\Rightarrow \begin{bmatrix} 1 & 0 & 4 \\ 0 & 1 & -3 \\ 0 & 0 & 1 \end{bmatrix} \Rightarrow \begin{bmatrix} 1 & 0 & 0 \\ 0 & 1 & 0 \\ 0 & 0 & 1 \end{bmatrix}$

23. $\begin{bmatrix} 1 & 2 & 3 & -5 \\ 1 & 2 & 4 & -9 \\ -2 & -4 & -4 & 3 \\ 4 & 8 & 11 & -14 \end{bmatrix} \Rightarrow \begin{bmatrix} 1 & 2 & 3 & -5 \\ 0 & 0 & 1 & -4 \\ 0 & 0 & 2 & -7 \\ 0 & 0 & -1 & 6 \end{bmatrix} \Rightarrow \begin{bmatrix} 1 & 2 & 0 & 7 \\ 0 & 0 & 1 & -4 \\ 0 & 0 & 0 & 1 \\ 0 & 0 & 0 & 2 \end{bmatrix}$

$\Rightarrow \begin{bmatrix} 1 & 2 & 0 & 0 \\ 0 & 0 & 1 & 0 \\ 0 & 0 & 0 & 1 \\ 0 & 0 & 0 & 0 \end{bmatrix}$

25. $4x + 3y = 8$

$x - 2y = 3$

27. $x \qquad + 2z = -10$

$\qquad 3y - \ z = \quad 5$

$\quad 4x + 2y \qquad = \quad 3$

29. $x - 2y = 4$

$y = -3$

$x = 4 + 2y$

$= 4 + 2(-3)$

$= -2$

$(-2, \ -3)$

31. $x - y + 2z = 4$

$y - \ z = 2$

$z = -2$

$y = 2 + z$

$= 2 + (-2)$

$= 0$

$x = 4 + y - 2z$

$= 4 + 0 - 2(-2)$

$= 8$

$(8, \ 0, \ -2)$

33. Row 1: $x = 7$

Row 2: $y = -5$

$(7, \ -5)$

35. Row 1: $x = -4$

Row 2: $y = -8$

Row 3: $z = 2$

$(-4, \ -8, \ 2)$

37. $x + 2y = 7$

$2x + \ y = 8$

$$\begin{bmatrix} 1 & 2 & \vdots & 7 \\ 2 & 1 & \vdots & 8 \end{bmatrix} \Rightarrow \begin{bmatrix} 1 & 2 & \vdots & 7 \\ 0 & -3 & \vdots & -6 \end{bmatrix} \Rightarrow \begin{bmatrix} 1 & 2 & \vdots & 7 \\ 0 & 1 & \vdots & 2 \end{bmatrix}$$

$y = 2$

$x + 2(2) = 7 \quad \Rightarrow \quad x = 3$

Solution: $(3, \ 2)$

39. $-3x + 5y = -22$

$\quad\quad 3x + 4y = \quad 4$

$\quad\quad 4x - 8y = \quad 32$

$$\begin{bmatrix} -3 & 5 & \vdots & -22 \\ 3 & 4 & \vdots & 4 \\ 4 & -8 & \vdots & 32 \end{bmatrix} \Rightarrow \begin{bmatrix} 1 & -3 & \vdots & 10 \\ 3 & 4 & \vdots & 4 \\ 4 & -8 & \vdots & 32 \end{bmatrix} \Rightarrow \begin{bmatrix} 1 & -3 & \vdots & 10 \\ 0 & 13 & \vdots & -26 \\ 0 & 4 & \vdots & -8 \end{bmatrix}$$

$$\Rightarrow \begin{bmatrix} 1 & -3 & \vdots & 10 \\ 0 & 1 & \vdots & -2 \\ 0 & 0 & \vdots & 0 \end{bmatrix}$$

$y = -2$

$x - 3(-2) = 10 \quad \Rightarrow \quad x = 4$

Solution: $(4, -2)$

41. $8x - 4y = 7$

$\quad\quad 5x + 2y = 1$

$$\begin{bmatrix} 8 & -4 & \vdots & 7 \\ 5 & 2 & \vdots & 1 \end{bmatrix} \Rightarrow \begin{bmatrix} 24 & -12 & \vdots & 21 \\ 25 & 10 & \vdots & 5 \end{bmatrix} \Rightarrow \begin{bmatrix} -1 & -22 & \vdots & 16 \\ 25 & 10 & \vdots & 5 \end{bmatrix}$$

$$\Rightarrow \begin{bmatrix} -1 & -22 & \vdots & 16 \\ 0 & -540 & \vdots & 405 \end{bmatrix} \Rightarrow \begin{bmatrix} 1 & 22 & \vdots & -16 \\ 0 & 1 & \vdots & -\frac{3}{4} \end{bmatrix}$$

$y = -\frac{3}{4}$

$x + 22\left(-\frac{3}{4}\right) = -16 \quad \Rightarrow \quad x = \frac{1}{2}$

Solution: $\left(\frac{1}{2}, -\frac{3}{4}\right)$

43. $-x + 2y = 1.5$

$\quad\quad 2x - 4y = \quad 3$

$$\begin{bmatrix} -1 & 2 & \vdots & 1.5 \\ 2 & -4 & \vdots & 3 \end{bmatrix} \Rightarrow \begin{bmatrix} -1 & 2 & \vdots & 1.5 \\ 0 & 0 & \vdots & 6 \end{bmatrix}$$

The system is inconsistent and there is no solution.

45. $x \qquad -\ 3z = -2$

$3x + y \quad -\ 2z = 5$

$2x + 2y + z \quad\ = 4$

$$\begin{bmatrix} 1 & 0 & -3 & \vdots & -2 \\ 3 & 1 & -2 & \vdots & 5 \\ 2 & 2 & 1 & \vdots & 4 \end{bmatrix} \Rightarrow \begin{bmatrix} 1 & 0 & -3 & \vdots & -2 \\ 0 & 1 & 7 & \vdots & 11 \\ 0 & 2 & 7 & \vdots & 8 \end{bmatrix} \Rightarrow \begin{bmatrix} 1 & 0 & -3 & \vdots & -2 \\ 0 & 1 & 7 & \vdots & 11 \\ 0 & 0 & -7 & \vdots & -14 \end{bmatrix}$$

$$\Rightarrow \begin{bmatrix} 1 & 0 & -3 & \vdots & -2 \\ 0 & 1 & 7 & \vdots & 11 \\ 0 & 0 & 1 & \vdots & 2 \end{bmatrix}$$

$z = 2$

$y + 7(2) = 11 \quad \Rightarrow \quad y = -3$

$x - 3(2) = -2 \quad \Rightarrow \quad x = 4$

Solution: $(4,\ -3,\ 2)$

47. $x + y - 5z = 3$

$x \qquad -\ 2z = 1$

$2x - y - \ z = 0$

$$\begin{bmatrix} 1 & 1 & -5 & \vdots & 3 \\ 1 & 0 & -2 & \vdots & 1 \\ 2 & -1 & -1 & \vdots & 0 \end{bmatrix} \Rightarrow \begin{bmatrix} 1 & 1 & -5 & \vdots & 3 \\ 0 & -1 & 3 & \vdots & -2 \\ 0 & -3 & 9 & \vdots & -6 \end{bmatrix} \Rightarrow \begin{bmatrix} 1 & 1 & -5 & \vdots & 3 \\ 0 & -1 & 3 & \vdots & -2 \\ 0 & 0 & 0 & \vdots & 0 \end{bmatrix}$$

$$\Rightarrow \begin{bmatrix} 1 & 0 & -2 & \vdots & 1 \\ 0 & 1 & -3 & \vdots & 2 \\ 0 & 0 & 0 & \vdots & 0 \end{bmatrix}$$

$z = a$

$y = 3a + 2$

$x = 2a + 1$

Solution: $(2a + 1,\ 3a + 2,\ a)$

49. $x + 2y + \ z = \ 8$

$3x + 7y + 6z = 26$

$$\begin{bmatrix} 1 & 2 & 1 & \vdots & 8 \\ 3 & 7 & 6 & \vdots & 26 \end{bmatrix} \Rightarrow \begin{bmatrix} 1 & 2 & 1 & \vdots & 8 \\ 0 & 1 & 3 & \vdots & 2 \end{bmatrix} \Rightarrow \begin{bmatrix} 1 & 0 & -5 & \vdots & 4 \\ 0 & 1 & 3 & \vdots & 2 \end{bmatrix}$$

$z = a$

$y = -3a + 2$

$x = 5a + 4$

Solution: $(5a + 4,\ -3a + 2,\ a)$

51. $3x + 3y + 12z = 6$

   $x + y + 4z = 2$

   $2x + 5y + 20z = 10$

   $-x + 2y + 8z = 4$

$$\begin{bmatrix} 3 & 3 & 12 & \vdots & 6 \\ 1 & 1 & 4 & \vdots & 2 \\ 2 & 5 & 20 & \vdots & 10 \\ -1 & 2 & 8 & \vdots & 4 \end{bmatrix} \Rightarrow \begin{bmatrix} 1 & 1 & 4 & \vdots & 2 \\ 1 & 1 & 4 & \vdots & 2 \\ 2 & 5 & 20 & \vdots & 10 \\ -1 & 2 & 8 & \vdots & 4 \end{bmatrix}$$

$$\Rightarrow \begin{bmatrix} 1 & 1 & 4 & \vdots & 2 \\ 0 & 0 & 0 & \vdots & 0 \\ 0 & 3 & 12 & \vdots & 6 \\ 0 & 3 & 12 & \vdots & 6 \end{bmatrix}$$

$$\Rightarrow \begin{bmatrix} 1 & 1 & 4 & \vdots & 2 \\ 0 & 0 & 0 & \vdots & 0 \\ 0 & 3 & 12 & \vdots & 6 \\ 0 & 0 & 0 & \vdots & 0 \end{bmatrix}$$

$$\Rightarrow \begin{bmatrix} 1 & 1 & 4 & \vdots & 2 \\ 0 & 0 & 0 & \vdots & 0 \\ 0 & 1 & 4 & \vdots & 2 \\ 0 & 0 & 0 & \vdots & 0 \end{bmatrix}$$

$$\Rightarrow \begin{bmatrix} 1 & 0 & 0 & \vdots & 0 \\ 0 & 0 & 0 & \vdots & 0 \\ 0 & 1 & 4 & \vdots & 2 \\ 0 & 0 & 0 & \vdots & 0 \end{bmatrix}$$

$z = a$

$y = -4a + 2$

$x = 0$

Solution: $(0, -4a + 2, a)$

53. $2x + y - z + 2w = -6$

$3x + 4y \quad\ + w = 1$

$x + 5y + 2z + 6w = -3$

$5x + 2y - z - w = 3$

$$\begin{bmatrix} 2 & 1 & -1 & 2 & \vdots & -6 \\ 3 & 4 & 0 & 1 & \vdots & 1 \\ 1 & 5 & 2 & 6 & \vdots & -3 \\ 5 & 2 & -1 & -1 & \vdots & 3 \end{bmatrix} \Rightarrow \begin{bmatrix} 1 & 5 & 2 & 6 & \vdots & -3 \\ 3 & 4 & 0 & 1 & \vdots & 1 \\ 2 & 1 & -1 & 2 & \vdots & -6 \\ 5 & 2 & -1 & -1 & \vdots & 3 \end{bmatrix}$$

$$\Rightarrow \begin{bmatrix} 1 & 5 & 2 & 6 & \vdots & -3 \\ 0 & -11 & -6 & -17 & \vdots & 10 \\ 0 & -9 & -5 & -10 & \vdots & 0 \\ 0 & -23 & -11 & -31 & \vdots & 18 \end{bmatrix}$$

$$\Rightarrow \begin{bmatrix} 1 & 5 & 2 & 6 & \vdots & -3 \\ 0 & -1 & 1 & 3 & \vdots & -2 \\ 0 & -9 & -5 & -10 & \vdots & 0 \\ 0 & -23 & -11 & -31 & \vdots & 18 \end{bmatrix}$$

$$\Rightarrow \begin{bmatrix} 1 & 5 & 2 & 6 & \vdots & -3 \\ 0 & 1 & -1 & -3 & \vdots & 2 \\ 0 & -9 & -5 & -10 & \vdots & 0 \\ 0 & -23 & -11 & -31 & \vdots & 18 \end{bmatrix}$$

$$\Rightarrow \begin{bmatrix} 1 & 5 & 2 & 6 & \vdots & -3 \\ 0 & 1 & -1 & -3 & \vdots & 2 \\ 0 & 0 & -14 & -37 & \vdots & 18 \\ 0 & 0 & -34 & -100 & \vdots & 64 \end{bmatrix}$$

$$\Rightarrow \begin{bmatrix} 1 & 5 & 2 & 6 & \vdots & -3 \\ 0 & 1 & -1 & -3 & \vdots & 2 \\ 0 & 0 & 238 & 629 & \vdots & -306 \\ 0 & 0 & -238 & -700 & \vdots & 448 \end{bmatrix}$$

$$\Rightarrow \begin{bmatrix} 1 & 5 & 2 & 6 & \vdots & -3 \\ 0 & 1 & -1 & -3 & \vdots & 2 \\ 0 & 0 & 238 & 629 & \vdots & -306 \\ 0 & 0 & 0 & -71 & \vdots & 142 \end{bmatrix}$$

$$\Rightarrow \begin{bmatrix} 1 & 5 & 2 & 6 & \vdots & -3 \\ 0 & 1 & -1 & -3 & \vdots & 2 \\ 0 & 0 & 1 & \frac{37}{14} & \vdots & -\frac{9}{7} \\ 0 & 0 & 0 & 1 & \vdots & -2 \end{bmatrix}$$

$w = -2$

$1 + \frac{37}{14}(-2) = -\frac{9}{7} \quad \Rightarrow \quad z = 4$

$y - 4 - 3(-2) = 2 \quad \Rightarrow \quad y = 0$

$x + 5(0) + 2(4) + 6(-2) = -3 \quad \Rightarrow \quad x = 1$

Solution: $(1,\ 0,\ 4,\ -2)$

55. $x + 2y = 0$

$-x - y = 0$

$$\begin{bmatrix} 1 & 2 & \vdots & 0 \\ -1 & -1 & \vdots & 0 \end{bmatrix} \Rightarrow \begin{bmatrix} 1 & 2 & \vdots & 0 \\ 0 & 1 & \vdots & 0 \end{bmatrix} \Rightarrow \begin{bmatrix} 1 & 0 & \vdots & 0 \\ 0 & 1 & \vdots & 0 \end{bmatrix}$$

$x = 0$

$y = 0$

Solution: $(0, 0)$

57. $x + y + z = 0$

$2x + 3y + z = 0$

$3x + 5y + z = 0$

$$\begin{bmatrix} 1 & 1 & 1 & \vdots & 0 \\ 2 & 3 & 1 & \vdots & 0 \\ 3 & 5 & 1 & \vdots & 0 \end{bmatrix} \Rightarrow \begin{bmatrix} 1 & 1 & 1 & \vdots & 0 \\ 0 & 1 & -1 & \vdots & 0 \\ 0 & 2 & -2 & \vdots & 0 \end{bmatrix} \Rightarrow \begin{bmatrix} 1 & 0 & 2 & \vdots & 0 \\ 0 & 1 & -1 & \vdots & 0 \\ 0 & 0 & 0 & \vdots & 0 \end{bmatrix}$$

$z = a$

$y = a$

$x = -2a$

Solution: $(-2a,\ a,\ a)$

59. $x =$ amount at 8% $x + y + z = 1{,}500{,}000$

$y =$ amount at 9% $0.08x + 0.09y + 0.12z = 133{,}000$

$z =$ amount at 12% $x - 4z = 0$

$$\begin{bmatrix} 1 & 1 & 1 & \vdots & 1{,}500{,}000 \\ 0.08 & 0.09 & 0.12 & \vdots & 133{,}000 \\ 1 & 0 & -4 & \vdots & 0 \end{bmatrix} \Rightarrow \begin{bmatrix} 1 & 1 & 1 & \vdots & 1{,}500{,}000 \\ 0 & 0.01 & 0.04 & \vdots & 13{,}000 \\ 0 & -1 & -5 & \vdots & -1{,}500{,}000 \end{bmatrix}$$

$$\Rightarrow \begin{bmatrix} 1 & 1 & 1 & \vdots & 1{,}500{,}000 \\ 0 & 1 & 4 & \vdots & 1{,}300{,}000 \\ 0 & -1 & -5 & \vdots & -1{,}500{,}000 \end{bmatrix}$$

$$\Rightarrow \begin{bmatrix} 1 & 0 & -3 & \vdots & 200{,}000 \\ 0 & 1 & 4 & \vdots & 1{,}300{,}000 \\ 0 & 0 & -1 & \vdots & -200{,}000 \end{bmatrix}$$

$$\Rightarrow \begin{bmatrix} 1 & 0 & -3 & \vdots & 200{,}000 \\ 0 & 1 & 4 & \vdots & 1{,}300{,}000 \\ 0 & 0 & 1 & \vdots & 200{,}000 \end{bmatrix}$$

$z = 200{,}000,\quad y = 500{,}000,\quad x = 800{,}000$

Solution: \$800,000 at 8%, \$500,000 at 9%, \$200,000 at 12%

61. $\dfrac{4x^2}{(x+1)^2(x-1)} = \dfrac{A}{x-1} + \dfrac{B}{x+1} + \dfrac{C}{(x+1)^2}$

$$4x^2 = A(x+1)^2 + B(x-1)(x+1) + C(x-1)$$

$$4x^2 = Ax^2 + 2Ax + A + Bx^2 - B + Cx - C$$

Equating coefficients of like powers of x:

$$A + B \qquad = 4$$

$$2A \qquad + C = 0$$

$$A - B - C = 0$$

The solution to this system is $A = 1$, $B = 3$, and $C = -2$. Thus,

$$\frac{4x^2}{(x+1)^2(x-1)} = \frac{1}{x-1} + \frac{3}{x+1} + \frac{-2}{(x+1)^2}.$$

63. At $(1,\ 7)$: $7 = a(1)^2 + b(1) + c \quad \Rightarrow \quad a + b + c = 7$

At $(2,\ 12)$: $12 = a(2)^2 + b(2) + c \quad \Rightarrow \quad 4a + 2b + c = 12$

At $(3,\ 19)$: $19 = a(3)^2 + b(3) + c \quad \Rightarrow \quad 9a + 3b + c = 19$

$$\begin{bmatrix} 1 & 1 & 1 & \vdots & 7 \\ 4 & 2 & 1 & \vdots & 12 \\ 9 & 3 & 1 & \vdots & 19 \end{bmatrix} \Rightarrow \begin{bmatrix} 1 & 1 & 1 & \vdots & 7 \\ 0 & -2 & -3 & \vdots & -16 \\ 0 & -6 & -8 & \vdots & -44 \end{bmatrix} \Rightarrow \begin{bmatrix} 1 & 1 & 1 & \vdots & 7 \\ 0 & 1 & \frac{3}{2} & \vdots & 8 \\ 0 & 0 & 1 & \vdots & 4 \end{bmatrix}$$

$$c = 4$$

$$b + \tfrac{3}{2}(4) = 8 \quad \Rightarrow \quad b = 2$$

$$a + 2 + 4 = 7 \quad \Rightarrow \quad a = 1$$

Solution: $y = x^2 + 2x + 4$

65. At $(1,\ 1)$: $(1)^2 + (1)^2 + D(1) + E(1) + F = 0 \quad \Rightarrow \quad D + D + F = -2$

At $(3,\ 3)$: $(3)^2 + (3)^2 + D(3) + E(3) + F = 0 \quad \Rightarrow \quad 3D + 3E + F = -18$

At $(4,\ 2)$: $(4)^2 + (2)^2 + D(4) + E(2) + F = 0 \quad \Rightarrow \quad 4D + 2E + F = -20$

$$\begin{bmatrix} 1 & 1 & 1 & \vdots & -2 \\ 3 & 3 & 1 & \vdots & -18 \\ 4 & 2 & 1 & \vdots & -20 \end{bmatrix} \Rightarrow \begin{bmatrix} 1 & 1 & 1 & \vdots & -2 \\ 0 & 0 & -2 & \vdots & -12 \\ 0 & -2 & -3 & \vdots & -12 \end{bmatrix} \Rightarrow \begin{bmatrix} 1 & 1 & 1 & \vdots & -2 \\ 0 & 1 & \frac{3}{2} & \vdots & 6 \\ 0 & 0 & 1 & \vdots & 6 \end{bmatrix}$$

$$F = 6$$

$$E + (\tfrac{3}{2})6 = 6 \quad \Rightarrow \quad E = -3$$

$$D + (-3) + 6 = -2 \quad \Rightarrow \quad D = -5$$

Solution: $x^2 + y^2 - 5x - 3y + 6 = 0$

Section 9.6   Operations with Matrices

- $A = B$ if and only if they have the same order and $a_{ij} = b_{ij}$.

- You should be able to perform the operations of matrix addition, scalar multiplication, and matrix multiplication.

- Some properties of matrix addition, scalar multiplication, and matrix multiplication are:

  (a) $A + B = B + A$ (b) $A + (B + C) = (A + B) + C$

  (c) $(cd)A = c(dA)$ (d) $1A = A$

  (e) $c(A + B) = cA + cB$ (f) $(c + d)A = cA + dA$

  (g) $A(BC) = (AB)C$ (h) $A(B + C) = AB + AC$

  (i) $(A + B)C = AC + BC$ (j) $c(AB) = (cA)B = A(cB)$

- You should remember that $AB \neq BA$ in general.

- The zero matrix is the additive identity, and the identity matrix I_n is the multiplicative identity.

1. $x = -4$, $y = 22$

3.
$$\left.\begin{array}{l} 5 = 2x + 1 \\ 6 = 3x \end{array}\right\} \Rightarrow x = 2$$
$$4 = 3y + 5 \quad \Rightarrow y = 3$$
$$x = 2, \ y = 3$$

5. (a) $A + B = \begin{bmatrix} 1 & -1 \\ 2 & -1 \end{bmatrix} + \begin{bmatrix} 2 & -1 \\ -1 & 8 \end{bmatrix} = \begin{bmatrix} 1+2 & -1-1 \\ 2-1 & -1+8 \end{bmatrix} = \begin{bmatrix} 3 & -2 \\ 1 & 7 \end{bmatrix}$

(b) $A - B = \begin{bmatrix} 1 & -1 \\ 2 & -1 \end{bmatrix} - \begin{bmatrix} 2 & -1 \\ -1 & 8 \end{bmatrix} = \begin{bmatrix} 1-2 & -1+1 \\ 2+1 & -1-8 \end{bmatrix} = \begin{bmatrix} -1 & 0 \\ 3 & -9 \end{bmatrix}$

(c) $3A = 3\begin{bmatrix} 1 & -1 \\ 2 & -1 \end{bmatrix} = \begin{bmatrix} 3(1) & 3(-1) \\ 3(2) & 3(-1) \end{bmatrix} = \begin{bmatrix} 3 & -3 \\ 6 & -3 \end{bmatrix}$

(d) $3A - 2B = \begin{bmatrix} 3 & -3 \\ 6 & -3 \end{bmatrix} - 2\begin{bmatrix} 2 & -1 \\ -1 & 8 \end{bmatrix} = \begin{bmatrix} 3 & -3 \\ 6 & -3 \end{bmatrix} + \begin{bmatrix} -4 & 2 \\ 2 & -16 \end{bmatrix} = \begin{bmatrix} -1 & -1 \\ 8 & -19 \end{bmatrix}$

7. (a) $A + B = \begin{bmatrix} 6 & -1 \\ 2 & 4 \\ -3 & 5 \end{bmatrix} + \begin{bmatrix} 1 & 4 \\ -1 & 5 \\ 1 & 10 \end{bmatrix} = \begin{bmatrix} 6+1 & -1+4 \\ 2-1 & 4+5 \\ -3+1 & 5+10 \end{bmatrix} = \begin{bmatrix} 7 & 3 \\ 1 & 9 \\ -2 & 15 \end{bmatrix}$

(b) $A - B = \begin{bmatrix} 6 & -1 \\ 2 & 4 \\ -3 & 5 \end{bmatrix} - \begin{bmatrix} 1 & 4 \\ -1 & 5 \\ 1 & 10 \end{bmatrix} = \begin{bmatrix} 6-1 & -1-4 \\ 2+1 & 4-5 \\ -3-1 & 5-10 \end{bmatrix} = \begin{bmatrix} 5 & -5 \\ 3 & -1 \\ -4 & -5 \end{bmatrix}$

(c) $3A = 3\begin{bmatrix} 6 & -1 \\ 2 & 4 \\ -3 & 5 \end{bmatrix} = \begin{bmatrix} 3(6) & 3(-1) \\ 3(2) & 3(4) \\ 3(-3) & 3(5) \end{bmatrix} = \begin{bmatrix} 18 & -3 \\ 6 & 12 \\ -9 & 15 \end{bmatrix}$

(d) $3A - 2B = \begin{bmatrix} 18 & -3 \\ 6 & 12 \\ -9 & 15 \end{bmatrix} - 2\begin{bmatrix} 1 & 4 \\ -1 & 5 \\ 1 & 10 \end{bmatrix} = \begin{bmatrix} 18 & -3 \\ 6 & 12 \\ -9 & 15 \end{bmatrix} + \begin{bmatrix} -2 & -8 \\ 2 & -10 \\ -2 & -20 \end{bmatrix} = \begin{bmatrix} 16 & -11 \\ 8 & 2 \\ -11 & -5 \end{bmatrix}$

9. (a) $A + B = \begin{bmatrix} 2+1 & 2+1 & -1+(-1) & 0+1 & 1+0 \\ 1+(-3) & 1+4 & -2+9 & 0+(-6) & -1+(-7) \end{bmatrix}$

$= \begin{bmatrix} 3 & 3 & -2 & 1 & 1 \\ -2 & 5 & 7 & -6 & -8 \end{bmatrix}$

(b) $A - B = \begin{bmatrix} 2-1 & 2-1 & -1-(-1) & 0-1 & 1-0 \\ 1-(-3) & 1-4 & -2-9 & 0-(-6) & -1-(-7) \end{bmatrix}$

$= \begin{bmatrix} 1 & 1 & 0 & -1 & 1 \\ 4 & -3 & -11 & 6 & 6 \end{bmatrix}$

(c) $3A = \begin{bmatrix} 3(2) & 3(2) & 3(-1) & 3(0) & 3(1) \\ 3(1) & 3(1) & 3(-2) & 3(0) & 3(-1) \end{bmatrix} = \begin{bmatrix} 6 & 6 & -3 & 0 & 3 \\ 3 & 3 & -6 & 0 & -3 \end{bmatrix}$

(d) $3A - 2B = \begin{bmatrix} 6 & 6 & -3 & 0 & 3 \\ 3 & 3 & -6 & 0 & -3 \end{bmatrix} - \begin{bmatrix} 2 & 2 & -2 & 2 & 0 \\ -6 & 8 & 18 & -12 & -14 \end{bmatrix}$

$= \begin{bmatrix} 4 & 4 & -1 & -2 & 3 \\ 9 & -5 & -24 & 12 & 11 \end{bmatrix}$

11. (a) $AB = \begin{bmatrix} 1 & 2 \\ 4 & 2 \end{bmatrix}\begin{bmatrix} 2 & -1 \\ -1 & 8 \end{bmatrix} = \begin{bmatrix} 1(2)+2(-1) & 1(-1)+2(8) \\ 4(2)+2(-1) & 4(-1)+2(8) \end{bmatrix} = \begin{bmatrix} 0 & 15 \\ 6 & 12 \end{bmatrix}$

(b) $BA = \begin{bmatrix} 2 & -1 \\ -1 & 8 \end{bmatrix}\begin{bmatrix} 1 & 2 \\ 4 & 2 \end{bmatrix} = \begin{bmatrix} 2(1)+(-1)4 & 2(2)+(-1)2 \\ -1(1)+8(4) & -1(2)+8(2) \end{bmatrix} = \begin{bmatrix} -2 & 2 \\ 31 & 14 \end{bmatrix}$

(c) $A^2 = \begin{bmatrix} 1 & 2 \\ 4 & 2 \end{bmatrix}\begin{bmatrix} 1 & 2 \\ 4 & 2 \end{bmatrix} = \begin{bmatrix} 1(1)+2(4) & 1(2)+2(2) \\ 4(1)+2(4) & 4(2)+2(2) \end{bmatrix} = \begin{bmatrix} 9 & 6 \\ 12 & 12 \end{bmatrix}$

13. (a) $AB = \begin{bmatrix} 3 & -1 \\ 1 & 3 \end{bmatrix} \begin{bmatrix} 1 & -3 \\ 3 & 1 \end{bmatrix} = \begin{bmatrix} 3(1)+(-1)(3) & 3(-3)+(-1)(1) \\ 1(1)+3(3) & 1(-3)+3(1) \end{bmatrix} = \begin{bmatrix} 0 & -10 \\ 10 & 0 \end{bmatrix}$

(b) $BA = \begin{bmatrix} 1 & -3 \\ 3 & 1 \end{bmatrix} \begin{bmatrix} 3 & -1 \\ 1 & 3 \end{bmatrix} = \begin{bmatrix} 1(3)+(-3)(1) & 1(-1)+(-3)(3) \\ 3(3)+1(1) & 3(-1)+1(3) \end{bmatrix} = \begin{bmatrix} 0 & -10 \\ 10 & 0 \end{bmatrix}$

(c) $A^2 = \begin{bmatrix} 3 & -1 \\ 1 & 3 \end{bmatrix} \begin{bmatrix} 3 & -1 \\ 1 & 3 \end{bmatrix} = \begin{bmatrix} 3(3)+(-1)(1) & 3(-1)+(-1)(3) \\ 1(3)+3(1) & 1(-1)+3(3) \end{bmatrix} = \begin{bmatrix} 8 & -6 \\ 6 & 8 \end{bmatrix}$

15. (a) $AB = \begin{bmatrix} 1 & -1 & 7 \\ 2 & -1 & 8 \\ 3 & 1 & -1 \end{bmatrix} \begin{bmatrix} 1 & 1 & 2 \\ 2 & 1 & 1 \\ 1 & -3 & 2 \end{bmatrix}$

$= \begin{bmatrix} 1(1)+(-1)2+7(1) & 1(1)+(-1)(1)+7(-3) & 1(2)+(-1)1+7(2) \\ 2(1)+(-1)2+8(1) & 2(1)+(-1)(1)+8(-3) & 2(2)+(-1)(1)+8(2) \\ 3(1)+1(2)+(-1)1 & 3(1)+1(1)+(-1)(-3) & 3(2)+1(1)+(-1)(2) \end{bmatrix}$

$= \begin{bmatrix} 6 & -21 & 15 \\ 8 & -23 & 19 \\ 4 & 7 & 5 \end{bmatrix}$

(b) $BA = \begin{bmatrix} 1 & 1 & 2 \\ 2 & 1 & 1 \\ 1 & -3 & 2 \end{bmatrix} \begin{bmatrix} 1 & -1 & 7 \\ 2 & -1 & 8 \\ 3 & 1 & -1 \end{bmatrix}$

$= \begin{bmatrix} 1(1)+1(2)+2(3) & 1(-1)+1(-1)+2(1) & 1(7)+1(8)+2(-1) \\ 2(1)+1(2)+1(3) & 2(-1)+1(-1)+1(1) & 2(7)+1(8)+1(-1) \\ 1(1)+(-3)(2)+2(3) & 1(-1)+(-3)(-1)+2(1) & 1(7)+(-3)(8)+2(-1) \end{bmatrix}$

$= \begin{bmatrix} 9 & 0 & 13 \\ 7 & -2 & 21 \\ 1 & 5 & -19 \end{bmatrix}$

(c) $A^2 = \begin{bmatrix} 1 & -1 & 7 \\ 2 & -1 & 8 \\ 3 & 1 & -1 \end{bmatrix} \begin{bmatrix} 1 & -1 & 7 \\ 2 & -1 & 8 \\ 3 & 1 & -1 \end{bmatrix}$

$= \begin{bmatrix} 1(1)+(-1)(2)+7(3) & 1(-1)+(-1)(-1)+7(1) & 1(7)+(-1)8+7(-1) \\ 2(1)+(-1)(2)+8(3) & 2(-1)+(-1)(-1)+8(1) & 2(7)+(-1)8+8(-1) \\ 3(1)+1(2)+(-1)(3) & 3(-1)+1(-1)+(-1)(1) & 3(7)+1(8)+(-1)(-1) \end{bmatrix}$

$= \begin{bmatrix} 20 & 7 & -8 \\ 24 & 7 & -2 \\ 2 & -5 & 30 \end{bmatrix}$

17. A is 3×2 and B is 3×3. Since the number of columns of A does not equal the number of rows of B, the multiplication is not possible.

19. A is 3×2 and B is $2 \times 2 \Rightarrow AB$ is 3×2.

$$AB = \begin{bmatrix} -1 & 3 \\ 4 & -5 \\ 0 & 2 \end{bmatrix} \begin{bmatrix} 1 & 2 \\ 0 & 7 \end{bmatrix}$$

$$= \begin{bmatrix} -1 & 19 \\ 4 & -27 \\ 0 & 14 \end{bmatrix}$$

21. A is 3×3 and B is $3 \times 3 \Rightarrow AB$ is 3×3.

$$AB = \begin{bmatrix} 5 & 0 & 0 \\ 0 & -8 & 0 \\ 0 & 0 & 7 \end{bmatrix} \begin{bmatrix} \frac{1}{5} & 0 & 0 \\ 0 & -\frac{1}{8} & 0 \\ 0 & 0 & \frac{1}{2} \end{bmatrix}$$

$$= \begin{bmatrix} 1 & 0 & 0 \\ 0 & 1 & 0 \\ 0 & 0 & \frac{7}{2} \end{bmatrix}$$

23. A is 4×1 and B is $1 \times 2 \Rightarrow AB$ is 4×2.

$$AB = \begin{bmatrix} 6 \\ -2 \\ 1 \\ 6 \end{bmatrix} \begin{bmatrix} 10 & 12 \end{bmatrix}$$

$$= \begin{bmatrix} 60 & 72 \\ -20 & -24 \\ 10 & 12 \\ 60 & 72 \end{bmatrix}$$

25. $X = 3A - 2B = 3 \begin{bmatrix} -2 & -1 \\ 1 & 0 \\ 3 & -4 \end{bmatrix} - 2 \begin{bmatrix} 0 & 3 \\ 2 & 0 \\ -4 & -1 \end{bmatrix}$

$$= \begin{bmatrix} -6 & -3 \\ 3 & 0 \\ 9 & -12 \end{bmatrix} - \begin{bmatrix} 0 & 6 \\ 4 & 0 \\ -8 & -2 \end{bmatrix} = \begin{bmatrix} -6 & -9 \\ -1 & 0 \\ 17 & -10 \end{bmatrix}$$

27. $X = -\frac{3}{2}A + \frac{1}{2}B = -\frac{3}{2} \begin{bmatrix} -2 & -1 \\ 1 & 0 \\ 3 & -4 \end{bmatrix} + \frac{1}{2} \begin{bmatrix} 0 & 3 \\ 2 & 0 \\ -4 & -1 \end{bmatrix}$

$$= \begin{bmatrix} 3 & \frac{3}{2} \\ -\frac{3}{2} & 0 \\ -\frac{9}{2} & 6 \end{bmatrix} + \begin{bmatrix} 0 & \frac{3}{2} \\ 1 & 0 \\ -2 & -\frac{1}{2} \end{bmatrix} = \begin{bmatrix} 3 & 3 \\ -\frac{1}{2} & 0 \\ -\frac{13}{2} & \frac{11}{2} \end{bmatrix}$$

29. $A = \begin{bmatrix} -1 & 1 \\ -2 & 1 \end{bmatrix}$, $X = \begin{bmatrix} x \\ y \end{bmatrix}$, $B = \begin{bmatrix} 4 \\ 0 \end{bmatrix}$

$$\begin{bmatrix} -1 & 1 & \vdots & 4 \\ -2 & 1 & \vdots & 0 \end{bmatrix} \Rightarrow \begin{bmatrix} 1 & -1 & \vdots & -4 \\ 0 & -1 & \vdots & -8 \end{bmatrix} \Rightarrow \begin{bmatrix} 1 & 0 & \vdots & 4 \\ 0 & 1 & \vdots & 8 \end{bmatrix}$$

$x = 4, \ y = 8$

31. $A = \begin{bmatrix} 1 & -2 & 3 \\ -1 & 3 & -1 \\ 2 & -5 & 5 \end{bmatrix}$, $X = \begin{bmatrix} x \\ y \\ z \end{bmatrix}$, $B = \begin{bmatrix} 9 \\ -6 \\ 17 \end{bmatrix}$

$$\left[\begin{array}{ccc:c} 1 & -2 & 3 & 9 \\ -1 & 3 & -1 & -6 \\ 2 & -5 & 5 & 17 \end{array}\right] \Rightarrow \left[\begin{array}{ccc:c} 1 & -2 & 3 & 9 \\ 0 & 1 & 2 & 3 \\ 0 & -1 & -1 & -1 \end{array}\right]$$

$$\Rightarrow \left[\begin{array}{ccc:c} 1 & 0 & 7 & 15 \\ 0 & 1 & 2 & 3 \\ 0 & 0 & 1 & 2 \end{array}\right]$$

$$\Rightarrow \left[\begin{array}{ccc:c} 1 & 0 & 0 & 1 \\ 0 & 1 & 0 & -1 \\ 0 & 0 & 1 & 2 \end{array}\right]$$

$x = 1,\ y = -1,\ z = 2$

33. $AC = \begin{bmatrix} 1 & 2 & 3 \\ 0 & 5 & 4 \\ 3 & -2 & 1 \end{bmatrix} \begin{bmatrix} 0 & 0 & 0 \\ 0 & 0 & 0 \\ 4 & -2 & 3 \end{bmatrix} = \begin{bmatrix} 12 & -6 & 9 \\ 16 & -8 & 12 \\ 4 & -2 & 3 \end{bmatrix}$

$BC = \begin{bmatrix} 4 & -6 & 3 \\ 5 & 4 & 4 \\ -1 & 0 & 1 \end{bmatrix} \begin{bmatrix} 0 & 0 & 0 \\ 0 & 0 & 0 \\ 4 & -2 & 3 \end{bmatrix} = \begin{bmatrix} 12 & -6 & 9 \\ 16 & -8 & 12 \\ 4 & -2 & 3 \end{bmatrix}$

Thus, $AC = BC$ even though $A \neq B$.

35. $1.20 \begin{bmatrix} 60 & 40 & 20 \\ 30 & 90 & 60 \end{bmatrix} = \begin{bmatrix} 72 & 48 & 24 \\ 36 & 108 & 72 \end{bmatrix}$

37. $BA = [3.75 \quad 7.00] \begin{bmatrix} 100 & 75 & 75 \\ 125 & 150 & 100 \end{bmatrix}$

$= [\$1250.00 \quad \$1331.25 \quad \$981.25]$

The entries in the last matrix represent the profit for both crops at each of the three outlets.

39. (a) We multiply the entries in the first row of S by those of the second column of T.

$3(1100) + 2(1350) + 2(1650) + 3(3000) + 0(3200) = \$18{,}300$

(b) We multiply the entries in the third row of S by those in the first column of T.

$4(840) + 2(1200) + 1(1450) + 3(2650) + 2(3050) = \$21{,}260$

(c) $ST = \begin{bmatrix} 3 & 2 & 2 & 3 & 0 \\ 0 & 2 & 3 & 4 & 3 \\ 4 & 2 & 1 & 3 & 2 \end{bmatrix} \begin{bmatrix} 840 & 1100 \\ 1200 & 1350 \\ 1450 & 1650 \\ 2650 & 3000 \\ 3050 & 3200 \end{bmatrix} = \begin{matrix} \text{Wholesale} & \text{Retail} \\ \begin{bmatrix} \$15{,}770 & \$18{,}300 \\ \$26{,}500 & \$29{,}250 \\ \$21{,}260 & \$24{,}150 \end{bmatrix} & \begin{matrix} 1 \\ 2 \\ 3 \end{matrix} \end{matrix} \Bigg\} \text{Outlet}$

This represents the wholesale and retail price of the inventory at each outlet. Note that the answers to parts (a) and (b) are in ST.

41. $P^2 = \begin{bmatrix} 0.6 & 0.1 & 0.1 \\ 0.2 & 0.7 & 0.1 \\ 0.2 & 0.2 & 0.8 \end{bmatrix} \begin{bmatrix} 0.6 & 0.1 & 0.1 \\ 0.2 & 0.7 & 0.1 \\ 0.2 & 0.2 & 0.8 \end{bmatrix} = \begin{bmatrix} 0.40 & 0.15 & 0.15 \\ 0.28 & 0.53 & 0.17 \\ 0.32 & 0.32 & 0.68 \end{bmatrix}$

Section 9.7   Inverse Matrices and Systems of Linear Equations

- The inverse of a square matrix A is a matrix A^{-1} satisfying $AA^{-1} = I_n = A^{-1}A$.
- You should be able to find the inverse, if it exists, of a 2×2 matrix.
- You should be able to find inverses using your graphing utility.
- You should be able to use inverse matrices to solve systems of equations.

1. $AB = \begin{bmatrix} 2 & 1 \\ 5 & 3 \end{bmatrix} \begin{bmatrix} 3 & -1 \\ -5 & 2 \end{bmatrix} = \begin{bmatrix} 6-5 & -2+2 \\ 15-15 & -5+6 \end{bmatrix} = \begin{bmatrix} 1 & 0 \\ 0 & 1 \end{bmatrix}$

$BA = \begin{bmatrix} 3 & -1 \\ -5 & 2 \end{bmatrix} \begin{bmatrix} 2 & 1 \\ 5 & 3 \end{bmatrix} = \begin{bmatrix} 6-5 & 3-3 \\ -10+10 & -5+6 \end{bmatrix} = \begin{bmatrix} 1 & 0 \\ 0 & 1 \end{bmatrix}$

3. $AB = \begin{bmatrix} 1 & 2 \\ 3 & 4 \end{bmatrix} \begin{bmatrix} -2 & 1 \\ \frac{3}{2} & -\frac{1}{2} \end{bmatrix} = \begin{bmatrix} -2+3 & 1-1 \\ -6+6 & 3-2 \end{bmatrix} = \begin{bmatrix} 1 & 0 \\ 0 & 1 \end{bmatrix}$

$BA = \begin{bmatrix} -2 & 1 \\ \frac{3}{2} & -\frac{1}{2} \end{bmatrix} \begin{bmatrix} 1 & 2 \\ 3 & 4 \end{bmatrix} = \begin{bmatrix} -2+3 & -4+4 \\ \frac{3}{2}-\frac{3}{2} & 3-2 \end{bmatrix} = \begin{bmatrix} 1 & 0 \\ 0 & 1 \end{bmatrix}$

5. $AB = \frac{1}{3} \begin{bmatrix} -2 & 2 & 3 \\ 1 & -1 & 0 \\ 0 & 1 & 4 \end{bmatrix} \begin{bmatrix} -4 & -5 & 3 \\ -4 & -8 & 3 \\ 1 & 2 & 0 \end{bmatrix}$

$= \frac{1}{3} \begin{bmatrix} -8+8+3 & 10-16+6 & -6+6 \\ -4+4 & -5+8 & 3-3 \\ -4+4 & -8+8 & 3 \end{bmatrix} = \frac{1}{3} \begin{bmatrix} 3 & 0 & 0 \\ 0 & 3 & 0 \\ 0 & 0 & 3 \end{bmatrix} = I_3$

$BA = \frac{1}{3} \begin{bmatrix} -4 & -5 & 3 \\ -4 & -8 & 3 \\ 1 & 2 & 0 \end{bmatrix} \begin{bmatrix} -2 & 2 & 3 \\ 1 & -1 & 0 \\ 0 & 1 & 4 \end{bmatrix} = \frac{1}{3} \begin{bmatrix} 8-5 & -8+5+3 & -12+12 \\ 8-8 & -8+8+3 & -12+12 \\ -2+2 & 2-2 & 3 \end{bmatrix} = I_3$

7. $AB = \begin{bmatrix} 2 & 0 & 1 & 1 \\ 3 & 0 & 0 & 1 \\ -1 & 1 & -2 & 1 \\ 4 & -1 & 1 & 0 \end{bmatrix} \begin{bmatrix} -1 & 2 & -1 & -1 \\ -4 & 9 & -5 & -6 \\ 0 & 1 & -1 & -1 \\ 3 & -5 & 3 & 3 \end{bmatrix}$

$= \begin{bmatrix} -2+0+0+3 & 4+0+1+(-5) & -2+0+(-1)+3 & -2+0+(-1)+3 \\ -3+0+0+3 & 6+0+0+(-5) & -3+0+0+3 & -3+0+0+3 \\ 1+(-4)+0+3 & -2+9+(-2)+(-5) & 1+(-5)+2+3 & 1+(-6)+2+3 \\ -4+4+0+0 & 8+(-9)+1+0 & -4+5+(-1)+0 & -4+6+(-1)+0 \end{bmatrix}$

$= \begin{bmatrix} 1 & 0 & 0 & 0 \\ 0 & 1 & 0 & 0 \\ 0 & 0 & 1 & 0 \\ 0 & 0 & 0 & 1 \end{bmatrix}$

$BA = \begin{bmatrix} -1 & 2 & -1 & -1 \\ -4 & 9 & -5 & -6 \\ 0 & 1 & -1 & -1 \\ 3 & -5 & 3 & 3 \end{bmatrix} \begin{bmatrix} 2 & 0 & 1 & 1 \\ 3 & 0 & 0 & 1 \\ -1 & 1 & -2 & 1 \\ 4 & -1 & 1 & 0 \end{bmatrix}$

$= \begin{bmatrix} -2+6+1+(-4) & 0+0+(-1)+1 & -1+0+2+(-1) & -1+2+(-1)+0 \\ -8+27+5+(-24) & 0+0+(-5)+6 & -4+0+10+(-6) & -4+9+(-5)+0 \\ 0+3+1+(-4) & 0+0+(-1)+1 & 0+0+2+(-1) & 0+1+(-1)+0 \\ 6+(-15)+(-3)+12 & 0+0+3+(-3) & 3+0+(-6)+3 & 3+(-5)+3+0 \end{bmatrix}$

$= \begin{bmatrix} 1 & 0 & 0 & 0 \\ 0 & 1 & 0 & 0 \\ 0 & 0 & 1 & 0 \\ 0 & 0 & 0 & 1 \end{bmatrix}$

9. $A^{-1} = \dfrac{1}{ad-bc} \begin{bmatrix} d & -b \\ -c & a \end{bmatrix} = \dfrac{1}{6} \begin{bmatrix} 3 & 0 \\ 0 & 2 \end{bmatrix} = \begin{bmatrix} \frac{1}{2} & 0 \\ 0 & \frac{1}{3} \end{bmatrix}$

11. $A^{-1} = \dfrac{1}{ad-bc} \begin{bmatrix} d & -b \\ -c & a \end{bmatrix} = \dfrac{1}{-3+4} \begin{bmatrix} -3 & 2 \\ -2 & 1 \end{bmatrix} = \begin{bmatrix} -3 & 2 \\ -2 & 1 \end{bmatrix}$

13. $A^{-1} = \dfrac{1}{ad-bc} \begin{bmatrix} d & -b \\ -c & a \end{bmatrix} = \dfrac{1}{-1+2} \begin{bmatrix} 1 & -1 \\ 2 & -1 \end{bmatrix} = \begin{bmatrix} 1 & -1 \\ 2 & -1 \end{bmatrix}$

15. Since $ad - bc = 16 - 16 = 0$, the inverse does not exist.

17. $A = \begin{bmatrix} 2 & 7 & 1 \\ -3 & -9 & 2 \end{bmatrix}$

A has no inverse because it is not square.

19. Using a graphing utility:

$$A^{-1} = \begin{bmatrix} 1 & 1 & -1 \\ -3 & 2 & -1 \\ 3 & -3 & 2 \end{bmatrix}$$

21. Using a graphing utility:

$$A^{-1} = \begin{bmatrix} -175 & 37 & -13 \\ 95 & -20 & 7 \\ 14 & -3 & 1 \end{bmatrix}$$

23. Using a graphing utility:

$$A^{-1} = \frac{1}{2} \begin{bmatrix} -3 & 3 & 2 \\ 9 & -7 & -6 \\ -2 & 2 & 2 \end{bmatrix}$$

25. Using a graphing utility:

$$A^{-1} = \frac{5}{11} \begin{bmatrix} 0 & -4 & 2 \\ -22 & 11 & 11 \\ 22 & -6 & -8 \end{bmatrix}$$

27. Using a graphing utility:

$$A^{-1} = \begin{bmatrix} 1 & 0 & 0 \\ -0.75 & 0.25 & 0 \\ 0.35 & -0.25 & 0.2 \end{bmatrix}$$

29. Using a graphing utility, we see that the inverse of A does not exist.

31. Using a graphing utility:

$$A^{-1} = \begin{bmatrix} -\frac{1}{8} & 0 & 0 & 0 \\ 0 & 1 & 0 & 0 \\ 0 & 0 & \frac{1}{4} & 0 \\ 0 & 0 & 0 & -\frac{1}{5} \end{bmatrix}$$

33. Using a graphing utility:

$$A^{-1} = \begin{bmatrix} -24 & 7 & 1 & -2 \\ -10 & 3 & 0 & -1 \\ -29 & 7 & 3 & -2 \\ 12 & -3 & -1 & 1 \end{bmatrix}$$

35. Using a graphing utility, the solution is $(2, -2)$.

37. Using a graphing utility, we find that the system is inconsistent.

39. Using a graphing utility, the solution is $\left(\frac{2}{3}, \frac{1}{2}\right)$.

41. Using a graphing utility, the solution is $(-1, 3, 2)$.

43. Using a graphing utility, we see that the coefficient matrix is not invertible. However, using row reduction, we find that there is an infinite number of solutions.

$$\left(\frac{5}{16}a + \frac{13}{16}, \frac{19}{16}a + \frac{11}{16}, a\right)$$

45. Using a graphing utility, the solution is $(5, 0, -2, 3)$.

For Exercises 47 and 49 we have: $A = \begin{bmatrix} 1 & 1 & 1 \\ 0.065 & 0.07 & 0.09 \\ 0 & 2 & -1 \end{bmatrix}$. **Using a graphing utility,**

we obtain: $A^{-1} = \frac{1}{11} \begin{bmatrix} 50 & -600 & -4 \\ -13 & 200 & 5 \\ -26 & 400 & -1 \end{bmatrix}$.

47. $B = \begin{bmatrix} 25,000 \\ 1,900 \\ 0 \end{bmatrix}$

$$X = A^{-1}B = \frac{1}{11} \begin{bmatrix} 50 & -600 & -4 \\ -13 & 200 & 5 \\ -265 & 400 & -1 \end{bmatrix} \begin{bmatrix} 25,000 \\ 1,900 \\ 0 \end{bmatrix} = \begin{bmatrix} 10,000 \\ 5,000 \\ 10,000 \end{bmatrix}$$

Answer: $10,000 in AAA-rated bonds, $5,000 in A-rated bonds, $10,000 in B-rated bonds

49. $B = \begin{bmatrix} 12,000 \\ 835 \\ 0 \end{bmatrix}$

$$X = A^{-1}B = \frac{1}{11} \begin{bmatrix} 50 & -600 & -4 \\ -13 & 200 & 5 \\ -26 & 400 & -1 \end{bmatrix} \begin{bmatrix} 12,000 \\ 835 \\ 0 \end{bmatrix} = \begin{bmatrix} 9000 \\ 1000 \\ 2000 \end{bmatrix}$$

Answer: $9,000 in AAA-rated bonds, $1,000 in A-rated bonds, $2,000 in B-rated bonds

For Exercise 51 we have: $A = \begin{bmatrix} 2 & 0 & 4 \\ 0 & 1 & 4 \\ 1 & 1 & -1 \end{bmatrix}$. **Using a graphing utility, we obtain:**

$A^{-1} = \frac{1}{14} \begin{bmatrix} 5 & -4 & 4 \\ -4 & 6 & 8 \\ 1 & 2 & -2 \end{bmatrix}$.

51. $B = \begin{bmatrix} 14 \\ 28 \\ 0 \end{bmatrix}$

$$X = A^{-1}B = \frac{1}{14} \begin{bmatrix} 5 & -4 & 4 \\ -4 & 6 & 8 \\ 1 & 2 & -2 \end{bmatrix} \begin{bmatrix} 14 \\ 28 \\ 0 \end{bmatrix} = \begin{bmatrix} -3 \\ 8 \\ 5 \end{bmatrix}$$

Answer: $I_1 = -3$ amps, $I_2 = 8$ amps, $I_3 = 5$ amps

Section 9.8   Systems of Inequalities

■ You should be able to sketch the graph of an inequality in two variables:

(a) Replace the inequality with an equal sign and graph the equation. Use a dashed line for $<$ or $>$, a solid line for $\leq$ or $\geq$.

(b) Test a point in each region formed by the graph. If the point satisfies the inequality, shade the whole region.

■ You should be able to sketch the solution set of a system of inequalities.

---

1. The graph of $x > 3$ is the half-plane to the right of the line $x = 3$. Graph (f)

3. The graph of $2x + 3y \leq 6$ is the half-plane below the line $2x + 3y = 6$ together with the line. Graph (e)

5. The graph of $x^2 + y^2 < 4$ is the interior of the circle centered at the origin with radius 2. Graph (a)

7. The graph of $xy = 2$ is a hyperbola with the axes as asymptotes. The graph of $xy > 2$ is graph (b).

9. $x \geq 2$ **11.** $y \geq -1$ **13.** $y < 2 - x$

15. $2y - x \geq 4$

17. $(x+1)^2 + (y-2)^2 < 9$

19. $y \leq \dfrac{1}{1+x^2}$

21. $x + y \leq 1$
   $-x + y \leq 1$
      $y \geq 0$

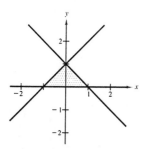

23. $x + y \leq 5$
      $x \geq 2$
      $y \geq 0$

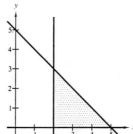

25. $-3x + 2y < 6$
     $x + 4y > -2$
      $2x + y < 3$

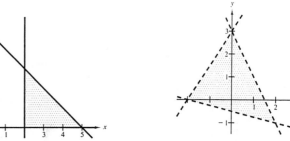

27. $2x + y > 2$
   $6x + 3y < 2$
   No solution

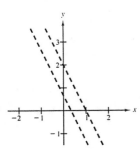

29. $x \geq 1$
      $x - 2y \leq 3$
      $3x + 2y \geq 9$
      $x + y \leq 6$

31. $x^2 + y^2 \leq 9$
     $x^2 + y^2 \geq 1$

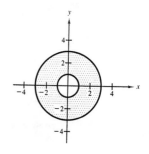

33. $x > y^2$

$x < y + 2$

35. $y \le \sqrt{3x} + 1$

$y \ge x + 1$

37. $y < x^3 - 2x + 1$

$y > -2x$

$x \le 1$

39. $x^2 y \ge 1$

$0 < x \le 4$

$y \le 4$

41. $2 \le x \le 5$

$1 \le y \le 7$

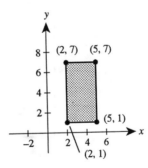

43. $y \ge 0$

$y \le \frac{3}{2}x$

$y \le -x + 5$

45. $x^2 + y^2 \le 16$

$x \ge 0$

$y \ge 0$

47. $x =$ number of tables

$y =$ number of chairs

$x + \frac{3}{2}y \le 12$

$\frac{4}{3}x + \frac{3}{2}y \le 15$

$x \ge 0$

$y \ge 0$

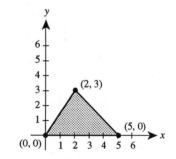

49. x = amount in one account

y = amount in other account

$x + y \leq 20,000$

$x \geq 5,000$

$y \geq 5,000$

$2x \leq y$

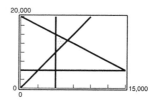

51. x = ounces of food X

y = ounces of food Y

Calcium: $20x + 10y \geq 280$

Iron: $15x + 10y \geq 160$

Vitamin B: $10x + 20y \geq 180$

$x \geq 0$

$y \geq 0$

53.   Demand = Supply

$50 - 0.5x = 0.125x$

$50 = 0.625x$

$80 = x$

$10 = p$

Point of equilibrium: $(80, \ 10)$

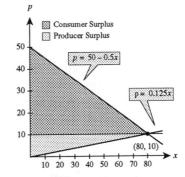

–CONTINUED ON NEXT PAGE–

53. –CONTINUED–

The consumer surplus is the area of the triangle bounded by

$$p \leq 50 - 0.5x$$

$$p \geq 10$$

$$x \geq 0.$$

Consumer surplus $= \frac{1}{2}(\text{base})(\text{height}) = \frac{1}{2}(80)(40) = \$1600$

The producer surplus is the area of the triangle bounded by

$$p \geq 0.125x$$

$$p \leq 10$$

$$x \geq 0.$$

Producer surplus $= \frac{1}{2}(\text{base})(\text{height}) = \frac{1}{2}(80)(10) = \$400$

55. Demand = Supply

$$300 - x = 100 + x$$

$$200 = 2x$$

$$100 = x$$

$$200 = p$$

Point of equilibrium: $(100, 200)$

The consumer surplus is the area of the triangle bounded by

$$p \leq 300 - x$$

$$p \geq 200$$

$$x \geq 0.$$

Consumer surplus $= \frac{1}{2}(\text{base})(\text{height}) = \frac{1}{2}(100)(100) = 5000$

The producer surplus is the area of the triangle bounded by

$$p \geq 100 + x$$

$$p \leq 200$$

$$x \geq 0.$$

Producer surplus $= \frac{1}{2}(\text{base})(\text{height}) = \frac{1}{2}(100)(100) = 5000$

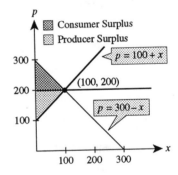

57.
$$\text{Demand} = \text{Supply}$$

$$140 - 0.00002x = 80 + 0.00001x$$

$$60 = 0.00003x$$

$$2,000,000 = x$$

$$100 = p$$

Point of equilibrium: (2,000,000, 100)

The consumer surplus is the area of the triangle bounded by

$$p \leq 140 - 0.00002x$$

$$p \geq 100$$

$$x \geq 0.$$

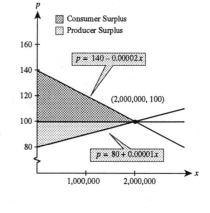

Consumer surplus $= \frac{1}{2}(\text{base})(\text{height}) = \frac{1}{2}(2,000,000)(40) = \$40,000,000$ or \$40 million

The producer surplus is the area of the triangle bounded by

$$p \geq 80 + 0.00001x$$

$$p \leq 100$$

$$x \geq 0.$$

Producer surplus $= \frac{1}{2}(\text{base})(\text{height}) = \frac{1}{2}(2,000,000)(20) = \$20,000,000$ or \$20 million

59. Inside track: $2x + \pi y \geq 125$

Body-building area: $xy \geq 500$

$$x \geq 0$$

$$y \geq 0$$

Chapter 9   Review Exercises

1. $x + y = 2$ Equation 1

$x - y = 0$ Equation 2

Solve for y in Equation 2: $y = x$
Substitute in Equation 1: $x + x = 2$ $\Rightarrow$ $x = 1$
Backsubstitute $x = 1$: $y = x$ $\Rightarrow$ $y = 1$
Solution: $(1, 1)$

3. $x^2 - y^2 = 9$ Equation 1

$x - y = 1$ Equation 2

Solve for x in Equation 2: $x = y + 1$
Substitute for x in Equation 1:
$$(y + 1)^2 - y^2 = 9 \quad \Rightarrow \quad 2y + 1 = 9 \quad \Rightarrow \quad y = 4$$
Backsubstitute $y = 4$: $x = y + 1 = 4 + 1 = 5$
Solution: $(5, 4)$

5. $y = 2x^2$ Equation 1

$y = x^4 - 2x^2$ Equation 2

Substitute for y in Equation 2:
$$2x^2 = x^4 - 2x^2 \Rightarrow 0 = x^2(x^2 - 4)$$
$$x = 0, \ \pm 2$$
Backsubstitute $x = 0$: $y = 2(0)^2 = 0$
Backsubstitute $x = 2$: $y = 2(2)^2 = 8$
Backsubstitute $x = -2$: $y = 2(-2)^2 = 8$
Solutions: $(0, 0)$, $(2, 8)$, $(-2, 8)$

7. $2x - \ \ y = \ \ 2 \Rightarrow 16x - 8y = 16$

$\underline{6x + 8y = 39 \Rightarrow \ \ 6x + 8y = 39}$

$22x = 55$

$x = \frac{5}{2}$

$y = \ \ 3$

Solution: $\left(\frac{5}{2}, \ 3\right)$

9. $3x - 2y = \ \ 0 \Rightarrow -3x + 2y = 0$

$\underline{3x + 2(y + 5) = 10 \Rightarrow \ \ 3x + 2y = 0}$

$4y = 0$

$y = 0$

$x = 0$

Solution: $(0, 0)$

11. $1.25x - 2y = 3.5 \Rightarrow \ \ 5x - 8y = \ \ \ 14$

$\underline{5x - 8y = \ \ 14 \Rightarrow -5x + 8y = -14}$

$0 = \ \ \ 0$

Solution: All points $(x, \ y)$ lying on the line $5x - 8y = 14$, or any points of the form $\left(\frac{14}{5} + \frac{8}{5}a, \ a\right)$.

13. $y^2 - 2y + x = 0$

    $x + y = 0$

One way to solve this problem is to reverse the roles of x and y. That is, let $x = Y$ and $y = X$, and graph

    $Y = 2X - X^2$

    $Y = -X.$

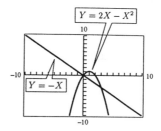

We see that there are two points of intersection, $(X, Y) = (0, 0)$ and $(X, Y) = (3, -3)$. Thus, the solutions to the original equations are $(x, y) = (0, 0)$ and $(x, y) = (-3, 3)$.

15. $y = 2(6 - x)$

    $y = 2^{x-2}$

The unique solution is $(x, y) = (4, 4)$.

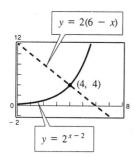

17. $C = 2.85x + 10,000$

    $R = 4.95x$

Break-even:

    $R = C$

    $4.95x = 2.85x + 10,000$

    $2.10x = 10,000$

        $x \approx 4762$ units

19. $x =$ amount of 75% solution

    $y =$ amount of 50% solution

$$x + \quad y = \quad 100 \Rightarrow -0.5x - 0.5y = -50$$
$$0.75x + 0.50y = 0.60(100) \Rightarrow \underline{\;0.75x + 0.5y = \quad 60\;}$$
$$0.25x \qquad\qquad = \quad 10$$
$$x = \quad 40$$
$$y = \quad 60$$

Solution: 40 gallons of 75% solution and 60 gallons of 50% solution

21. $x =$ ground speed of Pittsburgh to Philadelphia flight

$y =$ ground speed of Philadelphia to Pittsburgh flight

$$x = y + 25$$

$$\tfrac{2}{3}x + \tfrac{2}{3}y = 275$$

$$\tfrac{2}{3}(y + 25) + \tfrac{2}{3}y = 275$$

$$\tfrac{4}{3}y + \tfrac{50}{3} = 275$$

$$\tfrac{4}{3}y = \tfrac{775}{3}$$

$$y = 193.75$$

$$x = 218.75$$

Solution: 218.75 mph for the Pittsburgh to Philadelphia flight and 193.75 mph for the Philadelphia to Pittsburgh flight

23. Supply = Demand

$$22 + 0.00001x = 37 - 0.0002x$$

$$0.00021x = 15$$

$$x = \tfrac{500{,}000}{7}$$

$$y = \tfrac{159}{7}$$

Point of equilibrium: $\left(\tfrac{500{,}000}{7},\ \tfrac{159}{7}\right)$

25.
$$\begin{aligned}
x + 2y + 6z &= 4 \\
-3x + 2y - z &= -4 \\
4x \quad\ + 2z &= 16
\end{aligned}$$

$$\begin{aligned}
x + 2y + 6z &= 4 \\
8y + 17z &= 8 \\
-8y - 22z &= 0
\end{aligned}$$

$$\begin{aligned}
x + 2y + 6z &= 4 \\
8y + 17z &= 8 \\
-5z &= 8
\end{aligned}$$

$$-5z = 8 \ \Rightarrow\ z = -\tfrac{8}{5}$$
$$8y + 17\left(-\tfrac{8}{5}\right) = 8 \ \Rightarrow\ y = \tfrac{22}{5}$$
$$x + 2\left(\tfrac{22}{5}\right) + 6\left(-\tfrac{8}{5}\right) = 4 \ \Rightarrow\ x = \tfrac{24}{5}$$

Solution: $\left(\tfrac{24}{5},\ \tfrac{22}{5},\ -\tfrac{8}{5}\right)$

27.
$$\begin{aligned}
x - 2y + z &= -6 \\
2x - 3y &= -7 \\
-x + 3y - 3z &= 11
\end{aligned}$$

$$\begin{aligned}
x - 2y + z &= -6 \\
y - 2z &= 5 \\
y - 2z &= 5
\end{aligned}$$

$$\begin{aligned}
x \quad - 3z &= 4 \\
y - 2z &= 5 \\
z &= a
\end{aligned}$$

$$y - 2a = 5 \ \Rightarrow\ y = 2a + 5$$
$$x - 3a = 4 \ \Rightarrow\ x = 3a + 4$$

Solution: $(3a + 4,\ 2a + 5,\ a)$

29. $2x + 5y - 19z = 34$

$3x + 8y - 31z = 54$

$6x + 15y - 57z = 102$

$6x + 16y - 62z = 108$

$6x + 15y - 57z = 102$

$y - 5z = 6$

$6x \qquad + 18z = 12$

$y - 5z = 6$

$z = a$

$y - 5a = 6 \quad \Rightarrow \quad y = 5a + 6$

$6x + 18a = 12 \quad \Rightarrow \quad x = -3a + 2$

Solution: $(-3a + 2,\ 5a + 6,\ a)$

31. $\begin{bmatrix} -1 & 1 & 2 & \vdots & 1 \\ 2 & 3 & 1 & \vdots & -2 \\ 5 & 4 & 2 & \vdots & 4 \end{bmatrix} \Rightarrow \begin{bmatrix} 1 & -1 & -2 & \vdots & -1 \\ 0 & 5 & 5 & \vdots & 0 \\ 0 & 9 & 12 & \vdots & 9 \end{bmatrix} \Rightarrow \begin{bmatrix} 1 & 0 & -1 & \vdots & -1 \\ 0 & 1 & 1 & \vdots & 0 \\ 0 & 0 & 3 & \vdots & 9 \end{bmatrix}$

$$\Rightarrow \begin{bmatrix} 1 & 0 & 0 & \vdots & 2 \\ 0 & 1 & 0 & \vdots & -3 \\ 0 & 0 & 1 & \vdots & 3 \end{bmatrix}$$

$x = 2$

$y = -3$

$z = 3$

Answer: $(2,\ -3,\ 3)$

33. $\begin{bmatrix} 2 & 1 & 2 & \vdots & 4 \\ 2 & 2 & 0 & \vdots & 5 \\ 2 & -1 & 6 & \vdots & 2 \end{bmatrix} \Rightarrow \begin{bmatrix} 2 & 1 & 2 & \vdots & 4 \\ 0 & 1 & -2 & \vdots & 1 \\ 0 & -2 & 4 & \vdots & -2 \end{bmatrix} \Rightarrow \begin{bmatrix} 2 & 0 & 4 & \vdots & 3 \\ 0 & 1 & -2 & \vdots & 1 \\ 0 & 0 & 0 & \vdots & 0 \end{bmatrix}$

Let $z = a$.

$y - 2a = 1 \Rightarrow y = 2a + 1$

$2x + 4a = 3 \Rightarrow x = -2a + \frac{3}{2}$

Answer: $(-2a + \frac{3}{2},\ 2a + 1,\ a)$

35. $y = ax^2 + bx + c$

At $(0, -6)$: $-6 = c$

At $(1, -3)$: $-3 = a + b + c \Rightarrow a + b = 3 \Rightarrow -2a - 2b = -6$

At $(2, 4)$: $\quad 4 = 4a + 2b + c \Rightarrow 4a + 2b = 10 \Rightarrow \underline{\quad 4a + 2b = 10}$

$$2a \quad = \quad 4$$

$$a = \quad 2$$

$$b = \quad 1$$

Solution: $y = 2x^2 + x - 6$

37. $x^2 + y^2 + Dx + Ey + F = 0$

At $(2, 2)$: $\quad 4 + 4 + 2D + 2E + F = 0 \Rightarrow 2D + 2E + F = -8$

At $(5, -1)$: $\quad 25 + 1 + 5D - E + F = 0 \Rightarrow 5D - E - F = -26$

At $(-1, -1)$: $\quad 1 + 1 - D - E + F = 0 \Rightarrow -D - E + F = -2$

$$D + E - F = 2$$

$$5D - E + F = -26$$

$$2D + 2E + F = -8$$

$$D + E - F = 2$$

$$-6E + 6F = -36$$

$$3F = -12$$

$$3F = -12 \quad \Rightarrow \quad F = -4$$

$$-6E + 6(-4) = -36 \quad \Rightarrow \quad E = 2$$

$$D + 2 + 4 = 2 \quad \Rightarrow \quad D = -4$$

Solution: $y = x^2 + y^2 - 4x + 2y - 4 = 0$

39. $x = $ fraction of A to total

$y = $ fraction of B to total

$z = $ fraction of C to total

$\frac{1}{5}x \quad + \frac{1}{3}z = \frac{6}{27}$

$\frac{2}{5}x \quad + \frac{1}{3}z = \frac{8}{27}$

$\frac{2}{5}x + y + \frac{1}{3}z = \frac{13}{27}$

Solution: $x = \frac{10}{27}, \quad y = \frac{5}{27}, \quad z = \frac{12}{27}$

Thus, the ratio is $(10, 5, 12)$.

41.
$$5b + 10a = 17.8 \Rightarrow -10b - 20a = -35.6$$
$$10b + 30a = 45.7 \Rightarrow \underline{\quad 10b + 30a = \quad 45.7}$$
$$10a = \quad 10.1$$
$$a = \quad 1.01$$
$$b = \quad 1.54$$

Least squares regression line:

$$y = 1.01x + 1.54$$

43. $\begin{bmatrix} 2 & 1 & 0 \\ 0 & 5 & -4 \end{bmatrix} - 3 \begin{bmatrix} 5 & 3 & -6 \\ 0 & -2 & 5 \end{bmatrix} = \begin{bmatrix} 2 & 1 & 0 \\ 0 & 5 & -4 \end{bmatrix} + \begin{bmatrix} -15 & -9 & 18 \\ 0 & 6 & -15 \end{bmatrix}$

$$= \begin{bmatrix} -13 & -8 & 18 \\ 0 & 11 & -19 \end{bmatrix}$$

45. $\begin{bmatrix} 1 & 2 \\ 5 & -4 \\ 6 & 0 \end{bmatrix} \begin{bmatrix} 6 & -2 & 8 \\ 4 & 0 & 0 \end{bmatrix} = \begin{bmatrix} 14 & -2 & 8 \\ 14 & -10 & 40 \\ 36 & -12 & 48 \end{bmatrix}$

47. $\begin{bmatrix} 1 & 5 & 6 \\ 2 & -4 & 0 \end{bmatrix} \begin{bmatrix} 6 & 4 \\ -2 & 0 \\ 8 & 0 \end{bmatrix} = \begin{bmatrix} 6 - 10 + 48 & 4 \\ 12 + 8 & 8 \end{bmatrix} = \begin{bmatrix} 44 & 4 \\ 20 & 8 \end{bmatrix}$

49. $\begin{bmatrix} 1 & 3 & 2 \\ 0 & 2 & -4 \\ 0 & 0 & 3 \end{bmatrix} \begin{bmatrix} 4 & -3 & 2 \\ 0 & 3 & -1 \\ 0 & 0 & 2 \end{bmatrix} = \begin{bmatrix} 4 & 6 & 3 \\ 0 & 6 & -10 \\ 0 & 0 & 6 \end{bmatrix}$

51. $A = \begin{bmatrix} 2 & 6 \\ 3 & -6 \end{bmatrix}$

Using a graphing utility, we find

$$A^{-1} = \begin{bmatrix} 0.2 & 0.2 \\ 0.1 & -0.0667 \end{bmatrix}.$$

53. Using a graphing utility, we find:

$$A^{-1} = \begin{bmatrix} \frac{1}{2} & -1 & -\frac{1}{2} \\ \frac{1}{2} & -\frac{2}{3} & -\frac{5}{6} \\ 0 & \frac{2}{3} & \frac{1}{3} \end{bmatrix}$$

55. $\begin{bmatrix} x \\ y \end{bmatrix} = A^{-1}B$

$\qquad = \begin{bmatrix} -2 & 1 \\ \frac{3}{2} & -\frac{1}{2} \end{bmatrix} \begin{bmatrix} -1 \\ -5 \end{bmatrix} = \begin{bmatrix} -3 \\ 1 \end{bmatrix}$

Answer: $(-3,\ 1)$

57. $\begin{bmatrix} x \\ y \\ z \end{bmatrix} = \begin{bmatrix} 1 & 0 & 1 \\ 4 & 4 & 3 \\ -4 & -3 & -3 \end{bmatrix} \begin{bmatrix} 2 \\ -1 \\ -1 \end{bmatrix}$

$\qquad = \begin{bmatrix} 1 \\ 1 \\ -2 \end{bmatrix}$

Answer: $(1,\ 1,\ -2)$

59. $\begin{bmatrix} x \\ y \\ z \end{bmatrix} = \begin{bmatrix} 2 & 4 & \frac{7}{2} \\ -1 & -2 & -\frac{3}{2} \\ 1 & 1 & \frac{1}{2} \end{bmatrix} \begin{bmatrix} 2 \\ 10 \\ -12 \end{bmatrix}$

$\qquad = \begin{bmatrix} 2 \\ -4 \\ 6 \end{bmatrix}$

Answer: $(2,\ -4,\ 6)$

61. A has no inverse. The system is inconsistent.

63. Let $x =$ the number of carnations, and $y =$ the number of roses. Then,

$$x + y = 12$$

$$0.75x + 1.50y = \$12.00.$$

Using a graphing utility, we have $x = 8$ and $y = 4$. The florist should use 8 carnations and 4 roses.

65. $x + 2y \leq 160$

$$3x + y \leq 180$$

$$x \geq 0$$

$$y \geq 0$$

67. $3x + 2y \geq 24$
$x + 2y \geq 12$
$2 \leq x \leq 15$
$y \leq 15$

69. $y < x + 1$
$y > x^2 - 1$

71. $2x - 3y \geq 0$
$2x - y \leq 8$
$y \geq 0$

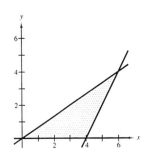

73. $-x + y \leq 4$
$2x + y \leq 22$
$-x + y \geq -2$
$2x + y \geq 7$

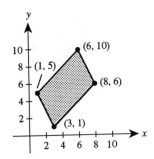

75. $x =$ Harrisburg market
$y =$ Philadelphia market
$x + y \leq 1500$
$x \geq 400$
$y \geq 600$

77. $\text{Demand} = \text{Supply}$

$$160 - 0.0001x = 70 + 0.0002x$$

$$90 = 0.0003x$$

$$x = 300{,}000 \text{ units}$$

$$p = \$130$$

Point of equilibrium: $(300{,}000, \ 130)$

Consumer surplus: $\frac{1}{2}(300{,}000)(30) = \$4{,}500{,}000$

Producer surplus: $\frac{1}{2}(300{,}000)(60) = \$9{,}000{,}000$

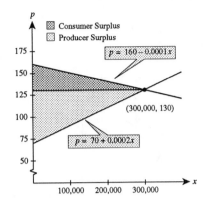

CHAPTER 10

Sequences, Mathematical Induction, and Probability

Section 10.1   Sequences and Summation Notation

- Given the general nth term in a sequence, you should be able to find, or list, some of the terms.
- You should be able to find an expression for the nth term of a sequence.
- You should be able to use and evaluate factorials.
- You should be able to use sigma notation for a sum.

1. $a_n = 2n + 1$

$a_1 = 2(1) + 1 = 3$

$a_2 = 2(2) + 1 = 5$

$a_3 = 2(3) + 1 = 7$

$a_4 = 2(4) + 1 = 9$

$a_5 = 2(5) + 1 = 10$

3. $a_n = 2^n$

$a_1 = 2^1 = 2$

$a_2 = 2^2 = 4$

$a_3 = 2^3 = 8$

$a_4 = 2^4 = 16$

$a_5 = 2^5 = 32$

5. $a_n = (-2)^n$

$a_1 = (-2)^1 = -2$

$a_2 = (-2)^2 = 4$

$a_3 = (-2)^3 = -8$

$a_4 = (-2)^4 = 16$

$a_5 = (-2)^5 = -32$

7. $a_n = \dfrac{1 + (-1)^n}{n}$

$a_1 = \dfrac{1 + (-1)}{1} = \dfrac{0}{1} = 0$

$a_2 = \dfrac{1 + (-1)^2}{2} = \dfrac{2}{2} = 1$

$a_3 = \dfrac{1 + (-1)^3}{3} = \dfrac{0}{3} = 0$

$a_4 = \dfrac{1 + (-1)^4}{4} = \dfrac{2}{4} = \dfrac{1}{2}$

$a_5 = \dfrac{1 + (-1)^5}{5} = \dfrac{0}{5} = 0$

9. $a_n = 3 - \dfrac{1}{2^n}$

$a_1 = 3 - \dfrac{1}{2^1} = \dfrac{5}{2}$

$a_2 = 3 - \dfrac{1}{2^2} = \dfrac{11}{4}$

$a_3 = 3 - \dfrac{1}{2^3} = \dfrac{23}{8}$

$a_4 = 3 - \dfrac{1}{2^4} = \dfrac{47}{16}$

$a_5 = 3 - \dfrac{1}{2^5} = \dfrac{95}{32}$

11. $a_n = \dfrac{1}{n^{3/2}}$

$a_1 = \dfrac{1}{1^{3/2}} = 1$

$a_2 = \dfrac{1}{2^{3/2}}$

$a_3 = \dfrac{1}{3^{3/2}}$

$a_4 = \dfrac{1}{4^{3/2}}$

$a_5 = \dfrac{1}{5^{3/2}}$

13. $a_n = \dfrac{3^n}{n!}$

$a_1 = \dfrac{3^1}{1!} = 3$

$a_2 = \dfrac{3^2}{2!} = \dfrac{9}{2}$

$a_3 = \dfrac{3^3}{3!} = \dfrac{9}{2}$

$a_4 = \dfrac{3^4}{4!} = \dfrac{27}{8}$

$a_5 = \dfrac{3^5}{5!} = \dfrac{81}{40}$

15. $a_n = \dfrac{(-1)^n}{n^2}$

$a_1 = \dfrac{(-1)^1}{1^2} = -1$

$a_2 = \dfrac{(-1)^2}{2^2} = \dfrac{1}{4}$

$a_3 = \dfrac{(-1)^3}{3^2} = -\dfrac{1}{9}$

$a_4 = \dfrac{(-1)^4}{4^2} = \dfrac{1}{16}$

$a_5 = \dfrac{(-1)^5}{5^2} = -\dfrac{1}{25}$

17. $a_1 = 3$

$a_{k+1} = 2(a_k - 1)$

$a_1 = 3$

$a_2 = 2(3 - 1) = 4$

$a_3 = 2(4 - 1) = 6$

$a_4 = 2(6 - 1) = 10$

$a_5 = 2(10 - 1) = 18$

19. $\dfrac{4!}{6!} = \dfrac{4!}{6 \cdot 5 \cdot 4!} = \dfrac{1}{30}$

21. $\dfrac{(n+1)!}{n!} = \dfrac{(n+1)n!}{n!} = n + 1$

23. $\dfrac{(2n-1)!}{(2n+1)!} = \dfrac{(2n-1)!}{(2n+1)(2n)(2n-1)!}$

$= \dfrac{1}{2n(2n+1)}$

25. $a_1 = 1 = 3(1) - 2$

$a_2 = 4 = 3(2) - 2$

$a_3 = 7 = 3(3) - 2$

$a_4 = 10 = 3(4) - 2$

$a_5 = 13 = 3(5) - 2$

$a_n = 3n - 2$

27. $a_1 = 0 = (1)^2 - 1$

$a_2 = 3 = (2)^2 - 1$

$a_3 = 8 = (3)^2 - 1$

$a_4 = 15 = (4)^2 - 1$

$a_5 = 24 = (5)^2 - 1$

$a_n = n^2 - 1$

29. $a_1 = \dfrac{1}{2} = \dfrac{(-1)^{1+1}}{2^1}$

$a_2 = -\dfrac{1}{4} = \dfrac{(-1)^{2+1}}{2^2}$

$a_3 = \dfrac{1}{8} = \dfrac{(-1)^{3+1}}{2^3}$

$a_4 = -\dfrac{1}{16} = \dfrac{(-1)^{4+1}}{2^4}$

$a_n = \dfrac{(-1)^{n+1}}{2^n}$

31. $a_1 = 1 + \dfrac{1}{1}$

$a_2 = 1 + \dfrac{1}{2}$

$a_3 = 1 + \dfrac{1}{3}$

$a_4 = 1 + \dfrac{1}{4}$

$a_5 = 1 + \dfrac{1}{5}$

$a_n = 1 + \dfrac{1}{n}$

33. $a_1 = 1 = \dfrac{1}{1!}$

$a_2 = \dfrac{1}{2} = \dfrac{1}{2!}$

$a_3 = \dfrac{1}{6} = \dfrac{1}{3!}$

$a_4 = \dfrac{1}{24} = \dfrac{1}{4!}$

$a_5 = \dfrac{1}{120} = \dfrac{1}{5!}$

$a_n = \dfrac{1}{n!}$

35. $a_1 = 1 = (-1)^{1+1}$

$a_2 = -1 = (-1)^{2+1}$

$a_3 = 1 = (-1)^{3+1}$

$a_4 = -1 = (-1)^{4+1}$

$a_5 = 1 = (-1)^{5+1}$

$a_n = (-1)^{n+1}$

37. $\displaystyle\sum_{i=1}^{5}(2i+1) = (2\cdot 1+1)+(2\cdot 2+1)+(2\cdot 3+1)+(2\cdot 4+1)+(2\cdot 5+1) = 35$

39. $\displaystyle\sum_{k=1}^{4}10 = 10+10+10+10 = 40$

41. $\displaystyle\sum_{i=0}^{4}i^2 = 0^2+1^2+2^2+3^2+4^2 = 30$

43. $\displaystyle\sum_{k=0}^{3}\dfrac{1}{k^2+1} = \dfrac{1}{0^2+1}+\dfrac{1}{1^2+1}+\dfrac{1}{2^2+1}+\dfrac{1}{3^2+1} = \dfrac{9}{5}$

45. $\displaystyle\sum_{i=1}^{4}[(i-1)^2+(i+1)^3] = [(1-1)^2+(1+1)^3+(2-1)^2+(2+1)^3+(3-1)^2$

$$+(3+1)^3+(4-1)^2+(4+1)^3] = 238$$

47. $\displaystyle\sum_{i=1}^{4}(9+2i) = (9+2\cdot 1)+(9+2\cdot 2)+(9+2\cdot 3)+(9+2\cdot 4) = 56$

49. $\displaystyle\sum_{k=0}^{4}\dfrac{(-1)^k}{k+1} = \dfrac{(-1)^0}{0+1}+\dfrac{(-1)^1}{1+1}+\dfrac{(-1)^2}{2+1}+\dfrac{(-1)^3}{3+1}+\dfrac{(-1)^4}{4+1} = \dfrac{47}{60}$

51. $\dfrac{1}{3(1)}+\dfrac{1}{3(2)}+\dfrac{1}{3(3)}+\cdots+\dfrac{1}{3(9)} = \displaystyle\sum_{i=1}^{9}\dfrac{1}{3i}$

53. $\left[2\left(\dfrac{1}{8}\right)+3\right]+\left[2\left(\dfrac{2}{8}\right)+3\right]+\cdots+\left[2\left(\dfrac{8}{8}\right)+3\right] = \displaystyle\sum_{i=1}^{8}\left[2\left(\dfrac{i}{8}\right)+3\right]$

55. $3-9+27-81+243-729 = 3^1-3^2+3^3-3^4+3^5-3^6 = \displaystyle\sum_{i=1}^{6}(-1)^{i+1}3^i$

57. $\dfrac{1}{1^2} - \dfrac{1}{2^2} + \dfrac{1}{3^2} - \dfrac{1}{4^2} + \cdots - \dfrac{1}{20^2} = \displaystyle\sum_{i=1}^{20} \dfrac{(-1)^{i+1}}{i^2}$ **59.** $\dfrac{1}{4} + \dfrac{3}{8} + \dfrac{7}{16} + \dfrac{15}{32} + \dfrac{31}{64} = \displaystyle\sum_{i=1}^{5} \dfrac{2^i - 1}{2^{i+1}}$

61. (a) $A_1 = 5000\left(1 + \dfrac{0.08}{4}\right)^1 = \$5100.00$ $A_5 = 5000\left(1 + \dfrac{0.08}{4}\right)^5 \approx \$5520.40$

$A_2 = 5000\left(1 + \dfrac{0.08}{4}\right)^2 = \$5202.00$ $A_6 = 5000\left(1 + \dfrac{0.08}{4}\right)^6 \approx \$5630.81$

$A_3 = 5000\left(1 + \dfrac{0.08}{4}\right)^3 = \$5306.04$ $A_7 = 5000\left(1 + \dfrac{0.08}{4}\right)^7 \approx \$5743.43$

$A_4 = 5000\left(1 + \dfrac{0.08}{4}\right)^4 \approx \$5412.16$ $A_8 = 5000\left(1 + \dfrac{0.08}{4}\right)^8 \approx \$5858.30$

(b) $A_{40} = 5000\left(1 + \dfrac{0.08}{4}\right)^{40} \approx \$11,040.20$

63. $a_0 = 242.67 + 42.67 \cdot 0 = 242.67$

$a_1 = 242.67 + 42.67 \cdot 1 = 285.34$

$a_2 = 242.67 + 42.67 \cdot 2 = 328.01$

$a_3 = 242.67 + 42.67 \cdot 3 = 370.68$

$a_4 = 242.67 + 42.67 \cdot 4 = 413.35$

$a_5 = 242.67 + 42.67 \cdot 5 = 456.02$

$a_6 = 242.67 + 42.67 \cdot 6 = 498.69$

$a_7 = 242.67 + 42.67 \cdot 7 = 541.36$

65. $\displaystyle\sum_{n=5}^{10}(0.20n + 1.17) = [0.20(5) + 1.17] + [0.20(6) + 1.17] + [0.20(7) + 1.17] + [0.20(8) + 1.17]$

$+ [0.20(9) + 1.17] + [0.20(10) + 1.17] = \$16.02$

$2.20 + 2.40 + 2.55 + 2.76 + 2.98 + 3.22 = \$16.11$

67. $\displaystyle\sum_{i=1}^{n}(x_i - \overline{x}) = \sum_{i=1}^{n} x_i - \sum_{i=1}^{n}\overline{x} = \sum_{i=1}^{n} x_i - n\overline{x} = \sum_{i=1}^{n} x_i - n\left(\dfrac{1}{n}\sum_{i=1}^{n} x_i\right) = 0$

69. $a_{n+2} = a_n + a_{n+1}, \quad a_1 = a_2 = 1$

(a) $a_1 = 1$ $\qquad\qquad a_7 = 5 + 8 = 13$

$\quad a_2 = 1$ $\qquad\qquad a_8 = 8 + 13 = 21$

$\quad a_3 = 1 + 1 = 2$ $\qquad a_9 = 13 + 21 = 34$

$\quad a_4 = 1 + 2 = 3$ $\qquad a_{10} = 21 + 34 = 55$

$\quad a_5 = 2 + 3 = 5$ $\qquad a_{11} = 34 + 55 = 89$

$\quad a_6 = 3 + 5 = 8$ $\qquad a_{12} = 55 + 89 = 144$

(b) $b_n = \dfrac{a_{n+1}}{a_n}$

$\quad b_2 = \dfrac{a_3}{a_2} = \dfrac{2}{1} = 2$ $\qquad\qquad b_7 = \dfrac{a_8}{a_7} = \dfrac{21}{13} = 1.615$

$\quad b_3 = \dfrac{a_4}{a_3} = \dfrac{3}{2} = 1.5$ $\qquad\quad b_8 = \dfrac{a_9}{a_8} = \dfrac{34}{21} = 1.619$

$\quad b_4 = \dfrac{a_5}{a_4} = \dfrac{5}{3} = 1.6\overline{6}$ $\qquad\quad b_9 = \dfrac{a_{10}}{a_9} = \dfrac{55}{34} = 1.618$

$\quad b_5 = \dfrac{a_6}{a_5} = \dfrac{8}{5} = 1.6$ $\qquad\quad b_{10} = \dfrac{a_{11}}{a_{10}} = \dfrac{89}{55} = 1.618$

$\quad b_6 = \dfrac{a_7}{a_6} = \dfrac{13}{8} = 1.625$ $\qquad b_{11} = \dfrac{a_{12}}{a_{11}} = \dfrac{144}{89} = 1.618$

(c) $b_n = \dfrac{a_{n+1}}{a_n} = \dfrac{a_n + a_{n-1}}{a_n} = 1 + \dfrac{a_{n-1}}{a_n} = 1 + \dfrac{1}{a_n/a_{n-1}} = 1 + \dfrac{1}{b_{n-1}}$

Section 10.2   Arithmetic Sequences

- You should be able to recognize an arithmetic sequence, find its common difference, d, and find its nth term, $a_n = dn + c$.

- You should be able to find the sum of an arithmetic sequence with n terms using the formula
$$S = \frac{n}{2}(a_1 + a_n).$$

- You should know that the arithmetic mean of a and b is $(a + b)/2$.

---

1. 4, 7, 10, 13, 16, ...

Arithmetic sequence, $d = 3$

3. 1, 2, 4, 8, 16, ...

Not an arithmetic sequence

5. $\frac{9}{4}$, 2, $\frac{7}{4}$, $\frac{3}{2}$, $\frac{5}{4}$, ...

Arithmetic sequence, $d = -\frac{1}{4}$

7. $\frac{1}{3}$, $\frac{2}{3}$, $\frac{4}{3}$, $\frac{8}{3}$, $\frac{16}{3}$, ...

Not an arithmetic sequence

9. 5.3, 5.7, 6.1, 6.5, 6.9, ...

Arithmetic sequence, $d = 0.4$

11. $a_n = 5 + 3n$

8, 11, 14, 17, 20

Arithmetic sequence, $d = 3$

13. $a_n = \dfrac{1}{n+1}$

$\dfrac{1}{2}, \dfrac{1}{3}, \dfrac{1}{4}, \dfrac{1}{5}, \dfrac{1}{6}$

Not an arithmetic sequence

15. $a_n = 100 - 3n$

97, 94, 91, 88, 85

Arithmetic sequence, $d = -3$

17. $a_n = 3 + \dfrac{(-1)^n 2}{n}$

1, 4, $\dfrac{7}{3}$, $\dfrac{7}{2}$, $\dfrac{13}{5}$

Not an arithmetic sequence

19. $a_1 = 1$, $d = 3$

$a_n = dn + c$

$a_1 = 1 = 3(1) + c \Rightarrow c = -2$

$a_n = 3n - 2$

21. $a_1 = 100$, $d = -8$

$a_n = dn + c$

$a_1 = 100 = -8(1) + c \Rightarrow c = 108$

$a_n = -8n + 108$

23. $a_1 = x$, $d = 2x$

$a_n = dn + c$

$a_1 = x = (2x)(1) + c \Rightarrow c = -x$

$a_n = 2xn - x$

25. 4, $\frac{3}{2}$, -1, $-\frac{7}{2}$, $\ldots \Rightarrow d = -\frac{5}{2}$

$a_n = dn + c$

$a_1 = 4 = -\frac{5}{2}(1) + c \Rightarrow c = \frac{13}{2}$

$a_n = -\frac{5}{2}n + \frac{13}{2}$

27. $a_1 = 5$, $a_4 = 15$

$a_n = dn + c$

$a_1 = 5 = d(1) + c$, $a_4 = 15 = d(4) + c$

$d + c = 5$

$4d + c = 15$

Solving this system of equations yields
$d = \frac{10}{3}$ and $c = \frac{5}{3}$.

$a_n = \frac{10}{3}n + \frac{5}{3}$

29. $a_3 = 94$, $a_6 = 85$

$a_n = dn + c$

$a_3 = 94 = d(3) + c$, $a_6 = 85 = d(6) + c$

$3d + c = 94$

$6d + c = 85$

Solving this system of equalities yields
$d = -3$ and $c = 103$.

$a_n = -3n + 103$

31. $a_1 = 5$, $d = 6$

$a_1 = 5$

$a_2 = 5 + 6 = 11$

$a_3 = 11 + 6 = 17$

$a_4 = 17 + 6 = 23$

$a_5 = 23 + 6 = 29$

33. $a_1 = -2.6$, $d = -0.4$

$a_1 = -2.6$

$a_2 = -2.6 - 0.4 = -3.0$

$a_3 = -3.0 - 0.4 = -3.4$

$a_4 = -3.4 - 0.4 = -3.8$

$a_5 = -4.2$

35. $a_1 = \frac{3}{2}$, $a_{k+1} = a_k - \frac{1}{4} \Rightarrow d = -\frac{1}{4}$

$a_1 = \frac{3}{2}$

$a_2 = \frac{3}{2} - \frac{1}{4} = \frac{5}{4}$

$a_3 = \frac{5}{4} - \frac{1}{4} = 1$

$a_4 = 1 - \frac{1}{4} = \frac{3}{4}$

$a_5 = \frac{3}{4} - \frac{1}{4} = \frac{1}{2}$

37. $a_1 = 2$, $a_{12} = 46$

$a_1 = 2 = d(1) + c$, $\quad a_{12} = 46 = d(12) + c$

$d + c = 2$

$12d + c = 46$

Solving this system yields $d = 4$ and $c = -2$.

$a_n = 4n - 2$

$a_1 = 2$

$a_2 = 6$

$a_3 = 10$

$a_4 = 14$

$a_5 = 18$

39. $a_8 = 26$, $a_{12} = 42$

$a_8 = 26 = d(8) + c$, $\quad a_{12} = 42 = d(12) + c$

$8d + c = 26$

$12d + c = 42$

Solving this system yields $d = 4$ and $c = -6$.

$a_n = 4n - 6$

$a_1 = -2$

$a_2 = 2$

$a_3 = 6$

$a_4 = 10$

$a_5 = 14$

41. 8, 20, 32, 44, $\ldots$, $n = 10$

$a_n = 12n - 4$

$a_1 = 8$ and $a_{10} = 116$

$S_{10} = \frac{10}{2}(8 + 116) = 620$

43. -6, -2, 2, 6, $\ldots$, $n = 50$

$a_n = 4n - 10$

$a_1 = -6$ and $a_{50} = 190$

$S_{50} = \frac{50}{2}(-6 + 190) = 4600$

45. 40, 37, 34, 31, $\ldots$, $n = 10$

$a_n = -3n + 43$

$a_1 = 40$ and $a_{10} = 13$

$S_{10} = \frac{10}{2}(40 + 13) = 265$

47. $a_1 = 100$, $a_{25} = 220$, $n = 25$

$S_{25} = \frac{25}{2}(100 + 220) = 4000$

49. $a_n = n$

$a_1 = 1$, $a_{50} = 50$

$S_{50} = \frac{50}{2}(1 + 50) = 1275$

51. $a_n = 5n$

$a_1 = 5$, $a_{100} = 500$

$S_{100} = \frac{100}{2}(5 + 500) = 25{,}250$

53. $\displaystyle\sum_{n=11}^{30} n - \sum_{n=1}^{10} n = \frac{20}{2}(11 + 30) - \frac{10}{2}(1 + 10) = 410 - 55 = 355$

55. $a_n = n + 3$

$a_1 = 4$, $a_{500} = 503$

$S_{500} = \frac{500}{2}(4 + 503) = 126{,}750$

57. $a_n = 2n + 5$

$a_1 = 7$, $a_{20} = 45$

$S_{20} = \frac{20}{2}(7 + 45) = 520$

59. $\displaystyle\sum_{n=0}^{50}(1000-5n)=1000+\sum_{n=1}^{50}(1000-5n)=1000+\frac{50}{2}(995+750)=44{,}625$

61. $5,\ m_1,\ m_2,\ 17$

$a_4=17=5+3d$

$d=4$

$m_1=5+4=9$

$m_2=9+4=13$

63. $3,\ m_1,\ m_2,\ m_3,\ 6$

$a_5=6=3+4d$

$d=\frac{3}{4}$

$m_1=3+\frac{3}{4}=\frac{15}{4}$

$m_2=\frac{15}{4}+\frac{3}{4}=\frac{9}{2}$

$m_3=\frac{9}{2}+\frac{3}{4}=\frac{21}{4}$

65. $a_1=1,\ a_{100}=199,\ n=100$

$S_{100}=\frac{100}{2}(1+199)=10{,}000$

67. (a) $a_n=a_1+(n-1)d$

$=27{,}500+(n-1)1500$

$=1500n+26{,}000$

$a_6=1500(6)+26{,}000=\$35{,}000$

(b) $S_6=\frac{6}{2}(27{,}500+35{,}000)=\$187{,}500$

69. $a_n=16+4n$

$a_1=20,\ a_{30}=136$

$S_{30}=\frac{30}{2}(20+136)=2340$ seats

71. $a_1=14,\ a_{20}=33$

$S_{20}=\frac{20}{2}(14+33)$

$=470$ bricks

73. Let $S=1+2+3+\cdots+(n-1)+n$ and $S=n+(n-1)+\cdots+2+1.$ Adding these two expressions for S:

$$2S=(n+1)+(n+1)+\cdots+(n+1)+(n+1)\qquad(n\text{ times})$$

$$2S=n(n+1)\Rightarrow S=\frac{n(n+1)}{2}$$

Section 10.3   Geometric Sequences

■ You should be able to identify a geometric sequence, find its common ratio, r, and find the nth term, $a_n = a_1 r^{n-1}$.

■ You should be able to find the sum of a geometric sequence with common ratio r using the formula
$$S = \frac{a_1(1 - r^n)}{1 - r}, \quad r \neq 1.$$

■ You should know that if $|r| < 1$, then
$$\sum_{n=0}^{\infty} a_1 r^n = \sum_{n=1}^{\infty} a_1 r^{n-1} = \frac{a_1}{1 - r}.$$

1. 5, 15, 45, 135, ...

Geometric sequence

$r = 3$

3. 3, 12, 21, 30, ...

Not a geometric sequence

5. $1, -\frac{1}{2}, \frac{1}{4}, -\frac{1}{8}, \ldots$

Geometric sequence

$r = -\frac{1}{2}$

7. $\frac{1}{2}, \frac{2}{3}, \frac{3}{4}, \frac{4}{5}, \ldots$

Not a geometric sequence

9. $1, \frac{1}{2}, \frac{1}{3}, \frac{1}{4}, \ldots$

Not a geometric sequence

11. $a_1 = 2, \; r = 3$

$a_1 = 2$

$a_2 = 2(3)^1 = 6$

$a_3 = 2(3)^2 = 18$

$a_4 = 2(3)^3 = 54$

$a_5 = 2(3)^4 = 162$

13. $a_1 = 1, \; r = \dfrac{1}{2}$

$a_1 = 1$

$a_2 = 1 \left(\dfrac{1}{2}\right)^1 = \dfrac{1}{2}$

$a_3 = 1 \left(\dfrac{1}{2}\right)^2 = \dfrac{1}{4}$

$a_4 = 1 \left(\dfrac{1}{2}\right)^3 = \dfrac{1}{8}$

$a_5 = 1 \left(\dfrac{1}{2}\right)^4 = \dfrac{1}{16}$

15. $a_1 = 5, \; r = -\dfrac{1}{10}$

$a_1 = 5$

$a_2 = 5 \left(-\dfrac{1}{10}\right)^1 = -\dfrac{1}{2}$

$a_3 = 5 \left(-\dfrac{1}{10}\right)^2 = \dfrac{1}{20}$

$a_4 = 5 \left(-\dfrac{1}{10}\right)^3 = -\dfrac{1}{200}$

$a_5 = 5 \left(-\dfrac{1}{10}\right)^4 = \dfrac{1}{2000}$

17. $a_1 = 1,\ r = e$

$a_1 = 1$

$a_2 = 1e^1 = e$

$a_3 = 1e^2 = e^2$

$a_4 = 1e^3 = e^3$

$a_5 = 1e^4 = e^4$

19. $a_1 = 3,\ r = \dfrac{x}{2}$

$a_1 = 3$

$a_2 = 3\left(\dfrac{x}{2}\right)^1 = \dfrac{3x}{2}$

$a_3 = 3\left(\dfrac{x}{2}\right)^2 = \dfrac{3x^2}{4}$

$a_4 = 3\left(\dfrac{x}{2}\right)^3 = \dfrac{3x^3}{8}$

$a_5 = 3\left(\dfrac{x}{2}\right)^4 = \dfrac{3x^4}{16}$

21. $a_1 = 4,\ r = \dfrac{1}{2},\ n = 10$

$a_{10} = 4\left(\dfrac{1}{2}\right)^9$

$= \dfrac{1}{128} = \left(\dfrac{1}{2}\right)^7$

23. $a_1 = 6,\ r = -\dfrac{1}{3},\ n = 12$

$a_{12} = 6\left(-\dfrac{1}{3}\right)^{11}$

$= -\dfrac{2}{3^{10}}$

25. $a_1 = 100,\ r = e^x,\ n = 9$

$a_9 = 100(e^x)^8 = 100e^{8x}$

27. $a_1 = 500,\ r = 1.02,$

$n = 40$

$a_{40} = 500(1.02)^{39}$

29. $a_1 = 16,\ a_4 = \dfrac{27}{4},\ n = 3$

$a_4 = 16r^3 = \dfrac{27}{4}$

$r^3 = \dfrac{27}{64}$

$r = \dfrac{3}{4}$

$a_3 = 16\left(\dfrac{3}{4}\right)^2 = 9$

31. $a_2 = -18,\ a_5 = \tfrac{2}{3},\ n = 6$

$a_2 r^3 = a_5$

$-18r^3 = \tfrac{2}{3}$

$r^3 = -\tfrac{1}{27}$

$r = -\tfrac{1}{3}$

$a_6 = a_5 r$

$a_6 = \tfrac{2}{3}\left(-\tfrac{1}{3}\right) = -\tfrac{2}{9}$

33. $A = P\left(1+\dfrac{r}{n}\right)^{nt} = 1000\left(1+\dfrac{0.10}{n}\right)^{n(10)}$

   (a) $n = 1,$ $A = 1000(1+0.10)^{10} \approx \$2593.74$

   (b) $n = 2,$ $A = 1000\left(1+\dfrac{0.10}{2}\right)^{2(10)} \approx \$2653.30$

   (c) $n = 4,$ $A = 1000\left(1+\dfrac{0.10}{4}\right)^{4(10)} \approx \$2685.06$

   (d) $n = 12,$ $A = 1000\left(1+\dfrac{0.10}{12}\right)^{12(10)} \approx \$2707.04$

   (e) $n = 365,$ $A = 1000\left(1+\dfrac{0.10}{365}\right)^{365(10)} \approx \$2717.91$

35. $V = $ value after n years

     $P = $ initial price $= \$135{,}000$

     $r = $ remaining value rate

     $ = 100\% - 30\% = 70\%$

     $n = $ number of years $= 5$

     $V = Pr^n = 135{,}000(0.7)^5 = \$22{,}689.45$

37. $\displaystyle\sum_{n=1}^{9} 2^{n-1} = \dfrac{1(1-2^9)}{1-2} = 511$

39. $\displaystyle\sum_{i=1}^{7} 64\left(-\dfrac{1}{2}\right)^{i-1} = \dfrac{64\left(1-(-1/2)^7\right)}{1-(-1/2)} = 43$

41. $\displaystyle\sum_{i=1}^{10} 8\left(-\dfrac{1}{4}\right)^{i-1} = \dfrac{8\left(1-(-1/4)^{10}\right)}{1-(-1/4)} = \dfrac{32(1-(-0.25)^{10})}{5} \approx 6.40$

43. $\displaystyle\sum_{n=0}^{20} 3\left(\dfrac{3}{2}\right)^n = \dfrac{3\left(1-(3/2)^{21}\right)}{1-(3/2)} = -6\left(1-\left(\dfrac{3}{2}\right)^{21}\right) \approx 29{,}921.31$

45. $\displaystyle\sum_{n=0}^{5} 300(1.06)^n = \dfrac{300(1-1.06^6)}{1-1.06} \approx 2092.60$

47. $A = \displaystyle\sum_{n=1}^{60} 100\left(1+\dfrac{0.10}{12}\right)^n = 100\left(1+\dfrac{0.10}{12}\right) \cdot \dfrac{\left[1-\left(1+\dfrac{0.10}{12}\right)^{60}\right]}{\left[1-\left(1+\dfrac{0.10}{12}\right)\right]} \approx \$7808.24$

49. Let $N = 12t$ be the total number of deposits.

$$A = P\left(1+\frac{r}{12}\right) + P\left(1+\frac{r}{12}\right)^2 + \cdots + P\left(1+\frac{r}{12}\right)^N$$

$$= \left(1+\frac{r}{12}\right)\left[P + P\left(1+\frac{r}{12}\right) + \cdots + P\left(1+\frac{r}{12}\right)^{N-1}\right]$$

$$= P\left(1+\frac{r}{12}\right)\sum_{n=1}^{N}\left(1+\frac{r}{12}\right)^{n-1}$$

$$= P\left(1+\frac{r}{12}\right)\frac{1-\left(1+\frac{r}{12}\right)^N}{1-\left(1+\frac{r}{12}\right)}$$

$$= P\left(1+\frac{r}{12}\right)\left(-\frac{12}{r}\right)\left[1-\left(1+\frac{r}{12}\right)^N\right]$$

$$= P\left(\frac{12}{r}+1\right)\left[-1+\left(1+\frac{r}{12}\right)^N\right]$$

$$= P\left[\left(1+\frac{r}{12}\right)^N - 1\right]\left(1+\frac{12}{r}\right)$$

$$= P\left[\left(1+\frac{r}{12}\right)^{12t} - 1\right]\left(1+\frac{12}{r}\right)$$

51. (a) $A = 50\left[\left(1+\frac{0.07}{12}\right)^{12(20)} - 1\right]\left(1+\frac{12}{0.07}\right) \approx \$26{,}198.27$

(b) $A = \dfrac{50e^{0.07/12}(e^{0.07(20)} - 1)}{e^{0.07/12} - 1} \approx \$26{,}263.88$

53. (a) $A = 100\left[\left(1+\frac{0.10}{12}\right)^{12(40)} - 1\right]\left(1+\frac{12}{0.10}\right) \approx \$637{,}678.02$

(b) $A = \dfrac{100e^{0.10/12}\left(e^{0.10(40)} - 1\right)}{e^{0.10/12} - 1} \approx \$645{,}861.43$

55. $P = W\left(1+\dfrac{r}{12}\right)^{-1} + W\left(1+\dfrac{r}{12}\right)^{-2} + \cdots + W\left(1+\dfrac{r}{12}\right)^{-12t}$

$= W\left(1+\dfrac{r}{12}\right)^{-1}\left[1+\left(1+\dfrac{r}{12}\right)^{-1} + \cdots + \left[\left(1+\dfrac{r}{12}\right)^{-1}\right]^{12t-1}\right]$

$= W\left(1+\dfrac{r}{12}\right)^{-1}\left[\dfrac{1-\left(1+\dfrac{r}{12}\right)^{-12t}}{1-\left(1+\dfrac{r}{12}\right)^{-1}}\right]$

$= \dfrac{W\left(\dfrac{12+r}{12}\right)^{-1}}{1-\left(\dfrac{12+r}{12}\right)^{-1}}\left[1-\left(1+\dfrac{r}{12}\right)^{-12t}\right]$

$= \dfrac{W\left(\dfrac{12}{12+r}\right)}{1-\dfrac{12}{12+r}}\left[1-\left(1+\dfrac{r}{12}\right)^{-12t}\right]$

$= \dfrac{W\left(\dfrac{12}{12+r}\right)}{\dfrac{12+r-12}{12+r}}\left[1-\left(1+\dfrac{r}{12}\right)^{-12t}\right]$

$= W\left(\dfrac{12}{r}\right)\left[1-\left(1+\dfrac{r}{12}\right)^{-12t}\right]$

57. $\displaystyle\sum_{n=0}^{9} 167.5e^{0.12n} = 167.5\dfrac{\left[1-\left(e^{0.12}\right)^{10}\right]}{1-e^{0.12}} \approx \$3048.1 \text{ million}$

59. $a_n = 30{,}000(1.05)^{n-1}$

$\displaystyle T = \sum_{n=1}^{40} 30{,}000(1.05)^{n-1} = 30{,}000\dfrac{(1-1.05^{40})}{(1-1.05)} \approx \$3{,}623{,}993.23$

61. $\displaystyle\sum_{n=0}^{\infty}\left(\dfrac{1}{2}\right)^{n} = 1 + \dfrac{1}{2} + \dfrac{1}{4} + \dfrac{1}{8} + \cdots = \dfrac{1}{1-\frac{1}{2}} = 2$

63. $\displaystyle\sum_{n=0}^{\infty}\left(-\dfrac{1}{2}\right)^{n} = 1 - \dfrac{1}{2} + \dfrac{1}{4} - \dfrac{1}{8} + \cdots - \dfrac{1}{1-\left(-\frac{1}{2}\right)} = \dfrac{2}{3}$

65. $\displaystyle\sum_{n=0}^{\infty} 4\left(\dfrac{1}{4}\right)^{n} = 4 + 1 + \dfrac{1}{4} + \dfrac{1}{16} + \cdots = \dfrac{4}{1-\frac{1}{4}} = \dfrac{16}{3}$

67. $8 + 6 + \dfrac{9}{2} + \dfrac{27}{8} + \cdots = \displaystyle\sum_{n=0}^{\infty} 8\left(\dfrac{3}{4}\right)^n = \dfrac{8}{1 - \frac{3}{4}} = 32$

69. $4 - 2 + 1 - \dfrac{1}{2} + \cdots = \displaystyle\sum_{n=0}^{\infty} 4\left(-\dfrac{1}{2}\right)^n = \dfrac{4}{1 - \left(-\frac{1}{2}\right)} = \dfrac{8}{3}$

71. The horizontal asymptote of f is the sum of the series.

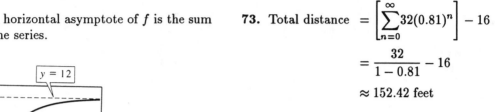

73. Total distance $= \left[\displaystyle\sum_{n=0}^{\infty} 32(0.81)^n\right] - 16$

$= \dfrac{32}{1 - 0.81} - 16$

≈ 152.42 feet

Section 10.4   Mathematical Induction

- You should be sure that you understand the principle of mathematical induction. If P_n is a statement involving the positive integer n, where P_1 is true and the truth of P_k implies the truth of P_{k+1}, then P_n is true for all positive integers n.

- You should be able to verify (by induction) the formulas for the sums of powers of integers and be able to use these formulas.

- You should be able to calculate finite differences of a sequence.

---

1. $P_{k+1} = \dfrac{5}{(k+1)[(k+1)+1]}$

$\qquad = \dfrac{5}{(k+1)(k+2)}$

3. $P_{k+1} = \dfrac{(k+1)^2[(k+1)+1]^2}{4}$

$\qquad = \dfrac{(k+1)^2(k+2)^2}{4}$

5. 1. When $n = 1$, $S_1 = 2 = 1(1+1)$.

    2. Assume that $S_k = 2 + 4 + 6 + 8 + \cdots + 2k = k(k+1)$. Then,

$$S_{k+1} = 2 + 4 + 6 + 8 + \cdots + 2k + 2(k+1)$$

$$= S_k + 2(k+1) = k(k+1) + 2(k+1) = (k+1)(k+2) = (k+1[(k+1)+1].$$

We conclude by mathematical induction that the formula is valid for all positive integer values of n.

7. 1. When $n = 1$, $S_1 = 2 = \frac{1}{2}(5(1) - 1)$.

    2. Assume that $S_k = 2 + 7 + 12 + 17 + \cdots + (5k - 3) = (k/2)(5k - 1)$. Then,

$$S_{k+1} = 2 + 7 + 12 + 17 + \cdots + (5k - 3) + [5(k+1) - 3]$$

$$= S_k + (5k + 5 - 3) = \frac{k}{2}(5k - 1) + 5k + 2$$

$$= \frac{5k^2 - k + 10k + 4}{2} = \frac{5k^2 + 9k + 4}{2}$$

$$= \frac{(k+1)(5k+4)}{2} = \frac{(k+1)}{2}[5(k+1) - 1].$$

We conclude by mathematical induction that the formula is valid for all positive integer values of n.

9. 1. When $n = 1$, $S_1 = 1 = 2^1 - 1$.

    2. Assume that $S_k = 1 + 2 + 2^2 + 2^3 + \cdots + 2^{k-1} = 2^k - 1$. Then,
$$S_{k+1} = 1 + 2 + 2^2 + 2^3 + \cdots + 2^{k-1} + 2^{k+1-1}$$
$$= S_k + 2^k = 2^k - 1 + 2^k = 2 \cdot 2^k - 1 = 2^{k+1} - 1.$$

Therefore, we conclude that this formula holds for all positive integer values of n.

11. 1. When $n = 1$, $S_1 = 1 = \dfrac{1(1+1)}{2}$.

    2. Assume that $S_k = 1 + 2 + 3 + 4 + \cdots + k = \dfrac{k(k+1)}{2}$. Then,
$$S_{k+1} = 1 + 2 + 3 + 4 + \cdots + k + (k+1)$$
$$= S_k + (k+1) = \frac{k(k+1)}{2} + \frac{2(k+1)}{2} = \frac{(k+1)(k+2)}{2}.$$

Therefore, we conclude that this formula holds for all positive integer values of n.

13. 1. When $n = 1$, $S_1 = 1^3 = 1 = \dfrac{1(1+1)^2}{4}$.

    2. Assume that $S_k = 1^3 + 2^3 + 3^3 + 4^3 + \cdots + k^3 = \dfrac{k^2(k+1)^2}{4}$. Then,
$$S_{k+1} = 1^3 + 2^3 + 3^3 + 4^3 + \cdots + k^3 + (k+1)^3$$
$$= S_k + (k+1)^3 = \frac{k^2(k+1)^2}{4} + (k+1)^3$$
$$= \frac{k^2(k+1)^2 + 4(k+1)^3}{4} = \frac{(k+1)^2[k^2 + 4(k+1)]}{4}$$
$$= \frac{(k+1)^2(k^2 + 4k + 4)}{4} = \frac{(k+1)^2(k+2)^2}{4}.$$

Therefore, we conclude that this formula holds for all positive integer values of n.

15. 1. When $n = 1$, $S_1 = 1^5 = \dfrac{1^2(1+1)^2(2 \cdot 1^2 + 2 \cdot 1 - 1)}{12}$.

2. Assume that $S_k = \displaystyle\sum_{i=1}^{k} i^5 = \dfrac{k^2(k+1)^2(2k^2 + 2k - 1)}{12}$. Then,

$$S_{k+1} = S_k + (k+1)^5$$

$$= \dfrac{k^2(k+1)^2(2k^2 + 2k - 1)}{12} + (k+1)^5$$

$$= \dfrac{k^2(k+1)^2(2k^2 + 2k - 1) + 12(k+1)^5}{12}$$

$$= \dfrac{(k+1)^2[k^2(2k^2 + 2k - 1) + 12(k+1)^3]}{12}$$

$$= \dfrac{(k+1)^2(k+2)^2(2k^2 + 6k + 3)}{12}$$

$$= \dfrac{(k+1)^2(k+2)^2(2(k+1)^2 + 2(k+1) - 1)}{12}.$$

Therefore, we conclude that this formula holds for all positive integer values of n.

17. 1. When $n = 1$, $S_1 = 2 = \dfrac{1(2)(3)}{3}$.

2. Assume that $S_k = 1(2) + 2(3) + 3(4) + \cdots + k(k+1) = \dfrac{k(k+1)(k+2)}{3}$. Then,

$$S_{k+1} = 1(2) + 2(3) + 3(4) + \cdots + k(k+1) + (k+1)(k+2)$$

$$= S_k + (k+1)(k+2)$$

$$= \dfrac{k(k+1)(k+2)}{3} + \dfrac{3(k+1)(k+2)}{3}$$

$$= \dfrac{(k+1)(k+2)(k+3)}{3}.$$

Thus, this formula is valid for all positive integer values of n.

19. $\displaystyle\sum_{n=1}^{20} n = \dfrac{20(20+1)}{2} = 210$ **21.** $\displaystyle\sum_{n=1}^{6} n^2 = \dfrac{6(6+1)(2 \cdot 6 + 1)}{6}$ **23.** $\displaystyle\sum_{n=1}^{5} n^3 = \dfrac{5^2(5+1)^2}{4} = 225$

$$= 91$$

25. $\displaystyle\sum_{n=1}^{6} n^4 = \dfrac{6(6+1)(2 \cdot 6 + 1)(3 \cdot 6^2 + 3 \cdot 6 - 1)}{30} = 2275$

27. $\displaystyle\sum_{n=1}^{6}(n^2 - n) = \sum_{n=1}^{6}n^2 - \sum_{n=1}^{6}n = \frac{6(6+1)(2 \cdot 6+1)}{6} - \frac{6(6+1)}{2} = 91 - 21 = 70$

29. 3, 7, 11, 15, ... is an arithmetic sequence with $a_1 = 3$, common difference $d = 4$, and $a_n = a_1 + (n-1)d = 3 + (n-1)4 = 4n - 1$. Hence, the sum of the first n terms is

$$S = \frac{n}{2}(a_1 + a_n) = \frac{n}{2}(3 + (4n - 1)) = \frac{n}{2}(4n + 2) = n(2n + 1).$$

31. 1, $\frac{9}{10}$, $\frac{81}{100}$, $\frac{729}{1000}$, ... is a geometric sequence with $a_1 = 1$ and common ratio $r = \frac{9}{10}$. Hence, the sum of the first n terms is

$$S = a_1 \left(\frac{1 - r^n}{1 - r}\right) = 1 \left(\frac{1 - (9/10)^n}{1 - (9/10)}\right) = 10(1 - (0.9)^n).$$

33. $\dfrac{1}{4}, \dfrac{1}{12}, \dfrac{1}{24}, \dfrac{1}{40}, \ldots, \dfrac{1}{2n(n-1)}, \ldots$. The sum of the first n terms is

$$\sum_{i=1}^{n}\frac{1}{2i(i-1)} = \frac{1}{2}\sum_{i=1}^{n}\frac{1}{i(i-1)} = \frac{1}{2}\left[\left(\frac{1}{1} - \frac{1}{2}\right) + \left(\frac{1}{2} - \frac{1}{3}\right) + \cdots + \left(\frac{1}{n} - \frac{1}{n+1}\right)\right]$$

$$= \frac{1}{2}\left(1 - \frac{1}{n+1}\right) = \frac{n}{2(n+1)}.$$

35. 1. When $n = 7$, $\left(\dfrac{4}{3}\right)^{7} \approx 7.4915 > 7.$

2. Assume that $\left(\dfrac{4}{3}\right)^{k} > k$, $k > 7$. Then,

$$\left(\frac{4}{3}\right)^{k+1} = \left(\frac{4}{3}\right)^{k}\left(\frac{4}{3}\right) > k\left(\frac{4}{3}\right) = k + \frac{k}{3} > k + 1 \text{ for } k > 7.$$

Thus, $\left(\dfrac{4}{3}\right)^{k+1} > k + 1$. Therefore, $\left(\dfrac{4}{3}\right)^{n} > n$.

37. 1. When $n = 4$, $4! = 24 > 2^4 = 16.$

2. Assume that $k! > 2^k$, $k > 4$.

$$(k + 1)! = (k + 1)k! > (k + 1)2^k > 2 \cdot 2^k = 2^{k+1}.$$

Therefore, $n! \geq 2^n$ for all integers $n \geq 4$.

39. 1. When $n = 1$, $(ab)^1 = a^1 b^1$.

2. Assume that $(ab)^k = a^k b^k$. Then,

$$(ab)^{k+1} = (ab)^k (ab) = a^k b^k ab = a^{k+1} b^{k+1}.$$

Thus, $(ab)^n = a^n b^n$.

41. 1. When $n = 1$, $(x_1)^{-1} = x_1^{-1}$.

2. Assume that $(x_1 x_2 x_3 \ldots x_k)^{-1} = x_1^{-1} x_2^{-1} x_3^{-1} \ldots x_k^{-1}$.

$$(x_1 x_2 x_3 \ldots x_k x_{k+1})^{-1} = (x_1 x_2 x_3 \ldots x_k)^{-1} (x_{k+1})^{-1} = x_1^{-1} x_2^{-1} x_3^{-1} \ldots x_k^{-1} x_{k+1}^{-1}.$$

Thus, $(x_1 x_2 x_3 \ldots x_n)^{-1} = x_1^{-1} x_2^{-1} x_3^{-1} \ldots x_n^{-1}$.

43. 1. When $n = 1$, $x(y_1) = xy_1$.

2. Assume that $x(y_1 + y_2 + \cdots + y_k) = xy_1 + xy_2 + \cdots + xy_k$. Then,

$$xy_1 + xy_2 + \cdots + xy_k + xy_{k+1} = x(y_1 + y_2 + \cdots + y_k) + xy_{k+1}$$
$$= x[(y_1 + y_2 + \cdots + y_k) + y_{k+1}]$$
$$= x(y_1 + y_2 + \cdots + y_k + y_{k+1}).$$

Hence, the formula holds.

45. 1. When $n = 1$, 3 is a factor of $(1^3 + 3 \cdot 1^2 + 2 \cdot 1) = 6$.

2. Assume that 3 is a factor of $k^3 + 3k^2 + 2k$. Then,

$$(k + 1)^3 + 3(k + 1)^2 + 2(k + 1) = k^3 + 6k^2 + 11k + 6$$
$$= (k^3 + 3k^2 + 2k) + (3k^2 + 9k + 6)$$
$$= (k^3 + 3k^2 + 2k) + 3(k^2 + 3k + 2)$$

Since 3 is a factor of each of the two terms, it follows that 3 is a factor of $(n^3 + 3n^2 + 2n)$ for all positive integers n.

47. $a_0 = 1$, $a_n = a_{n-1} + 2$

$a_1 = a_0 + 2 = 1 + 2 = 3$

$a_2 = a_1 + 2 = 3 + 2 = 5$

$a_3 = a_2 + 2 = 5 + 2 = 7$

$a_4 = a_3 + 2 = 7 + 2 = 9$

49. $a_0 = 4$, $a_1 = 2$, $a_n = a_{n-1} - a_{n-2}$

$a_2 = a_1 - a_0 = 2 - 4 = -2$

$a_3 = a_2 - a_1 = -2 - 2 = -4$

$a_4 = a_3 - a_2 = -4 - (-2) = -2$

51. $f(1) = 0, \quad a_n = a_{n-1} + 3$

$$\begin{array}{ccccc} 0 & 3 & 6 & 9 & 12 \\ & 3 & 3 & 3 & 3 \\ & & 0 & 0 & 0 \end{array}$$

Linear

53. $f(1) = 3, \quad a_n = a_{n-1} - n$

$$\begin{array}{ccccc} 3 & 1 & -2 & -6 & -11 \\ & -2 & -3 & -4 & -5 \\ & & -1 & -1 & -1 \end{array}$$

Quadratic

55. $a_0, \quad a_n = a_{n-1} + n$

$$\begin{array}{ccccc} 0 & 1 & 3 & 6 & 10 \\ & 1 & 2 & 3 & 4 \\ & & 1 & 1 & 1 \end{array}$$

Quadratic

57. $f(1) = 2, \quad a_n = a_{n-1} + 2$

$$\begin{array}{ccccc} 2 & 4 & 6 & 8 & 10 \\ & 2 & 2 & 2 & 2 \\ & & 0 & 0 & 0 \end{array}$$

Linear

59. $a_0 = 1, \quad a_n = a_{n-1} + n^2$

$$\begin{array}{ccccc} 1 & 2 & 6 & 15 & 31 \\ & 1 & 4 & 9 & 16 \\ & & 3 & 5 & 7 \end{array}$$

Neither linear nor quadratic

61. $a_0 = 3, \ a_1 = 3, \ a_4 = 15$

$f(n) = an^2 + bn + c$

$f(0) = a(0)^2 + b(0) + c = 3$

$f(1) = a(1)^2 + b(1) + c = 3$

$f(4) = a(4)^2 + b(4) + c = 15$

The system of three equations is:

$$c = 3$$
$$a + b + c = 3$$
$$16a + 4b + c = 15$$

The solution is

$a = 1, \ b = -1, \ c = 3 \Rightarrow f(n) = n^2 - n + 3.$

63. $a_0 = -3, \ a_2 = 1, \ a_4 = 9$

$f(n) = an^2 + bn + c$

$f(0) = a(0)^2 + b(0) + c = -3$

$f(2) = a(2)^2 + b(2) + c = 1$

$f(4) = a(4)^2 + b(4) + c = 9$

The system of three equations is:

$$c = -3$$
$$4a + 2b + c = 1$$
$$16a + 4b + c = 9$$

The solution is $a = \frac{1}{2}, \ b = 1, \ c = -3 \Rightarrow$
$f(n) = \frac{1}{2}n^2 + n - 3.$

Section 10.5   The Binomial Theorem

- You should be able to use the Binomial Theorem

$$(x + y)^n = x^n + nx^{n-1}y + \frac{n(n-1)}{2!}x^{n-2}y^2 + \cdots + {}_nC_m{}^n x^{n-m}y^m + \cdots + y^n$$

where ${}_nC_m = \dfrac{n!}{(n-m)!m!}$, to expand $(x+y)^n$.

- You should be able to use Pascal's Triangle in binomial expansion.

1. ${}_5C_3 = \dfrac{5!}{3!2!} = \dfrac{5 \cdot 4}{2 \cdot 1} = 10$

3. ${}_{12}C_0 = \dfrac{12!}{0!12!} = 1$

5. ${}_{20}C_{15} = \dfrac{20!}{15!5!}$

$= \dfrac{20 \cdot 19 \cdot 18 \cdot 17 \cdot 16}{5 \cdot 4 \cdot 3 \cdot 2 \cdot 1}$

$= 15{,}504$

7. ${}_{100}C_{98} = \dfrac{100!}{98!2!}$

$= \dfrac{100 \cdot 99}{2 \cdot 1}$

$= 4950$

9. ${}_{100}C_2 = \dfrac{100!}{2!98!} = \dfrac{100 \cdot 99}{2 \cdot 1} = 4950$

11. $(x+1)^4 = {}_4C_0x^4 + {}_4C_1x^3(1) + {}_4C_2x^2(1)^2 + {}_4C_3x(1)^3 + {}_4C_4(1)^4$

$\qquad = x^4 + 4x^3 + 6x^2 + 4x + 1$

13. $(a+2)^3 = {}_3C_0a^3 + {}_3C_1a^2(2) + {}_3C_2a(2)^2 + {}_3C_3(2)^3$

$\qquad = a^3 + 6a^2 + 12a + 8$

15. $(y-2)^4 = {}_4C_0y^4 - {}_4C_1y^3(2) + {}_4C_2y^2(2)^2 - {}_4C_3y(2)^3 + {}_4C_4(2)^4$

$\qquad = y^4 - 8y^3 + 24y^2 - 32y + 16$

17. $(x+y)^5 = {}_5C_0x^5 + {}_5C_1x^4y + {}_5C_2x^3y^2 + {}_5C_3x^2y^3 + {}_5C_4xy^4 + {}_5C_5y^5$

$\qquad = x^5 + 5x^4y + 10x^3y^2 + 10x^2y^3 + 5xy^4 + y^5$

19. $(r+3s)^6 = {}_6C_0r^6 + {}_6C_1r^5(3s) + {}_6C_2r^4(3s)^2 + {}_6C_3r^3(3s)^3 + {}_6C_4r^2(3s)^4 + {}_6C_5r(3s)^5 + {}_6C_6(3s)^6$

$\qquad = r^6 + 6(3s)r^5 + 15(9s^2)r^4 + 20(27s^3)r^3 + 15(81s^4)r^2 + 6(243s^5)r + 729s^6$

$\qquad = r^6 + 18r^5s + 135r^4s^2 + 540r^3s^3 + 1215r^2s^4 + 1458rs^5 + 729s^6$

21. $(x - y)^5 = {}_5C_0x^5 - {}_5C_1x^4y + {}_5C_2x^3y^2 - {}_5C_3x^2y^3 + {}_5C_4xy^4 - {}_5C_5y^5$

$\qquad = x^5 - 5x^4y + 10x^3y^2 - 10x^2y^3 + 5xy^4 - y^5$

23. $(1 - 2x)^3 = {}_3C_01^3 - {}_3C_11^2(2x) + {}_3C_21(2x)^2 - {}_3C_3(2x)^3$

$\qquad = 1 - 3(2x) + 3(2x)^2 - (2x)^3$

$\qquad = 1 - 6x + 12x^2 - 8x^3$

25. $(x^2 + 5)^4 = {}_4C_0(x^2)^4 + {}_4C_1(x^2)^3(5) + {}_4C_2(x^2)^2(5)^2 + {}_4C_3(x^2)(5)^3 + {}_4C_4(5)^4$

$\qquad = x^8 + 4x^6(5) + 6x^4(25) + 4x^2(125) + 625$

$\qquad = x^8 + 20x^6 + 150x^4 + 500x^2 + 625$

27. $\left(\dfrac{1}{x} + y\right)^5 = {}_5C_0\left(\dfrac{1}{x}\right)^5 + {}_5C_1\left(\dfrac{1}{x}\right)^4 y + {}_5C_2\left(\dfrac{1}{x}\right)^3 y^2 + {}_5C_3\left(\dfrac{1}{x}\right)^2 y^3 + {}_5C_4\left(\dfrac{1}{x}\right) y^4 + {}_5C_5y^5$

$\qquad = \dfrac{1}{x^5} + \dfrac{5y}{x^4} + \dfrac{10y^2}{x^3} + \dfrac{10y^3}{x^2} + \dfrac{5y^4}{x} + y^5$

29. $2(x - 3)^4 + 5(x - 3)^2 = 2[{}_4C_0x^4 - {}_4C_1x^3(3) + {}_4C_2x^2(3)^2 - {}_4C_3x(3)^3 + {}_4C_4(3)^4]$

$\qquad + 5[{}_2C_0x^2 - {}_2C_1x(3) + {}_2C_2(3)^2]$

$\qquad = 2[(1)x^4 - 4(3)x^3 + 6(9)x^2 - 4(27)x + 1(81)] + 5[(1)x^2 - 2(3)x + (1)9]$

$\qquad = 2x^4 - 24x^3 + 113x^2 - 246x + 207$

31. $(1 + i)^4 = {}_4C_01^4 + {}_4C_1(1)^3i + {}_4C_2(1)^2i^2 + {}_4C_31 \cdot i^3 + {}_4C_4i^4$

$\qquad = 1 + 4i - 6 - 4i + 1$

$\qquad = -4$

33. $(2 - 3i)^6 = {}_6C_02^6 - {}_6C_12^5(3i) + {}_6C_22^4(3i)^2 - {}_6C_32^3(3i)^3 + {}_6C_42^2(3i)^4 - {}_6C_52(3i)^5 + {}_6C_6(3i)^6$

$\qquad = 64 - 576i - 2160 + 4320i + 4860 - 2916i - 729$

$\qquad = 2035 + 828i$

35. $\left(-\dfrac{1}{2} + \dfrac{\sqrt{3}}{2}i\right)^3 = \dfrac{1}{8}(-1 + \sqrt{3}\,i)^3$

$\qquad = \dfrac{1}{8}[(-1)^3 + 3(-1)^2(\sqrt{3}\,i) + 3(-1)(\sqrt{3}\,i)^2 + (\sqrt{3}\,i)^3]$

$\qquad = \dfrac{1}{8}[-1 + 3\sqrt{3}\,i + 9 - 3\sqrt{3}\,i]$

$\qquad = 1$

37. 5th Row of Pascal's Triangle: 1   5   10   10   5   1

$$(2t - s)^5 = 1(2t)^5 + 5(2t)^4(-s) + 10(2t)^3(-s)^2 + 10(2t)^2(-s)^3 + 5(2t)(-s)^4 + 1(-s)^5$$
$$= 32t^5 - 80t^4s + 80t^3s^2 - 40t^2s^3 + 10ts^4 - s^5$$

39. 4th Row of Pascal's Triangle: 1   4   6   4   1

$$(3 - 2z)^4 = 3^4 - 4(3)^3(2z) + 6(3)^2(2z)^2 - 4(3)(2z)^3 + (2z)^4$$
$$= 81 - 216z + 216z^2 - 96z^3 + 16z^4$$

41. $_{12}C_7 x^5 (3)^7 = \dfrac{12!}{(12-7)!7!} \cdot 3^7 x^5$

$= 1{,}732{,}104 x^5$

$a = -326{,}592$

43. $_{10}C_2 x^8 (-2y)^2 = \dfrac{10!}{(10-2)!2!} \cdot 4x^8 y^2$

$= 180 x^8 y^2$

$a = 180$

45. $_9C_5 (3x)^4 (-2y)^5 = \dfrac{9!}{(9-5)!4!}(81x^4)(-32y^5)$

$= -326{,}592 x^4 y^5$

$a = -326{,}592$

47. $_{10}C_6 (x^2)^4 (1)^6 = \dfrac{10!}{(10-6)!6!} x^8$

$= 210 x^8$

$a = 210$

49. $_7C_4 \left(\dfrac{1}{2}\right)^4 \left(\dfrac{1}{2}\right)^3 = \dfrac{7 \cdot 6 \cdot 5}{3 \cdot 2} \left(\dfrac{1}{2}\right)^7$

$= \dfrac{35}{128} \approx 0.273$

51. $_8C_4 \left(\dfrac{1}{3}\right)^4 \left(\dfrac{2}{3}\right)^4 = \dfrac{8 \cdot 7 \cdot 6 \cdot 5}{4 \cdot 3 \cdot 2} \cdot \dfrac{2^4}{3^8}$

≈ 0.171

53. $(1.02)^8 = (1 + 0.02)^8 = 1 + 8(0.02) + 28(0.02)^2 + 56(0.02)^3 + 70(0.02)^4 + 56(0.02)^5$

$$+\, 28(0.02)^6 + 8(0.02)^7 + (0.02)^8$$
$$= 1 + 0.16 + 0.0112 + 0.000448 + \cdots \approx 1.172$$

55. $(2.99)^{12} = (3 - 0.01)^{12} = 3^{12} - 12(3)^{11}(0.01) + 66(3)^{10}(0.01)^2 - 220(3)^9(0.01)^3 + 495(3)^8(0.01)^4$

$$-\, 792(3)^7(0.01)^5 + 924(3)^6(0.01)^6 - 792(3)^5(0.01)^7 + 495(3)^4(0.01)^8$$
$$-\, 220(3)^3(0.01)^9 + 66(3)^2(0.01)^{10} - 12(3)(0.01)^{11} + (0.01)^{12}$$
$$= 531{,}441 - 21{,}257.64 + 389.7234 - 4.33026 + 0.03247695$$
$$-\, 0.0001732104 + \cdots$$
$$\approx 510{,}568.785$$

57. $f(x) = -x^2 + 3x + 2$

$\quad g(x) = f(x - 2)$

$\qquad = -(x - 2)^2 + 3(x - 2) + 2$

$\qquad = -(x^2 - 4x + 4) + 3x - 6 + 2$

$\qquad = -x^2 + 7x - 8$

$\quad g$ is f shifted 2 units to the right.

59. $f(x) = x^3 - 4x$

$\quad g(x) = f(x + 4)$

$\qquad = (x + 4)^3 - 4(x + 4)$

$\qquad = x^3 + 12x^2 + 48x + 64 - 4x - 16$

$\qquad = x^3 + 12x^2 + 44x + 48$

$\quad g$ is f shifted 4 units to the left.

61. $f(t) = 0.2187t^2 + 0.6715t + 26.67$

$\quad g(t) = f(t + 10)$

$\qquad = 0.2187(t + 10)^2 + 0.6715(t + 10) + 26.67$

$\qquad = 0.2187(t^2 + 20t + 100) + 0.6715t + 6.715 + 26.67$

$\qquad = 0.2187t^2 + 5.0455t + 55.255$

63. $_nC_m = \dfrac{n!}{(n - m)!m!} = \dfrac{n!}{m!(n - m)!} = \,_nC_{n-m}$

65. $_nC_m + {_nC_{m-1}} = \dfrac{n!}{(n-m)!m!} + \dfrac{n!}{(n-m+1)!(m-1)!}$

$$= \dfrac{n!(n-m+1)!(m-1)! + n!(n-m)!m!}{(n-m)!m!(n-m+1)!(m-1)!}$$

$$= \dfrac{n![(n-m+1)!(m-1)! + m!(n-m)!]}{(n-m)!m!(n-m+1)!(m-1)!}$$

$$= \dfrac{n!(m-1)![(n-m+1)! + m(n-m)!]}{(n-m)!m!(n-m+1)!(m-1)!}$$

$$= \dfrac{n!(n-m)![(n-m+1) + m]}{(n-m)!m!(n-m+1)!}$$

$$= \dfrac{n![n+1]}{m!(n-m+1)!}$$

$$= \dfrac{(n+1)!}{[(n+1)-m]!m!}$$

$$= {_{n+1}C_m}$$

67. $_nC_0 + {_nC_1} + {_nC_2} + {_nC_3} + \cdots + {_nC_n} = (1+1)^n = 2^n$

Section 10.6   Counting Principles, Permutations, Combinations

- You should know The Fundamental Principle of Counting.

- $_nP_m = \dfrac{n!}{(n-m)!}$ is the number of permutations of n elements taken m at a time.

- Given a set of n objects that has n_1 of one kind, n_2 of a second kind, and so on, the number of distinguishable permutations is

  $$\dfrac{n!}{n_1!n_2!\ldots n_k!}.$$

- $_nC_m = \dfrac{n!}{(n-m)!m!}$ is the number of combinations of n elements taken m at a time.

1. | *First Number* | *Second Number* |
   |:---:|:---:|
   | 1 | 7 |
   | 2 | 6 |
   | 3 | 5 |
   | 4 | 4 |
   | 5 | 3 |
   | 6 | 2 |
   | 7 | 1 |

   A total of 8 may be obtained 7 different ways.

3. $3 \cdot 4 = 12$ ways to fill the positions   5. $2 \cdot 3 \cdot 2 \cdot 1 = 12$ ways to be seated

7. $26 \cdot 26 \cdot 10 \cdot 10 \cdot 10 \cdot 10 = 6{,}760{,}000$ distinct license plate numbers

9. $2 \cdot 2 \cdot 2 \cdot 2 \cdot 2 \cdot 2 = 2^6 = 64$ different ways

11. (a) $9 \cdot 10 \cdot 10 = 900$ ways
    (b) $9 \cdot 9 \cdot 8 = 648$ ways
    (c) $9 \cdot 10 \cdot 2 = 180$ ways (The last digit must be 0 or 5.)
    (d) $6 \cdot 10 \cdot 10 = 600$ ways (The first digit must be greater than or equal to 4.)

13. $40 \cdot 40 \cdot 40 = 64{,}000$ different lock combinations

15. (a) $6 \cdot 5 \cdot 4 \cdot 3 \cdot 2 \cdot 1 = 720$ different ways
(b) $6 \cdot 4 \cdot 2 = 48$ different ways

17. $_4P_4 = \dfrac{4!}{(4-4)!} = \dfrac{4!}{0!} = 24$

19. $_8P_3 = \dfrac{8!}{(8-3)!} = \dfrac{8!}{5!} = 336$

21. $_{20}P_5 = \dfrac{20!}{(20-5)!}$
$= \dfrac{20!}{15!}$
$= 1{,}860{,}480$

23. $_{100}P_2 = \dfrac{100!}{(100-2)!}$
$= \dfrac{100!}{98!}$
$= 9900$

25. $_5P_4 = \dfrac{5!}{(5-4)!}$
$= \dfrac{5!}{1!}$
$= 120$

27.

ABCD	BACD	CABD	DABC
ABDC	BADC	CADB	DACB
ACBD	BCAD	CBAD	DBAC
ACDB	BCDA	CBDA	DBCA
ADBC	BDAC	CDAB	DCAB
ADCB	BDCA	CDBA	DCBA

29. $5! = 120$ ways

31. $_{12}P_4 = 12 \cdot 11 \cdot 10 \cdot 9 = 11{,}880$ ways

33. $\dfrac{7!}{2!1!3!1!} = 420$

35. $\dfrac{9!}{2!4!3!} = 1260$

37. $\dfrac{7!}{2!1!1!1!1!} = 2520$

39. AB, AC, AD, AE, AF, BC, BD, BE, BF, DC, CE, CF, DE, DF, EF

41. $_{20}C_4 = \dfrac{20!}{(20-4)!4!}$
$= \dfrac{20!}{16!4!}$
$= 4845$

43. $_{40}C_6 = \dfrac{40!}{(40-6)!6!}$
$= \dfrac{40!}{34!6!}$
$= 3{,}838{,}380$

45. $_{100}C_4 = \dfrac{100!}{(100-4)!4!}$
$= \dfrac{100!}{96!4!}$
$= 3{,}921{,}225$

47. $_8C_3\,_5C_2 = \dfrac{8!}{(8-3)!3!} \cdot \dfrac{5!}{(5-2)!2!}$
$= 560$

49. (a) $_8C_4 = \dfrac{8!}{(8-4)!4!} = \dfrac{8!}{4!4!} = 70$

   (b) $_3C_2 \, _5C_2 = \dfrac{3!}{(3-2)!2!} \cdot \dfrac{5!}{(5-2)!2!} = \dfrac{3!}{1!2!} \cdot \dfrac{5!}{3!2!} = 30$

51. (a) $_8C_4 = \dfrac{8!}{(8-4)!4!} = \dfrac{8!}{4!4!} = 70$

   (b) Number of ways to obtain no couples: $2^4 = 16$
   Number of ways to obtain at least one couple: $_8C_4 - 2^4 = 70 - 16 = 54$

   (c) $2^4 = 16$

53. $_5C_2 - 5 = \dfrac{5!}{(5-2)!2!} - 5$

   $= 10 - 5 = 5$

55. $_8C_2 - 8 = \dfrac{8!}{(8-2)!2!} - 8$

   $= 28 - 8 = 20$

57. $14 \cdot {}_nP_3 = {}_{n+2}P_4$

   $14n(n-1)(n-2) = (n+2)(n+1)(n)(n-1)$

   $\qquad\qquad 0 = (n+2)(n+1)(n)(n-1) - 14n(n-1)(n-2)$

   $\qquad\qquad 0 = n(n-1)[n^2 + 3n + 2 - 14n + 28]$

   $\qquad\qquad 0 = n(n-1)(n^2 - 11n + 30)$

   $\qquad\qquad 0 = n(n-1)(n-5)(n-6)$

   Since $n \geq 3$, $n = 5$ or $n = 6$.

59. $_nP_{n-1} = n(n-1)(n-2)\cdots 3 \cdot 2 = n(n-1)(n-2)\cdots 3 \cdot 2 \cdot 1 = {}_nP_n$

61. $_nC_{n-1} = \dfrac{n!}{(n-(n-1))!(n-1)!} = \dfrac{n!}{1!(n-1)!} = \dfrac{n!}{(n-1)!1!} = {}_nC_1$

63. $_nC_m = \dfrac{n!}{(n-m)!m!}$

   $= \dfrac{n(n-1)(n-2)\cdots(n-m+1)(n-m)!}{(n-m)!m!}$

   $= \dfrac{n(n-1)(n-2)\cdots(n-m+1)}{m!} = \dfrac{_nP_m}{m!}$

Section 10.7 Probability

You should know the following basic principles of probability.

■ If an event E has $n(E)$ equally likely outcomes and its sample space has $n(S)$ equally likely outcomes, then the probability of event E is

$$P(E) = \frac{n(E)}{n(S)}, \text{ where } 0 \le P(E) \le 1.$$

■ If A and B are mutually exclusive events, then $P(A \cup B) = P(A) + P(B)$. If A and B are not mutually exclusive events, then $P(A \cup B) = P(A) + P(B) - P(A \cap B)$.

■ If A and B are independent events, then the probability that both A and B will occur is $P(A)P(B)$.

■ The probability of the complement of an event A is $P(A') = 1 - P(A)$.

1. $\{(h, 1), (h, 2), (h, 3), (h, 4), (h, 5), (h, 6), (t, 1), (t, 2), (t, 3), (t, 4), (t, 5), (t, 6)\}$

3. $\{ABC, ACB, BAC, BCA, CAB, CBA\}$

5. $\{AB, AC, AD, AE, BC, BD, BE, CD, CE, DE\}$

7. $n(E) = \{HHT, HTH, THH\}$

$$P(E) = \frac{n(E)}{n(S)} = \frac{3}{8}$$

9. $P(TTT) = \frac{1}{8}$

$P(\text{at least one head}) = 1 - \frac{1}{8} = \frac{7}{8}$

11. There are three face cards (K, Q, and J) in each of the four suits. Therefore, there are 12 face cards in a deck.

$$P(E) = \tfrac{12}{52} = \tfrac{3}{13}$$

13. Twenty-six of the cards are black. Six of these are face cards (J, Q, K of clubs and spades). Therefore, there are 20 black cards that are not face cards.

$$P(E) = \tfrac{20}{52} = \tfrac{5}{13}$$

15. $n(S) = 6 \cdot 6 = 36$

$E = \{(1, 3), (2, 2), (3, 1)\}$

$P(E) = \tfrac{3}{36} = \tfrac{1}{12}$

17. $n(S) = 6 \cdot 6 = 36$

$E = \{(1,6),\ (2,5),\ (3,4),\ (4,3),\ (5,2),\ (6,1),\ (2,6),\ (3,5),\ (4,\ 4),\ (5,3),\ (6,2),$
$(3,6),\ (4,5),\ (5,4),\ (6,3),\ (4,6),\ (5,5),\ (6,4),\ (5,6),\ (6,6),\ (6,5)\}$

$P(E) = \frac{21}{36} = \frac{7}{12}$

19. $n(S) = 6 \cdot 6 = 36$

$E = \{(1,2),\ (1,4),\ (1,6),\ (2,1),\ (2,3),\ (2,5),(3,2),\ (3,4),\ (4,1),\ (4,3),\ (5,2),\ (6,1)\}$

$P(E) = \frac{12}{36} = \frac{1}{3}$

21. $n(S) = {}_6C_2 = 15$

$n(E) = {}_3C_2 = 3$

$P(E) = \frac{3}{15} = \frac{1}{5}$

23. $n(S) = {}_6C_2 = 15$

$n(E) = {}_4C_2 = 6$

$P(E) = \frac{6}{15} = \frac{2}{5}$

25. $1 - p = 1 - 0.7 = 0.3$

27. $1 - p = 1 - 0.15 = 0.85$

29. $n(S) = 1254$

(a) $n(E) = 672$

$P(E) = \frac{672}{1254} = \frac{112}{209}$

(b) $n(E) = 582$

$P(E) = \frac{582}{1254} = \frac{97}{209}$

(c) $n(E) = 672 - 124$

$= 548$

$P(E) = \frac{548}{1254} = \frac{274}{627}$

31. $p + p + 2p = 1$

$p = 0.25$

Taylor:	0.50
Moore:	0.25
Jenkins:	0.25

33. $n(S) = {}_{20}C_{10} = 184{,}756$

(a) $n(E) = {}_{15}C_{10} = 3003$

$P(E) = \frac{3003}{184{,}756} = \frac{21}{1292} \approx 0.016$

(b) $n(E) = {}_{15}C_8\ {}_5C_2 = 64{,}350$

$P(E) = \frac{64{,}350}{184{,}756} = \frac{225}{646} \approx 0.348$

(c) $n(E) = {}_{15}C_9\ {}_5C_1 +\ {}_{15}C_{10}$

$= 25{,}025 + 3003 = 28{,}028$

$P(E) = \frac{28{,}028}{184{,}756} = \frac{49}{323} \approx 0.152$

35. Total ways to insert 4 letters:

$4! = 24$ ways

4 correct:	1 way
3 correct:	not possible
2 correct:	6 ways
1 correct:	8 ways
0 correct:	9 ways

(a) $\dfrac{8}{24} = \dfrac{1}{3}$

(b) $\dfrac{8 + 6 + 1}{24} = \dfrac{15}{24} = \dfrac{5}{8}$

37. (a) $n(S) = 5! = 120$

$n(E) = 1$

$P(E) = \frac{1}{120}$

(b) $n(S) = 4! = 24$

$n(E) = 1$

$P(E) = \frac{1}{24}$

39. (a) $(\frac{4}{52})(\frac{4}{52}) = \frac{1}{169}$

(b) $(\frac{4}{52})(\frac{3}{51}) = \frac{1}{221}$

41. $n(S) = {}_{12}C_4 = 495$

(a) $n(E) = {}_9C_4 = 126$

$P(E) = \frac{126}{495} = \frac{14}{55}$

(b) $n(E) = {}_9C_2 \, {}_3C_2 = 108$

$P(E) = \frac{108}{495} = \frac{12}{55}$

(c) $n(E) = {}_9C_2 \, {}_3C_2 + {}_9C_3 \, {}_3C_1 + {}_9C_4 \, {}_3C_0 = 486$

$P(E) = \frac{486}{495} = \frac{54}{55}$

43. (a) $P(EE) = \frac{15}{30} \cdot \frac{15}{30} = \frac{1}{4}$

(b) $P(EO \text{ or } OE) = 2(\frac{15}{30})(\frac{15}{30}) = \frac{1}{2}$

(c) $P(N_1 < 10, \ N_2 < 10) = \frac{9}{30} \cdot \frac{9}{30} = \frac{9}{100}$

(d) $P(N_1 N_1) = \frac{30}{30} \cdot \frac{1}{30} = \frac{1}{30}$

45. (a) $P(SS) = (0.985)^2 \approx 0.9702$

(b) $P(S) = 1 - P(FF)$

$= 1 - (0.015)^2 \approx 0.9998$

(c) $P(FF) = (0.015)^2 \approx 0.0002$

47. (a) $P(SSSSS) = \left(\frac{1}{4}\right)^5 = \frac{1}{1024}$

(b) $P(NNNNN) = \left(\frac{3}{4}\right)^5 = \frac{243}{1024}$

(c) $P(\text{at least one contract})$

$= 1 - P(NNNNN)$

$= 1 - \frac{243}{1024} = \frac{781}{1024}$

49. (a) $P(BBBB) = (\frac{1}{2})(\frac{1}{2})(\frac{1}{2})(\frac{1}{2}) = \frac{1}{16}$

(b) $P(BBBB) + P(GGGG) = \frac{1}{16} + \frac{1}{16} = \frac{1}{8}$

(c) $1 - P(GGGG) = 1 - \frac{1}{16} = \frac{15}{16}$

51. $P(CC) = (0.32)(0.32) = 0.1024$

Chapter 10   Review Exercises

1. $\dfrac{1}{2(1)} + \dfrac{1}{2(2)} + \dfrac{1}{2(3)} + \cdots + \dfrac{1}{2(20)} = \displaystyle\sum_{k=1}^{20} \dfrac{1}{2k}$

3. $\dfrac{1}{2} + \dfrac{2}{3} + \dfrac{3}{4} + \cdots + \dfrac{9}{10} = \displaystyle\sum_{k=1}^{9} \dfrac{k}{k+1}$

5. $\displaystyle\sum_{i=1}^{6} 5 = 5+5+5+5+5+5 = 30$

7. $\displaystyle\sum_{j=3}^{10} (2j-3) = 3+5+7+9+\cdots+17$
$= 80$

9. Geometric, $a_0 = 1$, $r = 2$, $n = 7$
$\displaystyle\sum_{i=0}^{6} 2^i = 1\left(\dfrac{1-2^7}{1-2}\right) = 127$

11. $\displaystyle\sum_{i=0}^{\infty} \left(\dfrac{7}{8}\right)^i = \dfrac{1}{1-r} = \dfrac{1}{1-\frac{7}{8}} = 8$
(Sum of infinite geometric sequence)

13. Geometric, $a_0 = 4$, $r = \dfrac{2}{3}$
$\displaystyle\sum_{k=0}^{\infty} 4\left(\dfrac{2}{3}\right)^k = \dfrac{4}{1-\frac{2}{3}} = 12$

15. Arithmetic
$a_1 = \frac{14}{3}$, $a_{11} = \frac{34}{3}$, $n = 11$
$\displaystyle\sum_{k=1}^{11} \left(\tfrac{2}{3}k + 4\right) = \tfrac{11}{2}\left(\tfrac{14}{3} + \tfrac{34}{3}\right) = 88$

17. $\displaystyle\sum_{n=0}^{10} (n^2 + 3) = \displaystyle\sum_{n=0}^{10} n^2 + \displaystyle\sum_{n=0}^{10} 3 = \dfrac{10(10+1)(2 \cdot 10 + 1)}{6} + 3(11) = 418$

19. $a_1 = 3$
$a_2 = 3 + 4 = 7$
$a_3 = 7 + 4 = 11$
$a_4 = 11 + 4 = 15$
$a_5 = 15 + 4 = 19$

21. $a_4 = 10 = d(4) + c$
$a_{10} = 28 = d(10) + c$
$4d + c = 10$
$10d + c = 28$
Solving this system yields $d = 3$ and $c = -2$.
Thus, $a_n = 3n - 2$
$a_1 = 1$
$a_2 = 4$
$a_3 = 7$
$a_4 = 10$
$a_5 = 13.$

23. $a_1 = 100 = 1(-3) + c \implies c = 103$

$a_n = -3n + 103$

$a_{20} = 43, \; n = 20$

$\displaystyle\sum_{n=1}^{20} (-3n + 103) = \frac{20}{2}(100 + 43)$

$\qquad\qquad\qquad = 1430$

25. $\displaystyle\sum_{i=1}^{100} 5i = 5\sum_{i=1}^{100} i$

$\qquad = 5\left(\frac{100(101)}{2}\right)$

$\qquad = 25{,}250$

27. $a_1 = 4$

$a_2 = 4\left(-\dfrac{1}{4}\right) = -1$

$a_3 = 4\left(-\dfrac{1}{4}\right)^2 = \dfrac{1}{4}$

$a_4 = 4\left(-\dfrac{1}{4}\right)^3 = -\dfrac{1}{16}$

$a_5 = 4\left(-\dfrac{1}{4}\right)^4 = \dfrac{1}{64}$

29. $a_3 = 4 = (9)r^2, \; r^2 = \dfrac{4}{9}, \; r = \pm\dfrac{2}{3}$

$a_1 = 9 \qquad\qquad\qquad \text{or} \quad a_1 = 9$

$a_2 = 9\left(\dfrac{2}{3}\right) = 6 \qquad a_2 = 9\left(-\dfrac{2}{3}\right) = -6$

$a_3 = 9\left(\dfrac{2}{3}\right)^2 = 4 \qquad a_3 = 9\left(-\dfrac{2}{3}\right)^2 = 4$

$a_4 = 9\left(\dfrac{2}{3}\right)^3 = \dfrac{8}{3} \qquad a_4 = 9\left(-\dfrac{2}{3}\right)^3 = -\dfrac{8}{3}$

$a_5 = 9\left(\dfrac{2}{3}\right)^4 = \dfrac{16}{9} \qquad a_5 = 9\left(-\dfrac{2}{3}\right)^4 = \dfrac{16}{9}$

31. $r = \dfrac{a_2}{a_1} = \dfrac{-8}{16} = -\dfrac{1}{2}$

$a_n = 16\left(-\dfrac{1}{2}\right)^{n-1}$

$\displaystyle\sum_{n=1}^{20} 16\left(-\dfrac{1}{2}\right)^{n-1} = 16\left(\frac{1 - \left(-\dfrac{1}{2}\right)^{20}}{1 - \left(-\dfrac{1}{2}\right)}\right)$

$\qquad\qquad\qquad\qquad \approx 10.667$

33. (a) $a_t = 120{,}000(0.70)^t$

(b) $a_5 = 120{,}000(0.70)^5 = \$20{,}168.40$

35. $A = \displaystyle\sum_{i=1}^{24} 200\left(1 + \frac{0.06}{12}\right)^i = \sum_{i=1}^{24} 200(1.005)^i = 200(1.005)\left[\frac{1 - (1.005)^{24}}{1 - 1.005}\right] \approx \$5111.82$

37. 1. When $n = 1$, $1 = \frac{1}{2}[3(1) - 1] = 1$.

   2. Assume that $1 + 4 + 7 + \cdots + (3k - 2) = (k/2)(3k - 1)$. Then,

$$1 + 4 + 7 + \cdots + (3k - 2) + [3(k + 1) - 2] = [1 + 4 + 7 + \cdots + (3k - 2)] + (3k + 1)$$

$$= \frac{k}{2}(3k - 1) + (3k + 1)$$

$$= \frac{k(3k - 1)}{2} + \frac{2(3k + 1)}{2}$$

$$= \frac{3k^2 + 5k + 2}{2}$$

$$= \frac{(k + 1)(3k + 2)}{2}$$

$$= \frac{(k + 1)}{2}[3(k + 1) - 1].$$

Thus, the formula holds for all positive intergers n.

39. 1. When $n = 1$, $ar^0 = a = \dfrac{a(1 - r^1)}{1 - r} = a$.

   2. Assume that $\displaystyle\sum_{i=0}^{k-1} ar^i = \dfrac{a(1 - r^k)}{1 - r}$. Then,

$$\sum_{i=0}^{k+1-1} ar^i = \frac{a(1 - r^k)}{1 - r} + ar^k$$

$$= \frac{a(1 - r^k) + ar^k(1 - r)}{1 - r} = \frac{a(1 - r^k + r^k - r^{k+1})}{1 - r} = \frac{a(1 - r^{k+1})}{1 - r}.$$

Thus, the formula holds for all positive integers n.

41. $_6C_4 = \dfrac{6!}{(6 - 4)!4!} = 15$ **43.** $_{25}C_5 = \dfrac{25 \cdot 24 \cdot 23 \cdot 22 \cdot 21}{5 \cdot 4 \cdot 3 \cdot 2 \cdot 1} = 53{,}130$

45. $\left(\dfrac{x}{2} + y\right)^4 = \left(\dfrac{x}{2}\right)^4 + 4\left(\dfrac{x}{2}\right)^3 y + 6\left(\dfrac{x}{2}\right)^2 y^2 + 4\left(\dfrac{x}{2}\right) y^3 + y^4 = \dfrac{x^4}{16} + \dfrac{x^3 y}{2} + \dfrac{3x^2 y^2}{2} + 2xy^3 + y^4$

47. $\left(\dfrac{2}{x} - 3x\right)^6 = \left(\dfrac{2}{x}\right)^6 - 6\left(\dfrac{2}{x}\right)^5 (3x) + 15\left(\dfrac{2}{x}\right)^4 (3x)^2 - 20\left(\dfrac{2}{x}\right)^3 (3x)^3$

$$+ 15\left(\frac{2}{x}\right)^2 (3x)^4 - 6\left(\frac{2}{x}\right)(3x)^5 + (3x)^6$$

$$= \frac{64}{x^6} - \frac{576}{x^4} + \frac{2160}{x^2} - 4320 + 4860x^2 - 2916x^4 + 729x^6$$

49. $(5 + 2i)^4 = (5)^4 + 4(5)^3(2i) + 6(5)^2(2i)^2 + 4(5)(2i)^3 + (2i)^4$

$$= 625 + 1000i - 600 - 160i + 16$$

$$= 41 - 840i$$

51. (a) $_2C_2 = 1$

(b) $_4C_2 = 6$

(c) $_6C_2 = 15$

53. $26 \cdot 26 \cdot 10 \cdot 26 \cdot 26 \cdot 26$

$$= 118{,}813{,}760$$

55. $P(\text{pair}) = \frac{10}{10} \cdot \frac{1}{9} = \frac{1}{9}$

57. $E_3 = \{3\}, \ P(E_3) = \frac{1}{6}$

$E_6 = \{(1,5), \ (2,4), \ (3,3), \ (4,2), \ (5,1)\}, \quad P(E_6) = \frac{5}{36}$

The probability of rolling a 3 with a single die is greater than the probability of obtaining a total of 6 with two dice.

59. $1 - P(HHHHH) = 1 - \left(\frac{1}{2}\right)^5 = \frac{31}{32}$

61. $n(S) = {}_{52}C_5 = 2{,}598{,}960$

$n(E) = {}_{13}C_2 \ {}_4C_2 \ {}_4C_2 \ {}_{44}C_1 = 123{,}552$

$$P(E) = \frac{123{,}552}{2{,}598{,}960} \approx 0.0475$$

CHAPTER 11

Parametric Equations and Polar Coordinates

Section 11.1   Plane Curves and Parametric Equations

- If f and g are continuous functions of t on an interval I, then the set of ordered pairs $(f(t),\ g(t))$ is a *plane curve C*. The equations $x = f(t)$ and $y = g(t)$ are *parametric equations* for C and t is the *parameter*.

- You should be able to graph plane curves with your graphing utility.

- To eliminate the parameter:
  (a) Solve for t in one equation and substitute into the second equation.
  (b) Use trigonometric identities.

- You should be able to find the parametric equations for a graph.

---

1. $x = t,\ y = -2t$

$y = -2x$

3. $x = 3t - 1,\ y = 2t + 1$

$$y = 2\left(\frac{x+1}{3}\right) + 1$$

$$2x - 3y + 5 = 0$$

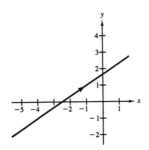

5. $x = \frac{1}{4}t,\ y = t^2$

$$y = (4x)^2$$

$$y = 16x^2$$

7. $x = t + 1, \ y = t^2$

$\quad y = (x - 1)^2$

9. $x = t^3, \ y = \dfrac{t}{2}$

$\quad y = \dfrac{1}{2}\sqrt[3]{x}$

11. $x = 3\cos\theta \Rightarrow \left(\dfrac{x}{3}\right)^2 = \cos^2\theta$

$\qquad y = 3\sin\theta \Rightarrow \left(\dfrac{y}{3}\right)^2 = \sin^2\theta$

$\qquad \left(\dfrac{x}{3}\right)^2 + \left(\dfrac{y}{3}\right)^2 = 1$

$\qquad\qquad x^2 + y^2 = 9$

13. $\qquad x = \cos\theta \Rightarrow x^2 = \cos^2\theta$

$\qquad y = 2\sin^2\theta \Rightarrow \dfrac{y}{2} = \sin^2\theta$

$\qquad x^2 + \dfrac{y}{2} = 1$

$\qquad y = 2 - 2x^2, \quad -1 \le x \le 1$

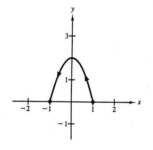

15. $\quad x = 4 + 2\cos\theta \Rightarrow \left(\dfrac{x-4}{2}\right)^2 = \cos^2\theta$

$\qquad y = -1 + 4\sin\theta \Rightarrow \left(\dfrac{y+1}{4}\right)^2 = \sin^2\theta$

$\qquad \left(\dfrac{x-4}{2}\right)^2 + \left(\dfrac{y+1}{4}\right)^2 = 1$

$\qquad \dfrac{(x-4)^2}{4} + \dfrac{(y+1)^2}{16} = 1$

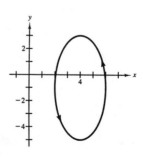

17. $x = e^{-t} \Rightarrow \dfrac{1}{x} = e^t$

$y = e^{3t} \Rightarrow y = (e^t)^3$

$y = \left(\dfrac{1}{x}\right)^3$

$y = \dfrac{1}{x^3}, \quad x > 0, \; y > 0$

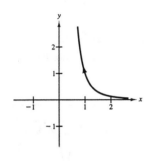

19. $x = t^3 \Rightarrow x^{1/3} = t$

$y = 3\ln t \Rightarrow y = \ln t^3$

$y = \ln(x^{1/3})^3$

$y = \ln x$

21. By eliminating the parameters in (a)–(d), we get $y = 2x + 1$. They differ from each other in restricted domain and in orientation.

(a) Domain: $-\infty < x < \infty$
   Orientation: up

(b) Domain: $-1 \le x \le 1$
   Orientation: Oscillates

(c) Domain: $0 < x < \infty$
   Orientation: Down

(d) Domain: $0 < x < \infty$
   Orientation: Up

23. $x = x_1 + t(x_2 - x_1)$

$y = y_1 + t(y_2 - y_1)$

$\dfrac{x - x_1}{x_2 - x_1} = t$

$y = y_1 + \left(\dfrac{x - x_1}{x_2 - x_1}\right)(y_2 - y_1)$

$y - y_1 = \dfrac{y_2 - y_1}{x_2 - x_1}(x - x_1)$

Notice that this is the point-slope form of the line.

25. $x = h + a\cos\theta$

$y = k + b\sin\theta$

$\dfrac{x - h}{a} = \cos\theta, \quad \dfrac{y - k}{b} = \sin\theta$

$\dfrac{(x - h)^2}{a^2} + \dfrac{(y - k)^2}{b^2} = 1$

27. From Exercise 23:

$$x = 5t$$

$$y = -2t$$

Solution not unique

29. From Exercise 24:

$$x = 2 + 4\cos\theta$$

$$y = 1 + 4\sin\theta$$

Solution not unique

31. From Exercise 25:

$a = 5$, $c = 4$, and hence, $b = 3$.

$$x = 5\cos\theta$$

$$y = 3\sin\theta$$

Center: $(0, 0)$

Solution not unique

33. From Exercise 26:

$a = 4$, $c = 5$, and hence, $b = 3$.

$$x = 4\sec\theta$$

$$y = 3\tan\theta$$

Center: $(0, 0)$

Solution not unique

35. $y = x^3$

Examples

$$x = t, \quad y = t^3$$

$$x = \sqrt[3]{t}, \quad y = t$$

$$x = \tan t, \quad y = \tan^3 t$$

37. $x = 2(\theta - \sin\theta)$
$y = 2(1 - \cos\theta)$

39. $x = \theta - \frac{3}{2}\sin\theta, \quad y = 1 - \frac{3}{2}\cos\theta$

41. $x = 2\cot\theta, \quad y = 2\sin^2\theta$

43. $x = 4\cos\theta,\ y = 2\sin 2\theta$

θ	0	$\pi/2$	π	$3\pi/2$	2π
x	4	0	-4	0	4
y	0	0	0	0	0

Matches graph (b).

45. $x = \cos\theta + \theta\sin\theta,\ y = \sin\theta - \theta\cos\theta$

θ	0	$\pi/2$	π	$3\pi/2$	2π
x	1	$\pi/2$	-1	$-3\pi/2$	1
y	0	1	π	-1	-2π

Matches graph (d).

47. When the circle has rolled θ radians, the center is at $(a\theta,\ a)$.

$$\sin\theta = \sin(180° - \theta)$$

$$= \frac{|AC|}{b} = \frac{|BD|}{b} \Rightarrow |BD| = b\sin\theta$$

$$\cos\theta = -\cos(180° - \theta)$$

$$= \frac{|AP|}{-b} \Rightarrow |AP| = -b\cos\theta$$

Therefore, $x = a\theta - b\sin\theta$ and $y = a - b\cos\theta$.

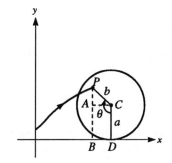

Section 11.2 Polar Coordinates

■ In polar coordinates you do not have unique representation of points. The point (r, θ) can be represented by $(r, \theta \pm 2n\pi)$ or by $(-r, \theta \pm (2n+1)\pi)$ where n is any integer. The pole is represented by $(0, \theta)$ where θ is any angle.

■ To convert from polar coordinates to rectangular coordinates, use the following relationships.

$$x = r \cos \theta$$
$$y = r \sin \theta$$

■ To convert from rectangular coordinates to polar coordinates, use the following relationships.

$$r = \pm \sqrt{x^2 + y^2}$$
$$\tan \theta = y/x$$

If θ is in the same quadrant as the point (x, y), then r is positive. If θ is in the opposite quadrant as the point (x, y), then r is negative.

■ You should be able to convert rectangular equations to polar form and vice versa.

---

1. Polar coordinates: $\left(4, \dfrac{3\pi}{6}\right)$

$$x = 4 \cos \left(\frac{3\pi}{6}\right) = 0$$

$$y = 4 \sin \left(\frac{3\pi}{6}\right) = 4$$

Rectangular coordinates: $(0, 4)$

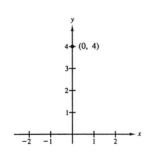

3. Polar coordinates: $\left(-1, \dfrac{5\pi}{4}\right)$

$$x = -1 \cos \left(\frac{5\pi}{4}\right) = \frac{\sqrt{2}}{2}$$

$$y = -1 \sin \left(\frac{5\pi}{4}\right) = \frac{\sqrt{2}}{2}$$

Rectangular coordinates: $\left(\dfrac{\sqrt{2}}{2}, \dfrac{\sqrt{2}}{2}\right)$

5. Polar coordinates: $\left(4, -\dfrac{\pi}{3}\right)$

$x = 4\cos\left(-\dfrac{\pi}{3}\right) = 2$

$y = 4\sin\left(-\dfrac{\pi}{3}\right) = -2\sqrt{3}$

Rectangular coordinates: $(2, -2\sqrt{3})$

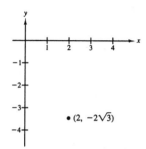

7. Polar coordinates: $\left(0, -\dfrac{7\pi}{6}\right)$

$x = 0\cos\left(-\dfrac{7\pi}{6}\right) = 0$

$y = 0\sin\left(-\dfrac{7\pi}{6}\right) = 0$

Rectangular coordinates: $(0, 0)$

9. Polar coordinates: $(\sqrt{2}, 2.36)$

$x = \sqrt{2}\cos(2.36) \approx -1.004$

$y = \sqrt{2}\sin(2.36) \approx 0.996$

Rectangular coordinates: $(-1.004, 0.996)$

11. Rectangular coordinates: $(1, 1)$

$r = \sqrt{2}, \quad \tan\theta = 1, \quad \theta = \dfrac{\pi}{4}$

Polar coordinates:

$\left(\sqrt{2}, \dfrac{\pi}{4}\right), \ \left(-\sqrt{2}, \dfrac{5\pi}{4}\right)$

13. Rectangular coordinates: $(-6, 0)$

$r = 6, \ \tan\theta = 0, \ \theta = 0$

Polar coordinates: $(6, \pi), \ (-6, 0)$

15. Rectangular coordinates: $(-3, 4)$

$r = \sqrt{9 + 16} = 5, \quad \tan\theta = -\frac{4}{3}, \quad \theta \approx 2.214$

Polar coordinates: $(5, 2.214), \ (-5, 5.356)$

17. Rectangular coordinates: $(-\sqrt{3}, -\sqrt{3})$

$r = \sqrt{3 + 3} = \sqrt{6}, \quad \tan\theta = 1, \quad \theta = \frac{\pi}{4}$

Polar coordinates:

$$\left(\sqrt{6}, \ \frac{5\pi}{4}\right), \ \left(-\sqrt{6}, \ \frac{\pi}{4}\right)$$

19. Rectangular coordinates: $(4, 6)$

$r = \sqrt{16 + 36} = 2\sqrt{13}$

$\tan\theta = \frac{3}{2}, \quad \theta \approx 0.983$

Polar coordinates:

$(2\sqrt{13}, \ 0.983), \ (-2\sqrt{13}, \ 4.124)$

21. $x^2 + y^2 = 9$

$\qquad r = 3$

23. $x^2 + y^2 - 2ax = 0$

$r^2 - 2ar\cos\theta = 0$

$r(r - 2a\cos\theta) = 0$

$r = 2a\cos\theta$

25. $\qquad y = 4$

$r\sin\theta = 4$

$r = 4\csc\theta$

27.
$$x = 10$$
$$r \cos \theta = 10$$
$$r = 10 \sec \theta$$

29.
$$3x - y + 2 = 0$$
$$3r \cos \theta - r \sin \theta + 2 = 0$$
$$r(3 \cos \theta - \sin \theta) = -2$$
$$r = \frac{-2}{3 \cos \theta - \sin \theta}$$

31.
$$xy = 4$$
$$(r \cos \theta)(r \sin \theta) = 4$$
$$r^2 = 4 \sec \theta \csc \theta = 8 \csc 2\theta$$

33.
$$(x^2 + y^2)^2 - 9(x^2 - y^2) = 0$$
$$(r^2)^2 - 9(r^2 \cos^2 \theta - r^2 \sin^2 \theta) = 0$$
$$r^2[r^2 - 9(\cos 2\theta)] = 0$$
$$r^2 = 9 \cos 2\theta$$

35.
$$r = 4 \sin \theta$$
$$r^2 = 4r \sin \theta$$
$$x^2 + y^2 = 4y$$
$$x^2 + y^2 - 4y = 0$$

37.
$$\theta = \frac{\pi}{6}$$
$$\tan \theta = \frac{\sqrt{3}}{3}$$
$$\frac{y}{x} = \frac{\sqrt{3}}{3}$$
$$y = \frac{\sqrt{3}}{3} x$$
$$\sqrt{3}\, x - 3y = 0$$

39.
$$r = 2 \csc \theta$$
$$r \sin \theta = 2$$
$$y = 2$$

41.
$$r = 2 \sin 3\theta$$
$$r = 2(3 \sin \theta - 4 \sin^3 \theta)$$
$$r^4 = 6r^3 \sin \theta - 8r^3 \sin^3 \theta$$
$$(x^2 + y^2)^2 = 6(x^2 + y^2)y - 8y^3$$
$$(x^2 + y^2)^2 = 6x^2 y - 2y^3$$

43.
$$r = \frac{6}{2 - 3 \sin \theta}$$
$$r(2 - 3 \sin \theta) = 6$$
$$2r = 6 + 3r \sin \theta$$
$$2(\pm\sqrt{x^2 + y^2}) = 6 + 3y$$
$$4(x^2 + y^2) = (6 + 3y)^2$$
$$4x^2 + 4y^2 = 36 + 36y + 9y^2$$
$$4x^2 - 5y^2 - 36y - 36 = 0$$

45.
$$r = 3$$
$$r^2 = 9$$
$$x^2 + y^2 = 9$$

47.
$$\theta = \frac{\pi}{4}$$
$$\tan\theta = \tan\frac{\pi}{4}$$
$$\frac{y}{x} = 1$$
$$y = x$$
$$x - y = 0$$

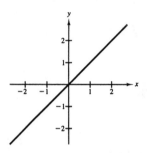

49.
$$r = 3\sec\theta$$
$$r\cos\theta = 3$$
$$x = 3$$
$$x - 3 = 0$$

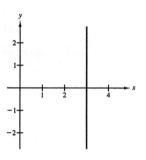

51. $(r_1, \theta_1) = (x_1, y_1)$ where $x_1 = r_1\cos\theta_1$ and $y_1 = r_1\sin\theta_1$.

$(r_2, \theta_2) = (x_2, y_2)$ where $x_2 = r_2\cos\theta_2$ and $y_2 = r_2\sin\theta_2$.

Then $x_1{}^2 + y_1{}^2 = r_1{}^2\cos^2\theta_1 + r_1{}^2\sin^2\theta_1 = r_1{}^2$ and $x_2{}^2 + y_2{}^2 = r_2{}^2$. Thus,

$$
\begin{aligned}
d &= \sqrt{(x_1 - x_2)^2 + (y_1 - y_2)^2} \\
&= \sqrt{x_1{}^2 - 2x_1x_2 + x_2{}^2 + y_1{}^2 - 2y_1y_2 + y_2{}^2} \\
&= \sqrt{(x_1{}^2 + y_1{}^2) + (x_2{}^2 + y_2{}^2) - 2(x_1x_2 + y_1y_2)} \\
&= \sqrt{r_1{}^2 + r_2{}^2 - 2(r_1r_2\cos\theta_1\cos\theta_2 + r_1r_2\sin\theta_1\sin\theta_2)} \\
&= \sqrt{r_1{}^2 + r_2{}^2 - 2r_1r_2\cos(\theta_1 - \theta_2)}.
\end{aligned}
$$

53.

$$r = 2(h\cos\theta + k\sin\theta)$$
$$r = 2\left(h\left(\frac{x}{r}\right) + k\left(\frac{y}{r}\right)\right)$$
$$r = \frac{2hx + 2ky}{r}$$
$$r^2 = 2hx + 2ky$$
$$x^2 + y^2 = 2hx + 2ky$$
$$x^2 - 2hx + y^2 - 2ky = 0$$
$$(x^2 - 2hx + h^2) + (y^2 - 2ky + k^2) = h^2 + k^2$$
$$(x - h)^2 + (y - k)^2 = h^2 + k^2$$

Center: $(h,\ k)$
Radius: $\sqrt{h^2 + k^2}$

Section 11.3   Graphs of Polar Equations

■ When graphing polar equations:
1. Test for symmetry
   (a) $\theta = \pi/2$: Replace (r, θ) by $(r, \pi - \theta)$ or $(-r, -\theta)$.
   (b) Polar axis: Replace (r, θ) by $(r, -\theta)$ or $(-r, \pi - \theta)$.
   (c) Pole: Replace (r, θ) by $(r, \pi + \theta)$ or $(-r, \theta)$.
   (d) $r = f(\sin \theta)$ is symmetric with respect to the line $\theta = \pi/2$.
   (e) $r = f(\cos \theta)$ is symmetric with respect to the polar axis.
2. Find the θ values for which $|r|$ is maximum.
3. Find the θ values for which $r = 0$.
4. Know the different types of polar graphs.

   (a) Limaçons   (b) Rose Curves, $n \geq 2$
   $\quad r = a \pm b \cos \theta$ $\quad r = a \cos n\theta$
   $\quad r = a \pm b \sin \theta$ $\quad r = a \sin n\theta$
   (c) Circles   (d) Lemniscates
   $\quad r = a \cos \theta$ $\quad r^2 = a^2 \cos 2\theta$
   $\quad r = a \sin \theta$ $\quad r^2 = a^2 \sin 2\theta$
   $\quad r = a$

■ You should be able to graph polar equations of the form $r = f(\theta)$ with your graphing
utility.

$$x = f(t) \cos t$$
$$y = f(t) \sin t$$

---

1. $r = 10 + 6 \cos \theta$

   $\theta = \dfrac{\pi}{2}$: $-r = 10 + 6 \cos(-\theta)$

   $\qquad\qquad -r = 10 + 6 \cos \theta$

   $\qquad\qquad$ Not an equivalent equation

   Polar $r = 10 + 6 \cos(-\theta)$
   axis:
   $\qquad\qquad r = 10 + 6 \cos \theta$

   $\qquad\qquad$ Equivalent equation

   Pole: $-r = 10 + 6 \cos \theta$

   $\qquad\qquad$ Not an equivalent equation

   Answer: Symmetric with respect to polar axis

3. $r = \dfrac{2}{1 + \sin\theta}$

$\theta = \dfrac{\pi}{2}$: $r = \dfrac{2}{1 + \sin(\pi - \theta)}$

$r = \dfrac{2}{1 + \sin\pi\cos\theta - \cos\pi\sin\theta}$

$r = \dfrac{2}{1 + \sin\theta}$

Equivalent equation

Polar axis: $r = \dfrac{2}{1 + \sin(-\theta)}$

$r = \dfrac{2}{1 - \sin\theta}$

Not an equivalent equation

Pole: $-r = \dfrac{2}{1 + \sin\theta}$

Not an equivalent equation

Answer: Symmetric with respect to $\theta = \pi/2$.

5. $r = 4\sec\theta\csc\theta$

$\theta = \dfrac{\pi}{2}$: $-r = 4\sec(-\theta)\csc(-\theta)$

$-r = -4\sec\theta\csc\theta$

$r = 4\sec\theta\csc\theta$

Equivalent equation

Polar axis: $-r = 4\sec(\pi - \theta)\csc(\pi - \theta)$

$-r = 4(-\sec\theta)\csc\theta$

$r = 4\sec\theta\csc\theta$

Equivalent equation

Pole: $r = 4\sec(\pi + \theta)\csc(\pi + \theta)$

$r = 4(-\sec\theta)(-\csc\theta)$

$r = 4\sec\theta\csc\theta$

Equivalent equation

Answer: Symmetric with respect to $\theta = \pi/2$, polar axis, and pole

7. $|r| = |5\cos 3\theta| = 5|\cos 3\theta| \le 5$

$|\cos 3\theta| = 1$

$\cos 3\theta = \pm 1$

$\theta = 0,\ \dfrac{\pi}{3},\ \dfrac{2\pi}{3}$

Maximum: $|r| = 5$ when $\theta = 0,\ \dfrac{\pi}{3},\ \dfrac{2\pi}{3}$.

9. $|r| = |10(1 - \sin\theta)|$

$= 10|1 - \sin\theta| \le 10(2) = 20$

$|1 - \sin\theta| = 2$

$1 - \sin\theta = 2$ or $1 - \sin\theta = -2$

$\sin\theta = -1$ $\sin\theta = 3$

$\theta = \dfrac{3\pi}{2}$ Not possible

Maximum: $|r| = 20$ when $\theta = \dfrac{3\pi}{2}$.

11. Circle: $r = 5$

13.

$$\theta = \frac{\pi}{6}$$

$$\tan \theta = \tan \frac{\pi}{6}$$

$$\frac{y}{x} = \frac{1}{\sqrt{3}}$$

$$y = \frac{x}{\sqrt{3}} \Rightarrow \text{Line}$$

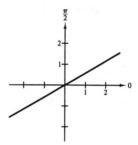

15. $r = 3 \sin \theta$

Symmetric with respect to $\theta = \pi/2$

Circle with a radius of $3/2$

17. $r = 4 + 4 \sin \theta$

Symmetric with respect to $\theta = \frac{\pi}{2}$

$$\frac{a}{b} = \frac{4}{4} = 1 \Rightarrow \text{Cardioid}$$

$$|r| = 8 \text{ when } \theta = \frac{\pi}{2}.$$

$$r = 0 \text{ when } \theta = \frac{3\pi}{2}.$$

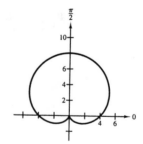

19. $r = 4 + 3\cos\theta$

Symmetric with respect to polar axis

$\dfrac{a}{b} = \dfrac{4}{3} > 1 \Rightarrow$ Dimpled limaçon

$|r| = 7$ when $\theta = 0$.

21. $r = 3 - 4\cos\theta$

Symmetric with respect to polar axis

$\dfrac{a}{b} = \dfrac{3}{4} < 1 \Rightarrow$ Limaçon with inner loop

$|r| = 7$ when $\theta = \pi$.

$r = 0$ when $\cos\theta = \dfrac{3}{4}$ or $\theta \approx 0.723, 5.560$.

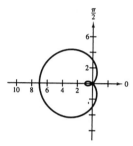

23. $r = 3\sin 2\theta$

Symmetric with respect to $\theta = \dfrac{\pi}{2}$,

polar axis, and pole

Rose curve $(n = 2)$ with 4 petals

25.
$$r = \dfrac{3}{\sin\theta - 2\cos\theta}$$

$$r(\sin\theta - 2\cos\theta) = 3$$

$$y - 2x = 3$$

$$y = 2x + 3 \Rightarrow \text{ Line}$$

27. $r^2 = 4 \cos 2\theta$

Symmetric with respect to polar axis

Lemniscate

29. $r = \dfrac{\theta}{2}$

Symmetric with respect to $\theta = \dfrac{\pi}{2}$

and polar axis

Spiral

31.
$$r = 2 - \sec \theta = 2 - \frac{1}{\cos \theta}$$
$$r \cos \theta = 2 \cos \theta - 1$$
$$r(r \cos \theta) = 2r \cos \theta - r$$
$$(\pm \sqrt{x^2 + y^2})(x) = 2x - (\pm \sqrt{x^2 + y^2})$$
$$(\pm \sqrt{x^2 + y^2})(x + 1) = 2x$$
$$(\pm \sqrt{x^2 + y^2}) = \frac{2x}{x + 1}$$
$$x^2 + y^2 = \frac{4x^2}{(x + 1)^2}$$
$$y^2 = \frac{-x^2(x^2 + 2x - 3)}{(x + 1)^2}$$
$$y = \pm \sqrt{\frac{x^2(3 - 2x - x^2)}{(x + 1)^2}} = \pm \left| \frac{x}{x + 1} \right| \sqrt{3 - 2x - x^2}$$

The graph has an asymptote at $x = -1$.

33. The graph of $r = f(\theta)$ is rotated about the pole through an angle ϕ. Let (r, θ) be any point on the graph of $r = f(\theta)$. Then $(r, \theta + \phi)$ is rotated through the angle ϕ, and since
$$r = f((\theta + \phi) - \phi) = f(\theta),$$
it follows that $(r, \theta + \phi)$ is on the graph of $r = f(\theta - \phi)$.

35. (a) $r = 2 - \sin\left(\theta - \dfrac{\pi}{4}\right)$

$$= 2 - \dfrac{\sqrt{2}}{2}(\sin\theta - \cos\theta)$$

(c) $r = 2 - \sin(\theta - \pi)$

$$= 2 + \sin\theta$$

(b) $r = 2 - \sin\left(\theta - \dfrac{\pi}{2}\right)$

$$= 2 + \cos\theta$$

(d) $r = 2 - \sin\left(\theta - \dfrac{3\pi}{2}\right)$

$$= 2 - \cos\theta$$

37. (a) $r = 1 - \sin\theta$

(b) $r = 1 - \sin\left(\theta - \dfrac{\pi}{4}\right)$

Section 11.4   Polar Equations of Conics

- The graph of a polar equation of the form

$$r = \frac{ep}{1 \pm e \cos \theta} \quad \text{or} \quad r = \frac{ep}{1 \pm e \sin \theta}$$

is a conic, where $e > 0$ is the eccentricity and $|p|$ is the distance between the focus (pole) and the directrix.

(a) If $e < 1$, the graph is an ellipse.

(b) If $e = 1$, the graph is a parabola.

(c) If $e > 1$, the graph is a hyperbola.

- Guidelines for finding polar equations of conics:

(a) Horizontal directrix above the pole: $r = \dfrac{ep}{1 + e \sin \theta}$

(b) Horizontal directrix below the pole: $r = \dfrac{ep}{1 - e \sin \theta}$

(c) Vertical directrix to the right of the pole: $r = \dfrac{ep}{1 + e \cos \theta}$

(d) Vertical directrix to the left of the pole: $r = \dfrac{ep}{1 - e \cos \theta}$

---

1. $r = \dfrac{6}{1 - \cos \theta} \Rightarrow e = 1$

Parabola with horizontal axis and vertex $(3, \pi)$

Matches graph (c)

3. $r = \dfrac{3}{1 - 2 \sin \theta} \Rightarrow e = 2$

Hyperbola with vertical transverse axis

Vertices: $\left(-3, \dfrac{\pi}{2}\right), \left(1, \dfrac{3\pi}{2}\right)$

Matches graph (a)

5. $r = \dfrac{6}{2 - \sin \theta} \Rightarrow e = \dfrac{1}{2}$

Ellipse with vertical major axis

Vertices: $\left(6, \dfrac{\pi}{2}\right)$, $\left(2, \dfrac{3\pi}{2}\right)$

Matches graph (b)

7. $r = \dfrac{2}{1 - \cos \theta}$

$e = 1$ so the graph is a parabola.

Vertex: $(1, \pi)$

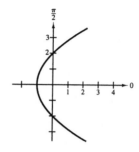

9. $r = \dfrac{5}{1 + \sin \theta}$

$e = 1$ so the graph is a parabola.

Vertex: $\left(\dfrac{5}{2}, \dfrac{\pi}{2}\right)$

11. $r = \dfrac{2}{2 - \cos \theta} = \dfrac{1}{1 - (1/2)\cos \theta}$

$e = \dfrac{1}{2} < 1$, the graph is an ellipse.

Vertices: $(2, 0)$, $\left(\dfrac{2}{3}, \pi\right)$

13. $r = \dfrac{4}{2 + \sin\theta} = \dfrac{2}{1 + (1/2)\sin\theta}$

$e = \frac{1}{2} < 1$, the graph is an ellipse.

Vertices: $\left(\dfrac{4}{3}, \dfrac{\pi}{2}\right)$, $\left(4, \dfrac{3\pi}{2}\right)$

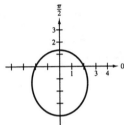

15. $r = \dfrac{3}{2 + 4\sin\theta} = \dfrac{3/2}{1 + 2\sin\theta}$

$e = 2 > 1$, the graph is a hyperbola.

Vertices: $\left(\dfrac{1}{2}, \dfrac{\pi}{2}\right)$, $\left(-\dfrac{3}{2}, \dfrac{3\pi}{2}\right)$

17. $r = \dfrac{3}{2 - 6\cos\theta}$

$= \dfrac{3/2}{1 - 3\cos\theta}$

$e = 3 > 1$, the graph is a hyperbola.

Vertices: $\left(-\frac{3}{4}, 0\right)$, $\left(\frac{3}{8}, \pi\right)$

19. $e = 1$, $x = -1$, $p = 1$

Vertical directrix to the left of the pole

$r = \dfrac{1(1)}{1 - 1\cos\theta} = \dfrac{1}{1 - \cos\theta}$

21. $e = \frac{1}{2}$, $y = 1$, $p = 1$

Horizontal directrix above the pole

$r = \dfrac{(1/2)(1)}{1 + (1/2)\sin\theta} = \dfrac{1}{2 + \sin\theta}$

23. $e = 2$, $x = 1$, $p = 1$

Vertical directrix to the right of the pole

$r = \dfrac{2(1)}{1 + 2\cos\theta} = \dfrac{2}{1 + 2\cos\theta}$

25. Vertex: $\left(1, -\dfrac{\pi}{2}\right) \Rightarrow e = 1$, $p = 2$

Horizontal directrix below the pole

$r = \dfrac{1(2)}{1 - 1\sin\theta} = \dfrac{2}{1 - \sin\theta}$

27. Vertex: $(5, \pi) \Rightarrow e = 1$, $p = 10$

Vertical directrix to the left of the pole

$$r = \frac{1(10)}{1 - 1\cos\theta} = \frac{10}{1 - \cos\theta}$$

29. Center: $(3, \pi)$; $c = 3$, $a = 5$, $e = \frac{3}{5}$

Vertical directrix to the right of the pole

$$r = \frac{(3/5)p}{1 + (3/5)\cos\theta} = \frac{3p}{5 + 3\cos\theta}$$

$$2 = \frac{3p}{5 + 3\cos 0}$$

$$p = \frac{16}{3}$$

$$r = \frac{3(16/3)}{5 + 3\cos\theta} = \frac{16}{5 + 3\cos\theta}$$

31. Center: $(8, 0)$; $c = 8$, $a = 12$, $e = \frac{2}{3}$

Vertical directrix to the left of the pole

$$r = \frac{(2/3)p}{1 - (2/3)\cos\theta} = \frac{2p}{3 - 2\cos\theta}$$

$$20 = \frac{2p}{3 - 2\cos 0}$$

$$p = 10$$

$$r = \frac{2(10)}{3 - 2\cos\theta} = \frac{20}{3 - 2\cos\theta}$$

33. Center: $\left(5, \frac{3\pi}{2}\right)$; $c = 5$, $a = 4$, $e = \frac{5}{4}$

Horizontal directrix below the pole

$$r = \frac{(5/4)p}{1 - (5/4)\sin\theta} = \frac{5p}{4 - 5\sin\theta}$$

$$1 = \frac{5p}{4 - 5\sin(3\pi/2)}$$

$$p = \frac{9}{5}$$

$$r = \frac{5(9/5)}{4 - 5\sin\theta} = \frac{9}{4 - 5\sin\theta}$$

35.

$$\frac{x^2}{a^2} + \frac{y^2}{b^2} = 1$$

$$\frac{r^2\cos^2\theta}{a^2} + \frac{r^2\sin^2\theta}{b^2} = 1$$

$$\frac{r^2\cos^2\theta}{a^2} + \frac{r^2(1 - \cos^2\theta)}{b^2} = 1$$

$$r^2 b^2 \cos^2\theta + r^2 a^2 - r^2 a^2 \cos^2\theta = a^2 b^2$$

$$r^2(b^2 - a^2)\cos^2\theta + r^2 a^2 = a^2 b^2$$

$$b^2 - a^2 = -c^2$$

$$-r^2 c^2 \cos^2\theta + r^2 a^2 = a^2 b^2$$

$$-r^2 \left(\frac{c}{a}\right)^2 \cos^2\theta + r^2 = b^2, \quad e = \frac{c}{a}$$

$$-r^2 e^2 \cos^2\theta + r^2 = b^2$$

$$r^2(1 - e^2 \cos^2\theta) = b^2$$

$$r^2 = \frac{b^2}{1 - e^2\cos^2\theta}$$

37. $\dfrac{x^2}{169} + \dfrac{y^2}{144} = 1$

$a = 13$, $b = 12$, $c = 5$, $e = \dfrac{5}{13}$

$$r^2 = \frac{144}{1 - (25/169)\cos^2\theta}$$

$$= \frac{24{,}336}{169 - 25\cos^2\theta}$$

39. $\dfrac{x^2}{9} - \dfrac{y^2}{16} = 1$

$a = 3, \quad b = 4, \quad c = 5, \quad e = \dfrac{5}{3}$

$r^2 = \dfrac{-16}{1 - (25/9)\cos^2\theta} = \dfrac{144}{25\cos^2\theta - 9}$

43. $r = \dfrac{2}{1 - \cos[\theta - (\pi/4)]}$

41. Hyperbola

One focus: $(5,\,0)$

Vertices: $(4,\,0),\ (4,\,\pi)$

$a = 4, \quad c = 5, \quad b = 3, \quad e = \dfrac{5}{4}$

$r^2 = \dfrac{-3^2}{1 - (5/4)^2 \cos^2\theta}$

$\quad = \dfrac{-144}{16 - 25\cos^2\theta} = \dfrac{144}{25\cos^2\theta - 16}$

45. When $\theta = 0, \quad r = c + a = ea + a = a(1 + e)$.

Therefore,

$$a(1 + e) = \dfrac{ep}{1 - e\cos 0}$$

$$a(1 + e)(1 - e) = ep$$

$$a(1 - e^2) = ep.$$

Thus, $r = \dfrac{ep}{1 - e\cos\theta} = \dfrac{(1 - e^2)a}{1 - e\cos\theta}.$

47. $r = \dfrac{[1 - (0.0167)^2](92.957 \times 10^6)}{1 - 0.0167\cos\theta}$

$\quad \approx \dfrac{9.2931 \times 10^7}{1 - 0.0167\cos\theta}$

Perihelion distance:

$\quad r = 92.957 \times 10^6 (1 - 0.0167)$

$\quad \approx 9.1405 \times 10^7$

Aphelion distance:

$\quad r = 92.957 \times 10^6 (1 + 0.0167)$

$\quad \approx 9.4509 \times 10^7$

49. Directrix: $y = 8200, \ e = 1, \ p = 8200$

$$r = \dfrac{1(8200)}{1 + 1\sin\theta} = \dfrac{8200}{1 + \sin\theta}$$

Chapter 11   Review Exercises

1. $x = 2t, \quad y = 4t$

$$t = \frac{x}{2}$$

$$y = 4\left(\frac{x}{2}\right) = 2x$$

3. $x = 1 + 4t, \quad y = 2 - 3t$

$$t = \frac{x-1}{4}$$

$$y = 2 - 3\left(\frac{x-1}{4}\right)$$

$$3x + 4y = 11$$

5. $x = \dfrac{1}{t}, \quad y = t^2$

$$t = \frac{1}{x}$$

$$y = \frac{1}{x^2}$$

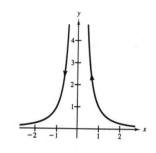

7. $x = 6\cos\theta, \quad y = 6\sin\theta$

$$\cos\theta = \frac{x}{6}, \quad \sin\theta = \frac{y}{6}$$

$$\frac{x^2}{36} + \frac{y^2}{36} = 1$$

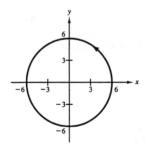

9. $x = \cos^3\theta, \quad y = 4\sin^3\theta$

$$\cos\theta = x^{1/3}, \quad \sin\theta = \left(\frac{y}{4}\right)^{1/3}$$

$$x^{2/3} + \left(\frac{y}{4}\right)^{2/3} = 1$$

11. $x = e^t$, $y = e^{-t}$

$t = \ln x$

$y = e^{-\ln x}$

$y = \dfrac{1}{e^{\ln x}} = \dfrac{1}{x}$

$xy = 1$, x, $y > 0$

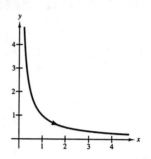

13. $r = 4$

Circle of radius 4 centered at the pole

15. $r = 4 \sin 2\theta$

Symmetric with respect to $\theta = \pi/2$, polar axis, and pole

Rose curve $(n = 2)$ with 4 petals

17. $r = -2 - 2 \cos \theta$

Symmetric with respect to polar axis

$\dfrac{a}{b} = \dfrac{2}{2} = 1 \Rightarrow$ Cardioid

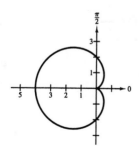

19. $r = 4 - 3 \cos \theta$

Symmetric with respect to polar axis

$\dfrac{a}{b} = \dfrac{4}{3} > 0 \Rightarrow$ Dimpled limaçon

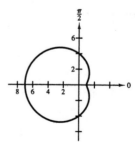

21. $r = -3 \cos 3\theta$

Symmetric with respect to polar axis

Rose curve $(n = 3)$ with 3 petals

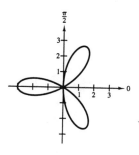

23. $r^2 = 4 \sin 2\theta \Rightarrow r = \pm 2 \sin 2\theta$

Symmetric with respect to pole

Lemniscate

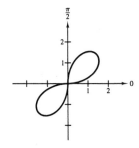

25.
$$r = \frac{3}{\cos(\theta - (\pi/4))}$$

$$r \cos\left(\theta - \frac{\pi}{4}\right) = 3$$

$$r\left[\frac{\sqrt{2}}{2}\cos\theta + \frac{\sqrt{2}}{2}\sin\theta\right] = 3$$

$$r\cos\theta + r\sin\theta = 3\sqrt{2}$$

$$x + y = 3\sqrt{2}$$

Line

27. $r = \dfrac{2}{1 - \sin\theta}$, $e = 1$

Parabola symmetric with $\theta = \pi/2$ and the vertex at $(1, \, 3\pi/2)$

29.
$$r = 3\cos\theta$$
$$r^2 = 3r\cos\theta$$
$$x^2 + y^2 = 3x$$

31.
$$r = \frac{2}{1 + \sin\theta}$$
$$r + r\sin\theta = 2$$
$$r = 2 - r\sin\theta$$
$$r^2 = (2 - r\sin\theta)^2$$
$$x^2 + y^2 = (2 - y)^2$$
$$x^2 + y^2 = 4 - 4y + y^2$$
$$x^2 + 4y - 4 = 0$$

33.
$$r^2 = \cos 2\theta$$
$$r^2 = 1 - 2\sin^2\theta$$
$$r^4 = r^2 - 2r^2\sin^2\theta$$
$$(x^2 + y^2)^2 = x^2 + y^2 - 2y^2$$
$$(x^2 + y^2)^2 - x^2 + y^2 = 0$$

35. $(x^2 + y^2)^2 = ax^2 y$
$$(r^2)^2 = ar^2\cos^2\theta r\sin\theta$$
$$r = a\cos^2\theta\sin\theta$$

37. Circle symmetric to $\theta = \pi/2$
Center: $(5,\ \pi/2)$
Solution point:
$(0,\ 0) \Rightarrow$ Radius $= 5 \Rightarrow a = 10$
$$r = a\sin\theta$$
$$r = 10\sin\theta$$

39. Parabola: $r = \dfrac{ep}{1 - e\cos\theta}$, $e = 1$
Vertex: $(2,\ \pi)$
Focus: $(0,\ 0) \Rightarrow p = 4$
$$r = \dfrac{4}{1 - \cos\theta}$$

41. Ellipse: $r = \dfrac{ep}{1 - e\cos\theta}$
Vertices: $(5,\ 0),\ (1,\ \pi) \Rightarrow a = 3$
One focus: $(0,\ 0) \Rightarrow c = 2$
$$e = \dfrac{c}{a} = \dfrac{2}{3},\quad p = \dfrac{5}{2}$$
$$r = \dfrac{(2/3)(5/2)}{1 - (2/3)\cos\theta}$$
$$= \dfrac{5/3}{1 - (2/3)\cos\theta} = \dfrac{5}{3 - 2\cos\theta}$$

43. $\dfrac{(x+3)^2}{16} + \dfrac{(y-4)^2}{9} = 1$
$$x = -3 + 4\cos\theta$$
$$y = 4 + 3\sin\theta$$
This solution is not unique.

45. $x = a(\theta - \sin\theta),\quad y = a(1 - \cos\theta)$
$$\cos\theta = 1 - \dfrac{y}{a}$$
$$\theta = \arccos\left(1 - \dfrac{y}{a}\right) = \arccos\left(\dfrac{a - y}{a}\right)$$
$$\sin\theta = \pm\sqrt{1 - \cos^2\theta} = \pm\sqrt{1 - \left(1 - \dfrac{y}{a}\right)^2}$$
$$= \pm\sqrt{\dfrac{2y}{a} - \dfrac{y^2}{a^2}} = \pm\dfrac{1}{a}\sqrt{2ay - y^2}$$
$$x = a\left[\arccos\left(\dfrac{a - y}{a}\right) \pm \dfrac{1}{a}\sqrt{2ay - y^2}\right]$$
$$x = a\arccos\left(\dfrac{a - y}{a}\right) \pm \sqrt{2ay - y^2}$$

47. $x = 2(\cos\theta + \theta\sin\theta)$
$$y = 2(\sin\theta - \theta\cos\theta)$$